SIX SIGMA:

A COMPLETE STEP-BY-STEP GUIDE

Using the most recent edition in your workplace?

Because we continually attempt to keep our Handbook up to date with the latest industry developments, be sure to check our website often for the most recent edition at www.sixsigmacouncil.org.

TABLE OF CONTENTS

UNIT 1:
INTRODUCTION TO SIX SIGMA

CHAPTER 1:
WHAT IS SIX SIGMA?

Six Sigma, or 6σ, is both a methodology for process improvement and a statistical concept that seeks to define the variation inherent in any process. The overarching premise of Six Sigma is that variation in a process leads to opportunities for error; opportunities for error then lead to risks for product defects. Product defects—whether in a tangible process or a service—lead to poor customer satisfaction. By working to reduce variation and opportunities for error, the Six Sigma method ultimately reduces process costs and increases customer satisfaction.

Data Driven Processes and Decisions

In applying Six Sigma, organizations, teams, and project managers seek to implement strategies that are based on measurement and metrics. Historically, many business leaders made decisions based on intuition or experience. Despite some common beliefs in various industries, Six Sigma doesn't remove the need for experienced leadership, and it doesn't negate the importance of intuition in any process. Instead, Six Sigma works alongside other skills, experience, and knowledge to provide a mathematical and statistical foundation for decision making. Experience might say a process isn't working; statistics prove that to be true. Intuition might guide a project manager to believe a certain change could improve output; Six Sigma tools help organizations validate those assumptions.

Decision Making Without Six Sigma

Without proper measurement and analysis, decision making processes in an organization might proceed as follows:

> **What is beta testing?**
>
> Beta testing is the act of implementing a new idea, system, or product with a select group of people or processes in as controlled an environment as possible. After beta testers identify potential problems and those problems are corrected, the idea, system, or product can be rolled out to the entire population of customers, employees, or processes. The purpose of beta testing is to reduce the risks and costs inherent in launching an unproven product or system to a widespread audience.

- Someone with clout in the organization has a good idea or takes interest in someone else's idea.
- Based on past experience or knowledge, decision makers within an organization believe the idea will be successful.
- The idea is implemented; sometimes it is implemented in beta mode so expenses and risks are minimized.
- The success of the idea is weighed after implementation; problems are addressed after they impact products or processes in some way in the present or the future.

Beta testing is sometimes used in a Six Sigma approach, but the idea or change in question goes through rigorous analysis and data testing first. The disadvantage of launching ideas into beta—or to an entire population--without going through a Six Sigma methodology is that organizations can experience unintended consequences from changes, spend money on ideas that don't end up working out as planned, and impact customer perceptions through trial-and-error periods rife with opportunities for error. In many cases, organizations that don't rely on data make improvements without first understanding the true gain or loss associated with the change. Some improvements may appear to work on the surface without actually impacting customer satisfaction or profit in a positive way.

Decision Making With Six Sigma

The Six Sigma method lets organizations identify problems, validate assumptions, brainstorm solutions, and plan for implementation to avoid unintended consequences. By applying tools such as statistical analysis and process mapping to problems and solutions, teams can visualize and predict outcomes with a high-level of accuracy, letting leadership make decisions with less financial risk.

Six Sigma methods don't offer a crystal ball for organizations, though. Even with expert use of the tools described in this book, problems can arise for teams as they implement and maintain solutions. That's why Six Sigma also provides for control methods: once teams implement changes, they can control processes for a fraction of the cost of traditional quality methods by continuing the use of Six Sigma tools and statistics.

Defining 6σ

Six Sigma as a methodology for process improvement involves a vast library of tools and knowledge, which will be covered throughout this book. In this section, we'll begin to define the statistical concept represented by 6σ.

At the most basic definition, 6σ is a statistical representation for what many experts call a "perfect" process. Technically, in a Six Sigma process, there are only 3.4 defects per million opportunities. In percentages, that means 99.99966 percent of the products from a Six Sigma process are without defect. At just one sigma level below—5σ, or 99.97 percent accuracy--processes experience 233 errors per million opportunities. In simpler terms, there are going to be many more unsatisfied customers.

Real World Examples

According to the National Oceanic and Atmospheric Administration, air traffic controllers in the United States handle 28,537 commercial flights daily.[1] In a year, that is approximately 10.416 million flights. Based on a Five Sigma air traffic control process, errors of some type occur in the process for handling approximately 2,426 flights every year. With a Six Sigma process, that risk drops to 35.41 errors.

The CDC reports that approximately 51.4 million surgeries are performed in the United States in a given year.[2] Based on a 99.97 accuracy rate, doctors would make errors in 11,976 surgeries each year, or 230 surgeries a week. At Six Sigma, that drops to approximately 174 errors a year for the entire country, or just over 3 errors each week. At Five Sigma, patients are 68 times more likely to experience an error at the hands of medical providers.

---

[1]"Air Traffic," Science on a Sphere, National Oceanic and Atmospheric Administration. http://sos.noaa.gov/Datasets/dataset.php?id=44
[2] "Inpatient Surgery," FastStats, Centers for Disease Control and Prevention. http://www.cdc.gov/nchs/fastats/inpatient-surgery.htm

While most people accept a 99.9 percent accuracy rate in even the most critical services on a daily basis, the above examples highlight how wide the gap between Six Sigma and Five Sigma really is. For organizations, it's not just about the error rate—it's also about the costs associated with each error.

Consider an example based on Amazon shipments. On Cyber Monday in 2013, Amazon processed a whopping 36.8 million orders.[3] Let's assume that each order error costs the company an average of $35 (a very conservative number, considering that costs might include return shipping, labor to answer customer phone calls or emails, and labor and shipping to right a wrong order).

Cost of Amazon Order Errors, 5σ			
Total Orders	Errors	Average Cost per Error	Total Cost of Errors
36.8 million	8574.4	$35	$300,104.00

Cost of Amazon Order Errors, 6σ			
Total Orders	Errors	Average Cost per Error	Total Cost of Errors
36.8 million	125.12	$35	$4,379.20

For this example, the cost difference in sigma levels is still over $295,000 for the Cyber Monday business.

For most organizations, Six Sigma processes are a constant target. Achieving and maintaining Six Sigma "perfection" is difficult and requires continuous process improvement. But even advancing from lower levels of sigma to a Four or Five Sigma process has a drastic impact on costs and customer satisfaction. Let's look at the Amazon Cyber Monday example at other levels of sigma.

[3] Siegel, Jacob, "Amazon sold 426 items per second during its 'best ever' holiday season," Boy Genius Reports, Dec. 26, 2013. http://bgr.com/2013/12/26/amazon-holiday-season-sales-2013/

Sigma Level	Defects per Million Opportunities	Estimated Cyber Monday Defects	Total Cost (at $35 estimate per error)
One Sigma	690,000	25,392,000	$888,720,000
Two Sigma	308,000	11,334,400	$396,704,000
Three Sigma	66,800	2,458,240	$86,038,400
Four Sigma	6,200	228,160	$7,985,600
Five Sigma	233	8,574.4	$300,104
Six Sigma	3.4	125.12	$4,379

At very low levels of sigma, any process is unlikely to be profitable. The higher the sigma level, the better the bottom line is likely to be.

Calculating Sigma Level

Organizations and teams can calculate the sigma level of a product or process using the equation below:

$$\left(\frac{\text{# of opportunities - # of defects)}}{\text{# of opportunities}} \right) \times 100 = \text{Yield}$$

Consider a process in a marketing department that distributes letters to customers or prospects. For the purposes of the example, imagine that the process inserts 30,000 letters in preaddressed envelopes each day. In a given business week, the process outputs 150,000 letters.

The marketing department begins receiving complaints that people are receiving letters in envelopes that are addressed to them, but the letters inside are addressed to or relevant to someone else. The marketing department randomly selects 1,000 letters from the next week's batch and finds that 5 of them have errors. Applying that to the total amount, they estimate that as many as 750 letters could have errors. (Sampling and extrapolation are covered in depth in the advanced chapters on statistics.)

The letter process has 150,000 opportunities for error each week and an estimated 750 defects.

$$((150,000 - 750) / 150,000) * 100 = \text{a yield of } 99.5$$

Look up a yield of 99.5 in the abridged Sigma table below and you'll see the process described above is currently between 4 and 4.1 sigma.

Yield %	DPMO	Sigma Level
99.7450	2,550	4.3
99.6540	3,460	4.2
99.5340	4,550	4.1
99.3790	6,210	4.0
99.1810	8,190	3.9

Sigma Level Is Not a Final Indicator

Sigma levels provide organization with a high-level look at how a process is performing, but comparing sigma levels between multiple processes doesn't always point to the particular process an organization should improve first. Leadership should also consider costs, resources, and the estimated impact of improvements.

For example, consider these processes that might be found in a food processing plant:

Process	Performance Metric(s)	Current Sigma Level
Attaching a decorative element to food item	Decorative touch is centered on food product and stable so it won't fall off in transit	2.2
Packing product	Product is sealed for freshness	3.1
Shipping of product	Product reaches the right customer in a timely manner	4.3

A glance at sigma levels indicates that the process that attaches the decorative element is in most need of improvement. While that process has the highest rate of defects, leadership within the plant would have to ask themselves: How much does that matter to the customer, and what is the hit to the bottom line?

It's likely that most customers will notice most that the product is sealed for freshness and reaches the right location. Since bad product has to be thrown away, the most expensive errors might be associated with improper sealing during packing. The plant is likely to use resources to improve the packing process before addressing the decorative element issue.

After the packing process is improved, the plant might then consider whether to improve the decorating process or the shipping process. As part of that consideration, the company might conduct customer surveys to reveal that some customers have stopped buying the product because of the decorative element issue. An analyst estimates that the loss of sales related to that issue are costing the company $1,000 a week. Shipping issues are costing the company $500 a week.

Should the company address the costlier issue first? What if you were told that the shipping process could be improved with staff training sessions, while the decorative element issue required an expensive machinery update? Sometimes, organizations have to consider the expense of an improvement. Applying a Six Sigma project to all situations isn't financially lucrative since those improvements take time and money. A Six Sigma culture is about continuous improvement, which means teams consider all options before embarking on the most lucrative improvement measures.

Common Six Sigma Principles

Organizations can impact their sigma level by integrating core principles from the Six Sigma methodology into leadership styles, process management, and improvement endeavors. The principles of Six Sigma, and the tools used to achieve them, are covered in detail in various sections of this book, but some common ideas are introduced below.

Customer-Focused Improvement

In the illustration about the food plant, we saw that the Six Sigma process doesn't just make improvements for the sake of driving up sigma levels. A primary principle of the methodology is a focus on the customer. In Chapter 5, we'll look at the Voice of the Customer (VoC) and ways for establishing what the customer really wants from a product or process. By combining that knowledge with measurements, statistics, and process improvement methods, organizations increase customer satisfaction, ultimately bolstering profits, customer retention, and loyalty.

A detailed understanding of the customer and customer desires not only lets businesses customize product offerings and services, but it also lets organizations:

- Offer additional features customers want and are willing to pay for
- Prioritize product development to meet current needs
- Develop new ideas based on customer feedback
- Understand changing trends in the market
- Identify areas of concern
- Prioritize work on challenges based on how customers perceive various problems or issues
- Test solutions and ideas before investing time and money in them

Value Streams The value stream is the sequence of all items, events, and people required to produce an end result. For example, the value stream for serving a hotdog with ketchup to someone would include:

- A hotdog supplier
- A bun supplier

- A ketchup supplier
- Hotdogs
- Buns
- Ketchup
- A cooking procedure for the hotdog
- A pot
- Tongs
- Someone to do the cooking
- A plate
- Someone to put the hotdog into the bun
- Someone to put the ketchup on the hotdog
- Someone to put the completed hotdog onto a plate
- Someone to serve the hotdog to another

If you combine all of the above processes into a pictorial representation of exactly how these elements become the served hotdog, then you have a value stream map.

The purpose for determining a value stream for a process is that you can identify areas of concern, waste, and improvement. In the above process, are there four different people putting the hotdog together and serving it, or is one person doing all four of those tasks? Is the supplier a single grocery store, or are you shopping for items at various stores and why? Do you get savings benefits to offset the added time spent working with multiple suppliers? These are some examples of the questions you can reveal and answer during value stream mapping.

Continuous Process Improvement

Inherent in the Six Sigma method is *continuous* process improvement. An organization that completely adopts a Six Sigma methodology never stops improving. It identifies and prioritizes areas of opportunity on a continuous basis. Once one area is improved upon, the organization moves on to improving another area. If a process is improved from 4 Sigma to 4.4 Sigma, the organization considers ways to move the sigma level up further. The goal is to move ever closer to the "perfect" level of 99.99966 accuracy for all processes within an organization while maintaining other goals and requirements, such as financial stability, as quickly as possible.

Variation

One of the ways to continuously improve a process is to reduce the variation in the process. Every process contains inherent variation: in a call center with 20 employees, variation will exist in each phone call even if the calls are scripted. Inflection, accents, environmental concerns, and caller moods are just some things that lead to variation in this circumstance. By providing employees with a script or suggested comments for common scenarios, the call center reduces variation to some degree.

Consider another example: A pizzeria. The employees are instructed to use certain amounts of ingredients for each size of pizza. A small gets one cup of cheese; a large gets two cups. The pizzeria owner notes a great deal of variation in how much cheese is on each pizza, and he fears it will lead to inconsistent customer experiences. To reduce variation, he provides employees with two measuring cups: a 1-cup container for small pizzas and a 2-cup container for large pizzas.

The variation is reduced, but it is still present. Some employees pour cheese into the cups and some scoop it. Some fill the cups just to the rim; others let the cheese create a mound above the rim. The owner acts to reduce variation again: he trains all employees to fill the cup over the rim and use a flat spatula to scrape excess cheese off. While variation will still exist due to factors such as air pockets or how cheese settles in the cup, it is greatly reduced, and customers experience more consistent pizzas.

Removing Waste

Remember the hotdog example for value streams? We asked the question: do four different people act to place the hotdog in the bun, put the ketchup on the hotdog, plate the hotdog, and serve it? If so, does the process take more time because the product has to be transferred between four people? Would it be faster to have one person perform all those actions? If so, then we've identified some waste in the process—in this case, waste of conveyance.

Removing waste—items, actions, or people that are unnecessary to the outcome of a process—reduces processing time, opportunities for errors, and overall costs. While waste is a major concern in the Six Sigma methodology, the concept of waste comes from a methodology known as Lean Process Management..

Equipping People

Implementing improved processes is a temporary measure unless organizations equip their employees working with processes to monitor and maintain improvements. In most organizations, process improvement includes a two-pronged approach. First, a process improvement team comprised of project management, methodology experts, and subject-matter experts define, plan, and implement an improvement. That team then equips the employees who work directly with the process daily to control and manage the process in its improved state.

Controlling the Process

Often, Six Sigma improvements address processes that are out of control. Out of control processes meet specific statistical requirements. The goal of improvement is to bring a process back within a state of statistical control. Then, after improvements are implemented, measurements, statistics, and other Six Sigma tools are used to ensure the process remains in control. Part of any continuous improvement process is ensuring such controls are put in place and that the employees who are hands-on with the process on a regular basis know how to use the controls.

Challenges of Six Sigma

Six Sigma is not without its own challenges. As an expansive method that requires commitment to continuous improvement, Six Sigma is often viewed as an expensive or unnecessary process, especially for small or mid-sized organizations. Leadership at Ideal Aerosmith, a manufacturing and engineering company in Minnesota, was skeptical of Six Sigma ideas and the costs associated with implementing them. Despite reservations, the company waded into Six Sigma implementations, eventually seeing worthwhile results after only 18 months. Those results included a production improvement of 25 percent, a 5 percent improvement in profits within the first year, and a 30 percent improvement in timely deliverables.[4]

Some obstacles and challenges that often stand in the way of positive results from Six Sigma include lack of support, resources, or knowledge, poor execution of projects, inconsistent access to valid statistical data, and concerns about using the methodology in new industries.

---

[4] Gupta, Praveen and Schultz, Barb, "Six Sigma Success in Small Business," Quality Digest. http://www.qualitydigest.com/april05/articles/02_article.shtml

Lack of Support

Six Sigma requires support and buy-in at all levels of an organization. Leaders and executives must be willing to back initiatives with resources—financial and labor related. Subject-matter experts must be open to sharing information about their processes with project teams, and employees at all levels must embrace the idea of change and improvement and participate in training. Common barriers to support include:

- Leaders that are unfamiliar with or don't understand the Six Sigma process
- Leaders willing to pursue improvements initially but who lose interest in overseeing and championing projects before they are completed
- Staff that is fearful of change, especially in an environment when change has historically caused negative consequences for employees
- Employees who are resistant to change because they believe improvements might make them obsolete, drastically change their jobs, or make their jobs harder
- Department heads or employees who constantly champion their own processes and needs and are unwilling to enter into big-picture thinking

Lack of Resources or Knowledge

Lack of resources can be a challenge to Six Sigma initiatives, but they don't have to be a barrier. Lack of knowledge about how to use and implement Six Sigma is one of the first issues small- and mid-sized companies face. Smaller businesses can't always afford to hire dedicated resources to handle continuous process improvement, but the availability of resources and Six Sigma training makes it increasingly possible for organizations to use some of the tools without an expert or to send in-house staff to be certified in Six Sigma.

Poor Project Execution

Companies implementing Six Sigma for the first time, especially in a project environment, often turn away from the entire methodology if the first project or improvement falls flat. Proponents of Six Sigma within any organization really have to hit it out of the ballpark with the first project if leadership and others are on the fence about the methodology. Teams can help avoid poor project performance by taking extreme care to execute every phase of the project correctly. By choosing low-risk, high-reward improvements, teams can also stack the deck in their favor with first-time projects. The only disadvantage with such a tactic is that it can be hard to duplicate the wow factor with subsequent improvements, making it important to remember that long-term implementation and commitment is vital in Six Sigma.

Data Access Issues

Data and analytics issues are a common challenge for organizations of all sizes. Gaining access to consistent and accurate data streams—and applying statistical analysis to that data in an appropriate manner—is difficult. Some data-related challenges include:

- Discovering that an important process metric is not being captured
- The use of manual data processes in many processes
- Automated data processes that capture enormous amounts and create scope challenges
- Data that is skewed due to assumptions, human interaction in the process, or incorrect capture
- Lengthy times between raw data capture and access
- Industry or company compliance rules that make it difficult to gain access to necessary data

Concerns about Using Six Sigma in a Specific Industry

Six Sigma originated in the manufacturing industry and many of the concepts and tools of the methodology are still taught in the context of a factory or industrial environment. Because of this, organizations often discount the methods or believe they will be too difficult to implement in other industries. In reality, Six Sigma can be customized to any industry.

CHAPTER 2:
SIX SIGMA HISTORY AND APPLICATION

While the roots of Six Sigma are commonly attributed to companies such as Toyota and Motorola, the methodology is actually grounded in concepts that date as far back as the 19th century. Before delving into the history of Six Sigma, it's important to understand the difference between traditional quality programs, such as Total Quality Management, and continuous process improvement methods, such as Six Sigma.

Most modern quality and improvement programs can be traced back to the same roots. Both quality programs and continuous process improvement methods look to achieve goals such as reducing errors and defects, making processes more efficient, improving customer satisfaction, and boosting profits. But quality programs are concerned with achieving a specific goal. The program either runs forever, constantly working toward the same goal, or it achieves the end goal and must be reset for a new goal.

Six Sigma seeks to instill a culture of *continuous* improvement and quality that optimizes performance of an organization from the inside out. It's the cultural element inherent in Six Sigma that lets organizations enact both small and sweeping improvements that drastically impact efficiencies and costs. Six Sigma does work toward individual goals with regard to each project, but the projects are part of the overall culture of improvement that, in practice, is never done. Six Sigma creates safeguards and tactics so that, even after a project is considered complete, controls are in place to ensure progress continues and it is impossible to revert to old ways.

The Development of Statistical Process Control

Six Sigma applies statistics to define, measure, analyze, verify, and control processes. In fact, Six Sigma teams usually use methodologies known as DMAIC or DMADV to accomplish improvements and develop controls for processes. DMAIC stands for Define, Measure, Analyze, Improve, and Control. These are the five phases of a Six Sigma project to improve a process that already exists. When developing a new process, teams use DMADV, which stands for Define, Measure, Analyze, Design, and Verify. Both methods are discussed in Chapter 11, and Unit 3 provides in-depth information about each phase of DMAIC.

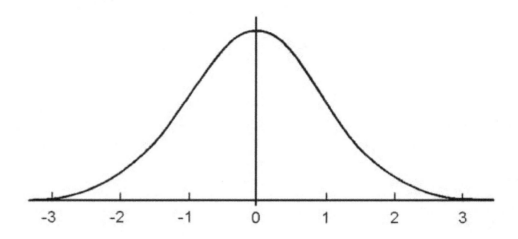

The Normal Curve

The roots of statistical process control, which provide a backbone for Six Sigma methods, began with the development of the normal curve by Carl Friedrich Gauss in the 19th century. We know today that the normal curve is just one of several possible probability distribution models. It is perhaps the most widely used model, and the other models developed from the normal curve. Probability distribution models are discussed in later chapters on statistics

In the early part of the 20th century, statistical process control received another big boost thanks to contributions from an engineer and scholar named Walter Shewhart. Shewhart's contributions to quality are many, but two specific ideas stand out. First, Shewhart was the first person to closely relate sigma level and quality. He defined a process in need of correction as one that is performing at three sigma. If you look back to Chapter 1 and the theoretical Amazon example, the cost difference between four sigma and three sigma is over $78 million; in comparison, the difference between five and four sigma is only approximately $7.6 million. Because errors and costs exponentially increase as sigma level decreases, Shewhart's definition has very practical applications in business. While Six Sigma as a method seeks to move ever toward less than 3.4 defects per million opportunities (dpmo), it is also true that if the quality of a process decreases, as it approaches three sigma, the costs associated with errors increase substantially.

Second, Shewhart is considered the father of control charts. Control charts, which are covered in depth in the chapters on advanced statistics, are a critical component of statistical process control that lets organizations maintain improved performance after a Six Sigma initiative. At a time when scholars were writing about the theoretical application of statistics in a growing number of fields, Shewhart developed ways to apply these concepts to manufacturing and industrial processes specifically.

During the same time period, W. Edwards Deming was working for the U.S. Department of Agriculture. A physicist and mathematician, Deming was in charge of teaching courses at the agency's graduate school and he arranged for Shewhart to come and speak there. Later, Deming brought Shewhart's statistical concepts to the United States Census Bureau, applying his theories outside of an industrial or manufacturing environment for possibly the first time.

One of Deming's ideas is called the PDCA cycle, or plan-do-check-act cycle. The idea is that improvement comes when you recognize there is a need for change and make a plan to create improvement. Next, you do something by testing your ideas. Using the results of the test, you check or verify that your improvements are working. Then you act, bringing your improvements to a production environment or scaling improvements outside of the test environment. The fact that PDCA is a cycle means it never ends; there are always improvements to be made. This is a core tenet of Six Sigma.

Following World War II, Deming worked in Japan on behalf of the United States government in several capacities. While in post-war Japan, Deming befriended statisticians and convinced at least one notable engineer that statistical process control was relevant to Japan's need to drastically drive economic and production performance to overcome damage from the war. In the end, Deming became a valued teacher and consultant to manufacturing companies in Japan, planting the ideas and concepts that would soon become the Toyota Production System, or Lean Six Sigma.

Continuous Process Improvement: Toyota and Lean

Deming's teachings and the need for Japanese industry to make a successful comeback following a catastrophic war combined to bear fruit for Toyota. Toyota's leadership had visited the concepts of quality prior to WWII, but improved performance and efficiency became a more critical goal given the nature of Japan's economy and resources in the 1940s and 50s. Taking manufacturing ideas attributed to Henry Ford, Toyota leaders applied statistics and new quality concepts to create a system they felt would increase production and allow for variable products while reducing costs and ensuring quality.

Several individuals were instrumental in the ultimate development of the Toyota Production System. They infused the process with automated machinery, quality controls to keep defects from occurring, and efficiency tools that had not yet been applied with such detail and consistency. One man, Kiichiro Toyoda, had previous factory experience. In his previous jobs, he

What is Jidoka?

Jidoka is a principle that creates control of defects inside a business process. Instead of identifying defects at the end of the production line and attempting to trace errors back to a source, jidoka demands that a process stop as soon as errors are detected so improvements or troubleshooting can happen immediately.

For jidoka to work properly, machines are often equipped to recognize bad outputs from good outputs; the machines are also equipped with a notification of some type to spark human interaction in the process when things go awry.

added efficiencies to processes in textile mills through conveyor and other automated systems. Toyoda introduced the same concepts on certain lines in the Toyota manufacturing process. Later, Eiji Toyoda and Taiichi Ohno introduced concepts known as Just-in-Time and jidoka, which are the pillars of the Toyota Production System.

The principles driving Toyota's system, and later, the foundation of Lean Process Management or Lean Six Sigma, include:

- Defining customer values
- Identifying the value stream for customer needs and desires
- Identifying waste in the process
- Creation of a continuous process flow
- Continually working to reduce the number of steps and time it takes to reach customer satisfaction

Lean management is highly concerned with removing waste from any process. Waste increases costs and time spent on a process, making it undesirable in any form.

Motorola's Focus on Defects

Though the basis for Six Sigma was laid in the late 19th and early 20th centuries, it wasn't until the mid-1980s that these concepts saw large-scale success in the United States. Decades after Toyota developed its system, engineers at Motorola began to question how effective their quality management programs were. Those questions first arose after a Japanese company took over a Motorola television manufacturing plant. By applying Lean concepts, the new company began creating televisions that demonstrated 1/20th the amount of defects as Motorola's own television sets.

At the time, departments across Motorola measured defects as a ratio of a thousand opportunities. Bob Galvin, the CEO of Motorola, issued a challenge to his team. He wanted to see an improvement in quality and production—not just any improvement; he wanted a ten-fold improvement in half a decade. Engineer Bill Smith and a new addition to the Motorola team – Dr. Mikel Harry – began to work on the problem.

The team realized that measuring errors against a thousand opportunities didn't provide the level of detail needed for true statistical process control. Instead, the engineers wanted to measure defects against a million opportunities. We know that sigma levels were already defined and the idea of using sigma levels as a measure of quality began with Shewhart. It wasn't a long jump for the Motorola engineers to make from their desire for more accurate data to the basic concepts of Six Sigma as both a goal and a methodology.

Throughout the next two decades, Motorola worked to perfect its Six Sigma methodology, seeing positive results along the way. In addition to statistical tools, the team created a step-by-step process by which any team--in almost any industry--could make gains and improvements. For the first time, this type of statistical process control was taken out of the manufacturing environment on a large scale company-wide. Motorola applied the method to customer service, engineering, and technical support. It used the process to create a collaborative environment between stakeholders inside and outside of the organization. It was highly successful; according to Motorola, the company saved more than $16 billion as a result of continuous process improvement initiatives within 12 years.[5]

Motorola did more than improve its own systems and products, though. Galvin directed his team to share Six Sigma with the world. Motorola and its team published articles and books on the Six Sigma method and implemented efforts to train others. In this way, they created a methodology based on statistics that could be taught and implemented within any organization or industry.

ABB, Allied Signal, and General Electric

After leaving Motorola, Dr. Harry joined Asea Brown Boveri. At ABB, Harry worked with Richard Schroeder, who would also become a champion for Six Sigma. In fact, the two men later cofounded the Six Sigma Academy. At ABB, Harry came to realize a key idea in the evolution of Six Sigma: business, or profits, in some ways came before quality. Quality, in fact, was a driving factor of business. Customers didn't make purchases if quality was poor. Because the individuals with the ability to decide in favor of Six Sigma initiatives were highly motivated by dollars, Harry incorporated financial tactics into the Six Sigma methodology. For the first time, the method was focused on the bottom-line as a primary goal with other concerns and goals stemming from financially-led goals.

In 1993, both Schroeder and Harry changed jobs, joining the team at Allied Signal. Allied Signal's CEO at the time was Larry Bossidy. He was interested in Six Sigma but realized that executives and other high-level leaders experienced knowledge barriers while attempting to interact and collaborate with analysts, process engineers, and Six Sigma experts. Bossidy

---

[5] "The History of Six Sigma," iSixSigma. http://www.isixsigma.com/new-to-six-sigma/history/history-six-sigma/

suggested that leadership at a company had to be well-versed in Six Sigma to pick the right projects for success and support those projects on a company-wide basis to ensure success.

Harry, who is sometimes referred to as the father of Six Sigma, created a system for educating executive leaders. In conjunction with others at Allied Signal, he developed systems that allowed Six Sigma to be effectively deployed by leadership throughout an organization in its entirety.

Around the same time, GE CEO Jack Welch entered into the Six Sigma arena. Prior to learning about Six Sigma, Welch had stated he was not a proponent of quality measures. He'd previously criticized quality programs as heavy-handed approaches that did little to deliver results. Welch invited Larry Bossidy to speak at a GE corporate meeting in 1995. He also requested an analysis regarding the benefits of implementing Six Sigma at GE. At that time, GE was performing at between three and four sigma. The potential savings should the company rise to six sigma were enormous; estimates were $7 to $10 billion.[6]

Welch is known as a champion of Six Sigma not because he contributed in major ways to the development of statistical process controls or the Six Sigma toolsets, but because he demonstrated exactly how leaders should approach Six Sigma. He also made GE a historically successful Six Sigma organization by tying Six Sigma goals to employee reward structures. Employees were no longer only compensated based on financial performance factors; they were also evaluated based on Six Sigma performance. Suddenly, employees at every level had a personal reason to become involved in continuous process improvement, and employees and managers were supplied with the Six Sigma training to succeed.

Continued Growth of Six Sigma

Following the success of corporations such as GE and Motorola, companies across the country rushed to implement Six Sigma. Unfortunately, in the rush to implement the process, many organizations executed improvements poorly or failed to gain an adequate understanding of statistical process control before moving forward with improvements. Although Six Sigma methods have been used by organizations to gain millions—even billions—in savings and efficiencies, some companies walked away with a bad taste for the process. That bad taste has resulted in the following misconceptions and myths that are still prevalent today in many industries:

---

[6] "The Evolution of Six Sigma," PQA.net.
http://www.pqa.net/ProdServices/sixsigma/W06002009.html

- *Six Sigma is solely concerned with metrics and ignores common sense.* The opposite is actually true: Six Sigma often starts with traditional common sense ideas, often arrived at through brainstorming, and validates those assumptions with data. The reason for this myth is twofold. First, managers and others who are used to making calls without being questioned are suddenly questioned in a Six Sigma environment. Not only are they questioned, but hard data sometimes proves them wrong. Second, in some cases data is improperly used to support conclusions that are against common sense or tradition. When those conclusions turn out to be faulty, it's easy to blame the process of Six Sigma there is a lack of adequate understanding of the statistical theories involved.
- *Six Sigma is too expensive.* While enterprise-wide adoption of Six Sigma can be costly at first, due in part to training needs, slowly integrating the concepts into a company often costs very little in the long run. Organizations have to balance how they adopt Six Sigma with budgetary concerns—but when implemented correctly, Six Sigma generally leads to savings that more than cover its initial investment.
- *Six Sigma can fix anything.* Opposite the nay-sayers are Six Sigma cheerleaders who believe they can apply the method like a salve to any problem. While Six Sigma can be applied to any problem of process, it's not always relevant to problems of culture or people. If morale or other human resource problems are at the root of an issue, statistics can't help. However, if morale is low because a process is difficult to work with or is performing poorly, Six Sigma can be used to improve the process, thereby improving morale.

Applying Six Sigma Knowledge

Six Sigma is applied via a controlled project selection and management process. Once areas of concern are identified, leaders usually turn to analysts, Six Sigma experts, and subject-matter-experts for cost-benefit analyses. Six Sigma teams attempt to quantify how broken a process is (by calculating sigma level, costs of defects, downtime, and other metrics) and how much it might cost to address the problem. Problems are then prioritized according to severity as well as an organization's ability to address the issue. Teams begin working through the priority list, returning to the analysis from time to time to ensure the list has not changed. The majority of this book covers the methods by which teams identify and address problems using Six Sigma.

The Levels of Six Sigma Certification

Possessing a Six Sigma certification proves that an individual has demonstrated practical applications and knowledge of Six Sigma. Some organizations offer in-house certification processes. Most people seek certification by enrolling in online or onsite Six Sigma training course. Most organizations that offer Six Sigma education also offer a path to certification. You can take courses for certification at various levels; Six Sigma levels are differentiated by belt level.

White Belt

A certified Six Sigma White belt is familiar with the basic tenets of the Six Sigma methodology, though they aren't often regular members of process improvement teams. White belt training is a good introduction to Six Sigma for auxiliary staff members within an organization and can provide the information necessary for understanding why project teams do what they do. The training lets employees review project processes, understand information presented in milestone meetings, and better participate in project selection processes. White belt training can also be used across all levels of employees when organizations are attempting to implement a Six Sigma culture. It is worth noting that White Belt training usually only provides a very basic introduction and overview of Six Sigma, so much so that not all Six Sigma professionals recognize it as a true Six Sigma certification.

Yellow Belt

A yellow belt certification is a step above white belt: it is still considered a basic introduction to the concepts of Six Sigma, but a yellow belt learns basic information about the DMAIC method often used to improve processes. The following concepts are often included in Six Sigma yellow belt training:

- Six Sigma roles
- Team development and management
- Basic quality tools such as Pareto charts, run charts, scatter diagrams and histograms
- Common Six Sigma metrics
- Data collection
- Measurement system analysis
- Root cause analysis
- An introduction to hypothesis testing

At the yellow belt level, training is often geared toward understanding of the overall methodology and basic data collection. Yellow belts don't need to know how to conduct hypothesis testing, but they must understand the language of hypothesis testing and the conclusions that are drawn from such tests. Yellow belts are often employees who need to know about the overall process and why it is being implemented.

Green Belt

Certified green belts work within Six Sigma teams, usually under the supervision of a black belt or master black belt. In some cases, green belts might lead or handle smaller projects on their own. Green belts are generally equipped with intermediate statistical analysis capabilities; they might address data and analysis concerns, help Black Belts apply Six Sigma tools to a project, or teach others within an organization about the overall Six Sigma methodology.

Green Belts can be middle managers, business analysts, project managers, and others who have a reason to be involved regularly with process improvement initiatives but who might not be a full-time Six Sigma expert within an organization. Sometimes, Green Belts are considered the worker bees of the Six Sigma methodology because they undertake most of the statistical data collection and analysis under the supervision of certified Black Belts.

The following concepts are often included in Green Belt training:

- All of the information listed for yellow belt certification
- Failure mode and effects analysis
- Project and team management
- Probability and the Central Limit Theorem
- Statistical distributions
- Descriptive statistics
- How to perform basic hypothesis testing
- Waste elimination and Kaizen
- Basic control charts

Black Belt

A certified Six Sigma Black Belt usually works as the project leader on process improvement projects. They might also work within management, analyst, or planning roles throughout a company. Common minimum requirements for black belt certification include everything listed for yellow and green belts in addition to:

- Advanced project and team management skills
- Knowledge of the expansive list of Six Sigma brainstorming and project tools
- Intermediate to advanced statistics
- An understanding of other process improvement and quality programs, including Lean and Total Quality Management
- An ability to design processes
- Advanced capabilities for diagraming processes, including flow charts and value stream maps
- Use of software to conduct analysis, such as Excel or Minitab

Master Black Belt

A Master Black Belt is the highest certification level achievable for Six Sigma. Within a business organization, Master Black Belts usually manage Black Belts and Green Belts, consult on especially difficult project concerns, offer advice and education about challenging statistical concepts, and train others in Six Sigma methodology.

Certification Exams

Most certification programs require individuals to pass an exam for certification; some require that green and black belt candidates also demonstrate their knowledge in the form of Six Sigma project experience.

If an exam is required for white or yellow belt certification, it is usually fairly short and covers basic concepts about the methodology. Green belt exams are longer and might include questions about statistics and some basic calculations. Black belt exams often take up to four hours to complete; they test for understanding and application. Exams might include difficult statistical problems or questions about how a project leader might handle various situations. While exams differ by organization, this book is designed based on The Council for Six Sigma Certification's (CSSC) published body-of-knowledge requirements.

Note: *For those that are utilizing this textbook in preparation for one of the certification exams administered directly by the Council for Six Sigma Certification (www.sixsigmacouncil.org), the following material should be reviewed as follows in preparation for the open-book examination(s):*

White Belt Certification *or* **Lean White Belt Certification**: *Chapter 1 thru Chapter 3*

Yellow Belt Certification or ***Lean Yellow Belt Certification***: *Chapter 1 thru Chapter 11*
Green Belt Certification or ***Lean Green Belt Certification***: *Chapter 1 thru Chapter 24*
Black Belt Certification or ***Lean Black Belt Certification***: *Chapter 1 thru Chapter 33*
Master Black Belt Certification or ***Lean Master Black Belt Certification***: *Chapter 1 thru Chapter 33*

CHAPTER 3:
OTHER PROCESS IMPROVEMENT AND QUALITY METHODS

By studying the history of Six Sigma, you've already realized that the methodology is closely related to a number of other quality-driven initiatives developed over the past century. This is true in part because all successful businesses ultimately seek to do the same thing: serve a customer a product or service they need while making as much profit as possible.

While Six Sigma encompasses all the tools you need to approach virtually any problem of process, familiarity with other types of process improvement and quality methods is important. Some of these methods, such as Lean and JumpStart, add value within a Six Sigma approach. Others might be used by outside resources alongside a Six Sigma project. Even if you don't use or work with some of these programs, you will need to communicate with leadership and business partners who are more familiar with other methods. The ability to frame Six Sigma concepts in a more global quality management approach can help you win support for your own projects.

Other Formal Quality or Process Improvement Programs

Lean Process Management

Lean principles often go hand-in-hand with Six Sigma principles. While Lean originally developed as a concept for reducing waste in a manufacturing environment, the ideas of Lean Process Management can be applied to any process that involves the movement or creation of goods or services. This is true even if those services are virtual or digital, such as in a computerized workflow process.

One of the ways that Lean is similar to Six Sigma is that it is concerned with continuous improvements; like Six Sigma, Lean provides waste-removal tools so daily control and improvements can be made to processes. In fact, one of Lean's continuous improvement tools is called Kaizen, a Japanese word that translates loosely to "change for the better."

The purpose of every change in a Kaizen environment is to eliminate waste and/or create more value for the customer on a continuous basis.

Lean Process Management can be deployed within a project environment or in daily production. Like Six Sigma, Lean is more about an overall culture of quality than a single quality event. Many organizations use Lean principles to make improvements in processes. By simply instituting some of the Lean principles, managers can drastically increase production and reduce costs for their departments.

Because Lean principles are so effective and fit so well with Six Sigma principles, for the purpose of this book, we will often treat Lean as a part of the Six Sigma methodology.

Total Quality Management

Total Quality Management, or TQM, is a phrase well-known by anyone who worked in business in the last quarter of the 20th century. The TQM approach to quality is one of the first formal methods enacted in business environments in the United States. Originally developed in the 1950s, Total Quality Management didn't become popular with companies across the country until the 80s. At one point, TQM was so popular with executives and other leaders that it actually became something of a joke among certain workforces who believed that much effort and expense was expended on quality without an equal resulting benefit. In fact, if you remember from the last chapter, Jack Welch at GE felt this way.

While Total Quality Management programs were often somewhat lackluster when it came to results, the method was an essential stepping point to current improvement and quality methods such as Six Sigma. TQM was not without its results: as with any method, results depended highly on the way the program was implemented and the culture of the organization. For this reason, TQM and its variations are still in play in many industries today. Some requirements for a successful TQM program include:

- A strict quality commitment at all levels of the organization, especially among leaders
- Empowered employees who can make quality decisions while working within the process without constantly seeking leadership approval for those decisions
- A reward and recognition structure to promote quality work so that employees have a reason to make quality-making decisions
- Strategic planning that takes quality and quality improvement goals into account when making long-term decisions
- Systems that let organizations make improvements and monitor quality

Successful TQM initiatives require eight key elements: ethics, integrity, trust, training, teamwork, leadership, recognition, and communication. You can view these elements as if they were part of the components needed to build a high-quality, lasting building. Ethics, integrity, and trust become the foundation for quality. Training, teamwork, and leadership are the bricks by which quality organizations are built. Honest, open, and concise communication is the mortar that binds everything else together, and recognition is the roof that covers everything, providing employees with a reason to seek and maintain quality.

One of the biggest advantages of the TQM mentality is that it began to force organizations to see themselves as one entity rather than a number of loosely related entities or departments. Prior to the quality methods developed in the last half of the 20th century, many organizations were run via heavily siloed departments. One department often did not understand what another was doing, which caused a great deal of rework and waste. Each department might seek higher quality levels or process improvements, but in the end, the organization was only as strong as the weakest element.

TQM began to change departmental thinking on a massive scale: organizations began to take enterprise approaches to decision making, quality, and customer service. Business leaders started to look at companies as a series of linked processes operating toward a single end goal. Within the bounds of TQM, the ideas for business process reengineering began to develop.

Organizations using TQM often experienced benefits such as:

- Improved employee engagement and morale
- A reduction in production or product costs
- Decreased cycle times
- More satisfied customers

Business Process Reengineering

Six Sigma, Lean and TQM are all concerned with making *continuous* changes on both a large and small scale that bring an organization ever closer to a model of perfection. In the case of Lean, that model is a process that has zero waste; in Six Sigma, the model is statistically 6 sigma. In TQM, organizations often define their own version of perfection before working toward it. Business Process Reengineering, or BPR, is less concerned with incremental quality wins and more concerned with a radical change across an entire organization or process architecture.

Business process reengineering, which is also called business process redesign, is most often concerned with the technical processes that occur throughout an organization. Those processes might include systems, software, data storage, cloud and web processes, and computer-based workflows operated and maintained by human users. Because of the intense integration of automation and computer elements into processes with BPR, organizations that enter BPR endeavors have to rely heavily on both inside and outside technical resources. Inside resources provide programming, integration, and troubleshooting services as processes are developed or redesigned. Outside resources can be BPR consultants, contracted programmers and developers, or vendors bringing new software products to the table.

As you can probably imagine, BPR initiatives can be costly, which is why they are often deployed only when an organization expects exponential gain or has determined that current processes are obsolete or badly broken.

BPR projects tend to follow a common map, though there isn't a defined set of principles as there is with Six Sigma. Most projects go through planning, design, and implementation phases. During planning, teams use process mapping and process architecture principles to define enterprise-wide processes in their current state. Teams look for opportunities for improvement and brainstorm new architectures for processes throughout the organization.

During the design phase, BPR teams use validation techniques 3 to ensure solutions they are planning will work within the enterprise structure. They also begin to build tools and programs to integrate the changes; technical teams might use the Scrum methods described later in this chapter at this point in the process.

Finally, organizations implement the changes they have made. Since changes are often programmatic in nature, implementation usually includes a rigorous change management and testing procedure. Testing in technical environments includes steps such as:

- Sandbox testing of basic functionality
- Quality assurance testing by trained technical resources
- Beta testing during which experienced subject matter experts vet all aspects of a program in a limited live environment

- A rollout of the program to the enterprise, often conducted in a phased approach during which technical resources are on call to immediately resolve troubleshooting issues
- A conversion to regular function where technical resources are available in a normal capacity to deal with occasional issues

Rummler-Brache

As process improvement methods became increasingly popular in the 1980s and later, individuals often took portions of one method or another and integrated it into new improvement or quality programs. In this manner, companies outside of the manufacturing industry began implementing bits and pieces of methods that incorporated Lean and Six Sigma elements. One such program is known as Rummler-Brache.

Rummler-Brache was pioneered in the 80s by Geary Rummler and Alan Brache. They developed what remains a proprietary program used by their own consulting firm, but details of the method have been published and used by others. The method seeks to affect positive change in processes and organizations by using a set of practical tools to address business issues and process problems.

One of the foundational components of Rummler-Brache is known as the Nine Boxes Model. The model is created by a matrix of three performance levels and three performance dimensions. Performance levels are the performer, the process, and the organization. Dimensions are management, design, and goal. When placed on a grid, the levels and dimensions form nine boxes, as seen below.

	Management	Design	Goals
Performer	Concerned with feedback, consequences, and rewards	Concerned with the tools and training needed to do the job as well as job documentation	Concerned with performance metrics and requirements at an individual level
Process	Concerned with who owns the process and how they might improve it	Concerned with the design of the process, work space, or system	Concerned with the requirements of the business and the customer
Organization	Concerned with overall leadership culture and the requirements of performance evaluation	Concerned with overall org charts and process architecture	Concerned with operating plans and top-level metrics

Rummler-Brache approaches improvement in six phases:

- **Improvement planning.** During the first phase, leadership and subject-matter-experts commit to making improvements and begin to identify opportunities for change.
- **Definition.** During the second phase, project goals and scopes are defined and teams are formed to create improvements.
- **Analysis and Design.** Teams use analysis to understand the current problem and to define and validate workable solutions.
- **Implementation.** Teams implement process changes. Depending on the type of change, this might include programming changes, retraining staff, changes in machinery or equipment, or policy changes.
- **Management of process.** Teams monitor the process during and immediately following the change to ensure improvements function as planned.

- **Processes are turned over to daily teams**. Management of the process is turned over to daily teams, often with some type of control in place to ensure continued success.

Scrum

Scrum is a project development method specific to Agile programming endeavors in technical departments. Scrum is used when teams want to create new technical products or integrate new developments on existing products within a short time frame. Commonly, Scrum projects last between two and four weeks, which is traditionally a very tight timeline for programming projects. Scrum was developed as programming and development teams needed a way to meet continuous technical design and improvement needs from other departments without substantially increasing programming, testing employee hours, or hiring more technical staff. Scrum can also be used to drive faster times to production or market for software and application products.

Scrum is a related concept to other process improvement initiatives discussed in the book because many projects today call for some type of technical resource or change. While project teams are working to validate and measure, technical departments often simultaneously deploy Scrum concepts to meet development needs for the improvement project by deadline.

Scrum projects feature three main phases:

- **The pregame**. Development teams analyze available data and business requirements. They use this information to come up with the concept for the new product or upgrade. Often, this involves translating business and process concepts into computer and technical concepts.
- **The game**. Teams begin to develop the product via programming sprints. Sprints are smaller phases of development that are completed in sequence, usually with a review and validation of the work before moving on to the next sprint. By validating work during development, teams are able to create working products faster.
- **The postgame**. Even though validation occurs during development, teams still have to follow quality assurance, testing, and change management procedures. Quality preparation for product release is handled in the final phase.

The Customer Experience Management Method (CEM)

Like Rummler-Brache, the Customer Experience Management Method, or CEM Method, was created by process improvement consultants to address needs in organizations outside of manufacturing. CEM combines some process improvement tools with customer relations management. It was developed in the 1990s by the Virgin Group and became popular throughout the 90s and early part of the 21st century.

The CEM Method takes an outside-in approach to process improvement, focusing on what the customer wants or needs and how each process in an organization serves that need. The primary purpose of CEM is to align processes throughout an organization with customer satisfaction goals. As such, even processes without a direct relation to customers are defined in terms of customers.

For example, shipping processes are obviously directly related to end customers, so it's easy to define how those processes can best serve customers. Shipments should arrive on time, be accurate to orders, and shipping costs should be affordable.

In-house human resource processes are harder to link to customer-facing goals. However, the morale and functionality of employees *is* directly related to how those employees can serve customers. You can make a customer-facing statement about almost any process in an organization in this manner. If organizations cannot link a process to the customer, then they must ask whether the process is necessary or broken.

Like Six Sigma, CEM relies heavily on data. Organizations can't make determinations about customer goals and the success of processes without collecting and analyzing customer feedback. The advantage of CEM is that organizations are able to deploy customer-facing tactics across the enterprise, which often results in enormous gains in customer satisfaction, loyalty, and spending. A disadvantage of this method is that traditionally inward-facing departments, such as human resources, legal, and accounting, often have a difficult time implementing customer-focused cultural change.

JumpStart

JumpStart differs from the other programs and methods described in this chapter in that it is a fast-paced method for identifying problems and solutions in a single session. JumpStart can be used within almost all of the other methods described in this book as a way to spark discussion regarding processes or to identify possible solutions. It can also be used as a management tool for helping teams come to tenable solutions outside of project environments or in the absence of project resources.

Because JumpStart doesn't take the time for rigorous verification or statistical analysis on its own, teams should not use this method to enact sweeping changes or attempt to improve processes that could seriously impact customer experience or the bottom line. One disadvantage of using JumpStart alone is that changes are sometimes made on a wait-and-see mentality, which is safe for many inner-team changes but often dangerous for department or enterprise-wide processes, or for making changes to processes that are closely tied to regulatory or compliance rules.

JumpStart usually begins when leaders at some level identify an area of concern or opportunity. The manager, supervisor, or other delegate identifies a team of employees who they believe would offer appropriate insight on the issue at hand. In most cases, JumpStart doesn't work to define the problem: the group is close enough to the issue that they already know what is wrong. Instead, the group spends several hours brainstorming root causes for the problem and coming up with possible solutions.

Six Sigma and other process improvement tools can be deployed during JumpStart sessions. Fishbone diagrams and solutions selections matrixes, both covered in later chapters, can be used to validate assumptions using only the knowledge of the people in the room and some quick research.

The benefit of JumpStart is that it lets teams create and implement small-scale solutions quickly, often providing problem resolution the same day. It also lets teams identify issues that need to be addressed in a more comprehensive project environment.

When to Use Six Sigma

Some organizations make use of various project improvement methods. As a Six Sigma expert, you might have to champion your own method on occasion. Here are some reasons to choose Six Sigma over other methods described in this chapter.

When facing the unknown

Six Sigma is designed so you can begin a project even when you don't know the cause of the problem. In some cases, teams aren't even sure what the exact problem is – they only know some metric is not performing as desired. For example, an organization might experience a drop in profits that doesn't correct itself in several consecutive quarters. Six Sigma methods can begin to seek the causes of the problem, prioritize them, and work toward solutions.

When problems are widespread and not defined

Even when a problem is understood, if it is wide in scope and not well defined, improvement projects that are not tightly managed can escalate in scope to a point that they become unmanageable. In this situation, teams attempt to solve increasingly bigger issues. As a result, no problem is ever completely solved. Six Sigma includes controls for avoiding such scope creep so teams can make incremental improvements that steadily improve a process over time. We'll talk about scope creep more in later chapters.

When solving complex problems

If processes are complex and feature many variables, it is difficult to determine how to approach a solution, much less define and measure success. Knowledge of statistical analysis and process control lets teams approach problems that involve enormous amounts of data and many variables. Through analysis and graphical representation, complex ideas can be distilled to specific hypotheses, premises, and conclusions.

When costs are closely tied to processes

Because Six Sigma's statistical process control component lets teams make more accurate assumptions than almost any other method, it is very appropriate for situations that are closely tied to revenue or cost. When a single tiny change can result in millions of dollars in gains or losses, teams must validate assumptions with an extremely small margin of error. Guesswork, basic research, and even years of experience cannot do that as accurately as properly implemented Six Sigma methods.

CHAPTER 4:
LEAN CONCEPTS

We've discussed Lean concepts in the previous three chapters because most Six Sigma approaches today incorporate Lean concepts into problem solving and the control of a process. In fact, organizations often use the term Lean Six Sigma when describing a process improvement approach that incorporates tenants from both Six Sigma and Lean methodologies. This is a popular approach because the greatest results usually come when you improve a process so that both defects and waste are eliminated. That statement rings true whether you're measuring from a business-driven bottom-line or a customer-satisfaction approach.

A Six Sigma defect is a failure to meet a requirement in a process. We'll talk more about requirements in Chapter 8 when we define quality. For now, know that **defects** cost money because businesses have to replace parts, equipment, or products that are not perfect. Organizations also experience financial loss associated with defects when quality reputation is so low that customers choose not to return or purchase from the company. From a customer satisfaction standpoint, defects can increase the time it takes for a customer to get what they want or can cause the customer to be unhappy with the end product or service.

Waste costs money because it is unnecessary time, labor, or material in the process. Generally, waste is something that is used in the process that isn't required for a satisfactory outcome. In some cases, waste creates a customer satisfaction issue because it holds up the process or introduces undesirable elements or defects in the end product.

In this chapter, we'll look at some specific types of waste and how to avoid them as well as touch on some Lean concepts for creating the most efficient processes.

The Seven Muda

Muda is a Japanese word that translates to waste. It describes a concept of being useless, unnecessary, or idle. The concept that muda must be eliminated in a process is a driving concept of the Toyota Production System and Lean manufacturing. Muda is a non-value-added task (NVA) within a process. Some types of muda are easier to identify than others, which is why Lean Six Sigma deploys tools such as value stream mapping. By understanding a process at all levels, teams are more likely to identify various forms of muda. According to Taiicho Ohno, chief engineer for Toyota, there are seven muda, or resources that are commonly misused and mismanaged: overproduction, correction, inventory, motion, conveyance, over processing, and waiting.

Overproduction

Overproduction is one of the easiest forms of muda to spot, as it tends to result in what we commonly think of as waste. Overproduction means a product, part, or service was produced too fast, at the wrong time, or in too much quantity for the process. To understand the idea of overproduction, consider a basic fast food restaurant that offers hamburgers and French fries for lunch. The restaurant does not serve breakfast, and it opens its doors at 11:00 a.m. for the lunch crowd.

If the cooks light up the grill at 11:00 a.m., then they might start the day behind, as it is possible that several orders will be placed immediately. However, if the cooks start making hamburger patties at 10:30 a.m., they might have patties that sit for some time before being consumed, which leads to customer dissatisfaction or waste if the patties are thrown out. Making 10 patties every 10 minutes starting at 10:30 a.m. is overproduction—the patties are being made too soon.

What if the restaurant owners have done some research and they know the average number of orders between 11:00 and 11:15 a.m. on a Tuesday is 10 hamburgers? They might instruct the cooks to begin making patties at 10:50 a.m. and to make 5 patties every 10 minutes. The goal is to align patty-making with customer orders so that wait times are reduced but customers are still able to enjoy fresh patties.

By noon, the owners know orders tend to come in quickly, so they ask the cooks to make 15 patties every 10 minutes. By 2:00 p.m., however, the order traffic usually drops to 10 hamburgers an hour. If the cooks are still making 15 every 10 minutes, then the process suffers from overproduction.

At some point, the traffic in the restaurant may call for made-to-order grilling—a process where the cook only makes hamburger patties as they are ordered to avoid wasting any materials. By understanding the traffic trends in their restaurant, the owners are able to estimate needs and create processes that reduce the amount of waste made in the kitchen while still meeting the quality demands of customers.

Overproduction is most often associated with tangible outcomes from a process, though these outcomes don't have to be final, or "end products" of said processes. Consider a business that prints business cards, stationary, invitations, and other documents. Perhaps this business offers a printing and mailing service; to complete this service, the company uses a machine-driven process that prints, folds, and stuffs mailings. The printer is capable of delivering 1,000 pages an hour, but the folding machine is only able to fold 800 pages an hour.

Even if a customer wants 1,000 pages printed and mailed, the printer is overproducing if the first machine is set to operate at maximum speed. The process will take longer than one hour because it is contingent upon the slowest machine. Since the overproduction doesn't result in tangible waste – the printed pages will eventually be folded and mailed – the company's process owners have to consider other factors in order to decide if the temporary overproduction is detrimental to the process. Does the stacking of extra paper before the folding process create an extra risk for error? Does operating the printing machine at maximum capacity without necessity put unnecessary strain or wear and tear on it? If the answer is yes to either question, then there exists waste that should be eliminated from the process.

Overproduction can also exist with regard to reporting, digital assets, and preparation for processes. Almost anyone working in a business environment is familiar with reporting requirements—just as almost anyone who has created reports knows the unfortunate truth that the information often goes unread. Creating reports no one reads—or creating highly detailed reports when an overview would suffice—is overproduction.

Preparing equipment that isn't used in a process is also overproduction. Surgery centers often prepare machines, equipment trays, and operating rooms before shifts begin. The goal is to create efficient processes for any patient operation; staff must also be able to access equipment quickly if issues arise during procedures. Preparing 20 trays of equipment on a day when only 10 surgeries are scheduled might be considered overproduction if there is no use for the extra trays.

In some situations, such as the medical example above, processes might call for slight overproduction. If 10 surgeries are scheduled, staff might prepare 13 or 14 equipment trays. This way, if an emergency surgery arrives, or if an issue comes up with an existing tray, stand-by equipment is available. By understanding nuances within processes and requirements, Six Sigma teams can better identify muda of overproduction versus overproduction that might be required by regulation or problem-solving policies.

The key to eliminating overproduction is planning. In the examples above, you'll note that each solution came when the process operator understood the needs inherent within the process. When the owners knew how many orders were likely, they were able to plan to reduce waste. When the printer knows the capability of each machine in the process, he or she can plan for the most efficient printing run.

Correction

Also known as muda of rework, this form of waste often plagues organizations that are keen on traditional quality programs. In a desire to eliminate defects from the end product, organizations institute in-process quality checks that route work with defects back for correction. While rework might be necessary in some cases, especially if materials are particularly valuable and work is worth saving rather than scrapping, it is still waste in the process that should be identified and analyzed.

When rework occurs, it increases overall process time and uses additional labor and materials to create a smaller amount of products or outputs. Let's look at an example that might be found in the call center for a large automobile insurance company. Some of the calls coming into the center are from individuals who have sustained damage to vehicles in an accident. Consider the following process for handling such calls:

- The caller reports damage to the car.
- The representative records information in a computer form.
- The representative makes a decision based on the information provided by the caller:
    - The claim is routed for immediate handling if it is deemed an emergency
    - The claim is routed to team A if it is a single-car or act-of-God incident
    - The claim is routed to team B if it is a multi-car accident

Now, imagine a claim that arrives in the work queue for an employee working on team B. The information entered into the computer is incomplete, so the employee cannot determine for sure if the claim is related to a multi-car accident. The employee might send the claim back to the original queue, which means a call-center employee would have to call the insured back to gather additional information. The claim would then be routed again, according to the new information, and would wait in a work queue again.

One of the biggest problems with muda of correction is that a case can often be made that the processing is necessary. Perhaps team B is not equipped to deal with single-car incidents, so the work has to be rerouted if the claim is to be completed. But why not equip down-line team members to handle any claim, or create a process for rerouting claims to the correct team without sending the work back to the original queue?

Correction, or rework, can occur in any type of process. Manufacturing processes cull out defective parts and products; sometimes materials are reworked for a better outcome and sometimes they are scrapped—also a form of waste. Call centers and digital work queues are famous for rework, as it's easy to send work back and forth in a digital format. In some cases, rework occurs not because of correction, but simply because departmental or worker responsibilities overlap.

To eliminate rework or correction, organizations must use a twofold approach. First, the root cause of the rework—that which is causing the errors—must be addressed. Is further employee training required? Could a process be changed to make it more mistake proof? In some cases, the principles discussed in later units on process control, including a strategy called a poka yoke, can be deployed to make it more difficult to create defects than to not create defects during a process. When defects are avoided, rework is also avoided.

In addition to addressing the root cause of errors, organizations should create quality steps that reduce rework waste. In the example about the insurance company call center, we noted that it would be more efficient for the down-line worker to reroute the claim to the correct team than to return it to the original team. This method sometimes causes a problem of culture, though; there is a feeling among leaders and staff that the first team or first team member should be held accountable for the error. One way of seeking accountability is to have that person correct his or her mistake. While reworking errors can be a good training method when time and resources allow, it isn't always feasible and doesn't make for an efficient daily process. Instead, employees might be more efficiently held accountable through goal-setting and metrics for the greater good of the organization as a whole.

Inventory

Muda of inventory is similar to muda of overproduction; in fact, overproduction can cause a waste of inventory. Muda of inventory occurs when materials or inputs stack up before a step in the process; this phenomenon is also called a bottleneck. Remember the printing example for overproduction? If the first machine is set to the highest production level, it will generate 1,000 pages an hour. The folding machine can only handle 800 pages an hour, so you would have an inventory of 200 pages created every hour. If both machines ran at highest production for four hours, the process would have developed an inventory of 800 pages. Until and unless the folding process becomes faster, then those extra pages are wasted inventory and will continue to pile up.

Inventory waste can occur when items are purchased or created before they are needed in a manufacturing or service process. Inventory can also occur in work queues, digital data queues, or even email inboxes. If you receive 300 emails a day and you are only handling 30 of them on a regular basis, you have a process problem with your communications.

While inventory waste can occur in any process, it is especially common in processes that operate in batches. Traditional lean wisdom says to avoid batch process – processes that involve creating a certain number of products or outputs before pushing them down the line. Reducing batch size lowers lead times—the time it takes to deliver the end product. It also reduces the amount of inventory that occurs before each step of the process.

While Lean mindsets usually push a batching-is-bad mentality, you can't always avoid it—and reduced lead times on individual outputs aren't always a primary goal of a process. Consider a baker who is preparing an order of one dozen cupcakes. He could prepare the order as a batch, or he could prepare each cupcake separately. Obviously, mixing the ingredients and baking the cupcakes as a batch makes more sense. Decorating them as a batch also works well—the baker might frost all of the cupcakes, add piping to all the cupcakes, and then top all the cupcakes with a candy. Batching works for the baker because the first cupcake is not going to leave the bakery before the 12th is finished—they all move together because they are considered a unit.

You can also reduce waste of inventory by understanding a process and basing inventory decisions on historic metrics. A shipping center that processes between 50,000 and 100,000 boxes a week wouldn't place an order for 300,000 boxes if they only wanted to have a week's supply on hand. A baker doesn't whip cream for seven pies if he or she only intends to make two.

Motion

Muda of motion has to do with how employees themselves move during a process. This type of waste is often relevant to people-powered processes in manufacturing, warehousing, shipping, delivery, or industrial fields, but waste of motion can even crop up in processes that are computerized.

For example, if a data-entry employee has to click back and forth between screens when entering information, this could be muda of motion. If the system is designed so that a number is to be entered in one window and a second number entered in a different window, the click between windows is wasting motion. Moving to another window involves a mouse or keyboard action that could be eliminated if the data were entered on the same window. It seems like an inconsequential detail, but imagine what happens when the data employee completes this process hundreds or thousands of times a day. The waste can absolutely add up:

- If each data-entry employee completes 600 entries an hour on average, and there are 10 employees on a team, the team is completing 48,000 entries each day.
- If it takes only half a second more to toggle between the two windows, the team is still spending a collective 400 minutes a day – just over 6.5 hours – toggling.
- If the average hourly wage for a data worker is $10, the team is spending an extra $325 each week – almost $17,000 each year – to cover the act of toggling between windows.

Given those numbers, a programing change that includes both data elements on the same window could save the company $17,000 in a single year. This same concept can be applied to any form of muda when you can apply a time and dollar figure to the waste.

Other examples of muda of motion include a task that requires an individual to physically move back and forth between work, extra motion that stems from a poor layout of work, or movement that occurs when an employee leaves an area and has to return one or more times because he or she forgot something. Public libraries have long employed a simple tool to avoid muda of motion in the reshelving process: books are first ordered on a cart. The cart allows an employee to carry many books without moving back and forth, and placing the books in order on the cart lets the individual move through the stacks once. If books are placed at random on the cart, the subsequent movement between shelves wastes motion and time.

Streamlining company processes eliminates muda of motion, and data must be collected and analyzed to identify unnecessary movement. A common tool used in manufacturing and similar environments to track movement is known as a spaghetti diagram. Begin with a basic, bird's eye drawing of the workspace. Include furniture, computer stations, machinery, doors, and walls. Observe an actual process, tracking any and all movements with a line on the diagram.

When drawn correctly, the diagram looks like a string of spaghetti fell onto your page. Once the process is complete, you can look at the diagram to see where the movements cross paths multiple times or go out of the way unnecessarily. This helps you find opportunities for streamlining the movement in a process—sometimes, it's as simple as moving furniture or resources around to reduce unnecessary movement. It's worth noting that a spaghetti diagram only reveals a snapshot of movement in time; sometimes, it is worthwhile to complete more than one such diagram at different times of day or with different employees to reveal an overall picture of a process and possible muda.

Conveyance

Muda of conveyance is similar to muda of movement except conveyance involves the movement of outputs, products, or resources. It is sometimes also referred to as muda of transportation. For example, in a doll-making facility, if the glue that binds doll eyes to doll faces is kept in an inventory room and carried, as needed, to the process, there might be muda of conveyance.

If an expense report is printed and then carried to a manager for approval who then routes it in an inner-office envelope to a director, who then carries it to the accounting department, the muda of conveyance is occurring. This is especially true because appropriate technology used correctly and efficiently lets organizations handle expensive reporting via computer with little conveyance at all.

If a plate is prepared by a chef and placed on a counter where a kitchen assistant moves the plate to a different table where wait staff know to pick it up, conveyance is occurring. The wait staff then carries the plate to the customer.

Conveyance can relate to physical movement of items or digital movement of data or workflow. Email strings, which are present in many work environments, often present muda of digital conveyance. A CEO might email a director with a request for data. The director emails a manager, who emails a supervisor, who emails a subject-matter-expert. The SME delivers the information to her supervisor, and the emails work their way back up the chain. The same request and information was conveyed multiple times when it only may have needed to be conveyed once. This allows for many opportunities for error.

Some might point to chain-of-command concerns, but for the purpose of this example, if the data request is a repeated process, then it makes sense for the chain of command to inform the CEO where this information comes from. To go even further, a truly Lean process would require all waste be removed from this process. If the data requirement comes on a weekly basis, then Lean ideals require that the SME automatically generate the data and send it to the CEO weekly.

Physical conveyance is often easier to locate and address than digital conveyance. A spaghetti diagram, process map, or value stream map can help you identify areas where muda of conveyance might exist. Spaghetti diagrams work well in physical conveyance situations, and process maps help you identify conveyance in digital settings.

Once you identify muda of conveyance, you can eliminate it by making changes in the process, layout, or inventory requirements for the work. If conveyance waste isn't due to poor process design or work-area layout, it might be related to another form of muda. Conveyance is often seen in processes that involve a lot of correction, because work is transferred back and forth between staff or areas. By addressing the muda of correction, you often also address the muda of conveyance.

Over-processing

Over-processing occurs when an employee or process inputs more resources into a product or service than is valued by the customer. This could occur because of ignorance, a desire for perfection, or even excitement. Sometimes over-processing occurs because an employee hasn't had training on the most efficient way to handle a task. Other times, it occurs because an employee or process is more thorough than is worthwhile. A goal of any process should be to do just enough useful and necessary work to ensure that customer or end-user expectations are met.

One example of over-processing often occurs in healthcare administrative offices during the insurance verification process. Insurance verification occurs when a healthcare provider's office attempts to verify that a person is covered by insurance for the services that are about to be rendered. Depending on the type of insurance coverage and the office's policies, a staff member either checks benefits via a computer program or calls the insurance company.

In most cases, the goal of insurance verification is simply to ensure that the insured is covered by the plan for the date the services are to be rendered. Sometimes, however, an office worker delves deeper into the verification, spending up to an hour on the phone with an insurance company to receive detailed benefits or calling back to check with another representative to ensure the original information provided was correct. While specific cases exist that require in-depth insurance verification, basic doctor's visits don't require this level of work. A staff member who is taking up to an hour to verify insurance coverage is overproducing, and it's probably causing productivity problems for the office as a whole.

In consumer-centric processes, over-processing occurs when you put more into a product than the value afforded by the customer. While product excellence is important, at some point the work you put into a product exceeds that which is deemed necessary or useful by the customer, and this is often tied to price point. A customer expects more out of a premium, more expensive model, for example.

An example of over-processing might be painting the bottom of an inside cabinet shelf when no one will ever see it. In a restaurant, ironing table linens to an exacting standard could be considered over-processing, especially if you remove the linens between meals for washing. In most restaurants, much of the table linen drapes over the table; owners might want linens that aren't full of wrinkles, but they don't need crisp and perfect seams. In the technical world, building an app with 100 features when 99 percent of people only want to use 10 main functions can be considered both over-processing and over-producing.

A value stream map, covered in Chapter 35, is a good tool for identifying any points of over-processing. Any part of the process that doesn't provide value could be considered over-processing; when the process features a series of linked events and none provide value, it's even more likely that over-processing is occurring.

In a true Lean process, every step of a process provides value, but it can be tricky to determine when value is not occurring. Quality is important to both the success of the process and the end customer, for example, but the customer doesn't care, or usually even realize, that your process is imbued with quality checks throughout. They care instead that a process takes 10 minutes longer because of those quality checks—teams have to dig deep into processes, metrics, and customer voice to determine if those 10 extra minutes are providing enough added value to cover the annoyance or loss of customer because of the added time. This knowledge is all ascertained through data collection and statistical analysis discussed in detail throughout this book.

Waiting

Muda of waiting refers to any idle time in a process, whether that idle time is for machinery or people. In other words, an employee or machine is working below capacity or is not working at all due to waiting on inputs from another part of the process. Waiting occurs when steps in the process are not properly coordinated, when processes are unreliable, when work is batched too large, during rework, and during long changeovers between staff or machines.

In a retail or fast food environment, when one cashier's shift is over, another cashier takes over at the station. To maintain financial integrity, almost all companies switch out cash register drawers during the change between cashiers; if there is a mistake with the drawer, the company knows who was running the register at that point in time, making it easier to find trends or issues. However, when the drawer is being changed out, the register usually can't be used. The cashier is simply waiting, sometimes along with the customer.

To reduce the muda of waiting in this cash register example, most organizations use a process that includes a series of register drawers that are prepped at the beginning of the day or shift. The drawers are designed to be interchangeable in the registers, so the old drawer can be pulled and the new drawer put in in less than 30 seconds, solving the waste of waiting.

Waste of waiting is common in construction environments. Construction of roads, bridges, buildings and other structures requires close attention to order and detail: you can't build the roadway of a bridge until the pillars are in place and steady. This concept is seen even on a small scale in construction, causing paid employees to often stand around waiting for others to complete a piece of the job before they can finish the assigned task.

Because construction is a field of specialists and certifications, one employee often cannot do the work another can. In other words, employee tasks are not interchangeable. This causes additional muda of waiting; one group of construction workers might have to wait on the forklift operator to come and move some items. Meanwhile, the forklift operator is finishing up with a task on the other side of the construction lot. This isn't a problem limited to construction: some offices have policies requiring an official IT staff member to handle any computer issue. Whether it's a software glitch, a troubleshooting error, or simply the need to switch out an underperforming mouse, regular office staff must send a support ticket or make a phone call and wait for IT staff to solve the problem.

You can eliminate waste of waiting within many processes by balancing machinery, people, and production. The process will only perform as fast as the slowest link; beefing up the production of a single element does nothing for the whole, so teams must work to balance and improve the entire process.

Sometimes, scheduling is a key component in eliminating waiting. In the construction example, advanced planning and scheduling tactics could reduce the chance that one team would be waiting for a forklift operator while he or she is busy elsewhere. Understanding organizational, team, project, and process needs also helps leadership provide the right amount of resources to reduce waiting. The construction site might benefit from two forklift operators, for example. In the IT example, a company can reduce wait times by maximizing IT staffing at high-volume times or implementing processes within the IT department to create more efficient responses to help tickets. An auxiliary IT staff member can be hired to handle less technical issues such as switching out an under-performing mouse.

Other Forms of Waste

While Toyota originally defined seven common muda, even Taiichi Ohno agreed that other types of waste exist. In some cases, what seems like other types of waste are just more defined or specific types of the seven muda discussed above. Some forms of waste don't seem to fit neatly into one of the seven muda categories.

Talent

Talent can be wasted when a process doesn't make the most use of the labor or staff available. If a process calls for data to be entered, and the staff member slowest on 10-key is assigned to the task, resources are being wasted. Hiring the wrong person, putting staff in the wrong position, or ignoring a staff member's growth potential could all be instances of muda of talent. Wasted talent is more a concern for leadership and human resources than for process improvement specialists, though Six Sigma experts should be aware that the way personnel resources are handled can drastically impact the efficiency of a process.

Ideas

Muda of ideas occurs when the thoughts and ideas of people are discounted, not sought out, or misappropriated in a way that doesn't make sense. Leadership and project teams can often overlook subject matter experts who have detailed insight into a process and, as such, could offer first-hand knowledge and ideas. The result could be the design of a process that works great in theory but falls flat on a granular level once it's instituted.

One reason waste of ideas is such a concern for organizations is that people themselves rarely come forward with thoughts. Staff members might think they don't have anything real to contribute, might feel like their ideas won't be heard, or could be anxious about looking silly or ignorant.

Six Sigma Green or Black Belts in charge of projects can facilitate less muda of ideas by encouraging subject matter experts to contribute and encouraging leaders to seek all ideas before moving forward with change. Brainstorming tools, which are covered in later chapters, are valuable for this purpose because they are designed to create a safe haven for all ideas. By fostering all ideas in a safe environment, teams can foster valuable ideas and avoid waste of ideas.

Capital/Cash

Saving for a rainy day is smart, but banking cash when there are profits to gain isn't always the right decision. Muda of capital or cash occurs when leadership decides not to invest in upgrades or improvements that would create additional cash flow. This type of waste is very similar to waiting, except the cash itself is waiting, often for a time when leadership feels safe enough to spend it.

Six Sigma helps reduce muda of cash because statistical analysis helps point leaders to decisions that involve the least risk or most gain. No business decision is 100 percent guaranteed, but Six Sigma helps leaders hedge bets by using statistical data in the decision-making process so they don't sit on cash or capital that could be used to drive gains in efficiency, production, and profit.

Two Types of Muda

All muda is waste that fails to add value to a product or process as defined by the customer or end-user. All muda can also be divided into two overall types, which can help organizations prioritize waste for project and improvement purposes. Muda can be referred to as type I or type II.

Type I Muda

Type I muda are non-value-added tasks that might actually be essential or required by circumstances. Inspection of products during a process might be required if the process is known to produce defects. Organizations don't want defects to reach customers, so they put quality controls in place. The act of the inspection, and the time and expense it adds to a process -- are all muda. However, an organization can't remove that waste until it addresses the cause of the defects within the process.

Sometimes, auxiliary processes within an organization are Type I muda. For example, the external end customer doesn't receive direct value from human resource processes within an organization. At the same time, if employees don't receive pay checks or support regarding benefits, they aren't likely to continue performing work. Those processes are then essential to the organization. Instead of removing the muda completely, teams might look for ways to make essential muda as efficient and cost-effective as possible.

Type II Muda

Type II muda are non-value-added tasks that are not essential and can be immediately removed from a process. For example, if a product is carried to and from several work stations while it is being completed, it's likely type II muda of conveyance exists. By rearranging the workflow, teams might be able to reduce the muda by a substantial amount without making any actual changes to how the product is put together.

5S

5S is a Japanese Lean approach to organizing a workspace, so that by making a process more effective and efficient, it will become easier to identify and expunge muda. 5S relies on visual cues and a clean work area to enhance efficiencies, reduce accidents, and standardize workflows to reduce defects. The method is based on five steps:

- Sort (Seiri)
- Straighten (Seiton)
- Shine (Seiso)
- Standardize (Seiketsu)
- Sustain (Shitsuke)

Phase I: Sort

During the sort phase, all items or materials in a workspace are reviewed, removing unneeded items and keeping necessary resources.

Consider the copy room in an office: over the years, supplies, tools, and machinery have piled up. When going through the room, teams might decide that the stapler and Scotch tape stay; people still need to staple pages or access tape. The old paper cutter isn't necessary for the team, since no one ever performs paper-cutting duties. However, someone notes that the team in shipping and warehousing has to manually cut pages down sometimes, so the paper cutter is relocated to that department. The team decides to toss a bin of miscellaneous loose paper and an old fax machine because a new copy machine includes fax capability. By eliminating obstacles and unnecessary items, costs, time, and employee frustration are also removed.

The sort step lets you take inventory of an area, discover unused or wasted resources, and make room for reorganization. Sort can also be applied with computerized processes.

Phase 2: Straighten

Once excess is removed from the work area, teams must provide a streamlined and easy-to-use location for everything necessary to the workspace. During the straighten phase, every item, tool, or material is given a home. To facilitate ongoing organization, the location of resources should be labeled clearly. The idea is to create a workspace that anyone could use: if someone from another area comes to your copy room, it should only take a few seconds to locate the right size paper. Employees in a factory should be able to move from station to station, finding equipment and tools with ease. The goal is to provide the visual controls that allow for common-sense operation. Labeling a shelf for letter-sized paper, arranging sockets in size order in a drawer labeled sockets, or parking the forklift in a marked area of factory floor when not in use are all good examples. Labeling the stapler with a label maker is an example of things going beyond common sense: you don't need to label items that most people in the workplace would recognize on site.

The straighten phase also works well in a digital environment, especially when computers or systems are used by a variety of people. In an office that has a shared workspace policy, computer desktops might be pushed out by technical resources so that the same programs are available to everyone. Not only are all programs the same, but the icons are in the same location on each desktop so users don't have to search for programs if they move to a new workstation.

Phase 3: Shine

The third phase in the 5S methodology is targeted to keeping the workplace clean and neat. Seiso can also be translated to "sweep, sanitize, or scrub." The goal is to shine the work space by cleaning it, maintaining equipment, and returning items to the proper place after use. In a computerized environment, the shine phase can be accomplished by naming files in a manner that makes them easy to locate, keeping folder structures intact, and deleting or archiving files that are no longer necessary.

Shine can be applied to any environment, physical or digital.

Phase 4: Standardize

The standardize phase is used to maintain the progress achieved in all previous phases. By keeping high standards of orderliness in place, the benefits of the 5S methodology can be long-term. The stress and speed of a daily workday can make it hard to keep up with the 5S standards. If everyone is committed to working together, the benefits can be ongoing.

Phase 5: Sustain

5S only works if everyone on the team or within the organization commits to the process. Employees must follow the rules that are set up for standardizing and sustaining the organization. Otherwise, the team enters a cycle of cleaning up after a period of failing to keep up with the standards of 5S.

The overall benefits the 5S method includes:

- Reduced risks of accidents and safety issues
- Increased compliance with regulations from organizations such as OSHA
- A foundation that makes additional improvements easier to implement
- Waste is easier to identify and eliminate
- Production and quality are generally improved

All of these benefits translate to increased profits and customer satisfaction, which are the overall goals of the Six Sigma methodology.

Just-in-Time Manufacturing

Just-in-Time manufacturing, or JIT, is another Lean concept that originated with Toyota. Originally, JIT took a literal meaning. The goal of JIT manufacturing was to produce an output "just in time," or "as needed" by the customer. The customer was the person or process that required the output; sometimes, that meant the end customers, and, other times, the customer was a different employee or process within the organization.

In a JIT processing situation, one machine might produce a part required by another machine. JIT manufacturing means that the first machine supplies only the amount of parts that the second machine can process. If the second machine can process one part per minute, the first machine is set to produce one part per minute. You'll recognize this idea from the sections on muda of inventory and overproduction.

It's obviously not always possible to run a process just-in-time for the end customer, but most modern companies do try to come as close as possible. Using predictive analytics, companies attempt to estimate how many of each product will sell before they produce those products. In some cases, such as with book publishing, companies run a smaller number of items first. If those items sell well or sell out, the company orders bigger and bigger runs of the product.

Some entrepreneurs have applied JIT manufacturing to DVD sales. These individuals and companies buy the rights to films that have never been released on DVD or Blu-ray before. They usually go after low-cost films that are likely to have a small cult or niche following. Because the demand is small, it isn't feasible to print and market these DVDs in traditional fashion. However, the companies make a stable profit by selling the DVDs through online retailers such as Amazon.com and printing the DVDs to order. Modern technology lets this process occur with minimal expense and waiting.

Today, JIT mentalities are less about the literal idea of providing the product just in time; rather, it has become a more general concept of Lean manufacturing that helps organizations eliminate waste in the process.

Lean Concepts Crop Up in Many Improvement Methodologies

We've covered many of the high level Lean concepts, and you'll see some of these concepts repeat throughout the rest of this book. While Six Sigma is concerned with improving processes and reducing defects, eliminating waste and increasing efficiencies goes hand-in-hand with these goals.

CHAPTER 5:
BASIC SIX SIGMA CONCEPTS

In the last chapter, we covered some of the major concepts associated with Lean. In this chapter, we'll look at some of the major concepts of the Six Sigma methodology. These, along with the concepts introduced in Chapter 1, are some of the building blocks used in improvement projects and statistical process control.

Standard Deviation

The driving goal of Six Sigma is to reduce defects. By reducing defects, teams can increase productivity, decrease overall costs, increase customer satisfaction, and create maximum profit. One idea inherent in the Six Sigma methodology is that variance is the root of many defects.

For example, if an oven heats to exactly 350 degrees in five minutes and stays at that temperature until it is turned off, it is less likely to burn cookies. If a cook measures each ingredient exactly, he or she is more likely to turn out cookies that consistently taste good. Add variation in the process, and consistency is lost. When consistency is lost, defects are introduced. If the oven doesn't maintain an exact temperature all the time, the cookies might burn. If the cook puts in a cup of sugar instead of a cup and a half, the cookies might not be sweet enough. Variation makes for inconsistent quality.

It's important to note that removing variation alone doesn't always improve quality. What if the cook set the oven to 400 degrees all the time and only used half a cup of sugar for each batch? The process has no variation, and neither do the results. The cookies will always be bland and burnt.

Six Sigma process improvement teams usually take a two-step approach to improvements. First, they have to determine if the process is functional. In the cookie example, does the recipe work at all? Is there even a recipe? Once the team determines there is a workable recipe, they make improvements to remove the variation that causes outputs to deviate from the result intended by the recipe.

The statistical measure used by teams to understand variation in a process is known as standard deviation. Standard deviation is represented in math by the lower case Greek letter Sigma – the σ you saw in Chapter 1.

Standard deviation measures the distance between data points and the mean of all data. A large standard deviation means an overall wide spread of points; a smaller standard deviation means a closely clustered set of points.

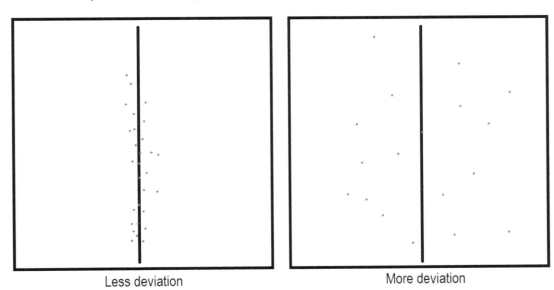

Less deviation   More deviation

The image above provides a graphical representation of deviation. Imagine the vertical axis is a measure of time and the horizontal axis is a measure of temperature. The center line in each image represents the mean temperature. You can see that the temperature over time varies much more in the figure on the right.

Calculating Standard Deviation for Population Data

Standard deviation is a statistical concept. The formula for standard deviation when dealing with data of the entire population is:

You would use this formula if you have all the data elements of a population and not just a random sampling of data elements. For example, if you wanted to find out what the deviation was in the size of pizzas made, you could ask staff to measure each pizza before serving it. You would have the data for the entire population of pizzas for the day, so you could use the equation above. However, if you wanted to calculate standard deviation when you have sample data, you would use the equation from the next section.

$$\sigma = \sqrt{\frac{1}{N}\sum_{i=1}^{N}(x_i - \mu)^2}$$

Formula Key:

σ = Standard deviation

μ = mean

Σ tells you to add up the results of all the calculations done for the items listed in the parentheses

N = the number of data elements for which you calculated standard deviation

X = a place holder for each data element

If you're new to statistics, the equation for standard deviation looks complicated. We'll break it down and run through some exercises on calculating standard deviation manually, but in practice, you will usually use a statistical software tool to make this calculation automatically.

For our explanation, we'll use a data set from a teacher. She wants to find the standard deviation of scores on the latest test. The scores from her class of 15 students are:

67, 68, 73, 74, 81, 85, 88, 88, 90, 90, 90, 93, 94, 98, 99

1. Calculate the mean.

To begin the standard deviation calculation, you need to know the mean for the population. The mean is represented mathematically by the Greek letter mu, or μ. Mean is calculated by adding all of the numbers and dividing that sum by the number of items in a data set. In this case, there are 15 items.

67 + 68 + 73 + 74 + 81 + 85 + 88 + 88 + 90 + 90 + 90 + 93 + 94 + 98 + 99 = 1278

1193/15 = 85.2

2. Subtract the mean and square it.

The formula calls for you to take each number in the data set, subtract the mean from it, and square the result. The first number is 67, so:

67 – 85.2 = -18.2

-18.2 * -18.2 = 331.24

If you apply that concept to all 15 numbers, you end up with a list of results:

331.24
295.84
148.84
125.44
17.64
0.04
7.84
7.84
23.04
23.04
23.04
60.84
77.44
163.84
190.44

3. Find the mean of the results.

The rest of the formula under the square root sign simply tells you to add up all the numbers you just calculated and divide by N, where N is the number of items in your data set. Or, to put it another way, you need to find the mean of the new numbers you just calculated.

The sum of the numbers above is 1496.4.

1496.4 / 15 = 99.76

This new number, 99.76, is called the variance.

4. Find the square root of the variance.
The standard deviation is the square root of the variance. In this case, the square root of 99.76, which is 9.987.

The standard deviation for the test scores is **9.987.**

Calculating Standard Deviation with Sample Data

While statistics based on total population data are always more accurate than those based on sample data, you'll probably work from sample data more often. It just becomes too expensive or even impossible to get population data for many elements. Sometimes, the data is measuring events or states over time, which means population data doesn't exist. For example, if you wanted to understand temperature fluctuations in a warehouse, you might record the temperature at a certain location every ten minutes. After several days, you have sufficient sample data to analyze.

Other examples of sample data include:

- A random sample of reasons for denied medical claims
- Measurements for river height taken three times per day for a month

The formula for standard deviation based on sample data is:

$$S = \sqrt{\frac{1}{N-1}\sum_{i=1}^{N}(x_i - \bar{x})^2}$$

Formula Key:

s = Standard deviation of a sample

x-bar = the mean of the sample

Σ tells you to add up the results of all the calculations done for the items listed in the parentheses

N = the number of data elements for which you calculated standard deviation

X = a place holder for each data element

Since mu is the mean of *population* data, it's been replaced in this formula with x-bar, which is the average of the data points in your sample. Sigma has been replaced with s, but the only mathematical difference is that you divide by N-1 instead of N to get the variance as a way to make up for some of the accuracy lost in using a sampling.

Using the same data from the population example above, let's assume that the 15 grades the teacher had were a random sampling from all of her classes. The only difference in the math would come in the second to last step, where we divide by 14 instead of 15, so:

1496.4 / 14 = 106.885

The square root of 106.885 is 10.338, which would be the standard deviation for the sample.

See for yourself:

Lab techs are measuring the response of bacteria to an ingredient in a potential treatment. They want to know how long it takes bacteria to show a response. Sample data for response times in minutes is:

2, 3.5, 2.3, 2, 2.5, 3.1, 2.2, 3.2, 4

Calculate the standard deviation.

Standard Deviation in Excel

Admittedly, if you're calculating standard deviation by hand, it's a lot of arithmetic. Luckily, once the statistical concepts behind the numbers are understood, statistical analysis software, such as Excel and Minitab, can be used to accurately crunch numbers. Standard deviation is automatically calculated in most statistical analysis software programs by clicking a button after you enter your data sets. The standard deviation is also calculated automatically by such software programs when you initiate other calculations that require standard deviation. We'll look at some of these functions more in-depth in the chapters on using Excel add-ons and Minitab for statistical analysis.

In the meantime, you can quickly calculate standard deviation in Excel using the standard deviation function. To do so:

1. Enter your data set in a column

	A
1	2
2	3.5
3	2.3
4	2
5	2.5
6	3.1
7	2.2
8	3.2
9	4

2. In a new cell, enter =STDEV()

3. Select the cells with data you want to calculate standard deviation for.

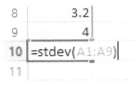

4. Hit enter

7	2.2
8	3.2
9	4
10	0.719568
11	

Note: The formula in Excel calculates a sample standard deviation using the N-1 math, which means you can use this formula for samples and not for populations.

Why Calculate Standard Deviation?

Standard deviation gives you an idea of how much variation actually exists in a process while taking outliers somewhat into account. In the example of the grades from above, the sample standard deviation indicates that most of the grades are going to fall within 10.33 points on either side of the average.

That tells the teacher that students have a fairly wide performance on her test. If the results were an average score of 90 with a standard deviation of 3, he or she might assume that students in class were learning and retaining the knowledge as expected. If the average score was 64 with a standard deviation of 2, then he or she might assume students in class were not retaining the knowledge as expected or there was some issue with the test structure. Both of these situations indicate a small variance in the way students are performing, which points to the success or problem being tied to the class, the teaching, or the test.

On the other hand, if the average score was 60 with a standard deviation of 30, then some students were performing very well while others were performing poorly. This might indicate to the teacher that some students are falling behind. If he or she took samples from several classes, he or she might investigate and realize that the lowest scores were mostly from one class, which could indicate that he or she forgot to adequately cover a certain concept in that class.

Standard deviation alone serves as a pointer for where to investigate within the process for problems or solutions. Another reason to calculate it is because it is involved in many of the other statistical processes we cover in later chapters. Standard deviation becomes an important concept in both analysis and statistical process control and often serves as the starting point for further Statistical Six Sigma analysis.

The Pareto Principle

The Pareto principle, also called the 80/20 rule, says that 20 percent of the causes lead to 80 percent of the effects. This there is also called the law of the vital few: the vital few inputs drive the majority of the outputs.

The Pareto principle was first suggested by a management consultant named Joseph Juran. Juran named the principle for Vilfredo Pareto, an economist in Italy who wrote that 20 percent of the nation's people owned 80 percent of its land. The principle has become common in various circles. Business professionals commonly state that 80 percent of sales come from 20 percent of customers, and volunteer organizations usually operate with 20 percent of the people doing 80 percent of the work.

The principle is critical to Six Sigma not because causes and effects line up nicely via an 80/20 breakdown, but because it almost universally applies that a few inputs create more impact than all of the other inputs. Individuals seeking to reduce defects can almost always identify three to four inputs that, if improved, will create dramatic impact on the outcome. While resources, costs, and difficulty of improvements also play a role in solution selections, understanding which inputs or root causes are high on a Pareto chart let project teams determine where improvements will make the biggest impact to the bottom line.

The Pareto principle is best displayed using a Pareto chart, which is a graphical representation of data elements – usually inputs or causes – in a ranked bar chart. Unlike a regular bar chart, the bars are arranged in order of height, with the highest on the left and the lowest on the right. Statistical software used to create such charts adds formatting and other elements automatically, but you can also create a basic Pareto chart in Excel.

To illustrate the Pareto principle, we'll look at a common situation involving defects in the medical field—specifically in the process for submitting medical claims. Payers often deny claims, and they do so for a variety of reasons. When claims are denied, provider offices have to rework, resubmit, or appeal the denials. Some denial reasons are not appealable, which means the provider's office loses the revenue associated with the claim.

We'll imagine a medical office that is experiencing a cash flow problem because of claim denials. The office gathers data about the denials and creates a Pareto chart so the team can see where the bulk of the denials are coming from. The data is listed below, followed by a basic Pareto chart created in Excel.

Reasons for Denying Medical Claims

Reason	Count
Duplicate claim	18012
Timely Filing	13245
No beneficiary found	10215
Claim lacks information	4548
Service not covered	2154
Medical necessity	1423
Date of service issue	526

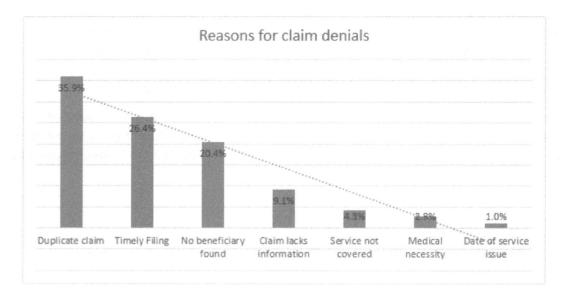

From the Pareto chart, you can see that the top three denial reasons account for 80 percent of the denied claims. An experienced billing team could tell you three things just from looking at this data:

- The office has muda of rework. They are sending a large percentage of claims more than one time.
- The office has an efficiency problem. Almost a fourth of their claims are not making it to the payer pior to timely filing deadlines.
- The office has an insurance verification problem, because a fifth of their claims are being sent with information that doesn't match anything on the payer's end.

Addressing duplicate claims is important because it reduces rework and could enhance the office's relationship with insurance companies. However, the team might choose to work on the timely filing problem first because timely filing denials are final, which means the office is losing the revenue associated with all those claims. Filing claims on time is not difficult in many cases, given the fact that most payers allow months or even a year for claims to be filed, so this could be an "easy" win for the team. A Pareto chart often uncovers low-hanging fruit in this manner.

Creating a Basic Pareto Chart in Excel

If you don't have statistical software, you can create a basic Pareto chart like the one above in Excel. Use the claims denial data or data of your own to practice making a Pareto chart.

1. Create a column for the data labels. Pareto charts work well when you have quantifiable causes for a defect or other effect. In the example, the data labels are the reason for the denial. No matter what type of data you are using, enter it in order from largest to smallest for Pareto chart purposes.
2. Create a column for count. Enter the total for each cause in that column.
3. Create a column for cumulative count. This column provides a running total. You can calculate the numbers manually or using Excel. In the data table below, you would set C3 = B3. In C4, you would enter the formula =C3+B4. You can drag that formula down and Excel will change the references for each cell so you get =C4+B5, =C5+B6…and so forth.
4. Create a column for percent. In the data table below, the formula for D3 is =B3/$C$9. Cell C9 has the total of all denials, so we want to divide each individual denial total by C9. The dollar signs in the formula let you copy it into each lower cell. The first reference will change, moving to the next line, but the dollar signs tell Excel to keep the C9 reference for each calculation. The final result is a table that looks like this:

Reason	Count	Cumulative	Percent
Duplicate claim	18012	18012	35.9%
Timely Filing	13245	31257	26.4%
No beneficiary found	10215	41472	20.4%
Claim lacks information	4548	46020	9.1%
Service not covered	2154	48174	4.3%
Medical necessity	1423	49597	2.8%
Date of service issue	526	50123	1.0%

5. To create the Pareto chart, highlight the information in both the Reason and Percent column and select Insert → Chart → Bar chart.

BASIC SIX SIGMA CONCEPTS

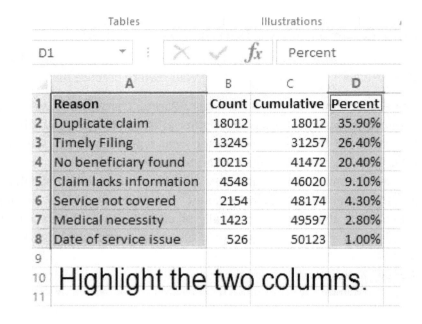

Highlight the two columns.

Click insert, then click on bar charts.

6. The bar chart will be created automatically. Select Add Chart Element → Trendline, and add either an exponential or linear trendline.

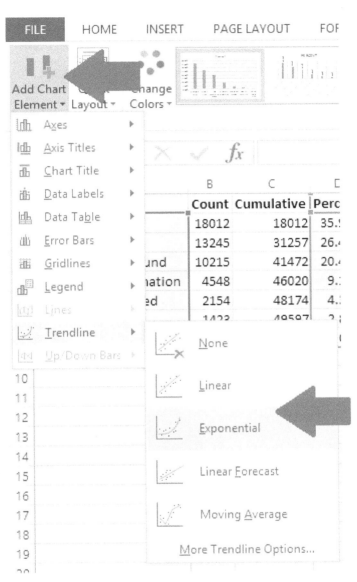

7. Select Add Chart Element → Data Labels, and select the format of data label you prefer for your chart.

Use of Pareto Charts

Pareto charts are helpful analytical tools when you need to analyze frequencies or causes of problems. They also help narrow an approach for a problem that has many causes or is too broad to address in a single improvement project. Like the claims denials example above, you can find a single cause to work on that can yield large results across the entire process.

Pareto charts are also helpful when communicating information about causes to others, especially those outside of the Six Sigma process. Although Pareto charts are a powerful analytical tool, they also represent complex data in a visual format that is familiar to most anyone. Business professionals know how to read a bar chart, and putting the chart in order only makes it easier for individuals to see the true causes behind issues. For this reason, many Six Sigma experts regularly include Pareto charts when presenting to business leaders and others, especially if the data might be considered surprising or need visual reinforcement.

Voice of the Customer

Voice of the Customer, or VOC, is a foundational concept in many quality programs. The goal of quality is to make a better, more consistent product. One of the ways you know you've reached this goal is that your customers will be more consistently satisfied. The only way to reach this goal is to seek feedback from the customer, making VOC data critical to collect before, during, and after improvement projects.

Successful VOC programs are proactive and constant in their desire for feedback, and technology makes it possible to seek customer feedback in numerous ways. Some methods for capturing feedback include:

- Surveys via telephone, mail, email, or online
- Focus groups in person or online
- Interviews
- Beta or user testing
- Feedback forms
- Customer complaints
- Social media or site interaction
- Reviews
- Forums

The VOC can be sought as a means to clarify needs and desires, clarify specific problems with a process, or as a regular part of improvement, customer service, and marketing agendas.

Building a VOC Campaign

Asking the right questions, in the right way, helps you create powerful VOC campaigns that provide useable data for Six Sigma teams. We'll talk about two specific types of VOC campaigns in this section: general customer feedback and specific customer feedback.

General Feedback

General customer feedback is often obtained through feedback forms, customer complaint records, and passive information gathering via websites or social media. Through such methods, organizations are usually testing general waters to get a temperature reading: are customers happy overall, dissatisfied overall, and is there any direction as to the cause of customer feelings?

Pick up a feedback form in any fast food restaurant or access the online survey usually linked to on a receipt and you'll get a good idea of the type of information sought in general VOC campaigns.

Kroger, a grocery store chain in the United States, includes a link to a survey on most of its receipts. The survey first asks for the date, time, and an entry code from the receipt. This helps the company know where and when a person shopped so they can attribute feedback to the right location and staff.

Next, the Kroger survey asks in which areas of the store a person shopped. The rest of the survey asks specific questions about each area of the store a person visited, including:

- What was the overall satisfaction with the store?
- What was the customer's satisfaction with:
  - Employee friendliness
  - Prices
  - Service
  - Cleanliness
  - Items being available
  - Weekly specials
  - Ease of movement
  - Quality of brands
  - Check out times
- Whether the shopper is likely to recommend the store to another person in the next 30 days.

These questions are designed to gauge general customer feelings on critical quality elements for the store. Understanding your critical to quality factors, or CTQs, is important to designing a strong VOC campaign. We'll cover CTQs more in depth in Chapter 8.

General VOC feedback is often used as a smoke alarm. A smoke alarm is designed to alert individuals in a business, home, or other building that the possibility of a fire exists. Smoke alarms are set at a sensitive level, so they go off when smoke is present and people within the building can take action. Often, the alarm and early action saves lives and can even reduce damage associated with a potential fire.

VOC data can work the same way. If numbers change suddenly in a certain area, an organization knows to look deeper into the issue. It's an indicator that a problem could exist; early investigation and action can help prevent problems from becoming bigger or more costly. For example, if a certain Kroger store always scored high in cleanliness, and the numbers dropped consistently across a month, then store management might need to revisit maintenance and cleaning training.

Results from general VOC feedback are also used in some organizations as an indicator of quality for certain employees. Sales and services staff are often rewarded financially and in other ways for high customer satisfaction scores. This also increases employee drive and satisfaction.

Specific Feedback

Sometimes, organizations want feedback that is specific to a problem, product, or idea. The same tools used in general feedback campaigns can be used in specific campaigns, but you can also tailor the VOC tool to the need. If you want feedback about a new app, you could use a beta test. If you want to test a product, idea, or marketing campaign, an in-person or online focus group might be best.

For specific feedback, you have to ask specific questions. This is especially true if you are seeking additional information or clarification of general feedback. For example, if Kroger did see a problem with ratings on cleanliness, it might want more information about how and where customers note uncleanliness. Without additional feedback, managers might have staff mopping the floors more when customers really felt the store was dirty because of a lack of lighting or because shelves were stocked in a sloppy manner.

Selecting the Right VOC Tools

Getting the right type of feedback—and keeping costs and timelines within budget—requires selecting the right VOC tool for your project. The table below rates each tool on relative cost and provides some brief pros and cons.

Tool	Cost	Benefits	Disadvantages
Feedback form	Low	-Gathers a lot of data from many sources -Can be geared toward numeric data for easier analysis	-An individual must decide to leave feedback, skewing results to people who feel strongly one way or the other
Survey via phone	High	-Can randomly select, which allows you to draw conclusions for the entire population	-Requires a lot of labor hours -Customers may be annoyed by unwanted phone calls
Survey via mail	Medium	-Can randomly select, which allows you to draw conclusions for the entire population. -Lower cost alternative to phone or in-person surveys.	-The customer must send it back for it to count. Because many people won't do so, you have to send more surveys to get a statistical sampling.
Social media	Low	-Ongoing ability to seek feedback. -Ability to ask questions on the fly. -Possibly the least expensive option for VOC.	-Requires an established social media following. -Relies on followers and fans, which means you are asking for feedback from people who

			already favor your brand in some way.
Focus groups in person	High	-Lets moderators seek more in-depth answers or feedback immediately	-Limits data pool to local customers or those willing to travel. -Can't use data to make assumptions about the general population. -Customers may be less inclined to be honest when face-to-face with surveyors
Focus groups online	Low	-Lets moderators seek more in-depth answers or feedback immediately -Doesn't require travel and you can access customers across the globe	-Can't use data to make assumptions about general population.
User or beta testing	High	-Provides feedback about a specific produce, service, or process.	-Takes time and requires experienced users or testers.

The Likert Scale

When designing your own VOC tool, keep in mind how you intend to use the information gained. If you want to input data into statistical analysis software to test hypothesis or create visual charts, then you need to ask questions that yield actual data points that can be analyzed using statistics. A popular way to do this is with a Likert Scale.

Using a Likert Scale, you would frame all questions so they are answered via a 5-point ranking. The ranking can be any number of things, but most commonly is some variation of:

- Strongly agree
- Agree
- Neutral
- Disagree
- Strongly disagree

The answers are coded with numbers when data is entered into statistical software. For example, an answer of strongly agree might be coded as 10. Agree would be 7, neutral 5, disagree 3, and strongly disagree 1. By using numerical data, you can easily create charts and graphs and run more in-depth statistical analysis, which is covered in future chapters.

Basic Metrics

We introduced some ideas about Six Sigma metrics in Chapter 1 when we talked about sigma level and defects per million opportunities, or DPMO. Metrics are extremely utilized when applying Six Sigma to processes and improvements, requiring that anyone working in a Six Sigma environment be familiar with them.

Defects per Million Opportunities

Many Six Sigma metrics come with an equation, just like standard deviation. For example, the equation for DPMO is:

(number of defects in a sample/opportunities for a defect in the sample) * 1,000,000

For example, if a mail-order retailer examines quality of the order process, it might sample forms entered by customer service representatives. If each form has 10 fields, then there are 10 opportunities for an error on each form. If the retailer reviews 90 forms, then there are 10 * 90, or 900, total opportunities for errors.

During the review, the retailer finds 2 errors, or defects. To calculate DPMO, the math would be as follows:

(2/900) * 1,000,000 = 2,222 defects per million opportunities.

Defects per Unit

DPU is a measure of how many defects there are in relation to the number of units tested. DPU is concerned with total defects, and one unit could have more than one defect. The formula for DPU is:

Number of defects found / number of units in the sample

For example, if a publisher printed 1,000 books and pulled out 50 books for quality checks, it might be looking for the following defects:

- Incorrect printing
- Incorrect alignment
- Missing pages
- A loose spine
- Torn cover

Out of 50 books, the publisher discovers:

- 3 books are missing pages
- 1 book is missing pages and has a torn cover
- 2 books have loose spines
- 1 book has incorrect printing and incorrect alignment

There are 9 total errors, as two books had two defects each.

The DPU is calculated by dividing defects by number of units sampled. In this case, 9/50 = 0.18.

DPU provides an average level of quality—it tells you how many defects on average each unit can be expected to have. In this case, that is 0.18 defects on average.

First Time Yield (FTY)

First time yield is the ratio of units produced to units attempted to produce. For example, if you put 12 cookies in the oven, but only 10 come out edible, then you haven't produced 12 cookies.

The formula for FTY is:

Number of good units produced / number of units entering the process

In the cookie example, the FTY is 10/12, or .833.

Most products or services are created via multiple processes; you multiply the FTY for each process to calculate an overall FTY. For example, consider the following process chain:

- 100 units enter process A and 95 units exit.
- 95 units enter process B and 85 good units are achieved.
- 85 units enter process C and 80 good units exit.

The FTY would be calculated as follows:

- 95/100 = 0.95 = FTY of process A
- 85/95 = 0.89 = FTY of process B
- 80/85 = 0.94 = FTY of process C
- 0.95 * 0.89 * 0.94 = 0.79

The overall FTY of the process is 0.79.

Rolled Throughput Yield (RTY)

The rolled throughput yield, or RTY, provides a probability that a unit will be generated by a process with no defects. One of the main differences between RTY and basic yield or first time yield is that RTY considers whether rework was needed to generate the number of final units. This is a valuable concern, because organizations don't always think about the rework that is inherent in a process, which means they often measure a process and deem it successful even if muda is present.

RTY is calculated in a similar manner to FTY, but it takes rework into account. If process A from the FTY example only achieved a yield of 95 because someone reworked five items to make them good, then RTY calculations add five instances of rework into the ratio. The formula is:

(Number of units entering - (scrap + rework))/number of units entering process

In the case of process A: (100 - (5+5))/100 = 90/100 = 0.9

Consider the following process chain:

- 100 units enter process A. Five are scrapped, 5 are reworked, and a total of 95 are produced.

- 95 units enter process B. Ten are scrapped, 5 are reworked, and a total of 85 are produced.
- 85 units enter process C. Five are scrapped, 15 are reworked, and a total of 80 are produced.

The RTY is calculated as follows:

- $100 - (5 + 5) = 90$, $90/100 = 0.9$ RTY for A
- $95 - (10 + 5) = 80$, $80/95 = 0.84$ RTY for B
- $85 - (5 + 15) = 65$, $65/85 = 0.76$ RTY for C
- $0.9 * 0.84 * 0.76 = 0.574$

The overall RTY for the process is 0.574, which is a much lower rate than when you look at FTY alone. RTY doesn't provide an indication of final production or sales, but a low RTY indicates that there is waste in the process in the form of rework.

See for yourself

A government agency handles applications for assistance for local families. The process for each application includes:

- A representative enters the family's information into a computer system
- A separate staff member reviews the information and uses an income scale to determine if the family is eligible for any assistance
- The second staff member sends the family a letter stating their options for assistance

All of the applications and customer feedback for March were reviewed, and the team found the following information:

- 643 families sought assistance in March
- 3 families were not able to complete the application process because the representative took too long to see them
- 50 applications could not be passed to the second rep because of incomplete information
- 45 applications did not have complete information at first but that information was later received
- The second staff member was able to process all completed applications she received
- Of all letters that went out to families, 10 included incorrect information

Calculate the FTY and the RTY for this process.

CHAPTER 6:
APPROACHING THE PROBLEM

Understanding how to approach the problem – beginning to identify the problem and defining it with a statement – is critical to creating a foundation for successful Six Sigma projects. In later chapters, we'll cover the importance of defining a variety of project, process, and problem aspects, but in this chapter, we're going to discuss the project in general, digging deeper via a series of why questions, and creating a general problem statement as a launching point for a project.

Problem Functions: $y = f(x)$

Because Six Sigma approaches things with a statistical mindset, it considers all problems as a function. Using mathematical symbols, this looks like:

$$y = f(x)$$

Y, the problem   is   a function   of x, the cause(s)
or outcome   or input (s)

The y=f(x) statement can be used in two ways. First, it is a general map for stating a problem. Y (the problem) occurs because some X (input or cause) is occurring. In reality, Y is usually occurring because of some group of causes or inputs, which means there are going to be more than one X inputs.

The idea can also be applied to specific processes and outcomes within the problem. As you get more and more granular, the y=f(x) concept becomes increasingly mathematical; in many cases, you can graph the relationship between the output (y) and the input (x).

To understand the concept of thinking of problems as a function, let's look at a problem that might occur for a large HVAC service provider. The manager of a service team has discovered that service calls are taking much longer than expected; in fact, his five team members take 1.75 times longer on average than other service reps in the company to handle all types of calls.

To find out what might be causing the situation, the manager researches the problem by talking to the reps, talking to the customers, and going out on random calls with all five representatives. He makes the following observations:

- One representative is a native to the area the team services, which means he or she knows many of the customers personally. This results in friendly chatter that lengthens the time on the job.
- One representative is providing homeowners with very in-depth explanations and education about HVAC issues, sometimes over and beyond what the homeowner would ever need to know regarding his or her HVAC unit.
- One representative is new to the job and takes longer to complete each task because he or she is unsure of the work, has to double-check the work, or calls another rep to ask questions about the work.
- The remaining two reps perform work in times that are on par with company averages.

The manager distills this data down to two overall causes for the problem:

- Too much talking (reps one and two)
- Inadequate training

The problem can now be stated as a function:

The extra time is a function of too much talking and inappropriate training.

The manager also now has two root causes to address. The example is simple, but it illustrates the basic concept in defining a y=f(x) relationship for a problem and its causes. It's not always so easy to conduct the research and analysis to find the relationship, but the relationship is *always* present.

Some other examples of y=f(x) relationships include:

- Low customer satisfaction with hamburger taste is a function of an uncalibrated grill.

- Low employee morale is a function of a poor time-off approval system.
. Customer wait times are a function of technology distractions for employees.

The 5 Whys

Data analysis is one of the best ways to validate a $y=f(x)$ assumption, but teams who are familiar with processes can often arrive at some basic relationships through a process known as the 5 Whys. This is a brainstorming tool that asks increasingly granular why questions about a problem or process, seeking to understand the root cause or actual problem. The 5 Whys can be used to define a problem or to begin seeking causes.

For example, consider the hamburger example above. Teams addressing a problem of customer satisfaction might begin doing so because feedback forms have shown a lower-than-normal satisfaction with food quality over the past week.

The team first asks: *Why are customers dissatisfied with the food?*

Looking at feedback tied to orders, the team notes that the customers who are rating the food poorly are mostly customers who ordered hamburgers of some type. The answer to the first question is that the customers are dissatisfied with the food because they are dissatisfied with the hamburgers.

Why are customers dissatisfied with hamburgers?

The team looks at written feedback on forms or speaks with customers directly and discovers that many customers feel that their hamburgers were undercooked. The new answer is that customers are dissatisfied with hamburgers because the meat is undercooked.

Why is the meat undercooked?

An investigation into the kitchen reveals that the grill is not properly calibrated and is providing inconsistent results. At this point, you have the $y=f(x)$ relationship, but the team could keep asking questions.

Why is the grill not properly calibrated?

Further investigation shows that the morning shift, responsible for calibrating the grill, has a new grill cook. During training, education on performing this function was omitted. The grill is not properly calibrated because the employee responsible was not properly trained. Now the team has a specific cause and a solution: train the grill cook.

In a Six Sigma environment, the team might move on with one more question: Why was the grill cook not properly trained? This might lead to the development of a consistent training policy so the problem doesn't occur the next time a new grill cook is hired.

In the hamburger example, it only took four why questions to get to the root of the problem, and a fifth question started pointing to controls or long-term solutions. It isn't always this easy; the tool is called the 5 Whys because it often leads to answers within five questions. However, teams could ask a dozen questions if they begin at a very high level and work down through a complex process.

When to Use 5 Whys

One benefit of 5 Whys is that it only costs your team a small amount of time to use—a team familiar with a process can conduct a complete 5 Whys session in less than an hour if a moderator keeps things on task. Because of its simplicity, the 5 Whys tool can be used for almost any problem. Use it to address a problem team members bring up, to address a problem a supervisor noticed, or to address the vague feeling that there is a problem when no one has been able to define what is actually wrong. At the very least, a 5 Whys session facilitates communication and thought.

In a Six Sigma project environment, 5 Whys is usually deployed when processes involve human interactions or people-powered inputs, though it can be an effective start to brainstorming on any process.

Conducting a 5 Whys Session

Since a 5 Whys session is usually based on input from subject-matter-experts, gather people who are close to the process. On a white board or web conference screen, display a basic problem statement as you understand it. This problem statement is not going to be detailed like the statements we'll discuss in the next session—a 5 Whys session is often one of the tools you use to get to that detailed statement.

Examples of statements you might see in a 5 Whys station include:

- Customers are not happy with the selection of produce
- Customers are receiving orders late
- The printing process is resulting in too many defects
- Lead times on the bottling process are excessive
- Employees are not happy with vacation schedules

These are all fairly general statements that simply say something about defects or dissatisfaction. Begin by asking the highest-level "Why?" question possible about the statement. "Why are employees not happy with vacation schedules?" Write this question down.

The team works together to provide a high level answer to the question. Employees are not happy with vacation schedules because it's rare to get the exact time off requested. Write the answer down under the question, then create the highest-level "Why?" question you can about the new answer.

"Why are employees not getting their first choice time off for vacation?" Perhaps the answer is that supervisors take so long to approve vacation requests that other employees have also asked off for the same time, so it's hard for supervisors to accommodate everyone.

The next question is "Why are supervisors taking too long to approve requests?" The answer might be that the time-off system is too cumbersome, so supervisors put off approvals until they have a lot of time to manage them.

"Why do supervisors see the system as cumbersome?" Because there are wait times when moving from screen to screen and each approval requires a vast number of clicks and entries.

Now, the team has a root cause: the system itself is inefficient, which leads to problems down the line. If the team can correct the programing issues and encourage supervisors to approve vacation requests faster, employee morale can be improved.

Creating a Problem Statement

A Six Sigma improvement project usually starts with a formal project statement. This is different from the basic statements used to launch a 5 Whys session. A strong problem statement is similar to a 30-second elevator pitch, which executives and sales people across the globe use to hook clients or business investors on an idea. The problem statement, like that pitch, provides enough information that a busy executive can understand what the issue is and why there is a need for an improvement effort.

Project statements should include:

- Where and when the problem was recorded or was occurring
- A measurement of magnitude for the problem, preferably with some tie to cost

- A brief description of the problem that could be understood by professionals not closely aligned with the process (avoid too many niche words and acronyms if you will be presenting information to non-niche professionals)
- A brief notation about the metric used to measure or describe the problem

Example of a Strong Problem Statement

In the first quarter, the California distribution center sent 108,000 packages. Of those packages, 15,000 were returned, resulting in a 13.8 percent return rate. The rate of return is above the accepted 7 percent rate and cost the company an additional $372,000 for the quarter. Over the course of the year, the current process could result in additional costs of over $1.4 million.

This problem statement covers all the basic information:

- When? During the first quarter of this year.
- Where? The California distribution center
- What? Returns
- How many? 15,000, or 6.8 percent above expectations
- What is the magnitude? The cost could be $1.4 million a year

The problem statement doesn't talk about solutions or provide too many details. This is a strong problem statement because it answers all the basic questions *and* it provides a significant reason for leadership to invest interest: $1.4 million a year is a big loss.

Example of a Weak Problem Statement

The Canton, Ohio bakery is producing undercooked bread. Customer dissatisfaction with the bread is resulting in returns and bad word of mouth. The bread is supposed to be baked at 350 degrees for 40 minutes.

This statement introduces a problem, but it doesn't provide details about when the problem occurred, how it was measured, and what the true magnitude is. The problem statement also begins going into possible root causes when it includes how the bread should be baked; the problem statement isn't the place to begin this type of analysis.

This statement might be better framed as:

In November and December 2014, customer satisfaction complaints were traced back to bread baked in the Canton, Ohio facility. The facility produced 300,000 loaves during that *time period and received 50,000 complaints of bread being undercooked. Bread returns and loss of sales related to quality are estimated to be $125,000 per month.*

Writing Your Own Problem Statement

When you first start writing problem statements, it's sometimes harder than you might expect to get all the information into a couple of sentences. To avoid leaving out information, it helps to use a list and to consider yourself a problem-statement journalist.

When journalists write a report, they are looking to answer some specific questions: What happened? Who did it happen to? When did it happen? Why does the audience care?

The same is true when you are writing a problem statement. Follow the problem statement checklist:

- o   Where did the problem occur?
- o   When did the problem occur?
- o   What process did the problem involve?
- o   How is the problem measured?
- o   How much is the problem costing (in money, time, customer satisfaction, or another critical metric)?

Use the checklist to construct the problem statement, and then ask yourself: Could someone else answer all the questions in the checklist from your problem statement alone? Before you present your statement to a boss or other decision-maker, test it out with a coworker or someone who is not as familiar with the issue as you are.

Here are two problem statements. See if you can answer all of the questions in the checklist just using the information provided.

Problem Statement 1

The call center in Jacksonville, Florida, handled 36,000 calls in February 2015. Of those calls, 8,000 had an average speed of answer (ASA) over the contract-required 15 seconds. Those 8,000 service-level-agreement violations resulted in costs of $200,000.

Problem Statement 2

The call center in Ohio has a service-level-agreement issue that is costing approximately $9,000 per day.

Problem statement 1 answers all of the questions on the checklist:

- o   Where did the problem occur? Jacksonville, Florida
- o   When did the problem occur? February 2015
- o   What process did the problem involve? Answering phone calls
- o   How is the problem measured? Average speed of answer
- o   How much is the problem costing (in money, time, customer satisfaction, or another critical metric)? $200,000 per month

Problem statement 2 does not answer all of the questions:

- o   Where did the problem occur? Ohio
- o   When did the problem occur? Unknown
- o   What process did the problem involve? Unknown
- o   How is the problem measured? Unknown
- o   How much is the problem costing (in money, time, customer satisfaction, or another critical metric)? $9,000 per month

Problem statement 2 would benefit from adding a place, a specific reference to a process, and a specific metric.

Problem Statements Lead to Objective Statements/Goals

Another way to tell you have a strong problem statement is that you can create an overall project objective statement or goal directly from the problem statement. Consider the two examples above.

The team working with problem statement 1 might create an objective that states:

The goal is to reduce answer speed SLA violations in the Jacksonville call center by 50 percent within three months. The potential savings to the company is $100,000 per month.

The team working with problem statement 2 would not be able to create a goal statement with this much detail. They would simply be able to say they hope to reduce the service-level-agreement violations in the facility.

Specific problem and objective statements are critical to Six Sigma project success for several reasons. First, being as specific as possible sets up appropriate expectations. In the first example, leadership has a specific expectation of the project: the team is going to work to reduce average speed of answer, and success is a reduction of 50 percent. No one is going to expect the team to solve another problem, such as customer satisfaction with phone operators. That is out of scope for this project.

In the second situation, the problem and goal statements are not specific enough. What SLA violations is the team addressing? What, exactly, does success look like? Is the team expected to reduce costs completely? Not being specific enough sets you up for failure. Leadership might expect you to address service level agreements that have to do with how reps route phone calls, but you are only intending to address service level agreements that relate to the speed with which calls are answered. Leadership might think success is a 75 percent reduction in costs when you intend to work toward a 25 percent reduction.

Creating strong problem statements lays a stable foundation for the rest of your project, gives the team a beacon when they get overwhelmed with information, and reduces the chance of scope creep and misunderstanding.

Scope and Scope Creep

Scope is the definition of what is included – and what is not included – in a process or improvement project. You begin defining scope with your problem statement. The information you include in the statement gives clues to what you will be working on, and the goal statement provides appropriate limits on the work to be done.

Six Sigma projects are not everlasting initiatives, though the culture of improvement that comes from Six Sigma is. This means your individual project needs a specific, challenging, but attainable goal. Once that goal is met, the project is concluded and you begin looking for a new problem to improve upon.

Scope creep occurs when teams look to make infinite perfections on a process, attempt to reach unrealistic goals, or begin to reach for processes or problems that are out of the original scope. For example, consider the problem statement from one of our examples in this chapter:

In the first quarter, the California distribution center sent 108,000 packages. Of those packages, 15,000 were returned, resulting in a 13.8 percent return rate. The rate of return is above the accepted 7 percent rate and cost the company an additional $372,000 for the quarter. Over the course of the year, the current process could result in additional costs of over $1.4 million.

A related goal statement might be:

The goal is to reduce the return rate to the accepted 7 percent and save the company $372,000 per quarter.

In scope for this project are processes related to shipping and returns only insomuch that they impact the return process. At some point, the team might stumble upon a packing process that is using too much material, thus costing the company an additional $50,000 per month. Unless the packing process is causing the returns—which is not likely in this situation—this issue is not in scope for the team and they should not seek to fix it. The team can, however, note the issue or report it so that a future project might be launched to address the problem.

It takes discipline and organization to address only that which is in scope for a project. Understanding the relationship between problems and inputs and knowing how to create a strong problem statement are the first steps to controlling an improvement process.

UNIT 2:
PROJECTS AND PROCESSES

Chapter 7:
What is a Process?

In Unit 1, we introduced Six Sigma as a concept and covered a lot of principles that are foundational to creating and maintaining improvement in a business. In Unit 2, we'll begin looking at what a process is, why quality is important in a process, and how Six Sigma projects can improve processes. The concepts you learn in Units 1 and 2 become the bricks used to build project work that we discuss throughout the rest of the book.

What is a Process?

A process is a collection of tasks, steps, or activities that are performed, usually in a specific order, and result in an end product such as a tangible good or the provision of a service. In a business, multiple processes work together to achieve organizational goals. Technically, the business or organization itself can be seen as one enormous process. For example, a law firm that handles criminal defense cases operates via a huge, complex process. Defendants and their cases enter the process. The output of the process is the result of the case: a bargain with prosecutors, a win or loss in court, or dismissal of charges prior to court.

Within the huge process that sees the defendant through to his or her outcome, there are hundreds, possibly thousands, of smaller processes. There are processes within processes. A lawyer and team of paralegals might move through the process of negotiation; a legal secretary might go through the process of setting appointments. Holding depositions, making copies, sending letters, and filing legal documents are all examples of processes. At the most detailed level, even answering the phone or typing a letter can be considered processes.

In Chapter 6, we briefly introduced the idea of scope and scope creep. To define and maintain proper scope, we said that a Six Sigma team had to identify the processes that were related to a process improvement or project. In the legal firm example, a project to reduce the time it takes to set appointments would likely not include a process for filing a legal brief. To know that, however, you have to know that the legal brief process doesn't share components with the appointment setting process. In this chapter, we'll cover the components of processes and a format for mapping those components known as a SIPOC.

Four Layers of the Process Definition

As you continue with this chapter, you'll see that processes can be very complex. Our basic definition above is just that: Basic. Before we begin defining the components of a process, let's peel back the layers of this concept known as "a process."

The Steps

Whether physical, digital, or ideological, every process is a series of some number of steps. You can put those steps on paper in the form of instructions—often called a standard operating procedure in a formal business training or policy document -- or a visual diagram known as a process map. A process map uses standard shapes and connections to create a map of a process that can be understood by most employees and any Six Sigma team member.

Processing Time

Processes all take a certain amount of time, and processing time can change with a variety of factors. Process maps and documents can only record information such as the average time a process takes or measures of variation in the processing time. This information is often noted in such documents because it provides valuable information to teams, but real-time observation of a process almost always provides better information about processing time.

A retail chain might create a process map for restocking a certain area. The process documentation notes an average time of two hours to fully restock the shelves in the defined area. In an effort to obtain more data about the process, a Six Sigma team observes employees actually performing job functions in real time at various times of day for two weeks. Some notes that come from those observations include:

- Stocking in the evening takes only minutes.
- Stocking during the day is hampered by the movements of customers.

- Stocking work performed during peak shopping hours usually takes the longest.

With just this information, you can probably see an easy way to reduce stocking time in this example: move stocking duties to non-peak times when possible. Simply understanding the steps to stock the area is not enough to understand the process; you also have to gather data about process times.

Interdependencies

Almost any process in a business will be dependent upon one or more other processes. Remember, the business itself is a series of linked processes all working toward the same goal or goals. Sometimes, interdependencies are noted on processes maps. Other times, interdependencies are resource-related.

For example, consider a very simple passenger train scenario. The train leaves station A with passengers, carrying them to station B. Before the train can leave, the engineer must be on board and prepared to operate the machine. Safety checks, clearance from the rail yard, the closing of all the doors: these are all processes that must be completed before the train leaves the station. The process of the train transporting passengers is dependent upon the completion of other processes.

When working with processes during a Six Sigma improvement project, teams must be aware of interdependencies. What does any process you are working on rely? What relies on your process? The first is important because you might need help from processes or people upstream from your process when making improvements. The second is important because you have to know how your improvements will impact downstream processes and people – and improvement in the performance of your process doesn't do any good for the company or organization as a whole if it hinders the performance of a downstream process.

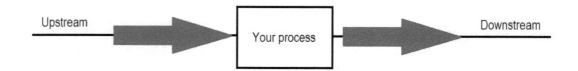

Resources and Assignment

Processes require resources. Like a motor vehicle requires fuel or electricity to run, a process requires resources such as power, people, cash, digital bandwidth, computer equipment, machinery, supplies, parts, and even skill. Since someone in an organization has to approve and pay for resources, project teams must understand the resources involved, the cost of those resources, and the owners of the processes and resources in question so they can make appropriate requests about needing additional resources.

Major Process Components

Processes are made up of components that include inputs, outputs, events, tasks (activities), and decisions. Inputs enter the process when a specific event occurs; tasks and decisions are performed upon or with the inputs. At the end of the process, an output is generated. Most of the time, the idea of process components is introduced with a simple factory-based illustration: raw goods of some type enter the factory, work is performed, and finished goods leave the factory. For example, if a factory makes hard candy, things such as sugar, water, plastic, and electrical power enter the factory. Equipment and employees take the inputs and work with them. The end result is a wrapped piece of candy ready for the store.

The figure below illustrates the idea of process components using a pizza shop example. An event – the ordering of a certain pizza – begins the process. You can see all of the components in the diagram, and we'll talk about each component in detail in the section that follows.

What is a Process?

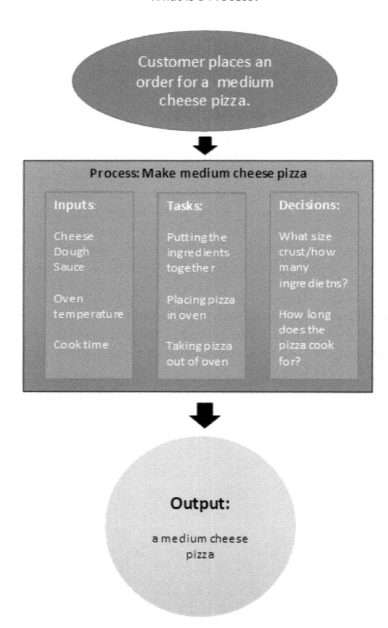

Customer places an order for a medium cheese pizza.

Process: Make medium cheese pizza

Inputs:	Tasks:	Decisions:
Cheese Dough Sauce	Putting the ingredients together	What size crust/how many ingredietns?
Oven temperature	Placing pizza in oven	How long does the pizza cook for?
Cook time	Taking pizza out of oven	

Output:

a medium cheese pizza

Figure 1 Medium Cheese Pizza Process

Inputs

Input refers to anything that enters a process or is required to enter a process to drive the creation of an output. In the pizza example above, the inputs are all the ingredients needed to make the pizza. You might also consider factors such as oven temperature, type of oven, and the cook's skill level to be inputs in the process.

Understanding all inputs to a process is important in Six Sigma because inputs are often causal – or related to causal – factors regarding a process. Inputs or the results of those inputs can cause errors or defects in the process. The cookies burn when the oven is too hot. The computers made in a factory don't function when the circuit boards are bad. A lawyer doesn't win his case if his or her information is wrong. The oven temperature, the circuit boards, and the lawyer's information: these are all inputs into processes that are also causing problems within the processes.

Other reasons for defining inputs when working with a process include:

- Understanding the resources required for a process to run
- Identifying extraneous inputs that aren't required
- Understanding costs for the process
- Understanding how the process relates to processes that come before it

Remember, in a business, processes are linked together to accomplish a final goal or goals. The inputs entering process B might be the outputs leaving process A.

Outputs

The output of a process is the service or product that is used by the customer of the process. In the pizza example, the output is the cheese pizza the customer is going to eat. In the candy factory example, the output is the hard candy that will be sold by the retail store.

The process customer is not always the traditional end customer who purchases a product or service. Customers can be internal or external. An example of a process serving an internal customer might be seen in a business office that employees a receptionist to answer phone calls. If the receptionist takes messages or transfers phone calls, he or she is serving both the person on the phone *and* the person who is receiving the call or message.

In some cases, the customer of a process is not even a person. Many processes feed other processes. In a pharmacy, the process of entering data about a prescription feeds the process that bills an insurance company for the medication.

From a Six Sigma perspective, an output is almost always of more value to the ultimate process than the input is. The process itself involves adding value of some kind to the inputs. A bakery puts raw bread dough through the oven to add value to it: the result is an edible and tasty product that a consumer is more likely to purchase or to pay more for.

Events

Events are specific, predefined criteria or actions that cause a process to begin working. A process that performs well responds to an event just like a light bulb responds to the action of a switch being pulled. Six Sigma teams must determine what events trigger a process because it helps them understand why a process is being performed and whether the process is being run when it isn't needed.

Consider an example about compliance audits in a financial sector company. Perhaps a company created a specific audit process that initiates when red flags on accounts are raised; the audit process is comprehensive and usually takes an average of 80 labor hours. You can imagine that it is an expensive process to run. In investigating, a Six Sigma team identifies the event associated with the process: anytime a discrepancy in an account is noted by a clerk, the compliance process is triggered.

The team investigates and realizes that this is true even when the discrepancy was minor – a few dollars or less – or the clerk was able to reconcile the discrepancy later in the day. The team might suggest that the relationship between the process and the event is a problem. The process is running at times when it might not be valuable for it to do so.

Tasks

Tasks, or activities, are the heart of a process. Just as the heart pumps blood through your body, the tasks within a process pump the inputs through, turning them into the outputs. Tasks are the physical, automated, or computerized actions within a process. Examples of tasks include:

- A machine joining two metal parts with a weld
- A person entering data into a software program
- A computer processing data to create a report
- An email being written
- A piece of computerized work being routed within a workflow system
- A chef chopping ingredients for a recipe

Decisions

Decisions are closely related to tasks and can be tasks themselves. A chef preparing ingredients for a soup dish has to chop those ingredients, but he also has to decide how much of each ingredient he needs. His decision will likely be guided by the recipe and the number of people he has to feed.

Decisions within a process are typically governed by a set of rules. Sometimes those rules are formally documented; other times, decisions are made via informal rules along with staff knowledge and experience. Processes that are governed by informal rules can have problems of consistency; even when all staff are experienced, they could have individual variations on performing a task. And, as we discussed in Unit 1, variation can lead to more opportunities for defects and a reduction in quality.

Using the task examples above, here are examples of decisions in a process:

- A person entering data into a software program makes a decision to select a certain drop down category because of training or rules provided by the software
- A computer processes a report; the result of that report is a number above a set threshold, so the computer sends the report to a person
- When writing an email, a person chooses to include certain specific information, such as an order number or customer number, because it is protocol to do so when sending this type of email

All Components Are Related

You're probably noticing that processes can be extremely complex, and the relationships between all the components are equally complex. Inputs can be outputs from previous processes; outputs can be inputs in the next process. A decision might result in an event that starts a new process, but it can also be the factor that decides which task begins. As Six Sigma teams work with processes – observing them, diagramming them, and measuring them – the teams begin to understand the relationships of the components, and that helps them make decisions about possible improvements and changes.

Process Owners

As teams work to improve processes, they need to understand who the process owners are. Depending on the business organization, process owners can be the people with the power to approve changes. In some organizations, the lowest-level owner might not have veto or decision power about all changes, but he or she is held responsible for the performance of the process.

A process owner can be:

- A person in charge of a very specific process or function
- A team supervisor or department manager
- An executive-level individual who is probably responsible for a number of processes in his or her division

What does a process owner do?

The responsibilities of a process owner are often defined by the infrastructure of a specific business, but commonly, a process owner will:

- Monitor how the process performs, usually using one or more metrics or regularly reported data elements.
- Understand how the process fits into the overall business, why the output of the process is critical to business goals, and what inputs feed the process.
- Ensures the process is documented via standard operating procedures (SOPs) and that process documentation is kept current and accurate.
- Ensures operators within the process have the resources and training they need to complete their jobs.

In a Six Sigma environment, process owners might also ensure a control plan is in place and regularly review the process for possible improvement opportunities.

Data

Finally, all processes generate some form of data. Even if data isn't yet being captured, information is inherent in any process. A computer program that automatically routes work in a workflow might generate data such as the number of items in work queues, how many items were worked that day, the time items have been waiting in queues, how many items were transferred, and where those items were transferred to. A process for filling bottles with liquid might generate data such as how much liquid is placed in each bottle, how many bottles per hour are filled, and perhaps variation between bottles.

Data is extremely valuable to Six Sigma teams because it's often how they define whether a process is in control and successful.

Defining Process Components: The SIPOC

The SIPOC diagram is often an important part of the define stage of a Six Sigma project. But you can use the SIPOC diagram anytime you want to learn more about a process or understand how a process in a business environment is linked to other processes.

SIPOC stands for Suppliers, Inputs, Process, Outputs, and Customer. For the purposes of a SIPOC, inputs and outputs follow the same guidelines described previously in this chapter. Suppliers are the people, processes, and organizations that supply inputs to your process. Customers are the people, processes, and organizations that make use of the outputs of your process. The process itself is the series of steps that take the inputs and make them outputs.

Benefits of a SIPOC Diagram

The SIPOC diagram is one of the most often used tools for understanding process components and process relevance because it is so effective and simple. Teams can create SIPOC diagrams in a single brainstorming session, though effective diagramming usually requires the presence of a process owner and one or more SMEs who are familiar with the process on a daily level.

SIPOC diagrams are also infinitely scalable. Teams can diagram processes at a very minute level, but they can also use SIPOC to diagram an entire business. We'll walk through creating a SIPOC diagram and then provide some examples of SIPOCs at various levels to illustrate scalability.

SME: Subject Matter Expert
An SME is someone who is closely associated with or familiar with a process or work function. Six Sigma teams invite SMEs to participate in discussion, process mapping sessions, or problem and solution brainstorming, because SMEs have valuable insight that might not be provided by high-level process owners or a review of the data.

Creating a SIPOC Diagram

You can create a SIPOC diagram as an individual exercise or within a team environment. SIPOCs can be created using a computer and software tool such as Word or Excel, but you can also draw them freehand on a whiteboard or piece of paper. Freehand diagramming is a valuable brainstorming tool because teams can quickly edit the rough draft of the diagram as they discuss a process. Keep this in mind :many of the diagrams presented in this book look clean because they have already been typed and edited. As you diagram your own processes, they can tend to look messy at first with edits, arrows, scratch outs, and inserts. "Editing" or putting rules on the brainstorming process can limit the ideas and information that flow during the process. You can always create a clean copy of the diagram for presentation purposes when you are finished brainstorming.

Step 1: Create Swim Lanes

A SIPOC diagram is based on swim lanes. Swim lanes let you show how cross-functional activities and resources relate to your process. A SIPOC diagram gets five lanes: one each for Suppliers, Inputs, Process, Outputs, and Customers. You'll end up with something that looks like the figure below.

Suppliers	Inputs	Process	Outputs	Customers

Step 2: Set Boundaries and Name Your Process

Before beginning a SIPOC session, set a definition for where your process or responsibility begins and ends. If you don't understand the scope of your process, then your SIPOC session can get out of hand or produce a diagram that isn't useful for your project.

Naming your process helps the team identify more readily with a specific aspect of the business. For example, a team working to improve processes within a medical office might look at a process named "Gathering New Patient Information." By naming the process, the team has put some scope limitations in place: the team will talk about things related to gathering information from patients. The scope is further limited to the process by which staff gathers information from *new* patients.

As you work through the SIPOC diagramming exercise, you can point back to the name and the scope you've defined to keep the team on task with the discussion.

Step 3: Complete Swim Lanes

You can complete SIPOC swim lanes in any order, but best practices usually have teams enter data in the following order:

- Process
- Outputs
- Customer
- Inputs
- Suppliers

Realistically, teams will think of things as they work through the process, so you'll be returning to swim lanes repeatedly to move information around and add new information.

A SIPOC isn't usually a low-level or detailed map of the actual process, so keep teams high-level when completing the process swim lane. You can simply enter the name of the process in that section, or you can list some of the high level steps required for the process. Listing steps is a good exercise if teams aren't sure about outputs and inputs – beginning to visualize the process usually helps ideas flow about how the process is connected to other processes and resources in the company.

To keep the session from turning into a detailed process mapping activity, ask the team to describe the process in less than five to seven steps. Keep things simple by limiting process steps to short verb-noun combos such as "Enter information," "Collect money," or "Place labels."

Name Outputs and Customers

Once you have a rudimentary process definition, begin with either inputs or outputs. Ask the team "What does this process make? What comes out of this process?" Those answers go into the outputs swim lane.

Next, ask the team "Who or what uses the things that come from this process?" Place those answers in the customer swim lane. Remember that customers can be external or internal, and another process can be the customer in cases of automation.

Name Inputs and Suppliers

Ask the team "What does the process need to perform? What raw goods or materials feed the process?" Record those answers in the inputs section.

You can divide the idea of inputs into two types, if you like. First, you have the actual inputs – the goods and services that are transformed by the process to create the outputs. Second, you have *enablers* of the process. These aren't technically inputs because they don't enter the process and aren't changed by the process; instead, they are required for the process to function. Machinery is an enabler. In a process that cuts metal parts from a steel sheet, the machine that does the cutting is an enabler. While it's not required, separating enablers on your SIPOC helps you define the process and provides additional information for later in the project.

Once you have a list of inputs, ask the team, "Where do the inputs come from? Who or what supplies the process with these things?" As with customers, suppliers can be external or internal. A vendor might provide the raw sugar that goes into the candy in a factory; the marketing department might provide the leads that the sales department uses to create orders.

Suppliers can also be other processes, particularly in an automated environment, and you can have a list of several suppliers for one input in a raw SIPOC diagram. For example, support tickets come into the Information Technology (IT) department. The supplier of the ticket could be both the end-user submitting the ticket and the automated process that routes the ticket to the appropriate work queue. If you are documenting enablers, you might record the end-user as the supplier and the automated process as the enabler.

Step 4: Validate the Information

Ensure that your understanding of the process at this high level is accurate by validating your diagram. If you've put together a comprehensive team that includes SMEs, the team can validate most of the information on its own. It's always a good idea to get a second opinion on anything the team isn't sure about, though. Invite other SMEs or the process owner to review the diagram briefly with the team and provide feedback.

Tips for a SIPOC Brainstorming Session

One of the best ways to create an initial SIPOC diagram during a team session is on large pieces of paper or a whiteboard. Create swim lanes by drawing them on the whiteboard or hanging a piece of paper for each swim lane on the wall. Provide the team with sticky notes and markers; write on sticky notes instead of writing directly on the board or paper. This lets you move components around quickly as you work through the diagram.

Sample SIPOC Diagrams

Here are some sample SIPOC diagrams. The first diagram is at the highest level: the process is the business itself. The second diagram features an automated process. The third diagram illustrates a people-powered factory process and includes enablers.

Business-Level SIPOC Diagram

This diagram shows the SIPOC for a mid-sized printing company. It's a very high-level, simplified SIPOC that shows how customers and vendors provide information and items; the printing company then turns those inputs into products such as printed business cards. The final product goes to individuals, businesses, and marketing professionals who placed the order.

Suppliers	Inputs	Process	Outputs	Customers
Paper vendor	Orders/customer specifications	Receive order	Business cards	Individuals
Ink vendor	Paper	Layout designs	Brochures	Business owners
Copy and print machine provider	Ink	Print designs	Banners and signs	Marketing departments
	Designs		Mailers	
Customer		Deliver printed product	Letterhead	

Most of the time, a Six Sigma team won't deal with a business-level SIPOC diagram. However, if the team includes members from outside the division or company, such as vendors or consultants assisting with an improvement, then starting with a high-level diagram can help those outside of the business understand the overall goals of the company.

SIPOC of an Automated Process

The diagram below represents an automated process in a mail-order pharmacy. The process in question puts labels on bottles that are to be filled with corresponding medications. The scope of the process is only the labeling of the bottles.

Suppliers	Inputs	Process	Outputs	Customers
Bottle sorting machine	Unlabeled bottles	Choose bottle size	Labeled bottle	Bottle-filling station
Label machine	Data for labels	Print label		
Prescription software	Labels	Affix label		
Ink and label vendors	Ink for printing			

Because this is a process within a chain of automated processes, almost all of the components are machines, processes, and things. Prior to labeling, a machine sorts bottles by size. That machine feeds the labeling station as needed. After the labeling is done, another station fills the bottles.

SIPOC with Enablers Noted

The SIPOC diagram below illustrates how enablers might be recorded for your process. The process in question takes place in a factory that makes furniture; in this process, a person attaches legs to a barstool on an assembly line. For the purposes of this illustration, leg attachment is the last step in the completion of the product, which means the product moves from the leg attachment station to packing and shipping.

Suppliers	Inputs	Process	Outputs	Customers
Upholstery station (provides final top of stool)	Stool top	Align legs	Barstool with legs attached	Packing station
	Legs	Attach legs with screws		
Warehouse (provides legs, screws, and protective cover)	Screws	Place protective cover		
	Protective cover			
Enablers:				
Conveyor machine that moves products				
Drill for application of screws				

Without the conveyor machine, the people in involved in this process would have to move items manually. The conveyor isn't 100 percent required for legs to be added to the stool, but it enables the process to move at a more efficient pace. A case could be made that the drill isn't required either – screws can be installed manually – but it's certainly what enables the process to move at a speed required for mass production.

With just this simple SIPOC diagram of a process, a Six Sigma team would already have some idea about where variation could be hiding, what drives efficiencies in the process, and how the process relates to the overall business.

Create Your Own SIPOC Diagram

Whether working in a team or on your own, choose a process you know about and practice creating your own diagram. Pick a process associated with your business or a business example you have experience with. Use the following templates to get started.

Suppliers	Inputs	Process	Outputs	Customers

Enablers:

What is a Process?

Suppliers	Inputs	Process	Outputs	Customers

CHAPTER 8:
QUALITY

One of the most concise definitions of quality comes from the International Organization for Standardization, or ISO. ISO 9000 defines quality as the "degree to which a set of inherent characteristics fulfills requirements."[7]

The same document defines requirements as expectations or needs that are implied, obligatory, or stated, and the ISO notes that requirements can be generated by different interest points. A Six Sigma team should be interested in requirements generated by all interest points, but often focuses most on those generated by the customer. Various types of requirements might include:

- Customer expectations, which are typically stated or implied values. It's implied that a customer wants the product he or she ordered. Expectations of delivery speed might be stated in the form of feedback in customer surveys.
- Compliance or regulatory rules, which are *obligatory*. For example, banks must protect credit card information—they are obligated by rules from government and the industry's Payment Card Information Data Security Standards (PCI-DSS). Similarly, healthcare organizations must protect the confidentiality and security of patient data; they are obligated to do so under the Health Insurance Portability and Accountability Act (HIPAA).
- Brand expectations, which come from in-house leadership. Brand expectations are typically stated; while not obligatory in the sense of being backed by regulation, companies for which high-quality, a specific voice, or other unique factor is a component of branding might treat brand expectations as obligatory. Coca-Cola, for example, has a brand that is recognizable around the globe. While components of that brand, such as the design of logos or soda cans, aren't mandated by regulations and might not be required by customers, Coca-Cola itself holds these components as important and puts resources and effort into them because it values its brand.

---

[7] https://www.iso.org/obp/ui/#iso:std:iso:9000:ed-3:v1:en:term:3.9.11

In this chapter, we'll take a look specifically at quality factors critical to processes and process improvement as well as costs associated with quality in general.

Critical to Quality Characteristics

Critical to quality characteristics, or CTQs, are the factors or parameters that are the major drivers of quality within an organization or process. Usually, CTQs are key characteristics that can be measured; where the performance of said metric provides information about whether or not the customer is going to be satisfied.

CTQs are closely related to CTCs, or critical to customer characteristics, but they are not the same thing. Something can be critical to quality – even critical to how a customer ultimately feels about a service or product – without being critical to the customer directly. CTQs are internal concerns, but they drive CTCs.

Let's look at some examples of CTQs and CTCs to understand the difference and the relationship between these two factors.

A Pair of Pants

When a customer purchases a pair of pants, he or she is usually concerned with how the pants fit and look. Are they comfortable, is the size correct, and does the clothing match the customer's personal style?

It's hard to create a measurement for whether pants are comfortable, but a manufacturer can take customer feedback on various types of pants and learn that a certain fabric with a certain cut is most comfortable for the target audience. The manufacturer can also determine appropriate measurements for each size. During the manufacturing process, these critical-to-quality factors are applied: only fabric that meets the specifications identified is used. The fabric is then cut to specific measurements and sewn together in a specific manner – measurements and sewing methods are critical to quality.

The average customer, however, doesn't want to hear about the exact measurements of each fabric piece or the way the seams were sewn. They want to put on a pair of pants and experience a comfortable fit.

Chocolate Bars

A chocolate company conducts a survey to find out why sales of its newest product haven't performed as expected. The feedback suggests that the chocolate is too sweet – the taste and the sweetness of the chocolate is a critical to customer characteristic.

The company might tweak its formula, reducing the amount of sugar that goes into the chocolate. The recipe – and the amount of sugar -- is a critical to quality factor in this case. But what if the customer feedback indicated that health-conscious consumers simply didn't want to buy a chocolate bar with so much sugar in it? Then the amount of sugar in the recipe becomes both a CTQ and a CTC. It is critical to the quality of the taste of the bar, but customers might also look at the nutritional information on the bar and make purchasing decisions based on the amount of sugar in the chocolate.

Mobile App Development

If a business wants to launch a mobile app for its customers, then an obvious customer-centric need is that the app works on the customer's phone. The customer doesn't care about the process the business needs to go through to launch the app on the platform in question, but the business must meet the criteria for Apple, Android, Windows, or other mobile operating systems. Those requirements become some of the CTQs for the mobile app development, even though certain requirements from the platforms might not appear to be at all related to statements from customers about desires or needs.

Why Identify CTQs?

In a process improvement environment, CTQs are critical to narrowing work scope and understanding how to enact change. Consider the 80/20 rule discussed in Chapter 5. Often, CTQs are the factors, characteristics, or outputs that drive 80 percent of customer satisfaction. By improving these few critical factors, teams can substantially impact customer satisfaction and the performance of the overall process. Identifying CTQs lets teams create the most improvement possible with the time, money, and people resources available.

Outside of a project environment, understanding CTQs lets organizations stay on top of quality. By managing a few critical metrics, teams can ensure excellent output in a continuous fashion and identify potential areas for improvement before they become customer-facing problems.

Using a CTQ Tree to Convert Customer Needs to Quality Metrics

In Chapter 5, we introduced the concept of the Voice of the Customer, or VoC. Six Sigma teams usually start with some type of VoC data when they are defining a problem and working on goals for a project. Either the team conducts surveys to hear from a statistically relevant group of customers during the first few phases of a project, or the team receives feedback from internal customers about a process. Sometimes, the VoC information a team begins with is something as simple as a champion or executive-level individual making a statement about expectations for an internal process or project. When VoC data is limited in such a fashion, teams might have to work harder to validate assumptions with data before moving on to CTQ analysis.

To gain a better understanding of how to measure the quality of a process, teams must convert VoC statements to CTQs. One of the best ways to do this is through a diagramming process known as a CTQ tree.

A CTQ tree begins with specific and critical customer needs, breaks that need down into drivers, and uses the drivers to create requirements. Specific requirements are easier to convert to measurable quality components. While each CTQ tree is unique, they begin with a common form. The common structure of a CTQ tree is shown below.

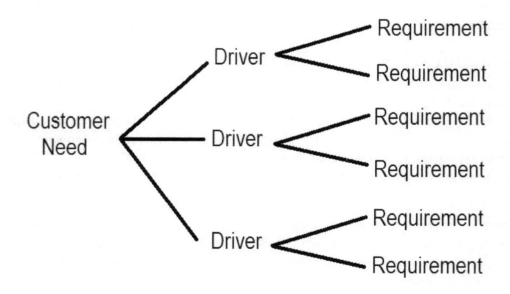

When creating a CTQ tree, you don't have to follow an equal pattern for drivers and requirements. Some customer needs will have more drivers than others; some drivers will have more requirements. You might also have multiple CTQ trees – you'll want to create one for every need you identify that is critical to a customer.

Identify Critical-to-Customer Needs

Begin the CTQ tree process by creating a list of needs that are critical to the customer. A bank working on processes dealing with online checking access might identify accessibility, user-friendly interfaces, and security of information as the major critical-to-customer needs, for example. Define needs in broad terms to help catch all drivers and requirements later in the diagramming process.

The best way to define needs is to directly ask customers for feedback, but time and resources don't always allow for surveys. Six Sigma teams might be able to take advantage of data collected via recent surveys or feedback forms, which is the next-best thing. In the absence of customer feedback, brainstorm critical needs with a group of employees who has knowledge of and experience with the customer. Subject matter experts from sales, customer service, and complaint departments can often provide viable information when the customer is the end-user. You can also begin a CTQ tree with the outputs of your SIPOC diagram; depending on how you structured the outputs on a SIPOC, you might need to define critical quality factors for the output as a starting point for your CTQ tree diagram.

Identify Drivers of Quality

Once you have a list of critical needs, work with one need at a time to create a tree similar to the diagram above. Identify quality drivers that must be present or met for the customer need to be fulfilled. For example, customers of an HVAC service company might require excellent service. Drivers for that need might include friendly service technicians, helpful and knowledgeable employees, and a timely response to service calls.

Drivers are the transition point between customer needs and requirements; you don't necessarily have to be able to measure drivers, but you want them to be a bit more detailed than the broad customer needs you already identified and you want to be flowing in the direction of measureable factors when possible.

List Requirements for Each Driver

Requirements are the most detailed breakdown regarding critical to quality characteristics. These are the things that you *can* measure that lead you to understand whether drivers are performing appropriately so customer needs are met.

For example, let's look at our HVAC example in a CTQ tree format.

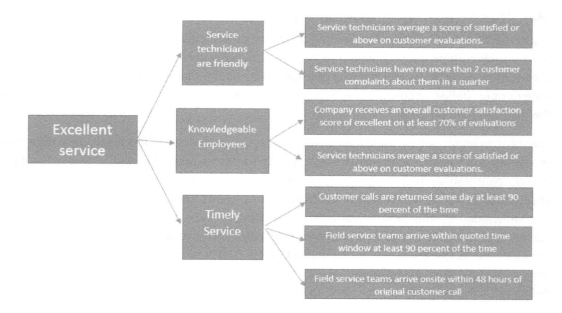

You can see in the above CTQ tree that drivers have been converted to requirements – and each of those requirements can be measured with numbers. In some cases, driver-to-requirement conversions equate to a hard number. The chocolate bar example at the beginning of this chapter features such a scenario: if the company deems that the recipe with a quarter cup of sugar is the correct recipe, then the process metric for quality is exactly a quarter cup of sugar.

In other examples, companies might provide leeway for exceptions or the understanding that a process is not going to hit an exact number every single time. For example, an HVAC team cannot possibly arrive at a customer's home exactly 24 hours after a phone call is made – and if the service technicians can arrive earlier than 24 hours, most people would want them to. That means the company has to create a definition for the requirement: how many hours is it before a customer considers a technician untimely? In the case of our example company, it's 48 hours. The requirement in another situation might be 24 hours.

Because teams will use the requirements from the CTQ trees to develop process measurements and metrics for success, it is extremely important that each requirement is vetted before teams incorporate it into the project or process. Requirements should be compared to VoC data, to existing measurements, and to experience and knowledge from subject matter experts and leaders. The team should ask themselves and others "If these requirements are met, will the customer be satisfied?" If the answer is ever no, then the requirements need work. The team might also consider asking "Are these requirements possible in the real world." If the answer is no, then either the process or the requirements needs work.

The CoQ and the CoPQ

Six Sigma teams must always be aware that quality comes at a cost. When talking about quality costs, many organizations consider what is known as the cost of poor quality, or CoPQ. The cost of poor quality is defined as the costs or expenses associated with defects created by a process. Quality actually has a broader cost – avoiding poor quality comes at an expense as well. The cost of quality, or CoQ, covers the expenses associated with maintaining good quality throughout an organization or process. Sometimes, this is referred to as the cost of good quality. In this section, we'll talk about both types of cost measurements, how they relate to Six Sigma in general, and how they relate to Six Sigma teams and projects.

The Cost of Poor Quality

In some ways, the cost of poor quality is easier to measure than the cost associated with overall quality. CoPQ is usually broken into two major categories: costs associated with external failures and costs associated with internal failures. External and internal failures are often referred to as the costs of nonconformity – they are the expenses that occur when outputs do not conform to critical to quality requirements.

External Failures

External failures usually occur after products or services have been delivered, which means they are directly associated with customer dissatisfaction. External failures might include revenue losses associated with a reduction in sales because of the quality of products, services, systems, or information. Other types of external losses include expenses associated with repairs, returns, or rework associated with a customer complaint; expenses associated with warranties; or loss of revenue or sales because of customer ill will or bad word-of-mouth.

Internal Failures

Internal failures occur when products, services, or processes don't conform to the requirements set by the company, and the product or service is provided to the customer in an unsatisfactory fashion. Internal failures are usually handled by scrapping the work, redoing the work, or repairing the work. Obviously, such rework results in added material and labor costs, but it also results in losses associated with delays, shortages of parts or inventory, and lack of flexibility or the ability to adapt. For example, if a process has such poor quality that 50 percent of the items produced by it require rework, then the process might be producing 40 percent less on a daily basis than it could be. That means the process can serve fewer customers, generate less output, and contribute less overall to the company's profit.

Calculating the Cost of Poor Quality

Understanding the cost of poor quality is critical to Six Sigma organizations because it lets leaders understand how financial needs are related to the need for quality improvements. The higher the cost of poor quality, the more likely an organization will work toward improvement.

At a project or process level, the cost of poor quality might help determine budgets for improvement. If poor quality within the process is costing an organization $5,000 a month, a project that costs $20,000 but saves $3,000 a month in quality would pay for itself in just seven months. On the other end, a project that costs $100,000 when the costs of poor quality are only $1,000 a month is less likely to make sense.

The equation for CoPQ is:

CoPQ = External Failure Costs + Internal Failure Costs

While the equation seems simple, identifying all of the costs associated with poor quality can be difficult. Most experts use the metaphor of an iceberg to explain the hidden costs of poor quality. On the surface, you see the very small tip of the iceberg—the obvious costs of poor quality. These might be things such as scrap, reprocessing, warranty claims, customer returns, and extra shipping.

Beneath the surface, however, an iceberg is always much bigger. The same is usually true of the cost of poor quality, and hidden costs might include:

- Loss of customer loyalty
- Loss of morale
- Loss of employees if morale remains low for extended periods
- Conflicts associated with scheduling or rescheduling
- Higher risks of compliance issues, including fines
- Higher administrative costs

- Unpredictable revenue, sales, or production

Calculating the cost of poor quality is extremely difficult on an enterprise-wide level and still moderately difficult on a process level. A method for listing all possible costs and formulizing them to dollar amounts doesn't exist. It's a good idea for organizations to develop a streamlined method that is used throughout the enterprise when calculating CoPQ. At the very least, Six Sigma experts in the organization might consider defining a specific way of listing costs of poor quality company-wide so that various process teams are using similar measures when they report to leadership.

The Cost of Quality

The cost of quality, or CoQ, includes the cost of poor quality *and* the cost of good quality. In addition to internal and external failure costs, CoQ includes prevention and appraisal costs. Prevention and appraisal costs are often referred to as the costs of conformity – they are the expenses related to ensuring outputs conform to critical to quality requirements.

Prevention Costs

The costs of prevention are the expenses that are related to any activity meant to stop an error or defect from occurring. Error-proofing, which is covered in detail in later chapters on controlling processes, results in prevention costs. For example, if a company produces baked goods, at some point in the process people or machines must measure ingredients to add to dough batches. One way to error-proof such a process is to provide specialized machinery that will only allow a specific amount of each ingredient to be introduced to a batch. Such a machine would likely be quite expensive; it would also have to be managed by a qualified operator and maintained by appropriate repair and cleaning staff. All of that activity would generate costs which might be considered preventative in nature.

Other types of prevention costs include expenses related to quality planning, reviews, or education and training focused on quality. Quality review and evaluation processes also create prevention costs, whether those reviews are related to suppliers, products, processes, or people. Customer surveys, the creation of technical manuals, work to create and manage requirements and specifications, and the management of job descriptions can all lead to prevention costs. Even housekeeping costs might be considered preventative costs, especially if a clean work environment is required to reduce flaws or errors in product manufacturing.

Appraisal Costs

Appraisal costs are those associated with any activity meant to ensure high levels of quality across a process or organization. If a manufacturing plant hires a quality control specialist, and that person's job is to review parts that come down the manufacturing line and either return the work for correction or report the level of quality as a metric, then the salary of that person and any expenses related to his or her employment are appraisal costs. In some cases, those expenses might also be considered prevention costs, *but they would not be counted twice when calculating CoQ.*

Other types of appraisal costs might include expenses related to quality audits on products, services, or processes, the cost of calibration and measurement equipment or software, and the costs of field tests. Prototype inspections, consulting expenses, financial reporting and auditing, security checks, safety checks, supplier certifications, employee surveys, and customer feedback are all further examples of areas where appraisal costs might exist.

Calculating the Cost of Quality

The equation for CoQ is:

CoQ = CoPQ + Prevention Costs + Appraisal Costs

The same challenges inherent in calculating CoPQ also exist when calculating CoQ. The same iceberg analogy is relevant, and prevention and appraisal activities often have hidden costs such as unnecessary overtime, paperwork, or system expenses.

The Cost of Quality and Six Sigma

Traditional wisdom might say that if the cost of poor quality goes down, the cost of good quality is likely to go up. You have to spend money on quality to have good quality, in other words. While historically that might be true for many organizations, it is not the case in a Six Sigma company. Because Six Sigma works to create quality that is inherent in the process – meaning things are done right the first time and defects are reduced – the costs of quality often go down while quality itself goes up.

In Chapter 1, we showed that a process with a higher sigma level (and thus, higher quality) has fewer defects. Defects decrease in an exponential manner as sigma level rises. Because there are fewer defects, the costs of poor quality are exponentially reduced as well. But time and again, Six Sigma has also reduced the cost of overall quality. As the sigma level of processes is increased via the application of Six Sigma tools and methodology, the cost of both prevention and appraisal goes down as well.

One way of relating the cost of quality – and perhaps the most common way of doing so among corporations – is as a percent of sales. The cost of quality as a percent of sales typically aligns so closely with sigma values that you can predict the cost of quality based on a company's or process's sigma value. The average ranges for CoQ in relation to sigma values are shown in the table below. As you can see, as companies improve their sigma levels, they experience a substantial savings in the cost of quality.

Sigma level	Cost of Quality as a Percent of Sales
2	Above 40%
3	25 to 40 %
4	15 to 25%
5	5 to 15%
6	Less than 1%

Managing Cost of Quality

Six Sigma is one of the best methodologies for managing the cost of quality because it works to build quality into every process. When approaching an organization or process that has a high cost of quality, teams and leadership can apply a triage-based method to reduce those costs. While no organization can remove quality costs 100 percent, the goal should be zero costs of failure, either internal or external, and minimal preventative and appraisal costs.

First, teams should concentrate on costs associated with failures. It's often easier and less expensive to detect costs associated with nonconformance, and improvements that seek to correct causes for a few critical failures can have a big impact on overall quality and total cost. Instead of adding layers of quality programs over processes to ensure quality – which only adds prevention or appraisal activities and increases the cost of quality – Six Sigma improvement projects build preventative measures into processes themselves. In other words, efficient Six Sigma processes are self-regulating. They have built in checks and balances that work to constantly reduce defects and rework.

The benefit of building failure stop-points into a process include:

- Earlier detection when errors do occur, which keeps hidden costs down. When the error can't make it to the next process or to the customer, you avoid many issues and costs associated with low morale, reduced customer loyalty, or product returns.
- Employees are able to support and manage higher quality. When quality is something employees have ownership of, they are more likely to work hard to create the best possible output. In contrast, appraisal-style quality programs can spark feelings of paranoia at being closely watched or create a relationship in employee minds between the idea of quality and the idea of reprisal or correction. Poor performance on a continuous basis does need to be addressed, but employees should not default to a negative mindset when they hear the word quality.
- In-process quality assurance is actually more effective than post-process or over-process prevention and appraisal methods. Statistical process control and Six Sigma improvements *can* push a process to six sigma level. To ensure the same level of performance – 3.4 defects per million opportunities – quality assurance employees would need to review millions of parts and ensure only a very tiny few had defects. It's simply not an economical option for most, if any, organization.

After teams use the Six Sigma and Lean process management methods discussed throughout this book to reduce failure costs, teams can turn to prevention and appraisal costs. Often, in a process that is functioning at a high sigma level, prevention and appraisal activities are a form of muda. They can be expunged from the process without impacting the end product, quality, customer satisfaction, or employee morale. In some cases, removing prevention or appraisal from processes actually creates a positive impact on quality, production, and customer and employee satisfaction.

Identifying Prevention and Appraisal Activities

The first step to removing quality-related muda is identifying it. Process maps, spaghetti diagrams, and value stream maps are valuable tools for uncovering activities that don't need to be included in a process. All of these tools are covered in depth in Unit 9.

Whether you're mapping a process or simply discussing various components with process owners or a Six Sigma team, asking questions about value and necessity can also help identify muda of prevention and appraisal. If you think an activity related to a process might be an unnecessary form of prevention or appraisal, ask:

- Does the activity itself add any value to the output?
- Does the activity substantially reduce the time it takes for the process to produce an output?
- Does the activity substantially increase the cost of the process?
- If the activity is designed to prevent defects within the process, can the activity be made more efficient?
- If the activity is designed to prevent defects, can the activity be made less expensive?
- If an activity is designed to capture quality data about the process for reporting purposes, are those reports necessary?
- If quality reports are necessary– either because of obligatory requirements such as compliance or because the reports provide value in another process – can the reports be automated to reduce associated expense?

The answers to these questions help teams identify areas where muda can be removed or where quality-related processes can be improved.

Quality is Critical to Success

When Six Sigma teams are expunging quality-related costs and unnecessary activities from processes, it is critical that they don't actually remove quality. While it's true that traditional quality programs and costs don't have to be present to ensure a reduction in defects and an improvement in customer satisfaction, it's equally true that you have to replace those programs with some other form of control. By the end of this book, you will have learned about a number of tools, from statistical process control to poka yokes, which you can use to create quality within a process.

It's also worth noting that a single Six Sigma team – or even an entire department devoted to Six Sigma – can't reduce the costs of quality in an organization on their own. Corporate leadership must buy into the belief that quality is better when controls are incorporated within the process, and they have to be willing to communicate this fact via training and example. Some companies choose instead to use Six Sigma to improve processes while maintaining the expense of traditional quality, compliance, and audit departments. For some industries, such as healthcare or finance, audits and other appraisal and prevention costs might be mandated by laws and regulations. Outside of that mandate, it's almost always best to remove any quality activity that doesn't provide additional value.

CHAPTER 9:
SELECTING THE RIGHT PROJECTS

Teams can bring abundant knowledge of Six Sigma to the table, but if organizations don't choose the right projects, improvements won't drive effective changes for the benefit of the bottom line and/or customer satisfaction. Since Six Sigma works best when it is implemented as a company-wide culture, project selection should work as an enterprise-wide function. This chapter covers a number of tools and methods for brainstorming and selecting projects that are most likely to bring significant improvement to processes and serve overall business goals.

Juggling the Right Amount of Projects

A critical part of Six Sigma success for organizations is knowing when teams reach maximum project load. Even when organizations hire employees dedicated to process improvement, they can only sustain a certain number of improvement projects without substantially reducing the positive outcomes of those projects. While project work, including data gathering and analysis, might be handled by employees committed 100 percent to improvement projects, teams usually have to engage with and pull resources from regular staff members. An organization that juggles too many projects puts daily output at risk. *In seeking to improve processes, a company that selects too many projects at one time could actually negatively impact quality.*

No formula exists for how many Six Sigma projects a company should run at a given time, but a few well-designed projects are more likely to make greater impact than many poorly designed, overlapping, or unfunded projects. Organizations should only launch projects they can:

- **Fund.** Six Sigma projects take monetary resources, which means organizations must prioritize based on financial criteria.
- **Support with people resources.** Six Sigma projects require work from employees at all levels. Companies shouldn't launch three projects at one time that draw heavily on IT resources or attempt multiple, simultaneous projects that need input from the Director of Compliance on a regular basis. Relying too heavily on resources for multiple projects can burn out employees, decrease

morale, impact quality, and impede work that is necessary to keep the business running from day to day.

- **Manage.** Project teams require leadership; Six Sigma teams are usually run by Black Belts, sometimes along with certified Project Managers. Since Black Belts are supported by Green Belts who handle much of the data collection and analysis work, a single Black Belt can usually manage more than one project at a time if needed. This is especially true for experienced Black Belts who are not responsible for any type of daily operation. Even so, organizations with limited Six Sigma experts on staff can't launch dozens of projects without putting a strain on those resources.

Enterprise-Level Selection Process

When companies are working to apply Six Sigma culture to the entire enterprise, executive leaders and other decision makers should work directly with Six Sigma experts to identify improvement opportunities and launch projects. Doing so lets leadership align project selection with organizational goals, ensure projects are organized in a way that matches resources, and keep a bird's eye view of improvement endeavors. Organizations can apply a five-step procedure for identifying viable Six Sigma improvement projects.

1. Data-Based Review of Current State of the Organization

Organizations can begin with a high-level look at internal and external sources of information about performance. Internal information might include complaints or issues raised by employees, existing performance metrics or reports, financial reports, and quality reports. External sources include all of the Voice of the Customer tools we covered in Chapter 5. In reviewing internal and external information, organizations should ask:

- What types of things are customers or employees complaining about?
- Where is the organization falling short of benchmarks or competitor performance?
- What needs do customers have that the organization is not meeting?
- What needs might customers have in the near future that the organization is not yet able to meet?
- What processes are outputting the most defects?
- What processes are known for the most rework?
- What are the slowest or most expensive processes in the organization?

- What are some obstacles keeping the organization from reaching its goals?

2. Brainstorm and Describe Potential Projects

Answers to the questions in step one become a brainstorming list for potential projects. What types of things are customers complaining about? Perhaps surveys and feedback forms show customers complaining about long shipment times, poor quality of products, or rude customer service. With just a single question, an organization has a list of possible projects:

- A project to reduce the time it takes for customers to receive orders
- A project to increase the quality of products
- A project to create better customer service

Admittedly, the scope is enormous with these examples, so organizations would need to look for a bit more detail. Why do customers think the quality of products is low? In Chapter 6, we covered the 5 Whys brainstorming method, and that method is relevant here. During the brainstorming process, organizations and teams should repeatedly ask "Why?" questions to get a more granular look at project possibilities.

For example, if a feedback form for a carpet installation company indicates that customers aren't satisfied with the service they receive, the team might ask "Why are customers dissatisfied?" Further investigation into customer feedback might indicate that the customers are unhappy because carpet edges are coming up shortly after the carpet is installed. Why is this happening? The short answer is that something is wrong in the installation process. The organization might add "Improve carpet installation process" to a list of possible projects.

Creating a list of possible projects in this manner isn't always a matter of a single brainstorming session. As issues are raised, more information might be required to list possible projects, but if you gather the right group of people for a few braining storming sessions, it's likely someone already has that information or knows some basic answers. Remember, the point of this exercise is to call out possible areas for improvement, not validate assumptions or come up with solutions.

Once teams have a large list of possible projects, they should begin creating short descriptions that will become the basis of step three. The descriptions also let teams quickly identify things that are not actually problems or would not apply within an improvement project environment. Descriptions should include answers to three questions:

- How is the issue painful to the customer, the employees, or the organization? In short, how does the issue impede someone from getting what they want or need?
- What is the goal that would be accomplished with an improvement?
- Why should an organization address this issue now?

If this is starting to sound familiar, it's because the answers to these questions create something similar to, though slightly less formal than, the problem statements discussed in Chapter 6. Using the carpet installation example, for example, the description might be:

Customers are not satisfied with carpet installation because edges are coming up within a few weeks of installation. The poor edges are creating safety and aesthetic issues and increasing expense and rework for teams who have to return to sites to address defects. The goal is to reduce the number of times carpet edges come up by 80 percent. The organization should address the issue because it is costing $20,000 per month in errors.

Some basic idea of what the team wants to do is provided, and leadership has a very real measurement of why the improvement is important. Even better, the measurement -- $20,000 in additional costs each month – can be compared to other project opportunities.

3. Apply Some Basic Criteria to Shorten the List

Once a list of possible projects is created, teams can apply some very basic criteria to remove projects that are inappropriate, would not work with Six Sigma methodology, are not property scoped, or have little likely return on investment. This step usually begins during the second part of step two, when teams are creating short descriptions of possible projects.

First, teams can remove items from the list where there is no real pain point. If a significant difference between desired state and current state doesn't exist, then there's nothing to improve. For example, if a single employee complaint about the efficiency of a piece of software made it onto the initial list, a company wouldn't pursue improvements further if it turned out no one else was having the issue.

Second, teams can remove issues that have very obvious problems and/or solutions. Consider the carpet installation problem: if the issue of edges cropped up in the last month and someone on the team reviewing potential problems recently received an email about defects in edging materials from a carpet vendor, the solution might be obvious. Perhaps the vendor sent notification that the materials in a certain batch of carpet were faulty and provided instructions for a solution. In this case, action is required on the part of the organization, but that action isn't a Six Sigma project. We'll talk more in Chapter 11 about the DMAIC process, but if a problem is already defined and a solution provided, you don't need to spend time going through the DMAIC phases.

4. Create Unique Business Criteria

After removing project ideas that don't fit Six Sigma methodology, teams should create and apply business criteria to further filter the list. Business criteria usually come in the form of expenses, monetary gains, impact on customer satisfaction, and urgency. Some questions teams might ask include:

- How will the improvement impact revenue-facing measurements such as profit, orders, or income?
- What savings will the improvement create?
- How is the problem trending? Is it becoming a bigger and more urgent issue quickly, or can the organization operate with minimal impact without making an immediate or near-future change?
- How much will the improvement cost?
- How many employees/employee hours will be required for the improvement?
- What resources are required for the improvement?

5. Use Business Criteria to Prioritize Project Lists

Using the business criteria, teams should prioritize projects and select projects from the top of the prioritized list for immediate work. One of the best ways to prioritize projects is to create a selection matrix with defined criteria and a numerical ranking system.

For example, using the example questions in step four, we might create the following list of criteria:

- Potential savings
- Potential cost
- Potential increase to revenue
- Ability to access resources needed

A matrix can be created using the criteria and a list of projects. Teams can then rate each project against each criteria using a numeric scale. In the example below, we applied a scale from 1 to 10, with 1 being the most negative and 10 being the most positive.

It's important to note that in this example, the numbers aren't associated with real-world numbers. For example, when rating savings, a higher number just means a more positive expectation. In this case, the positive expectation would be a high amount of savings. When rating costs, however, the higher number (and more positive expectation) would relate to a project with a lower overall cost.

	Savings	Costs	Revenue increase	Access to resources	**Total**
Project 1	1	8	9	10	28
Project 2	5	5	4	6	20
Project 3	10	2	2	2	16

In the table above, you can see that Project 1 has low expected savings, but the team also estimates it will have a low overall cost, drive a high increase in revenue, and has easy access to resources. Project 3, on the other hand, has a high expected savings, but negative ratings in all other categories.

To rank projects, add up the scores for all categories and order the projects from highest to lowest by total score.

The Project Viability Model

Teams can choose to create their own criteria for a project selection matrix, or they can use a 15-point viability model as defined below. One benefit of the project viability model is that it provides some weighting, letting teams make some criteria more important than others. It also removes some of the objective nature of the selection matrix defined in the previous section.

This model is based on 15 criteria, which are defined in the table below.

Criteria	Definition
1. Sponsorship	The project is likely to be sponsored at a high level. (For more information on project sponsorship, see the team building information in Chapter 10). Sponsorship increases the chance that teams will have access to the funds and resources required for a successful potential

	project.
2. Corporate alignment	The goals of the project are aligned with the goals of the business. Working on potential projects that aren't aligned with business goals can reduce business effectiveness.
3. Data	Data is available or can be accessed so the team can design project metrics. Without access to data, a Six Sigma methodology can't be applied. If data is excessively time-consuming or expensive to collect, then the potential project is usually not the best choice.
4. Definition of defect	There is a specific, well-defined defect or problem. Without a well-defined defect, potential projects run the risk of scope creep.
5. Stability	The potential process is stable and there are no expectations that the process is going to be overhauled, redesigned, or changed in the near future. There is usually no reason to spend time and money improving a process that will drastically change soon anyway.
6. Customer	The planned goal of the potential project would create a substantial and positive impact on customer satisfaction or perception of quality.
7. Benefits	The potential project has a strong cost-benefit ratio.
8. Timeline	The timeline for a potential project is relatively short. Timelines for most Six Sigma improvement projects are around 6 months, though some do run longer. Longer timelines decrease the chance that an improvement fits within the DMAIC methodology.

9. Solution	The potential project purpose is to find a solution that is not already known or defined. As we previously stated, if a solution is obvious, you don't need to run a project to find it.
10. Implementation is likely	A solution identified and verified by the potential project is likely to be implemented. If, for any reason, change is very unlikely within a process, then going through Six Sigma improvement work is a waste of resources.
11. Required investment	The potential project requires a large investment of cash. Generally, the greater the cash or capital investment required, the less likely a project will be selected or a solution will be implemented due to cost-benefit analysis.
12. Available Six Sigma Resources	The Black and Green Belts required for the project are available.
13. Inputs can be controlled	For a Six Sigma process improvement project to be successful, at least some of the inputs must be within control of the team or organization. For example, a team can't work to improve the quality of a part that is provided wholly by a vendor.
14. Redesign	The process can be improved as is and doesn't need a complete redesign.
15. Process quality is improved/maintained	The improvement doesn't negatively impact the quality of service or products along the value chain.

Based on the above criteria, teams create a matrix.

	Weig ht	No (1)	Most ly No (2)	Possibl y (3)	Most ly Yes (4)	Yes (5)
Is there a sponsor or champion?						
Do project goals align with corporate goals?						
Is data available or accessible?						
Are defects well defined?						
Is the process stable?						
Are there customer benefits to the project?						
Are there company benefits to the project?						
Can the project be completed within 6 months?						
Is the solution unknown?						
Is it likely a discovered solution will be implemented?						
Would a new solution cost little to no cash?						
Are Six Sigma team members available for the project?						
Can inputs in the process be controlled?						
Can the process be improved without a full redesign?						
Will the improvements maintain or improve quality across the value chain?						

Teams then apply a numerical weight to each criterion. Weight each criterion on a scale of 1 to 5, with 1 being least important and 5 being most important. For example, our team with the carpet installation issue might create weights as follows:

	Weight
Is there a sponsor or champion?	3
Do project goals align with corporate goals?	4
Is data available or accessible?	3
Are defects well defined?	3
Is the process stable?	1
Are there customer benefits to the project?	5
Are there company benefits to the project?	5
Can the project be completed within 6 months?	3
Is the solution unknown?	4
Is it likely a discovered solution will be implemented?	3
Would a new solution cost little to no cash?	5
Are Six Sigma team members available for the project?	3
Can inputs in the process be controlled?	5
Can the process be improved without a full redesign?	2
Will the improvements maintain or improve quality across the value chain?	5

Next, teams should answer each question by marking a 1 in the relevant box on the grid; the answers correspond with no, mostly no, possibly, mostly yes, and yes. The complete grid for our carpet installation problem is featured below.

	Weig ht	No (1)	Most ly No (2)	Possibl y (3)	Most ly Yes (4)	Yes (5)
Is there a sponsor or champion?	3		1			
Do project goals align with corporate goals?	4					1
Is data available or accessible?	3			1		
Are defects well defined?	3					1
Is the process stable?	1				1	
Are there customer benefits to the project?	5					1
Are there company benefits to the project?	5				1	
Can the project be completed within 6 months?	3			1		
Is the solution unknown?	4				1	
Is it likely a discovered solution will be implemented?	3			1		
Would a new solution cost little to no cash?	5			1		
Are Six Sigma team members available for the project?	3	1				
Can inputs in the process be controlled?	5		1			
Can the process be improved without a full redesign?	2					1
Will the improvements maintain or improve quality across the value chain?	5		1			

Once a matrix is completed for each project, teams must calculate and compare the score for potential projects. These calculations are completed via the following steps.

1. Divide each weight by 3; a weight of 3 equals 1, but a weight of 5 equals 5/3, or 1.7

2. Convert each of the 1s listed on your grid to a weighted value by multiplying it by the converted weight from step one. For example, the weight for the first question on the grid

above is 3. We divided 3/3 to get 1. We would multiple 1 * 1 for the first row. The next row is weighted 4; 4/3 is 1.3. The numbers have all been converted in the grid below.

	Weight	No (1)	Mostly No (2)	Possibly (3)	Mostly Yes (4)	Yes (5)
Is there a sponsor or champion?	3		1			
Do project goals align with corporate goals?	4					1.3
Is data available or accessible?	3			1		
Are defects well defined?	3					1
Is the process stable?	1				0.3	
Are there customer benefits to the project?	5					1.7
Are there company benefits to the project?	5				1.7	
Can the project be completed within 6 months?	3			1		
Is the solution unknown?	4				1.3	
Is it likely a discovered solution will be implemented?	3			1		
Would a new solution cost little to no cash?	5			1.7		
Are Six Sigma team members available for the project?	3	1.3				
Can inputs in the process be controlled?	5		1.7			
Can the process be improved without a full redesign?	2					0.4
Will the improvements maintain or improve quality across the value chain?	5		1.7			

3. Sum the numbers in each of the five columns.

	Weight	No (1)	Mostly No (2)	Possibly (3)	Mostly Yes (4)	Yes (5)
Is there a sponsor or champion?	3		1			
Do project goals align with corporate goals?	4					1.3
Is data available or accessible?	3			1		
Are defects well defined?	3					1
Is the process stable?	1				0.3	
Are there customer benefits to the project?	5					1.7
Are there company benefits to the project?	5				1.7	
Can the project be completed within 6 months?	3			1		
Is the solution unknown?	4				1.3	
Is it likely a discovered solution will be implemented?	3			1		
Would a new solution cost little to no cash?	5			1.7		
Are Six Sigma team members available for the project?	3	1.3				
Can inputs in the process be controlled?	5		1.7			
Can the process be improved without a full redesign?	2					0.4
Will the improvements maintain or improve quality across the value chain?	5		1.7			
		1.3	4.4	4.7	3.3	4.4

4. Multiply each of the summed weighted scores by the number at the top of the column. For example, the sum of the column for the "No" answers is 1.3. Multiplying that by 1 equals 1.3. The other columns are calculated as:

- $2 = 8.8$
- $4.7 * 3 = 14.1$
- $3.3 * 4 = 13.2$

- 4.4 * 5 = 22

5. Add up the answers from the previous step. In this case, the total is 59.4.

6. Divide the sum from step five by the sum of the weighted totals from step three. In this case, 59.4 / 18.1 = 3.28

7. The answer from step 6 is the score for your project.

Once you score each potential project, you can determine if it is a viable project within a DMAIC methodology with the following key:

Score	DMAIC Viability
< 2.0	Not viable for DMAIC
2.0 to 3.0	Possibility viable, but organizations should validate further
Above 3.0	A viable DMAIC project

It should be noted that the 15-point matrix described above can only be used to determine if a project is viable within a DMAIC structure. A process might still need to be improved even though it doesn't fit DMAIC methodology; in the case of a redesign, the DMADV structure might let Six Sigma teams approach the improvement. The differences between DMAIC and DMADV methodologies, and how to determine which method is best for a project, are covered more in-depth in Chapter 11.

Project Selection at a Process Level

The goal of a Six Sigma team is not to define appropriate projects at an enterprise level. A department or team responsible for only a few processes might be seeking to make an improvement. In an organization where Six Sigma is important to business culture, departmental leaders are likely familiar with some Six Sigma tools and might even be Green

Belts or Black Belts themselves. While these leaders have daily responsibilities that are not Six Sigma related, they can bring Six Sigma thought processes to their department.

Departmental leaders might want to identify potential opportunities to present to leadership. They might also want to identify areas where they and their teams can work toward improvement themselves. In some organizations, department leaders can run smaller versions of projects with the guidance of on-staff Six Sigma experts – especially when such projects would require little in the way of capital or resources.

Departmental staff can use all of the tools in this chapter to identify possible projects. Often, though, they are close enough to the situation that they can identify possibilities for improvement without going through brainstorming stages. If data is already present, departmental staff might use Pareto charts to identify some areas where improvement would create results; they can then use the selections matrix to validate those assumptions and prioritize efforts.

See for Yourself

Consider a problem or need for improvement in your own company or one you faced in a past work experience. Practice completing the project viability matrix using the template below.

	Weight	No (1)	Mostly No (2)	Possibly (3)	Mostly Yes (4)	Yes (5)
Is there a sponsor or champion?						
Do project goals align with corporate goals?						
Is data available or accessible?						
Are defects well defined?						
Is the process stable?						
Are there customer benefits to the project?						
Are there company benefits to the project?						
Can the project be completed within 6 months?						
Is the solution unknown?						
Is it likely a discovered solution will be implemented?						
Would a new solution cost little to no cash?						
Are Six Sigma team members available for the project?						
Can inputs in the process be controlled?						
Can the process be improved without a full redesign?						
Will the improvements maintain or improve quality across the value chain?						
	TOTALS:					
Score:						

CHAPTER 10:
BASIC SIX SIGMA TEAM MANAGEMENT

Six Sigma is typically managed on two levels within an organization. First, the culture of Six Sigma must be managed at an enterprise-wide level, usually by a group or council of senior managers, such as executives, with the guidance of a Master Black Belt or Black Belt. Ultimately, this group sets the tone for Six Sigma within an organization, provides final approval on projects, and holds others accountable for metrics, performance, and success. While many of these individuals might also work as sponsors or champions on projects, as a group they don't tend to get involved in the day-to-day project details.

Some roles of a high-level Six Sigma leadership group include:

- Creating a rationale for the use of Six Sigma in the organization and supporting process improvement as a cultural goal.
- Setting clear objectives for Six Sigma initiatives to ensure that project goals align with business goals.
- Holding Six Sigma teams and the organization accountable for improvements and performance.
- Demanding and reviewing measurements of results
- Communicating wins and losses to the team in an honest manner.
- Rewarding teams and individuals for Six Sigma successes.
- Advocating for resources and funding for necessary improvement projects.

Six Sigma must also be managed at the team level, which is the primary focus of this chapter. We'll cover building a team, detail the various common roles within a Six Sigma team, and talk about managing a team with timelines and schedules, milestones, budgets, and a defined measure of success.

Building a Six Sigma Team

You can't simply have a pre-made team ready to begin work on every project that comes up. Six Sigma teams must be uniquely tailored to the goals and processes at hand. The same

Six Sigma experts – Black Belt leaders, data analysts, or project managers – might work across multiple projects, but individual subject matter experts and team members only bring high value to the team if they are familiar with the process or have some related education, knowledge, or skill to offer. Not all team members will serve consistently throughout the entire life of a project, either. This is often why companies send existing employees for Six Sigma training rather than hire Six Sigma experts.

Executive leadership groups working with Six Sigma leaders and experts usually put teams together. Any process improvement team should have, at minimum:

- A Six Sigma leader
- A process owner
- An expert on the process
- Someone to manage budgeting and accounting

Some of those roles might be handled by the same person; the process owner might also be the process expert. Depending on expectations of needs, the team might also need to include technical resources, such as a programmer or IT leader, as well as individuals from human resources, compliance, legal, or other ancillary departments.

Three Types of Team Members

When putting teams together, organizations should remember that three basic team member types exist with relation to a Six Sigma project. First, there are the regular team members. These individuals participate in all activities of the team and attend all or almost all of the team's meetings. Regular team members include project leaders, process owners and experts, and identified subject matter experts who the team or executives feel would be critical components of their group.

Second, ad hoc team members provide expertise on an as-needed basis. Usually, these are subject matter experts or employees who work directly with the process. You don't want to take these employees from their job functions for every single team event, as that would negatively impact the state of current production. Instead, these employees are included in team meetings as needed when additional information or assistance is required.

Finally, resource team members are only included when the project team leader feels they are needed in a meeting or team event to provide expert information, counsel, or help in accessing resources. Resource team members are usually members of ancillary departments such as accounting, human resources, or compliance. Resource team members might also be managers or leaders in departments that are related to the process

BASIC SIX SIGMA TEAM MANAGEMENT

being improved. For example, if a team is seeking to improve a customer service department, they might need help with inputs from the marketing department; someone from the marketing department could be added as a resource team member.

Tips for Selecting Team Members

Most Six Sigma process improvement teams are relatively small: five regular team members is considered a good number on average. Adding too many regular team members can create communication problems, make it difficult to manage brainstorming sessions, and cause burnout. When all of a company's Six Sigma teams are large, there's a good chance that team members are serving on multiple projects. While ad hoc or resource team members can serve several projects and handle their own work on a daily basis, regular team members should not be asked to serve on more than one team *and* handle daily workloads. In fact, organizational leaders might want to consider reducing work requirements for team members who are serving as full-time members on a project.

Other tips for selecting team members include:

- Choosing employees who are knowledgeable about the customer, product, or process related to the project.
- Choosing employees who have shown a willingness and ability to work toward improvement in a team environment.
- Selecting employees who have access to and an understanding of the data required to learn about and measure the process or problem.
- Picking employees who can provide at least five hours of work per week to the team.
- Matching the skills of employees to the projects at hand; if a project is likely to include all technical improvements, you would be less likely to add a team member who is skilled in marketing.
- Removing political obstacles through team selection; if a specific person in an organization is likely to be an obstacle to a team, sometimes putting that person on the team can increase the chance that they will buy into the process.

Team Member Roles

The team member roles described in this section are based on Six Sigma process improvement best practices, but best practices also say that teams and team leaders should not be overly rigid. Experienced Six Sigma leaders and experts understand how to work within best practices while also creating unique team structures that are tailored to the project or process at hand.

Sponsors and Champions

We've briefly touched on sponsors and champions in previous chapters. In most Six Sigma environments, these are the senior-level leaders who oversee projects at the highest level. Even the Black Belt must report to the project sponsor or champion. The senior leader is usually responsible for the final result of a project, which means he or she usually wants regular reports about progress; sometimes, the sponsor or champion is the liaison between the team and the leadership council. As the senior leader, the champion or sponsor is also responsible for assisting the team with obtaining funds and resources to ensure project success. Some additional duties within this role include:

- Coaching the team, particularly at the project charter stage. The sponsor often provides input into what is in scope on a project and who might be included on a team.
- Locating resources for the team, including support from other departments, money, equipment, time, and labor hours.
- Handling matters of politics within a corporate structure so the team doesn't have to.
- Working with other managers within the organization to help the team succeed in improving a process and transitioning improvements to a daily work environment.

Business or Process Owners

The business or process owner is usually someone who is directly responsible for the process in a leadership capacity. Usually, the process owner is the person who is going to "receive" a solution implemented by a Six Sigma team once that solution is ready to be rolled out to all team members or used on a daily basis. Because of this, the process owner is usually included in the team because he or she must understand how and why any change is made. The process owner must also be familiar with methods of control that are created by the Six Sigma team as he or she will become responsible for maintaining and monitoring those controls once the process is transitioned from a team environment to day-to-day production.

A process owner usually also acts as a process expert on a Six Sigma team. The process owner has insight into the existing process, understands the needs of the customers and employees related to the process, and might already have access to data regarding the process. The process owner isn't always the only process expert on a team, however; in some cases, the person who owns the process doesn't have enough day-to-day interaction with the process to be an expert.

When leading or managing a Six Sigma team, Black Belts and others do have to be wary of process owners who are resistant to change or who believe they have all the answers. Someone who is set in his or her ways might not want to involve other team members or might believe certain changes are "impossible" because they are new. Some leaders who are also process owners might be afraid that a team member will outshine them or threaten their position, which could lead them to block team members from participating on a team. These are some of the political and human resource problems Six Sigma leaders run into, and Black Belts and project leaders must work tactfully with champions, sponsors, and process managers to resolve such issues.

Six Sigma Leaders

Six Sigma projects are usually led by certified Black Belts, although some organizations do allow Green Belts to act as leaders on small initiatives with occasional feedback and guidance from Black Belts. In most organizations, the Black Belt holds primary responsibility for the regular work performed by a team and usually only works with one team or project at a time.

Best case scenarios let organizations align Black Belts with projects in areas they are already familiar with. For example, a bank might have several Black Belts on staff. Each Black Belt might specialize in working with certain processes or departments; one might usually work with compliance and audit processes, another with accounting, a third with customer-facing processes, and a fourth with online processes. Since Black Belt resources might be limited, this isn't always possible. Most certified Black Belts can bring Six Sigma methods to process improvements even in areas they aren't closely familiar with. In some cases, various managers or other individuals are certified as Black Belts and can lead processes in addition to their regular responsibilities, although this can put an undue burden on employees and isn't always the best solution.

Black Belt project leaders often work to:

- Help create a rationale for a project.
- Provide input for the selection of project team members.
- Lead teams throughout all the phases of DMAIC, which are covered in depth in Unit 3.

- Educate and support team members as they learn about and use Six Sigma tools.
- Provide oversight through time management, decision making, and planning.
- Maintain schedules and timelines, sometimes in conjunction with a certified Project Manager.
- Provide expertise in the form of statistical analysis or guidance with analysis.
- Assist with project transition.
- Report to sponsor or champion on a regular basis.
- Provide documentation at the end of the project.

In some organizations, Master Black Belts play an overall role in leading multiple Six Sigma projects. Master Black Belts act as coaches to multiple teams; Black Belts leading Six Sigma teams can work with Master Black Belts to solve especially difficult problems or seek help for complex statistical analysis. Master Black Belts provide continuing education to both Black and Green Belts, helping team members to constantly improve their grasp of Six Sigma methodologies.

Project Managers

Some organizations use traditional project management techniques alongside Six Sigma improvement methodologies. In these organizations, a project manager is usually assigned to a Six Sigma project. While structures vary by organization, the project manager does not usually lead the team. Instead, the PM offers leader support to the Black Belt by keeping up with documentation and timelines, helping keep meetings on track, and ensuring items are followed up on after meetings. At first, you might think that adding a PM to a team would cause problems for a Black Belt, but when the two roles work together, the Black Belt benefits. With a PM worrying about timelines or whether the meeting is getting too far off track, a Six Sigma exert is free to concentrate on the brainstorming session or statistical analysis at hand.

Timekeeper

Not all Six Sigma teams use timekeepers, but they can help keep meetings on track, reduce the chance of scope creep, and increase overall productivity. The timekeeper can be any person on the team who is not regularly engaged in leading meetings, brainstorming activities or recording team activities and notes. The timekeeper shouldn't police time in a such a rigid fashion that the benefits of fluid discussion and brainstorming are lost, but he or she should gently steer teams toward following agenda schedules or provide the project leader with an indication that time is up for the topic at hand.

To function properly, a timekeeper needs an agenda to follow. It is usually the responsibility of the Black Belt or project manager to provide a detailed agenda for each meeting. The agenda should include clear indications regarding how long each item is expected to take, though teams should always be aware that agendas might be changed during the meeting at the discretion of the project manager or project leader.

Team leaders should pick a timekeeper who is organized and level-headed. In the heat of discussions and arguments, it's easy for any member of the team to lose track of time – and the timekeeper *is* a member of the team. In addition to regular duties as a team member, the timekeeper is expected to:

- Keep an eye on the agenda and the time
- Let team members know when the time for a certain agenda is almost up; teams might want to set up a five-minute warning rule so they have a few minutes to wrap up a discussion
- Signal that the time is up for a certain discussion or item

While project leaders can choose to ignore agendas, they should also back up the timekeeper's ability to interrupt politely. Timekeepers can't perform if they are being heckled by other team members for noting the time.

Scribes or Minute-Takers

A lot of discussion occurs in the midst of Six Sigma brainstorming and team sessions, and someone needs to record that information. Notes are important because they help team members review what was discussed, create lists of follow-ups and actions from a discussion, and record charts, graphs, and diagrams that were created during brainstorming processes. While everyone can take notes, the team leader should appoint one person as the official scribe for the team. Sometimes, that person is a certified project manager working in conjunction with a Six Sigma team leader. Other times, it is a member of the team who is seen as detailed and organized.

The Black Belt or other project leader should never be the scribe; it is too difficult to take notes while leading a discussion or exercise. The Black Belt might make some notes during the discussion, but he or she is likely to miss important details while working directly with other team members.

The scribe should create notes or minutes of the meeting in typed format and disseminate those notes to all team members as soon as possible following a meeting. Team members can review the notes and add any missing information if desired; often, organizations create portals or shared file systems so teams can keep notes and all other documents in an easy-to-access location.

One challenge in recording the discussions of a Six Sigma project meeting is in recording the diagrams and brainstorming that occurred. This is especially true if teams use whiteboards, paper, or sticky notes to create diagrams; the scribe is not always equipped with the skills or the software to recreate a computerized version of such documents. One tip for recording such information that is used by many modern Six Sigma teams is to take a picture of the diagrams with a smartphone or digital camera. The images can then be uploaded into the team's shared workspace; if necessary, a Black Belt or Green Belt can convert the raw diagrams to a computerized version for the purpose of presenting information to leadership or other departments if desired.

Team Members

In the beginning of this chapter, we covered the three major types of team members: regular, ad hoc, and resource. Selecting members for each of these roles is up to the project leader, the sponsor or champion, and the overall organizational leadership team. In addition to the project leader, process owner, and process expert, Six Sigma teams are usually comprised of one to three other regular team members. In addition to acting as timekeeper or scribe as directed by the team leader, team members also:

- Participate in brainstorming sessions, discussions, and other team activities.
- Collect data and perform analysis under the direction of the Black Belt. Often, team members performing these functions are Green Belts.
- Perform work between meetings as required by the project leader.
- Report the results of and progress on individual assignments to the team.

Review work performed by other team members and the team as a whole, offering suggestions and feedback.

Timelines, Scheduling, and Milestones

Scheduling and maintaining that schedule is an integral part of the Six Sigma project process. Organizational leaders need to understand how long a project will take, when results can be expected, and when team resources will be freed up for other endeavors. Without this information, leadership can't plan for ongoing improvement and employees can feel trapped in a project that seems to stretch on forever. In this section, we'll cover two methods for creating a project timeline or schedule and touch on the importance of milestones.

Phase-Based Timeline

Six Sigma projects usually follow a specific series of phases; we've briefly introduced the concept of the DMAIC method. DMAIC breaks a project up into five phases: Define, Measure, Analyze, Improve, and Control. Experienced Six Sigma experts with some data and information about a project and process can usually provide a very basic and raw estimate of time by assigning a certain number of weeks to each phase. It's also worth noting that most of the phases are likely to overlap.

To create a raw timeline for a project, a Black Belt or other Six Sigma leader usually starts with an overall time requirement. He or she either estimates the total time required for an improvement or works with a deadline imposed by the leadership group. For example, the leadership group might say that an improvement needs to be completed within four months.

Using a four month timeline and what information is already available about the process, problem, and resources, the Black Belt might create an estimated timeline for the DMAIC process that looks something like the figure below.

	Week															
	1	2	3	4	5	6	7	8	9	10	11	12	13	14	15	16
Define	▓	▓	▓													
Measure		▓	▓	▓	▓	▓										
Analyze				▓	▓	▓	▓	▓	▓							
Improve									▓	▓	▓	▓	▓			
Control														▓	▓	▓

The estimated timeline is for 16 weeks; the expert believes the Define phase will take 3 weeks and the Measure phase will take 5. The Measure phase overlaps with both the Define and Analyze phases, which is normal with Six Sigma projects.

The benefit of this approach is that you can generate a timeline quickly. The disadvantages are that someone without experience of Six Sigma and a fair amount of knowledge of the process being improved can easily misjudge the time required for each phase and leadership might consider this a hard timeline, which can create unrealistic expectations.

When presenting such a timeline, make sure everyone knows that it is a rough estimate and the time for each phase can change as you go through the process.

Critical Path Method

The critical path method is a more detailed way of defining timelines for various elements of a project, but it does require more information and input from a project team. This means you probably won't be able to provide a detailed timeline until the project is underway; a critical path diagram could be one of the activities the team undertakes as part of the Define phase.

Creating a Critical Path Diagram

A critical path diagram can be created for the entire project or for each phase of a project. As we go through the steps of creating a critical path diagram, we'll use the Define phase of a project to reduce bad debt (uncollected invoices) in a medical billing environment as an example.

1. Identify the critical needs or activities to complete the project or phase of a project.

To complete the define phase of our project to improve bad debt in a medical billing setting, the team needs to choose a team, charter the project, define the problem, and create a baseline metric.

2. Put critical activities in order.

The order with which the team should accomplish the tasks defined in step one is:

- Choose a team
- Charter the project and define the problem (these tasks can be done simultaneously)
- Create a baseline metric

3. Assign a time to each task.

A Six Sigma expert estimates it will take one week to choose a team, one week to create a charter, one day to create a problem statement, and two weeks to create a baseline metric.

4. Create a diagram of the tasks, stacking simultaneous or parallel process and including time figures.

151

The diagram is created from left to right. The items on the left must be done before the items to the right can be completed. When items can be done at the same time, they are stacked.

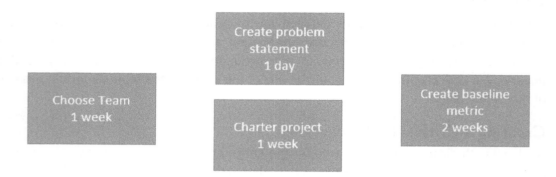

5. Draw a critical path through the diagram.

When steps are stacked, the critical path goes through the step with the longest time estimate. For example, the team might create a problem statement while they are working on a project charter; the project charter takes from Monday through Friday to complete. The problem statement is complete on Tuesday. However, the team is not done with all of the steps in that series until they are done with the project charter.

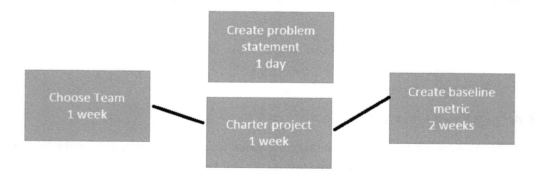

6. Add up the longest times from each section.

In this case, the team adds 1 week, 1 week, and 2 weeks to get to 4 weeks total for the Define phase.

We've used a very simple example, but you can use the critical path method to estimate timelines for extremely complex projects or processes.

Milestone Meetings

Once a timeline is established, set up milestone meetings and dates to help keep the team on track and notify the sponsor or champion of progress. In a DMAIC project, milestones are usually set at the end of each phase (Define, Measure, Analyze, Improve, and Control). However, teams can set custom milestones, and sponsors might require specific milestones if they are approving large resourcing or funding requests for a project.

You can also set up milestones within a team environment to manage goals and tasks; these milestones can be kept within the team. For example, a team working for a chain of sandwich shops is hoping to improve the process by which sandwiches are put together. They have set up the following milestones:

Define: January 21

Measure: February 12

Analyze: February 22

Improve: March 15

Control: April 10

The milestone dates are when the team or the Black Belt will meet with the sponsor to present the findings or results of each phase of the project. Each date gives the team something to work toward. However, the team has determined that certain tasks must be accomplished during the Measure phase. First, they have to create some definitions of terms so everyone is on the same page when discussing measurements. Second, the team has to gather data about the temperature at which ingredients are stored and cooked. Finally, the team wants to actively observe sandwich shop employees in order to measure the time it takes to make various sandwiches.

The team might set up internal milestones for the Measure phase, stating that definitions will be created by January 25, temperature data collected by February 5, and time data collected by February 10.

By breaking each phase, and each larger task, into smaller parts, it is easier for the team to stay on track and complete work. Smaller tasks seem more manageable, so they are more likely to be accomplished.

Budgets

Teams, and especially team leaders, must always be concerned with project budgets. While success is rated by end customers in terms of performance, quality, and satisfaction, Six Sigma teams also answer to corporate leadership. For leaders, success is also measured in terms of time and budget. A strong timeline and good milestones help you meet time requirements, and an understanding of financial drivers, strong communication, and financial oversight help you keep a project within budget.

One of the challenges when dealing with budgets in a Six Sigma project is that all team members are not always completely aware of financial drivers. In some cases, financial information might even be restricted; employers don't generally want specific data about employee pay made public to various team members, for example. Some information and analysis might need to be performed solely by a project-leading Black Belt in such cases, especially if data is critical or sensitive.

Outside of concerns with sensitive data, process improvement projects work best when all team members are made aware of as many of the drivers and data as possible. When teams know how much funding a champion is willing to seek on their behalf, they can make realistic decisions about how to improve a process. Sometimes, the solution that is most likely to generate the most improvement isn't viable because of budget. If an improvement project has a budget of $50,000, the team can't implement a solution that requires an $80,000 capital investment in machinery, for example.

Budget concerns vary by organization. In some organizations, leaders are most concerned with specific expenditures by a team, including expenses on new equipment, hiring new personnel, or purchasing new products or software. Some organizations take a more granular approach to project budgets, considering the expense of hours spent by the team on the project as well as the expenses associated with training and implementing a solution outside of the team environment.

Six Sigma team leaders must ensure they understand how leaders and organizations manage project budgets. Working for the first time with an organization or sponsor means having honest and thorough conversations about how budgets are calculated, how much sponsors are willing to work for increases in a budget, and what the Six Sigma leader's expected role in maintaining budgets is.

Defined Measures of Success

Finally, Six Sigma teams must create a well-defined measure of success. To best manage a Six Sigma project and team, leaders have to ensure all team members, leaders, and sponsors agree on what success means. If success isn't defined at all, the team risks scope creep and getting lost in a project that never seems to end. If success isn't well-defined, teams risk concluding a project without satisfying the customer, sponsor, or all members of the team. If a sponsor and the team don't agree on what success looks like, the team could think they've concluded a successful project while leadership believes the project was a failure.

In the end, successful Six Sigma team management hinges on many of the same concepts as successful leadership in other endeavors does. Choosing the right people, being clear about expectations, approaching work in an organized manner, and being honest and open about progress helps every member of the team succeed and provide value.

CHAPTER 11:
INTRODUCTION TO DMAIC AND DMADV

One of the things that sets Six Sigma apart from some other quality improvement and management methodologies is a structured approach to every project. Projects that are meant to improve an existing process follow a road-map for success known as the DMAIC process; DMAIC is broken into five phases: Define, Measure, Analyze, Improve, and Control. The main activities of a DMAIC project include identifying the critical inputs or causes (the Xs) that are creating the problem (the Y), verifying those causes, brainstorming and selecting solutions, implementing solutions, and creating a control plan to ensure the improved state is maintained.

The DMAIC methodology is designed to be fairly inclusive – the vast majority of teams who are seeking to improve a project will be able to fit their activities in to the DMAIC steps because those steps are designed to allow some flexibility. Sometimes, though, teams realize that fixing or improving a process isn't the right way to achieve sustained improvement for the organization. Instead, a process might need to be completely replaced or redesigned to meet goals for customer satisfaction or organizational improvement. In such cases, teams can employ the DMADV method.

DMADV stands for Define, Measure, Analyze, Design, and Verify. The principles governing the method are very similar to those governing DMAIC, but the last two phases are geared toward rolling out and testing a completely new process. Six Sigma teams might approach improvements through DMADV if:

- The business wants to launch a new service or product.
- Business leaders decide to replace a process because of upgrade needs or to align business processes, machinery, or employees with future goals.
- A Six Sigma team discovers that improving a process is not likely to provide the success desired from a project.

Most teams go into the project knowing whether they are employing DMAIC or DMADV approaches, but some DMAIC projects can become DMADV projects – usually during the

Define, Measure, or Analyze stages – when the team realizes the need for a complete process replacement. Switching to the new methodology during the middle of the project might require some shuffling of resources and could impact project schedules, which means keeping champions and sponsors informed of team progress and decisions is imperative.

It's worth noting that some organizations don't formally use the DMADV approach for any project, in part because they find it easier to stick with the nomenclature of a single methodology. These organizations might still complete process redesign projects by altering some of the activities handled in the Improve and Control stages of DMAIC. In short, the teams *do* use the DMADV approach, but they use the verbiage associated with DMAIC to streamline Six Sigma education across all levels of the organization.

DMAIC versus DMADV

The major differences between DMAIC and DMADV are the goals the team sets and the outcome of the completed project. In some ways, a DMADV project might feel like it has a more tangible outcome, but in reality, both methods are seeking to deliver better quality, better efficiency, more production, more profits, higher customer satisfaction, or some combination of these things. We'll introduce each of the phases of both methods in this chapter. But first, let's look at some quick definitions of each phase as they relate to DMAIC versus DMADV.

Phase 1: Define

During a DMAIC project, the Define phase is concerned with identifying the problem, defining requirements for the project, and setting goals for success. Requirements and goal setting might relate to a variety of factors and are dependent somewhat on guidance from the leadership team and expected budgets, and Six Sigma leaders can use various tools within the phase to create flexibility that allows for a variety of project types.

What is Change Management?

Change management refers to a closely-managed process of making changes in an organization. Often, companies use change management policies and rules to govern how changes are made to software, infrastructure, or processes that have compliance or audit elements.

During change management, teams must document all activity in keeping with corporate policies and report changes and results to an oversight committee. Sometimes, Six Sigma projects involve changes that are also governed by these policies, which means Six Sigma leaders must be prepared to report to change management committees.

In a DMADV project, the Define stage is slightly more rigid. Teams also have to identify a problem and begin defining requirements, but requirements must be made within a change-management environment. Sometimes, organizations have a change management program in place, which means Six Sigma teams must incorporate all requirements of that program into the DMADV phases. The team also works to define customer requirements to create a measuring stick to which the process development can be compared.

Phase 2: Measure

The DMAIC Measure phase is when teams use data to validate their assumptions about the process and the problem. Validation of assumptions also merges into the analyze phase. The bulk of the measure phase is occupied with actually gathering data and formatting it in a way that can be analyzed. Measuring can be one of the most difficult tasks in a Six Sigma project if data isn't already being captured. Teams might have to build tools to capture data, create queries for digital data, sift through enormous amounts of data to find relevant information, or capture data by hand in some manual process.

After validating assumptions from the Define stage with actual data, the team might revisit problem statements, goals, and other process-related definitions. If the team leaves Define with a "rough draft" of these things, they should leave Measure with a final draft. Teams also work during Measure phases to measure key inputs and steps in the process in preparation for Define.

Teams working through a DMADV approach might do some of the same things during the Measure phase, but activities are typically more targeted. Teams will likely collect data and measurements that help them define performance requirements for the new process.

Phase 3: Analyze

During the Analyze phase of a DMAIC project, teams develop hypotheses about causal relationships between inputs and outputs and between Xs and Ys, they narrow causation down to the vital few (using methods such as the Pareto principle), and they use statistical analysis and data to validate the hypotheses and assumptions they've made so far. The Analyze phase tends to flow into the Improve phase in a DMAIC project; hypothesis testing to validate assumptions and possible solutions might begin in Analyze and continue into the Improve phase.

A team using DMADV might also identify cause and effect relationships, but they are usually more concerned with identifying best practices and benchmarks by which to measure and design the new process. Teams might also begin process design work by identifying value- and non value-added activities, locating areas where bottlenecks or errors are likely, and refining requirements to better meet the needs and goals of the project.

Phase 4: Improve or Design

Six Sigma teams start developing the ideas that began in the Analyze phase during the Improve phase of a project. They use statistics and real-world observation to test hypotheses and solutions. Hypothesis testing actually begins in the analyze phase, but is continued during the improve phase as teams select solutions and begin to implement them. Teams also work to standardize solutions in preparation for rolling improved processes to daily production and non-team employees. Teams also start measuring results and lay the foundation for controls that will be built in the last phase.

The fourth phase is where DMADV projects begin to diverge substantially from DMAIC projects. The team actually works to design a new process, which does involve some of the solutions testing mentioned above, but also involves mapping, workflow principles, and actively building new infrastructures. That might mean putting new equipment in place, hiring and training new employees, or developing new software tools. Teams also start to implement the new systems and processes during the fourth phase.

Phase 5: Control or Verify

For DMAIC and DMADV teams, the control or verify phase is where loose ends are tied and the project is transitioned to a daily work environment. Controls and standards are established so that improvements can be maintained, but the responsibility for those improvements is transitioned to the process owner. During the transition, the Six Sigma team might work with the process owner and his or her department to troubleshoot any problems with the improvement.

Which Methodology Would You Use?

Consider the following improvement projects. Which methodology do you think a Six Sigma team might use to approach each project?

1. A business wants to create a smartphone app to help customers make and manage appointments.

2. A doctor's office has had numerous complaints from patients because it is too hard to get appointments, appointment communications are confusing, or patients show up for appointments and are told they don't have an appointment.
3. A company that manufactures pizza boxes isn't happy with the profit margins in the small size boxes.

The team handling an improvement for the business in example 1 would choose a DMADV approach. They are creating a product that doesn't yet exist; while the team is meeting a need that already exists and is improving an overall process – the setting of appointments – the app itself is a new process and a new product. The app will need to be designed, integrated into existing systems, and the final product tested before full implementation.

Example 2 is for an existing process, so the team would begin with a DMAIC approach. It's possible that the team might determine during the process that one solution might be to develop a new appointment-setting software or replace existing software with something from a different vendor. In some cases, that might warrant a switch to DMADV, but, as previously stated, not all organizations would do so. Some organizations would continue with the DMAIC process and modify the activities in each phase to fit the needs of the project at hand.

Example 3 is a classic example of what brings many teams to the DMAIC method. The problem hasn't yet been defined, but the organization knows that goals and expectations are not being met. A leadership team might work with subject matter experts and one or more Six Sigma experts to discover more about the processes involved before settling on one or more improvement projects.

Define

During the Define phase of a Six Sigma process improvement project, teams create what is known as a project charter and a basic plan for work. A charter is a synopsis of the project. It provides some common information and a summary of what the team hopes to accomplish. The charter usually features a list of team members, names of those responsible for outcomes, a problem statement, a goal, and some basic definitions of scope and metrics for success. Some charters also include a rough timeline estimate for the project.

Also during the Define phase, teams create or list measurable customer requirements and create high-level documents about the process (including process maps). Often, teams will start with a SIPOC diagram to help them begin to understand a process. Teams should also identify stakeholders during the Define phase. Stakeholders are individuals, both within and without an organization, who have some level of influence on the success of an improvement project. By understanding who stakeholders are, teams can remain in contact with various persons throughout the project, communicating with those stakeholders as needed to ensure future viability of any improvement that is created. One way to identify stakeholders is through a Stakeholder Analysis.

Tips for Positive Movement in the Define Stage

One of the biggest challenges Six Sigma teams face when in the Define phase of a project is generating positive, targeted momentum that sets the foundation for the rest of the project. As a Six Sigma team leader, you can increase chances of success by keeping the team as focused as possible during the Define stage. Begin by explaining the Six Sigma process and the purpose of the project for any ancillary team members who may not be familiar with Six Sigma and DMAIC. Next, work as a team to create ground rules for how the project will run – including how meetings are organized and managed, how information will be communicated, and what each team member might be responsible for during the project.

Create a charter and project plan so the team has something to focus on. If possible, have the Champion of the project spend time with the team. Hearing directly from an executive leader about expectations and the support of leadership for the project helps motivate a team. At the same time, ensure the Champion doesn't step in to take over the project, as this isn't his or her role.

Define is also a good time to explain the roles of scribe and time keeper and talk about the purpose of brainstorming. Some Six Sigma leaders like to let team members take turns facilitating various exercises for the group, as this integrates each person more tightly within the process and helps team members at all levels learn more about Six Sigma.

Measure

Once a team has a good grasp of what the process does and how it works, what the problem is, and what the goal for the project is, the team moves from Define to Measure. Usually, the transition between phases is marked by a tollgate review wherein the team presents its Define work to a champion or a Six Sigma leadership board. The champion or board provides feedback and makes the decision about whether the team is ready to move on to Measure.

During the Measure phase, the team is concerned with creating a baseline metric for the process and refining problem statements and other outputs of the Define stage. Creating a baseline metric lets teams understand how a process should be measured and how the process is really performing before improvements begin. It also provides a comparison point so teams can show how much improvement they've brought to a project at the end of the DMAIC method.

One of the biggest challenges, especially for teams and team members who are new to the Six Sigma method, can be deciding what to measure. Many times, inexperienced teams end up spending time collecting data that doesn't provide answers or can't be used for the process. Because the Measure phase starts with some educated guesswork and trial-and-error, teams and Six Sigma leaders have to keep a close eye on progress and redirect work when measurements are not creating the answers or production required.

A successful Measure phase requires strong observation skills, an understanding of the reasons behind measure, knowledge of data types such as discrete and continuous, tools for measurement assessment, and a strong background in statistical analysis. Some of the tools often deployed in the Measure phase, such as the CTQ tree and sigma level calculation, were covered in previous chapters.

Tips for an Effective Measure Phase

The Measure phase is often the most challenging phase for a Six Sigma team leader, especially when working with teams that are inexperienced in the methodology. When teams start to really dig deep into a process and begin to measure things, they often get a true idea about how challenging the problem really is. They might also have a difficult time understanding how and when to measure things, and collecting data that hasn't been collected before can be time consuming and tedious. Because of all these challenges, teams might enter what is called a storming stage—team members question the viability of the project, rail against the Champion or the team leader, complain how much time the project is taking from other duties, or stop showing up to meetings altogether.

Six Sigma leaders can reduce the impact of storming on a team by demonstrating a calm approach to each aspect of the project and redirecting the strong emotion of storming to more productive work. If you can identify an easy task or problem, letting the team work on that and accomplish something immediately can reduce the excitement of storming; Six Sigma leaders should also ensure work is fairly distributed and that each team member knows exactly what his or her responsibilities are.

Analyze

Once measurements are collected – or are in the process of being collected – Six Sigma teams usually move on to the Analyze phase. Again, a tollgate review is often conducted between phases, but the lines between Measure and Analyze are often blurrier than the lines between Define and Measure. In some cases, a team has to measure, analyze, and then measure some more – particularly if metrics aren't already in place for a process.

Analyze phases are when teams perform detective work on the process. Using the clues gathered during the Define and Measure phases, along with information provided by the sponsor, process owner, and subject matter experts, teams attempt to identify root causes for a problem; they also use statistical analysis and other tools to verify causes before turning to the work of identifying possible solutions. During the Analyze phase, teams use a variety of tools – some of which were introduced in earlier chapters. Tools common in the Analyze phase include Pareto charts, run charts, histograms, cause-and-effect diagrams, scatter diagrams, process maps, and value analysis.

As teams work through the Analyze phase, they also start preparing for the Improve phase. During Analyze, teams might begin working on possible solutions and selecting solutions, developing improvement plans, and preparing some basic documentation about improvement work. Whether a team begins this work during Analyze often depends on the individual project and the manner in which the Six Sigma team leader would like to proceed. The Six Sigma team leader should ensure that teams aren't taking on too much of the project at one time and that working on early Improve work doesn't reduce the efficacy of the work done for the Analyze phase.

Tips for a Strong Analyze Phase

Teams in the Analyze phase might continue to suffer from storming; if teams didn't storm during Define or Measure phases, they might begin to do so in Analyze. Six Sigma leaders can use the same tips for controlling storming in the Measure phase in the Analyze phase.

Another common challenge for Six Sigma team leaders is introducing and explaining statistical concepts during the Analyze phase. When other team members or even the champion of the process are not familiar with statistical analysis, presenting advanced analysis in terms of statistical verbiage only can be a mistake. Team members won't understand how you came to the conclusions you are presenting, which makes it less likely they will get behind the solution or improvement in a positive way.

Six Sigma experts should be aware of the knowledge limitations of various team members and work to both present information in a way that is understood by everyone *and* continue to add to team member knowledge by explaining concepts when possible.

Improve

During the Improve phase of a project, a Six Sigma team selects a final solution and begins to put it in place. Sometimes, teams will select more than one solution, especially if a few smaller solutions are highly related and work together for an overall solution. It can be hard to determine which solution actually improves a process, however, so it's usually a best practice to implement one change at a time and verify that change before moving on to something else.

Teams might also come up with many possible solutions, all of which would provide some improvement for the process. They should use a solutions selection matrix or other Six Sigma tool to evaluate solutions, choosing only the few best solutions. It's worth noting again that the best solution is not always the solution that provides the most improvement. Solutions that are so expensive or disruptive that they cause disadvantages that outweigh any benefits should never be selected by project teams.

During Improve, Six Sigma teams must continue to keep the project definitions in mind. The solution must address a root cause verified in the Analyze phase; the root cause must be directly related to the problem stated during the Define phase. After selecting solutions, teams must test them using statistical tools and real-world sampling to ensure effectiveness before deploying solutions to a live work environment.

Tips for Staying Strong Nearing the End of a DMAIC Project

Possibly the most common problem that plagues Six Sigma teams during the Improve phase is project fatigue. By the time teams come to Improve, they have been working on a project for weeks or even months; for many team members, the project work is on top of regular work. Fatigue or frustration might push team members to select and implement solutions just to have the project completed. Six Sigma leaders have to work to keep teams motivated on quality and improvement.

The best way for a Six Sigma team leader to create strength as the team nears project completion is to build a good foundation for Six Sigma in the earlier phases. Teams that understand the DMAIC process and have at least basic understanding of Six Sigma and statistical analysis by the Improve phase are more likely to stick with planning, analysis, and the DMAIC method.

Six Sigma team leaders should also continue to foster a team approach to all aspects of the project. One challenge for some leaders is the temptation to take measurements and analysis and begin performing much of the work themselves. Sometimes, it's faster and easier to handle decision-making and analysis on your own, especially when you are dealing with team members who aren't fluent in DMAIC or Six Sigma methods. Doing so alienates team members, though, and can result in a Six Sigma leader without direct process knowledge making the wrong decision. Keeping the team involved – and making exercises and meetings fun and productive – helps you make it through the Improve phase.

Control

Control is the final phase for Six Sigma teams employing the DMAIC process. During the Control phase, teams usually handle four tasks: creating the foundation for process discipline, finalizing documents regarding the improvement, establishing ongoing metrics to evaluate the process, and building a process management plan that lets the team transition the improvement to the process owner.

Tools used by a team during the Control phase include documentation checklists, control charts, response plans, process maps, and process dashboards.

The Control Phase is often easy for a team because the work of the team has already reached a crescendo. In a well-run DMAIC process, the Control phase is a time of wrapping up loose ends and arriving at the end of a project. At the same time, teams might find it challenging to let go of a process they have put so much time into. By the time teams reach the Control phase, they might have been working with a process for months. If a Six Sigma leader has done his or her job, the team has taken ownership of the process and feels personally tied to the quality and output, making it hard to turn the work over to other teams or employees.

Ending on a Positive Note

Six Sigma leaders can help team members transition a project by preparing them in advance for this phase. You might also find ways to incorporate team members into meetings or presentations where project results are being shared. Six Sigma leaders should always host a meeting to wrap up the project. The meeting should be somewhat celebratory in nature – if budget, time, and policy allows, Six Sigma leaders might consider having lunch or snacks at the meeting. Take time to recognize each team member's contribution, and ask team members to identify something they learned that can be applied to their own work. This helps team members see that Six Sigma is an ongoing culture within an organization, and the end of a particular project doesn't equate to the end of each person's involvement in continuous improvement.

Recognition is extremely important when ending a Six Sigma project. Team members might have put in extra hours to provide excellent work on a project while maintaining their own responsibilities. Often, work on a Six Sigma project is not part of a team member's regular duties, so they are going above and beyond what might normally be expected of them. Six Sigma leaders should make it a point to recognize the work of team members in front of a project sponsor or champion, and, when possible, in front of the department for which the improvement is being made.

Design

Design is the fourth phase of DMADV; it replaces the Improve phase of DMAIC. DMADV is one approach for what is called Design for Six Sigma, or DFSS. Another approach is called DMADOV, which stands for Define, Measure, Analyze, Design, Optimize, and Validate. Teams using the DMADV approach usually combine the activities from Design and Optimize, and we'll briefly introduce those activities in this section.

The Design phase of DMADV is when teams create a new process or develop a new product. A Six Sigma team would have previously done all the work to lay the foundation for development during the Define, Measure, and Analyze stages, which means most of the Design phase is taken up with the actual work involved in creating the process or project.

Using the plans, instructions, or maps created in earlier phases, the team either creates a product themselves or works with vendors, manufacturers, or other employees to create the product. For example, if the DMADV project involved the creation of a new app for customers or employees, the team might work with staff in the programming and technical departments. They might also work with a vendor who will be supplying the app or software in question; in such a case, a representative from the vendor should have been part of the team throughout all phases.

During Design, a team will also test the product, process, or service. Testing can be done in testing environments, in limited production environments, or via Beta testing. Usually, the team rolls out the new process or product to a limited number of internal or external customers; those customers provide feedback and the team uses the feedback to troubleshoot the new process or product as needed. Seeking feedback and troubleshooting the new process to create the best possible solution is where the Optimize in DMADOV comes in.

Tips for a Successful Design Phase

In a process redesign project, all phases are essential, but Design is often seen as the most critical. Teams that falter in the design phase can waste the work that was put into other phases, and it's easy for teams to fall prey to project fatigue just as work requirements pick up for everyone involved. Six Sigma team leaders can help improve the chances of a successful Design phase by following the tips for managing Improve phases. Teams should also be realistic about target dates for design work. Promising a complete solution in a short time period pleases leadership at first, but if teams are rushed, they tend to deliver low-quality processes. If you promise a too-good-to-be true timeline, you also run the risk of running far behind schedule, which can impede the work of other projects and process improvements.

Verify

The Verify phase of a DMADV or DMADOV project is very similar to the Control phase of a DMAIC project. The new process, product, or service is transitioned out of project mode and handed off to a process owner or employees who work daily with the process or product in question. Control plans, including control charts, might be put in place by the team to track ongoing results, and almost all of the tools used in a DMAIC Control phase are relevant to Verify.

One of the differences between Verify and Control is that DMADV teams might take time to complete further CTQ analysis at the end of a project so they can identify new critical-to-quality factors. This is done because the process or product is different than it was when the team first started working. While the team should have made educated guesses about CTQs for the new product – and used those CTQs in planning and designing – they could not predict 100 percent how the customer might react to the new product or process. A new process might have a capability the old one did not; having that capability, the customer might decide it is the most important factor in quality about the process or product.

At the end of the Verify phase, a team delivers a final product or process that meets the needs first identified in the Define stage. The process or product should be free of known problems and defects wherever possible, and teams should have provided a way to manage and control the process through statistical control charts, Lean templates, and policies.

Closing a DMADV Project

One of the major differences between DMAIC and DMADV is the possible timeline. We previously stated that a problem fits the DMAIC model if it can be solved in less than six months. While some DMADV projects might only take a few months, many process or product designs can take years. Because of this, the concluding challenges for a DMADV team are similar to those in a DMAIC environment, but they might be heightened by the length of time a team has spent on a project.

Team members who have spent a year or more working to develop a new process or product might feel like the end of the project threatens their job. This is especially true when team members have not been handling regular work duties in addition to product duties. Six Sigma leaders and champions can reduce these worries by communicating next steps and expectations clearly with staff.

Team members who have been working on regular job duties alongside project work for years might find it hard to return to regular duties without something else to work on. One of the benefits of Six Sigma is that team members learn to expect more of themselves, their coworkers, and an organization's processes. Six Sigma team leaders can work with employees returning to daily work and help them apply what they learned in a positive fashion within their respective departments.

Finally, Six Sigma team leaders should ensure that a DMADV project closes on a positive note by validating all team members and ensuring process owners have all the tools they need to accept the new process without disrupting work.

Breaking up the Elephant

You should now have a basic understanding of how a Six Sigma team approaches a problem or process improvement. Whether improving an existing process or creating a new process or product, teams work through phased approaches. The phases of DMAIC and DMADV provide control and organization for a project, help keep everyone on task, and let teams break up what can seem like enormous tasks into chunks that are tolerable. As the old adage says: How do you eat an elephant? One bite at a time. Similarly, the phased approach of Six Sigma breaks up the elephant so teams can work on it one bite at a time.

UNIT 3:
ADVANCED DMAIC

CHAPTER 12:
DEFINE

Six Sigma teams enter the project process with various levels of information. Sometimes, a problem is fairly well defined before the team begins work, particularly in organizations that use a Six Sigma leadership council to choose projects and create teams. Other times, teams begin work with little information except that a problem – of some type – exists because the outcomes of a process are not as expected. Teams might not know where errors are occurring or even begin a project with a complete understanding of the inputs and outputs associated with the process.

Whatever knowledge teams begin with, the define phase is when teams move from very basic information about a process or problem to the knowledge and organization necessary to enter measure and subsequent other phases with a successful foundation. In the define phase, teams set rules, create a charter that will govern efforts moving forward, identify stakeholders and customers, define a process through process mapping, and prepare for a define tollgate before entering the measure phase.

Creating a Project Charter

A project charter, or team charter, is a short document that includes information about the team and what they plan to accomplish. The purpose of the charter is to set expectations that can be agreed upon by the team as well as the sponsor or executive leaders, keep the team focused on the goal, ensure the project remains aligned with the goals of the business, and documents the fact that control of a process is being moved from a business executive or manager to a Six Sigma project team.

Minimally, team charters should include:

- A complete and concise problem statement that follows the guidelines set out in Chapter 6.
- A list of critical to quality metrics, or those measurements that will ultimately determine project or process success. Critical to quality was introduced in chapter 8.
- The names and roles of each person on the team. Selecting team members and appropriate team member roles are covered in Chapter 10.
- A list of both internal and external process customers. Use a SIPOC, discussed in Chapter 7, to begin defining internal or external customers.
- The name of a sponsor and/or champion.
- A duration for the project.

Teams might also include information such as a list of non-customer stakeholders, an estimated schedule for each phase of the project, scope definitions for the process or project, and financial drivers for the project.

The information for the team charter usually can't be gathered in a single brainstorming session; the charter is an outcome of the entire define phase, not a quick notation at the beginning. By taking time to properly consider all elements of a team charter, Six Sigma teams create a stronger foundation for the rest of their work.

Benefits of an Organizational Team Charter Template

Businesses that are implementing Six Sigma organization-wide might consider creating or using a specific template for team charters. Templates streamline define phases and make it easy for leadership teams and other employees to understand critical process components at a glance. While final team documentation is likely to be extensive, and even in the define phase, teams themselves might work with lengthy requirements documents, charters themselves should be as concise as possible. Some organizations distill charters to a single page while others use multipage documents. A sample one-page charter template is attached at the end of this chapter.

Details for Charter Elements

We've covered some of the most important elements of the charter in detail in previous chapters, but here's a quick look at some of the items we didn't cover in as much detail and are worth mentioning again.

Business Case

The business case might also be referred to as the financial drivers behind a project. Related closely to the problem statement, the business case is a short statement that provides a reason the project should be undertaken. The problem statement tells someone where, when, and how; the business case says why it's important. If you think back to Chapter 6, we said dollar amounts or another financial metric were important to include in the problem statement. If you include a business case in your charter, you would build on that basic financial statement to explain why, specifically, the loss of money, efficiency, or quality is important to consumers, employees, or the organization. You might also make an argument for why the problem must be solved now; in essence, why is this project being run now in place of another project?

Project Scope

We introduced the concept of scope briefly in Chapter 6. For the purposes of the team charter, the scope should include a hard beginning and end of the process or problem being considered. You might also include a short list of items or activities that are in scope and out of scope for your project. A SIPOC diagram helps teams identify the parameters for a project, and you can also use the In and Out of the Box method described later in this chapter to understand the intended scope of a project.

The scope should be clear. Listing the scope for a project or process as "beginning at the order stage and ending with fulfillment" isn't clear, because different people might consider different points the beginning of the order stage or the end of fulfillment. A better scope statement might be "beginning when a customer places an order and ending when the order is boxed for shipment." Going even further, a team might deem return and replacement processes out of scope for a project so that they are only dealing with original orders. Successful projects have a well-defined scope that is approved and backed by a project sponsor or champion.

List the Stakeholders

Listing major stakeholders on the charter helps the team remember who and what they are likely to impact in addition to end customers. Having the list visible during meetings reduces the chance that the team will initiate changes that might have a negative or unwanted effect on other process owners or processes, and it helps direct the team to resources outside of the team that can provide help, access, or information to areas related to the project.

Team Member Roles

Team members and roles were covered in Chapter 10, and the team charter simply needs to list the names of all team members along with their role and expected time commitment. Adding time commitments to the charter helps sponsors and executive leadership understand the human resource requirements for the project; often a Six Sigma team leader has to seek approval for staff members from other areas to devote a specified amount of time to the project.

Time commitments can be listed in hours per week but are often listed as a percent of the employee's overall time. For example, a subject matter expert who is expected to attend all of the team meetings to provide input, but is not expected to complete data collection, analysis, or improvement work, might be listed as providing 10 percent of his or her time to the team. A list of team members in a charter might look something like the list below. You don't have to list all the staff members you might possibility consult during the course of the project.

- Mike Smith, Black Belt, 100%
- Chase Michaels, Green Belt, 100%
- Lisa Javes, Green Belt, 100%
- Rosalie Myers, Process Owner, 25%
- Brent Reed, subject matter expert, 10%
- Brenda Tran, subject matter expert, 10%

Milestones

In Chapter 10, we covered creating a draft schedule for a Six Sigma project. The diagram included in Chapter 10 that broke down the timeline for a project is called a Gantt chart. Adapted by Henry Gantt in the early 20th century, a Gantt chart is a bar chart that displays the phases of a project according to time. One of the benefits of using a Gantt chart to display a rough project schedule is that it can easily be included in a one-page project charter; anyone reviewing the charter can quickly visualize the time element required for the project.

Teams should ensure a date is provided for the end of each of the DMAIC phases and that all team members agree that the dates are plausible given what the group wants to do. In some cases, milestones might be set by the project sponsor or champion, but the team should agree that milestone dates are possible. If dates seem implausible, teams can present a counter schedule with logical arguments regarding why the original schedule wouldn't work.

In addition to milestones at the end of each project phase, Six Sigma teams might also want to set milestones for work within each phase – specifically for the more laborious measure, analyze, and improve phases. While the team should document all milestones it agrees on, detailed milestones don't necessarily belong in the one-page charter document.

Measurement of Success

Everyone needs to know how the team is going to measure success. If a sponsor is measuring success on customer satisfaction scores and the team is measuring success on internal quality scores, ideas about the outcome of the project are likely to differ. Usually, measures of success can be pulled from the critical to quality metrics discussed in Chapter 8. If teams can convert a CTQ to a measurement, they can understand what major metrics determine success of a project. While teams might begin to gather measurements or look at existing measurements while in the define phase, finalization of metrics can extend into the measure phase.

Expected Financial Benefits

Financial information is already likely included on the charter in both the business case and the problem statement. Teams might include expected financial benefits in the business case section of a charter, but it must be included somewhere. For some sponsors and executive leaders, the financial benefit is the most important piece of information included in a charter. An estimated savings or increase in revenue also provides a measuring stick by which leaders can consider requests for resources for a project.

A Six Sigma expert should *never* over extend estimates regarding financial benefits; it's almost always better to under-promise and over-perform. If you tell leaders a project will save $500,000 in the first year because a big number means you're more likely to get project approval and all the resources you ask for, you're the one that answers when the project saves only $80,000. As with any aspect of a Six Sigma project, be as accurate as possible, but be conservative with estimates when accuracy is in question.

Review the Charter with Success in Mind

Before a Six Sigma team presents a charter for approval, it should take time to review the document as a group to ensure the charter lays a foundation for success. Some questions a team might ask itself about a charter include:

- Is everything—especially the goals, financial expectations, and timeline—challenging but realistic?

- Can everyone on the team devote the committed amount of time to the project?
- Is the project backed by a sponsor or champion with enough influence to drive critical assistance and resources?
- Does the team expect to be supported by auxiliary departments such as information technology, human resources, compliance, accounting, or legal as necessary for project success?
- Does the team expect to have the necessary freedom to implement a solution it designs after the solution is approved by the sponsor, champion, or executive steering committee?
- Does the team have a leader who is well-versed in Six Sigma tools and project management?

If the answer to any of the questions above is no, then the team could be setting itself up for failure. Before moving forward, the team should address these concerns and, if possible, make changes that convert no answers to yes answers.

Project Ground Rules

Before moving forward with any work – even defining a team charter – it's a good idea for a Six Sigma team to establish some basic rules and requirements for the team. We touched briefly on this in Chapter 10 when discussing management of a team. The ground rules for a project should be maintained in writing and approved by all team members, but they don't have to be part of an official charter document. The reason for documenting the rules and having all team members approve them is because a single team member cannot later claim to be ignorant of the rules.

At the same time, rule generation on a Six Sigma team shouldn't be a completely democratic process. Some of the more common sense or critical rules can be provided by the Black Belt or team leader. For example, ground rules should cover topics such as who should attend each meeting and the fact that team members should hold certain information confidential. A Black Belt might simply state that team members should observe confidentiality and attendance rules, be on time to meetings, and respect each other. The team itself will likely vote on the frequency of meetings and when meetings should be scheduled. Seeking team member input ensures that all team members can actually commit to meeting time slots. For consistency, it's best to hold meetings on the same days and at the same time each week, but it's understandably difficult to keep such a schedule through the entire life of some projects.

Black Belts might also provide some tips and suggestions for how team members should participate during meetings, particularly during group brainstorming sessions. For more information on running a brainstorming session, see Chapter 35. Black Belts should also dictate the rules for creating an agenda and running a meeting according to the agenda, though they might delegate some of these functions such as time keeper and secretary.

Define Toolset

We've covered a number of define tools in previous chapters, including the SIPOC diagram and the 5 Whys. Process maps and value stream mapping are two advanced Six Sigma tools that are often used in the define stage. Some Six Sigma teams begin using run charts to start defining a baseline in the define phase; run charts are covered in Chapter 13 on the measure phase.

In this section, we'll cover three additional tools that are common to the define phase: the Stakeholder Analysis, the In and Out of the Box Method, and the Is/Is Not Matrix.

Stakeholder Analysis

A stakeholder analysis is a quick way to identify how various people within an organization relate to a project and how the team should keep them informed. Begin the analysis with a grid drawn over an x and y axis. The vertical axis represents the amount of power a person has in the organization. The horizontal axis represents the amount of interest a person has in the team's project. The stakeholder analysis works best when teams conduct it on a whiteboard or large flipchart. Draw the basic diagram, as seen in the figure below, in large format.

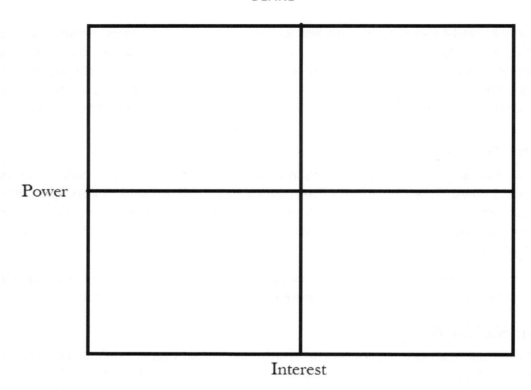

Provide the team with sticky notes. Ask them to write down possible stakeholders for a project or process. Stakeholders are anyone who has an interest in the project, who might benefit from the outcome of the project, or who might be impacted by the work done via the project. Take a few minutes to discuss the names that were brainstormed and discard any the team feels are not actually stakeholders.

Once the team decides who the stakeholders are, begin placing the names on the chart according to power and interest. People with both low power and little interest will be placed in the lower left corner. People with higher power and low interest are placed in the upper left; people with less power but a lot of interest are placed in the lower right corner, and people with high levels of power and a lot of interest are placed in the upper right corner. A name might be placed high and to the right of the lower-left corner if the stakeholder has a moderate amount of interest and power, but the team doesn't feel like the person quite crosses the line. Likewise, a name placed at the lower bounds of any quadrant might show lower amounts of power than those placed nearer the top of the box; the stakeholder analysis lets teams prioritize stakeholders in this manner, even within the four quadrants.

SIX SIGMA: A COMPLETE STEP-BY-STEP GUIDE

Each of the quadrants of the diagram correlate loosely to the type of stakeholder, providing some guidance on how the team might interact with each person or department listed.

Top Left: Keep Satisfied

Stakeholders that fall into the top left quadrant of the diagram have enough power that they could interfere with a project, but they aren't extremely interested in the day-to-day outcomes. The team should ensure these individuals are satisfied in whatever way they do interact with the project. Teams might also consult with these individuals at various times during the project. For example, a team working to solve problems of shipping in a warehouse might need to consult with procurement managers at some point because the team identifies a need for a different type of packing tape. Procurement leaders have power over obtaining the resource, but they might not have a great deal of interest in the project overall.

Sometimes, teams might identify a stakeholder that falls into this section and realize that it would be valuable to the team for that particular stakeholder to be more invested in the project. Six Sigma leaders can work with stakeholders to try to move someone from low interest to high interest categories – this is a political tactic that some teams use to bolster support for a project.

Bottom Left: Minimal Effort

Stakeholders that fall into the bottom left quadrant have the least important connection to a project. Teams will mostly communicate general information about a project via newsletters or email to these stakeholders. While these stakeholders take minimal effort from teams, some situations might exist where teams want to move stakeholders from this box to the lower-right box.

Bottom Right: Keep Informed

Individuals in the lower-right box have a strong tie or interest in the project, but do not have access to power to support projects from a resource standpoint. These stakeholders might include employees in departments related to the process being improved or subject matter experts that will be consulted about individual aspects of a project.

While stakeholders in the lower-right quadrant can't usually bring resources to bear, they *can* act in support of a project, often in the form of a goodwill ambassador.

Top Right: Key Player

Individuals in the top-right quadrant are either key players regarding a process or executive leaders with the ability to assign resources to a project. These are the individuals teams will report to at various tollgates; often, the executives responsible for the ultimate success of a process or project appear in the top-right quadrant.

In and Out of the Box Method

The In and Out of the Box method is a quick and easy method that helps teams define project or process scope. Begin by drawing a large box on a whiteboard or flip chart. Provide markers and sticky notes for the team. Ask the team to write down elements of the process to be worked on, including resources, activities, and people. Each item should be written on a sticky note. Work together to create as complete a list as possible, placing the sticky notes on a wall or table as you go. Make sure everyone on the team understands that there are no wrong answers and the first phase of the exercise doesn't require discussion. By brainstorming items with little-to-no discussion, teams can capture more ideas, leading to a more accurate picture of what is in and out of scope.

Once a comprehensive list is made, begin working as a team to assign each item to a place inside, on the line, or outside of the box. Items outside of the box are those that will be considered out of scope for the project. Teams might place items outside of the box because they don't have access or control over the items, they don't have time to work on the items, or they have specifically been told not to include the item in the project.

Items that are within the box are considered in scope for the project. These should be elements of the process the team can reasonably be expected to influence. If the team isn't sure yet where an item might fall, they should place it on the line. Items that go on the line might be ones that the team hopes to be able to impact but for which the team leader needs to seek permission or assistance from someone outside the team.

Once all items are placed on, in, or outside of the box, review the placements as a team and make any changes. Document the exercise by photographing the diagram or recreating it on a computer. The team might reflect back on the diagram when attempting to control scope creep or considering who they should approach for help with a project.

Is/Is Not Matrix

The Is/Is Not Matrix is another quick brainstorming tool teams can use to define scope. It can also be used to help define some of the information necessary to a problem statement. The matrix works by considering specific things about the process or project and coming up with both is and is not answers.

For example, if a Six Sigma team is tasked with determining why the furnaces in a certain factory are not heating to proper temperatures, they might create an Is/Is Not Matrix like the one below.

	Is	Is Not
Where	South plant	North or East plan
What	Steam furnaces	Wood furnaces
When	January 2015	Prior to January 2015

The matrix clearly shows that the scope of the project only includes work at the south plant on the steam furnaces. The problem was noted in January 2015, which provides the team with a starting point for gathering data. This is a very simple matrix; teams can ask as many questions as they like to narrow down scope or better understand processes and projects through the Is/Is Not structure.

Define Tollgate Checklist

A successful define phase ends with all of the following deliverables:

- o   A comprehensive project statement
- o   A team charter
- o   An understanding of the process and a project diagram or map
- o   An understanding of the Voice of the Customer

A definition of what success will look like that has been agreed on by the team members and any sponsors or executive leaders

o

179

Team Charter Template

Project Name:			
Team Members			Sponsor:
Name	Role	Time Commit	
			CTQs:
			Financial drivers:
			Internal Customers:
Non-Customer Stakeholders	In Scope		
			External Customers:
	Out of Scope		

Problem Statement:

Objective/Goal

Project Schedule:

CHAPTER 13:
MEASURE

Moving from the define phase to the measure phase of a project, Six Sigma teams continue to delve into the process, now coming to understand processes more fully through data. The measure phase is often the most laborious phase for the team, especially when data is not already available in digital formats. In this chapter, we'll review some of the metrics covered in previous chapters and introduce some concepts for data collection. We'll continue building on the concepts of measure introduced in later chapters on statistical analysis.

One of the first steps of the measure phase is determining the capability of a process. This step can be completed before a team formally leaves the define phase if the data needed to perform sigma level calculations is available. Calculating sigma levels for a process was covered in Chapter 1. In addition to sigma levels, teams might also calculate various metrics for a process, including defects per million opportunities, FTY, or RTY, which were all covered in Chapter 5.

Failure Modes and Effect Analysis

The Failure Modes and Effect Analysis is a tool that can be applied by a Six Sigma team in any phase from define to analyze. Often, teams begin working with FMEAs in measure because it helps them identify risk priorities for various inputs and errors within a process. Used properly, the FMEA uses systemic data and team input to set the stage for root cause analysis in the next DMAIC phase. Remember, while tollgates do occur and teams move through five phases during a DMAIC project, hard borders don't always exist between the phases. Teams might begin working on measure phase tasks before leaving the define phase, and it's almost certain that teams will begin some analysis while still collecting data.

Ultimately, an FMEA tool should be used when teams need more detailed information about inputs and possible associated fail-points than the tools discussed in the define chapter allow. The FMEA offers some of the information that is offered by SIPOC, but it also provides evaluations of the inputs. Teams typically create FMEAs in a spreadsheet program, as some calculations are required during the process.

To create an FMEA, create a spreadsheet with the following column headers:

1. Process step
2. Potential failure
3. Potential failure effect
4. SEV
5. Potential cause of failure
6. OCC
7. Current monitor/control
8. DET
9. RPN
10. Recommended changes/actions
11. Who and When?
12. Action completed
13. SEV
14. DET
15. RPN

Columns 1 through 9 of the FMEA might be completed during the measure phase while columns 10 through 15 are more appropriate for the improve phase.

Begin by identifying all possible process steps, activities, or inputs in column one. In column two, indicate what might go wrong for each process step. Note that you can list process steps more than once if there are multiple opportunities for error within each step. If the team has created a detailed enough list of steps, however, this won't likely be the case for a majority of the steps.

In column three, enter a short description of the impact of the failure on the customer. Incorrect measurement can result in increased variance in a product, for example. In the SEV column, rate the severity of the possible failure you described in the previous columns. Rate the severity from 1 to 10, with 1 being no effect, 5 being minor disruption to production, and 10 being severe enough to endanger a process or person.

In column five, enter the potential reasons the specific failure might occur, and in the OCC column, enter a numeric rating for how often the failure might be expected, with 1 being a very unlikely failure and 10 being an almost inevitable failure.

In column seven, create a short description of the current controls that are in place to monitor the process or prevent the failures the team has described. In the DET column, rate the ability of the process or staff to detect failure if it does occur. Rate detection between 1 and 10, with 1 being a process that includes automated detection that rarely fails and 10 being no detection at all.

Finally, calculate the risk priority number by multiplying the severity, occurrence, and detection ratings, as in the example below.

A Six Sigma team working on a project to improve the speed with which refunds are processed to customers is creating an FMEA. One row of the FMEA includes the following information:

- Process step: Refund request is entered in system.
- Potential failure: Incorrect amount is entered.
- Potential failure effect: The customer receives more or less refund than anticipated.
- SEV: 8
- Potential cause of failure: Data-entry employee transposes numbers or makes a similar typing mistake.
- OCC: 10
- Current monitor/control: A supervisor randomly reviews a sample of refund requests to ensure accuracy.
- DET: 7
- RPN: (SEV * OCC * DET) = (8*10*7) = 560

The team completes a second row as follows:

- Process step: Refund check is printed.
- Potential failure: The printed check has defects that make it difficult to cash.
- Potential failure effect: The customer can't cash the check and has to call for a new one.
- SEV: 9
- Potential cause of failure: Printer is misaligned or out of ink.
- OCC: 1
- Current monitor/control: The person who signs the checks reviews the checks as they sign them.
- DET: 2
- RPN: (SEV * OCC * DET) = (9*1*2) = 18

The potential failure in the first example has a much higher risk priority number, which means, as the team moves forward, they are more likely to work on solving that potential failure. During analyze and improve phases, the team would recommend changes, implement the recommended actions, and rescore the process to determine if the RPN of the changed process is lower. If it is higher or the same, then the change was not a good one and the team might need to try again.

Collecting Data

Creating a baseline metric for a process begins in the define phase, but teams cannot leave the measure phase without a strong understanding of current process performance. That understanding begins with figures such as sigma level, but teams should also define a process-specific metric where possible and gather historical data regarding that metric so they have something to compare future data against to prove that improvements were made.

Ideally, the team would have access to historical metrics for the process. In some cases, the team has to collect data from scratch. We'll introduce data collection later in this chapter and cover it in depth in the units on sampling.

Continuous versus discrete data

Before creating and displaying a baseline metric via graphical representation, you have to understand the type of data you are dealing with. Data is either discrete or continuous, and teams collect data either as a population sample or a process sample. How teams collect data and the type of data collected determine how the data can be viewed graphically and analyzed.

Discrete Data

Discrete data is categorical in nature; it is also referred to as qualitative data or attribute data. Discrete data falls into three categories: ordinal, nominal, and binary, or attribute, data; some data collected can be expressed in one or more of the discrete categories. For example, student test scores can be conveyed in an ordinal fashion via the grades A, B, C, D, and F or in a binary fashion via the Pass/Fail distinction.

Discrete data can be displayed via Pareto charts, pie charts, and bar charts. In some instances, the data can be converted to run and control charts using variation within the data or ratios as the item being charted. In the chapter on the control phase, you'll begin understanding why a team might want to convert discrete data to be used in a control chart.

Within discrete data, binary or attribute data is usually the easiest data to collect. Attribute data records one of the other answers. Does the person choose paper or plastic? Is the room hot or cold? Is the glass empty or full? Is the light on or off? Depending on the scenario, attribute data can be very accurate. The light is either on or off; the switch position tells you that. Attribute data in this case can be automated with the right technology, which means it would be highly accurate. Whether the cup is empty or full is another story, because there are so many variations between completely empty and completely full. If the data is being collected by people, personal biases might enter the equation. Teams can remove some of those biases and better ensure accurate measurements, which will be covered in the sections on measurement systems.

Continuous Data

Continuous data is quantitative data and is measured in units. For example, the time of day is measured in hours. Temperature is measured in degrees, and almost anything can be converted to continuous data by making it a percentage.

Continuous data is visualized in graphs such as histograms and box plots. Box plots are discussed in chapter 14, and histograms are covered in depth in the chapters on statistics. Continuous data can also be viewed in the form of run and control charts.

Choosing Between Discrete and Continuous Data

Sometimes, a process or activity can be measured in both discrete or continuous data. Depending on the purpose of the measurements, teams might need to pick between the two data types. For example, if a Six Sigma team has identified room temperature as an input into the quality of product, they will want to monitor the temperature of the room. They can do so by recording the temperature in degrees every ten minutes; that data would be continuous. Alternatively, the team might create a tick sheet, having someone make a mark every hour to note whether the temperature was in the 40s, 50s, 60s, 70s, or 80s with regard to the Fahrenheit scale. That data would be discrete.

In this particular example, most teams would choose to record the continuous data. Exact temperature measurements every 10 minutes provides a lot more information than whether the temperature of the room was in the 70s at the turn of the hour. The continuous data could be converted to provide teams with the discrete data easily; the discrete data in this case – and in most cases – could not be converted to continuous data.

What is true in the example is true for most scenarios. When possible, teams should convert measurements to continuous data. Continuous data:

- Provides more information than discrete data does.
- Is typically more time-consuming to collect than discrete data unless teams have access to automated or computerized data collection.
- Is more precise than discrete data.
- Lets teams remove variation and errors inherent in estimation and rounding.

Levels of Data

Data can be classified at four basic levels: nominal, ordinal, interval, and ratio. Attribute, or binary, data is actually a limited form of nominal data.

Nominal Data

Nominal is considered to be the lowest data classification level and simply involves applying number labels to a qualitative description so statistical analysis programs and tests can be applied to the data. The numbers assigned to each category don't provide any information about whether the data is better or worse than other data in the listing – in nominal data, numbers don't reflect a scale.

An example of nominal data might be applied in a list of birth states for a classroom. In a class of 30, the number of students born in various states breaks down as follows:

- Texas: 6
- Louisiana: 4
- Arkansas: 10
- Mississippi: 1
- Oklahoma: 9

In nominal data, each state would be provided a numeric label:

1. Texas
2. Louisiana
3. Arkansas
4. Mississippi
5. Oklahoma

That doesn't mean 5 students are from Oklahoma; it means 9 students fall into category 5 for the question "What state were you born in?"

For nominal data, central tendencies are calculated not with means or medians, but with mode. For example, a list of the nominal data in our example would be as follows:

1, 1, 1, 1, 1, 1, 2, 2, 2, 2, 3, 3, 3, 3, 3, 3, 3, 3, 3, 3, 4, 5, 5, 5, 5, 5, 5, 5, 5, 5

The mode is the number that appears most in the set; in this case, 3.

Statistically, analysis is limited with regard to nominal data, but some tests can be performed with statistical analysis software.

Ordinal Data

Ordinal data is considered to be a higher form of data than nominal, though it still uses numbers and categories to identify data elements. With ordinal data, though, the numbers themselves actually provide some meaning. The numbers used in the FMEA scales at the beginning of this chapter were ordinal data. The numbers are qualitative in nature, but they are also ranked. Central tendencies with ordinal data are measured by either the mode or the median, and common uses for this type of data include ranking various things against each other or rating a specific thing, such as a movie or pain level.

Ordinal data can be arranged in an order that makes sense: on a 1 to 10 scale, Suzy rated the movies as 2, 5, 6, and 9. If one is the worst and 10 is the best, then we can assume Suzy liked the last movie best.

While ordinal data comes with a logical order, the intervals between the numbers don't mean anything. If Suzy rated movie A as a 10 and movie B as a 9, the conclusion is that she liked movie A better. Exactly how much more she liked the movie is not discernible using ordinal data.

Interval Data

Interval data is an even higher form of data classification. Interval data provides numeric values that can be arranged in a logical order with meaning; the big difference between ordinal and interval data is that the difference between each interval value provides meaning. If Frank is keeping track of the temperature in his house and he sees that at 8:00 a.m. it was 76 degrees and at 9:00 a.m. it was 80 degrees, he not only knows that 9:00 a.m. was hotter; he knows that it was 4 degrees hotter at 9:00 a.m. than at 8:00 a.m. Interval data is continuous, or quantitative, and offers more flexibility when it comes to statistical analysis.

Ratio Data

Ratio data is considered to be the highest of the data classifications. Ratio data has an absolute zero point, can be both discrete or continuous in nature, and provides the highest capabilities for statistical analysis in many cases. Some examples of information that can be recorded using ratio data include force, defects per million opportunities, voltage, height, units per hour, and volume.

Choosing the Best Measurement Systems

Measurement systems analysis applies scientific principles to help teams analyze how much variation a system of measurement brings to a process. The purpose of the MSA is to identify errors of accuracy within data collection tools. Teams can then redress measurement systems to create more accurate data captures or, if that isn't possible, take the possibility of errors into account when performing analysis on data.

During measurement systems analysis, teams should review multiple components of possible measurement error. Six Sigma teams analyze:

- Whether bias occurs in the accuracy of measurements
- Whether the measurement has the proper resolution
- What measurement scale linearity exists
- Whether measurement activities are stable over time
- Whether measurements are repeatable and reproducible

Depending on the measurements the team is dealing with, the MSA can be time consuming and is often why the measure phase of a DMAIC project is one of the longest.

Creating Accuracy

In this stage of MSA, teams define the difference between the most accurate measurement possible and the data being collected by the current measurement system. The goal of a measurement system is accuracy: coming as close as possible to a defined target, if not the exact measurement. For example, in a computer manufacturing plant, one employee might solder a chip to the motherboard. For the rest of the chips and wires to be added to the motherboard, the chip must be placed within a 2 mm area. In this case, a measurement tool might be implemented with a required accuracy of plus or minus 0.5 mm to ensure the chip is placed within the area targeted.

Teams can ensure accuracy of data by verifying that the gauge used to collect data is performing accurately. If a digital scale is being used to weigh ingredients, teams should calibrate the scale using calibrated weights. If templates are used on a factory floor to make measurements more efficient, teams should ensure those templates are accurate by comparing them against known measurement tools such as verified rulers and scales. Note that, for the purpose of the MSA, accuracy reflects the performance of the measurement tool, not the operator. Whether the employee uses the measurement tool correctly or records the amount correctly is considered a concern of precision, which is covered later in this chapter under R&R Gages.

Once a Six Sigma team is confident that a measurement tool is properly calibrated, they can instruct employees or others who are responsible for recording data. Data should be accepted as it is collected for most efficient access and because early review can turn up specific problems with data collection. When possible, teams should not round data but collect it as it is recorded.

If data is being collected manually, employees should have a data collection template that prompts them to collect data at appropriate times and record information about the data collection event, including the person collecting the data, the machine or process involved, conditions of the environment – especially those that are different from normal conditions or might have a direct impact on measurements – and the measurement tool being used if multiple tools are an option. These details help Six Sigma teams rule out outliers, which are discussed in the next chapter.

Before measurements are passed to the analyze phase, Six Sigma experts should review data to ensure there are no misplaced or missing decimal points, that duplicate entries haven't been recorded, that frequency-based measurements aren't missing points, or that any other obvious issues haven't occurred with the data. Addressing obvious data problems before beginning analyze phases reduces the chance that teams will come to false conclusions about root causes or viable solutions for a process.

Addressing Resolution

Measuring at the correct resolution ensures that a measurement system can detect change in the data or process appropriately. For example, if a Six Sigma team is working to improve a process that cuts pipe for bathroom fixture installations, it might be concerned with the length of the pipe. In reviewing the measurement system for the cut pipe, the team finds that the process includes measuring the pipe to the nearest centimeter. If, however, pipes that are off by several millimeters cause issues in the installation, then the nearest centimeter measurement is not a small enough resolution.

A good rule of thumb to follow for resolution is called the 10-bucket rule. Break your measurement resolution into a tenth of what is required. If the pipe must measure within a range of 5 mm to perform, the measuring tool should measure to the ½ mm. In another example, a food service department might be tasked with maintaining the correct temperature in a freezer. To monitor the temperature, an employee records the temperature once per hour. If temperatures fluctuate quickly in the freezer, a change in temperature that would impact quality of food or ingredients might come and go between recordings. In this case, the proper resolution might be gained by recording measurements every 10 minutes or every six minutes for 10 readings per hour. Even better, in a freezer with a digital thermostat connected to a network, teams might be able to access readings recorded every minute.

Resolution is usually one of the easiest things to correct within a measuring system, but it isn't always cost-effective or plausible to measure at the most detailed resolutions. Teams should consider resource requirements when developing a measurement system. If, however, the most detailed resolution is possible, measurements obtained will provide more information about the process and a larger sample size from which to work.

Adjusting for Errors of Linearity

Linearity describes how a measurement system performs across a range. A standard metric ruler in the hands of most people is fairly accurate at measuring centimeters, but is less accurate at measuring millimeters or kilometers. A scale with a range between 0 and 10 kilograms might measure less accurately at either end of the range.

Taking measurements at various ranges with an existing measurement system and comparing those measurements to data gathered with tools known to be accurate across all ranges can help teams find errors of linearity. In some cases, teams can develop mathematical equations to account for the discrepancies. For example, if the scale is accurate at 5 kilograms, but is off by an extra quarter of a kilogram for each kilogram thereafter, a measurement of 8.5 kilograms would actually be:

$8.5 - ((8.5-5)*.25) = 7.625$

If mathematical adjustments are not possible, then teams should not use measurement systems to measure ranges where linearity errors regularly occur.

Stability

Stability describes the consistency of measurements over time. If operators are measuring in the same way and using the same tools – and those tools don't have any of the other problems described above – then measurements should reflect stability on a control chart. Control charts are introduced in Chapter 16 and covered in depth in later chapters on statistical process control.

If the variation of measurements, as reflected on a control chart, do not indicate stability, then teams might want to first rule out a problem with the measurement system before determining that the process is out of control.

Gage R&R

Gage R&R tools are used to ensure repeatability and reproducibility with regard to measurement systems. In most cases, Gage R&R tools apply to measurement systems that involve human operators and appraisers. Six Sigma teams apply Gage R&R tests to find weaknesses within such measurement systems.

In Gage R&R testing, repeatability means that a single employee, using the same measurement system and appraising the same things, can repeat his or her measurements. Reproducibility means that multiple employees using the same measurement system and appraising the same things come up with measurements that match or are very close to matching.

Most Gage R&R tests fall into two types: attribute and variable. The premise for testing each type of measurement is the same, though the criteria and statistical analysis following the test differ slightly.

Attribute Gage R&R

An attribute Gage R&R is used when Six Sigma teams are analyzing measurement systems for go/no go data. For example, if operators review an item in the product line and decide simply to pass or fail it, this would be an attribute measurement. In the example of the freezer measurements above, an employee might simply be tasked with recording whether the temperature was in an appropriate range: a yes/no measurement. As previously stated, attribute measurements provide the least information about a process, so in the case of the freezer temperature, it's better to record the actual temperature. Whether that recording was within appropriate range can be determined systemically from the temperature data.

When attribute data is used, an attribute Gage R&R is used to test the measurement system following the steps below.

1. Select at least two appraisers.
2. Provide a number of samples. Label the samples in a way that you know which one is which but that wouldn't identify the sample for the appraiser.
3. Record the actual attribute measurement for each sample according to the best possible (most accurate) measurement you have.
4. Have each appraiser record the attribute measurement for each sample provided (go/no go; yes/no; hot/cold; pass/fail; etc.).
5. Repeat the process with the same samples and appraiser, randomizing the order in which you present the samples. Randomizing sample order the second time appraisers are presented with them reduces the chance that appraisers remember what measurement they recorded the first time and record the same measurement by default.
6. Enter all data into a spreadsheet or Gage R&R file similar to the one below that shows a test of a pass/fail measurement.

Sample Label	Actual Attribute	Appraiser 1		Appraiser 2		Agreement
		Trial 1	Trial 2	Trial 1	Trial 2	Yes/No?
1	P	P	P	F	P	No
2	P	P	P	P	P	Yes
3	P	P	P	P	P	Yes
4	F	P	F	F	F	No
5	P	P	P	P	P	Yes
6	F	F	F	F	P	No
7	F	P	P	F	F	No
8	P	P	P	F	F	No
9	F	F	F	F	F	Yes
10	P	P	P	P	P	Yes

From the Gage R&R above, you can see that the measurement system is reproducible only 50 percent of the time, making it a poor measurement system. It is repeatable 90 percent of the time for Appraiser 1 and 80 percent of the time for Appraiser 2, and the appraisers are accurate 80 percent and 70 percent of the time respectively. Given these results, a Six Sigma team might determine that there is some problem of clarity with instructions for how to determine whether a sample is a pass or a fail. The chart above only provides data for a set of 10 samples; more accurate attribute Gage R&R testing usually requires at least 20 data points.

Variable Gage R&R

Not all data is attribute data, which is why teams can also perform variable Gage R&R tests. While the raw data from a variable Gage R&R test can provide a Six Sigma team with a picture of whether a measurement system is obviously failing or not, statistical analysis is usually required to make a true determination about the performance of a measurement system. This is because, with variable measurements, some differences between measurements and operators is likely, particularly when measuring to very small or large figures or capturing data in a moving measurement.

Set up a variable Gage R&R test in much the same way you set up an attribute test, using two to three appraisers and at least five to ten outputs to be measured. Have each appraiser measure each sample two or three times, randomizing the order in which samples are presented to avoid appraisers remembering the measurements initially entered. Record all data on a variable Gage R&R template, such as the example below.

Sample	Actual Measurement	Appraiser 1			Appraiser 2			Appraiser 3			Variation
1											
2											
3											
4											
5											
6											
7											

The statistical analysis performed in Excel SPC or Minitab by a Black Belt or Green Belt typically returns four figures:

- % Study Variation
- % Tolerance
- % Contribution
- Number of distinct categories

Teams should look to ensure all four elements of a variable Gage R&R test calculation are in what are considered "safe" ranges. Commonly, each element comes with a scale for safe, or green, zones along with caution zones and failure zones. If one of the elements falls into a caution zone and all others into the green, then a team will likely conclude that the measurement system is sufficient. In some cases, all or a majority of caution zone scores might be deemed acceptable, particularly if making the measurement system any more accurate would be costly or cause application issues for other processes. Measurement systems that score in the failure zone for any element should probably be repaired or replaced.

Common criteria used to judge each element of the variable Gage R&R calculations are as follows:

Element	Pass	Caution	Fail
% Study Variation	0 to 10	10 to 30	30 and above
% Tolerance	0 to 10	10 to 30	30 and above
% Contribution	0 to 1	1 to 9	10 and above
# of Distinct Categories	10 or more	6 to 10	1 to 5

Note: Another tool that is effective in identifying variation in a measurement system is called the ANOVA, or Analysis of Variance. ANOVA is also useful for analyzing variation of any type, and will be covered in Unit 5 on intermediate statistics.

Collecting Data Samples

Once teams are sure the best possible measurement tools are in place, they can begin collecting data to be used in the analyze phase of the DMAIC project. The most accurate conclusions come when a team can analyze data for the entire population, but that is rarely possible due to time and cost constraints. If you can gain access to automated data or data warehouses, you might be able to collect population data or extremely large sample sizes that better approximate population data. Otherwise, Six Sigma teams must randomly sample the population that is available and use those samples to draw conclusions about the population as a whole.

To ensure samples can be used to draw statistical conclusions, they must be handled correctly and be the appropriate size. In this section, we'll simply cover the types of sampling strategies that Six Sigma teams might use and why.

Simple Random Sampling

Simple random sampling works when there is an equal chance that any item within the population will be chosen. For example, if you put 20 marbles of the exact size, weight, and texture in a bag and blindly select one, each marble in the bag has a 1 in 20 chance at being selected. If the marbles are different sizes or weights, those differing attributes can impact the chance that each marble will be selected. Heavier marbles might sort to the bottom of the bag; bigger marbles might be more likely to be picked up.

Random sampling for statistical analysis requires that the sample will represent similar attributes and percentages as the entire population. The population is "N" items large. The sample size is "n" items large. How big the sample needs to be to statistically represent the population is decided by a number of factors.

Stratified Sampling

Stratified sampling occurs when the population as a whole is divided or can be divided into subgroups with differing attributes. For example, if a shipping company wants to test the accuracy of its estimated shipping times against actual shipping times, it might assume that the results will vary according to the distance a package has to travel. By randomly selecting samples from the entire package population, there's a chance the company might only end up with samples for packages delivered within a 200-mile radius.

To prevent bias in the data, the shipping company might divide the population into four subgroups:

- Deliveries within 200-mile radius
- Deliveries within 201 to 400-mile radius
- Deliveries within 401 to 600-mile radius
- Deliveries over 600 miles

By sampling randomly from the stratified subgroups, the team ensures a sample size with less bias.

Sequential Sampling

Sequential sampling involves selecting every X item for inclusion in the sampling. Sequential sampling can be used when teams are collecting data at intervals such as time. The team might collect data every 10 minutes. Sequential sampling can also be used to sample physical items; every 5th item on a product line might be reviewed. Given the right parameters and enough time, sequential sampling can provide valid statistical results. Teams must be cognizant, however, that the sequence of the sampling could, in rare cases, skew results. It is possible, for example, that something occurs during every 5th iteration of a process that causes a difference to occur.

Samples that Aren't Random

Non-random sampling should not be used when dealing with statistical analysis because it is more likely to introduce user or sampling error. While all sampling comes with some form of error, random sampling errors can be calculated and accounted for in analysis. The same cannot be said of non-random samples.

Non-random sampling includes convenience or judgment sampling. Convenience sampling occurs when a team takes the most convenient measurements. "We want to know about the process right now, so let's review the next dozen items that come off the line." That type of analysis only truly tells the team how the process performed at that exact moment in time.

Judgment sampling occurs when an expert or knowledgeable person is tasked with "selecting" appropriate samples. A supervisor might say to his or her team members, "Select some of your work that represents the normal way you function in a given day." In most cases, the team members select what they believe is better quality work, skewing any results from the sample.

Delivering a Baseline Metric

One of the major deliverables coming out of define and measure phases is the baseline metric. How is the process performing now, and what measurement will the team use to compare current performance to post-improvement performance?

Baseline metrics are numbers, but most teams find that presenting the metric graphically resonates best with business resources and executives. Visual representations also provide teams with a quick way to determine if progress is occurring.

The type of visual representation you use depends on whether your major metric is discrete or continuous. Discrete data can be displayed on Pareto charts (see Chapter 5) and continuous data can be displayed via run charts. You can also use variation or other calculations to convert discrete data to continuous data for display in run charts and control charts (see Chapter 16 for information about control charts).

Run Charts

A run chart can be used to monitor the performance of any variable or process over time. With a single, intuitive chart, Six Sigma teams can display trends, shifts, and cycles within a process; they can also monitor a process for concerns, though run charts are not as effective at this as the very similar control chart is.

A basic run chart is simply a line plot of the data over time, which means anyone can create the chart. Most Six Sigma run charts also feature a line representing the median of all data points for visual reference. Depending on the type of information being charted, you may need to convert data to a ratio for a more accurate run chart. For example, if you are plotting the temperature of a surface over time, there is no need to convert data. If you are plotting the number of patients readmitted to a hospital within 30 days of being discharged, then it helps to convert the data to a percentage of the number of patients discharged within the same time period. In a 30-day period where 10,000 patients were discharged, you can expect a higher number of returns than a period during which only 5,000 patients are discharged.

The figure below illustrates a run chart of temperature over time. You can see how temperature changes through time and begin to see some possible trends. A Six Sigma team would be able to zoom out, viewing the run chart over more time to validate trend assumptions. You can also see that the median temperature for the process is 33.

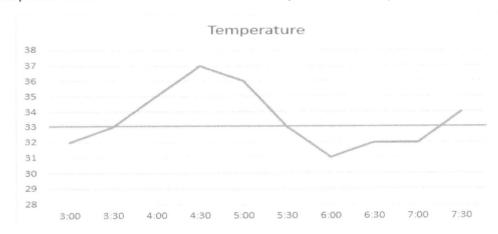

The run chart below indicates the number of returns per hundred sales for each month of the year. You can see that returns as a rate of sales increases steadily during the first part of the year before holding steady from May through November. The orange line indicates the median returns per hundreds sales, which is just under 7.

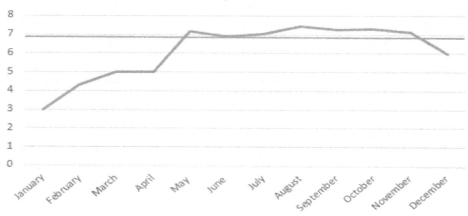

Returns per Hundred

Create Basic Run Charts in Excel

Statistical analysis software, including Minitab and Excel SPC, creates all elements of a run chart automatically from entered data, but anyone can use basic Excel functions to create a run chart if needed.

First, create a data table.

Creating a data table for a single attribute, such as temperature, just requires entering the time labels in one column and the attribute measurements in another. For the example, we'll walk through creating a rate data table, since it involves additional steps.

1. Enter the data labels (month, week, hour, etc.) in the first column of Excel.
2. In the next column, enter the corresponding measurements for the attribute you are interested in: in this case, the total number of returns per month.
3. In the third column, enter the total number of items you are comparing the attribute to: in this case, the total number of sales per month.

	A	B	C
1	Month	Number of Returns	Number of Sales
2	January	105	3500
3	February	95	2200
4	March	125	2500
5	April	140	2800
6	May	215	3000
7	June	200	2900
8	July	190	2700
9	August	245	3300
10	September	225	3100
11	October	270	3700
12	November	285	4000
13	December	250	4200
14			

4. In the fourth column, calculate the percentage the first column of data is of the second. In this case, the percentage of returns per sales for each month. The calculation is achieved in this case by the formula =B2/C2 for January, =B3/C3 for February, and so forth.

	A	B	C	D
1	Month	Number of Returns	Number of Sales	Rate of Returns per Sales
2	January	105	3500	0.03
3	February	95	2200	0.043181818
4	March	125	2500	0.05
5	April	140	2800	0.05
6	May	215	3000	0.071666667
7	June	200	2900	0.068965517
8	July	190	2700	0.07037037
9	August	245	3300	0.074242424
10	September	225	3100	0.072580645
11	October	270	3700	0.072972973
12	November	285	4000	0.07125
13	December	250	4200	0.05952381

5. Decide whether you want to create a run chart showing percentages, or if you would like to create the chart illustrating rate per 100, per 1,000, etc.
6. If you want to illustrate a rate per (x), multiply the percentage calculation in the fourth column by (x). In this case, the figures in column D are multiplied by 100.

Month	Number of Returns	Number of Sales	Rate of Returns per Sales	Returns per Hundred
	A	B	C	D	E
January	105	3500	0.03	3
February	95	2200	0.043181818	4.318181818
March	125	2500	0.05	5
April	140	2800	0.05	5
May	215	3000	0.071666667	7.166666667
June	200	2900	0.068965517	6.896551724
July	190	2700	0.07037037	7.037037037
August	245	3300	0.074242424	7.424242424
September	225	3100	0.072580645	7.258064516
October	270	3700	0.072972973	7.297297297
November	285	4000	0.07125	7.125
December	250	4200	0.05952381	5.952380952

7. Use Excel to calculate the median of the number you plan to chart. The median is calculated with the formula =Median(Number 1, Number 2,...), where the numbers in the formula correlate with the range of all the charted data points. In this case, the median is 6.96679
8. Highlight the data labels (in this case, column A) and the figures to be charted (column E)

A	B	C	D	E
Month	Number of Returns	Number of Sales	Rate of Returns per Sales	Returns per Hundred
January	105	3500	0.03	3
February	95	2200	0.043181818	4.318181818
March	125	2500	0.05	5
April	140	2800	0.05	5
May	215	3000	0.071666667	7.166666667
June	200	2900	0.068965517	6.896551724
July	190	2700	0.07037037	7.037037037
August	245	3300	0.074242424	7.424242424
September	225	3100	0.072580645	7.258064516
October	270	3700	0.072972973	7.297297297
November	285	4000	0.07125	7.125
December	250	4200	0.05952381	5.952380952

9. Select Insert > Charts > Line Chart to insert a line chart of the attribute or attribute calculation.

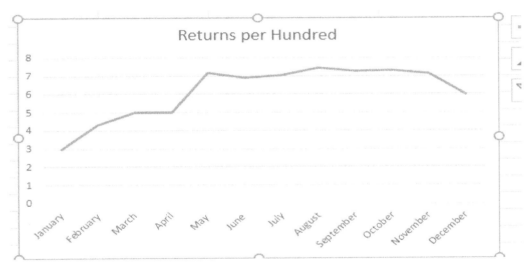

10. Select Insert > Shape > Draw Line.

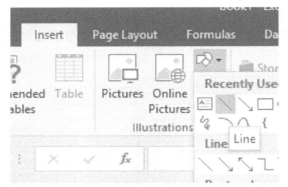

11. Draw a line on your run chart approximately where the median would be. Use Excel tools to select a color and thickness for the line that you desire.

Returns per Hundred

The completed run chart can be used to present information to the Six Sigma team or include a graphical representation of baseline process performance in a measure phase tollgate presentation. Again, it should be noted that manual creation of a run chart is not required for most Black Belts and Green Belts, who will have access to statistical analysis software.

Measure Tollgate Checklist

Use the checklist below to determine whether a team is ready to move from the measure phase to the analyze phase of a DMAIC project.

- o The team has agreed upon the key measurements and come up with a baseline measurement of process performance.
- o The team has analyzed measurement systems and identified any issues that might contribute to analysis errors.
- o Where possible, the team has corrected measurement systems to remove error risks.
- o The team has calculated process variation and sigma level.
- o The team has conducted appropriate sampling to allow for statistically valid conclusions in the next phase.
- o The sponsor or champion has reviewed and signed off on all elements of the measure phase.

CHAPTER 14: ANALYZE

If the chapter on the measure phase seemed especially long, it's because the phase itself is long and requires a great deal of work. Without a strong measure phase, the team cannot move on to analyze data and make data-based decisions that drive improve and control phases. Analyze phases also require a lot of work, but that work is usually performed by Black Belts and Green Belts, who report findings to the Six Sigma team and ask for feedback about analysis and verification of analysis.

In this chapter, we'll discuss a number of tools that might be used by Six Sigma teams during the analyze phase, but we'll also reference other chapters and units. Units 4, 5, 7 and 8 provide in-depth information about the statistical tools referenced throughout this chapter.

Root Cause Analysis

One of the fundamental activities of the analyze phase performed by the entire team with help from identified subject matter experts is the root cause analysis. Root cause analysis is used to identify root causes for problems or defects when a team has reached the analyze phase without a clear idea of primary causation. Some of the tools described for identifying root causes in this chapter could be used in either define or measure phases at the discretion of the Black Belt leading the team; the FEMA described in Chapter 13 on measure could likewise be used in the analyze phase as part of root cause analysis.

The Cause and Effect, or Fishbone Diagram

A popular method for brainstorming and analyzing causation in a process is the fishbone diagram. The fishbone diagram can be completed by a single Six Sigma expert, but it typically has more value when it is completed by the entire Six Sigma team. The diagram lets teams concentrate on a brainstorming process that generates ideas about possible problem causes, organizes those possibilities in a logical way, and lets teams visualize the information to identify priorities, trends, and relationships between ideas. When used as a team activity, the fishbone diagram encourages participation and input from all team members, which increases the chance of laying the foundational work for a viable and original solution.

The cause and effect diagram is called the fishbone diagram because you begin with what looks like a simple drawing of a fish skeleton. Reference the diagram below and follow the instructions to create a fishbone diagram as part of a team brainstorming exercise. You can also use these instructions now to practice a fishbone diagram based on a process or problem you have experience with.

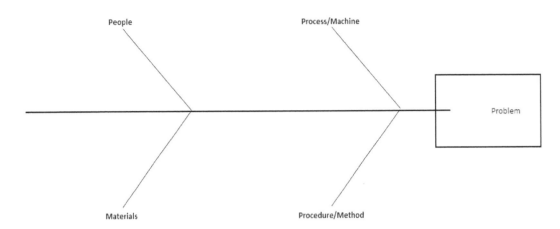

1. Sketch a basic fishbone shape on a whiteboard or large flipchart. Write a summarized version of the problem where the fish head should be. Note: You don't have to conduct a fishbone diagram only on the problem statement from the define phase. Teams might also conduct the diagram on a specific defect or issue found during the define or measure phase. For example, if the problem statement discusses the amount of waste in a restaurant, the team might have discovered during the measure phase that bread is being thrown away at a rate higher than all other food items. One of the activities handled in the analyze phase might be a fishbone diagram specifically about the reason for so much bread waste.
2. Draw a fish spine and four major connectors. Label each connector as People, Process, Materials, and Procedure. Some Black Belts also include two other major connectors: Equipment and Environment.
3. Explain the categories of the fishbone diagram to the team. Note that there are some places, especially with particular processes, where the various categories will overlap. Some ideas generated by the team as they complete the fishbone diagram might fit in more than one category, and that's okay.
    a. People references anyone who carries out or interacts with a process.
    b. Process or machine refers to the process by which inputs become outputs.

    c. Procedure or method refers to the way things are done, whether by written documents or unwritten rules.

    d. Materials are the inputs, such as raw goods, into the process.

    e. Equipment includes the technology or machines required to handle the work.

    f. Environment is the immediate area surrounding the process.

4. Begin with each category on the fishbone diagram, asking the team how something in that category might be responsible for a problem or defect.

5. Use sticky notes to write down ideas and place them on the fishbone diagram so you can move ideas around later. You can also write directly on the diagram.

6. Couple cause-and-effect brainstorming with the 5 Whys exercise described in Chapter 6. For each branch of the fishbone diagram, ask "Why?" at least five times to ensure the most granular detail possible.

7. Once the team has run out of ideas for the first category, repeat steps 4 through 6 for all other categories.

8. Take some time as a team to review the diagram, discussing the placement of potential causes, and moving them to appropriate categories and subsections to create an organized visual representation.

9. Remove or cross-out causes that don't prove to be valid after initial discussion.

10. As a team, decide which root causes seem most likely or highest priority. Circle those causes as high-priority possibilities for further investigation.

Cause and Effect Brainstorm Example

To provide a better idea of how a fishbone diagram works, consider the example image below and we'll walk through how the team came up with the information recorded on the procedure/method line of this diagram.

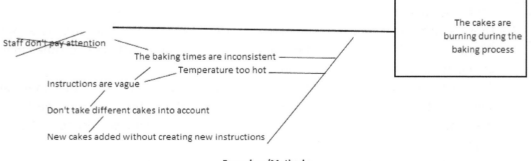

Procedure/Method

The team above was working to solve a problem of burnt cakes in a food-service bakery. When discussing the method by which the cakes are being baked, the team first came up the with the reason that the cakes were being baked at inconsistent times. Perhaps, suggested one team member, staff weren't paying attention and were leaving cakes in the oven too long. The idea was written down.

The instructions for baking cakes are vague, said another team member – this time, a subject matter expert from the bakery. "Why?" asked the team. The subject matter expert responded that the instructions in the bakery don't take various types of cakes into account, leaving staff guessing about bake times for some cakes. Further "Why?" questions helped the team determine that new cakes were added to the menu without the overall instructions for bakery staff being updated.

After digging deeper into the inconsistent baking times, the team again asked themselves how methods could be responsible for burnt cakes. Someone suggested that the temperature in the oven was too hot, and the team tied that suggestion to the same root cause as the inconsistent bake times. Upon final review, someone noted that the suggestion that staff not paying attention was a cause wasn't valid, because the bakery was equipped with alarms that sounded when baking time was done. The team crossed that idea off the diagram.

In this case, the Six Sigma team might prioritize the fact that instructions are not available for all types of items being prepared in the bakery. Because this would likely be a simple and common-sense improvement to make, the Black Belt might even assign someone to begin working on the improve phase as soon as the cause was verified. Many times, the root cause is not as obvious and the solution for the cause even less obvious, requiring additional analysis and validation before moving forward.

Root Cause Verification Matrix

Once teams identify possible root causes, they must verify that the causes are valid. Root cause verification can be completed via a variety of methods, including statistical analysis, design of experiments, logical questioning, observing a process, gathering additional data, analyzing data via graphical representation, and mapping processes at a more granular level than accomplished in the define phase. While this chapter touches briefly on statistical analysis and graphical representation, those topics, as well as experiments and process mapping, are covered in later units.

Whatever method is used to validate root cause assumptions, the Six Sigma team should document it. Documentation regarding root cause verification is usually completed on a matrix that includes the problem, possible root causes, the verification method, why the verification method was chosen, results of the verification, and, in some cases, whether a senior Six Sigma leader, such as a Master Black Belt, agrees. A template for such a matrix is included below, but teams can also create similar documents in Excel or Word.

Problem	Possible Root Causes	Method of Verification	Reason for Verification Method	Verified?	Notes

The root cause verification matrix for the burnt cake example might be completed as follows:

Problem	Possible Root Causes	Method of Verification	Reason for Verification Method	Verified?	Notes
Cakes in the Delaware bakery are coming out burnt 10 percent of the time.	Temperature too hot	Run chart of temperature against required temperature	Allows team to visually determine whether temperatures exceed requirements at any point during bake process	Yes	
	Bake times inconsistent	Box plot of bake times per type of cake	Provides visual representation of the variation per cake type; bake times should not vary widely by cake, so the boxes should be flat; lets teams determine if certain cake types are more of a problem.	Yes	
	Instructions not provided to staff	Process observation	Easy way to determine if bakery staff have the instructions necessary to complete work without defects	Yes	

Graphical Analysis

Six Sigma experts and teams can use a variety of graphical analysis tools to help generate ideas about root causes or understand how inputs and outputs really impact each other. Some of those graphical analysis tools require statistical analysis software, and those will be covered in later chapters. In this section, we'll look at a few graphical representations you can create easily with Excel.

Pareto Chart

The first graphical tool for validating root causes is the Pareto chart, which was covered in chapter 5. Chapter 5 discussed the Pareto Principle, or 80/20 rule, which says that 20 percent of the causes lead to 80 percent of the results. Because of this, a Pareto chart is a good starting point for root cause brainstorming – teams can start with the few inputs or attributes accounting for the bulk of the Pareto chart. Just as you can "drill down" using the fishbone diagram, asking deeper and deeper "Why?" questions, you can drill down using a Pareto chart.

Consider the Pareto chart illustrating reasons for medical claims denials from Chapter 5.

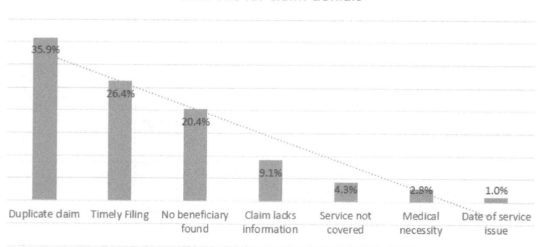

In this case, the team might decide to concentrate on the top two claims denial reasons: duplicate claim and timely filing. The team could use various methods for digging deeper into root causes for these two claims denial reasons. They might perform a fishbone diagram to discover why duplicate claims are being generated. To understand the timely filing problem, teams might gather additional data for graphical analysis.

Timely filing means that the claim was not originally filed with an insurance company prior to the deadline for claims submission. Different insurance companies have various timely filing requirements, and the countdown usually starts at the time of service to the patient or the time of discharge from a facility. The team might want to understand which payers are denying claims for timely filing, so they collect data as follows on how many timely filing denials are associated with each payer. Because Pareto analysis is concerned with the top few, you can lump the many others together in a single entry and, for the purposes of the Pareto analysis, ignore them. A medical provider might bill claims to dozens of providers; including every provider on the data table and Pareto chart would be a waste of both time and space for this particular exercise.

Payer	Denials
A	3512
B	2779
C	1575
D	1142
E	945
F	847
G	702
H	502
Others	1241

Converted to a basic Pareto chart, the data is illustrated in the graph below.

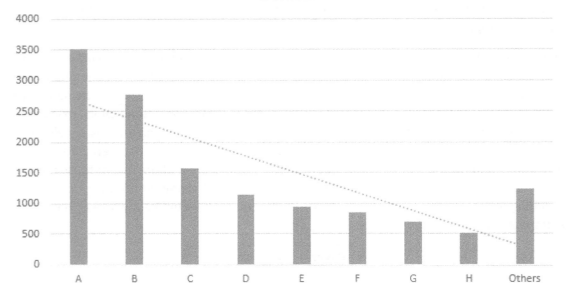

It's easy to see from the graph that the bulk of the problem is with payers A and B; perhaps these companies have shorter timely filing guidelines than the other companies or billing staff is unaware of the proper timely filing requirements for those payers. Six Sigma teams can begin asking questions specific to these payers as they continue analyzing data and discovering root causes.

Box Plots

Box plots are another graphical representation that can be handled with Excel. In later chapters on statistical analysis, we'll cover how box plots can be related to hypothesis testing and other analysis. When differences between distributions are marked, however, or when outliers are fairly obvious within data, the image of a box plot tells its own story without requiring advanced statistical knowledge.

Box plots are often called Box-and-Whisker graphs. To understand how to read a box plot, consider the data table and graph below. The data table shows the time in minutes in which various runners completed a one-mile race. The results are divided into the categories Children and Adults.

Children	Adults
9.9	4.1
10.2	4.1
11.6	4.5
12.7	4.6
13.8	4.7
13.4	7.5
13.4	8.3
13.9	8.9
15.2	9.7
15.8	9.8
15.7	10.1
16.2	11.6
16.7	13.5
18.9	13.7
19.4	14.8
20.1	14.9
29	15

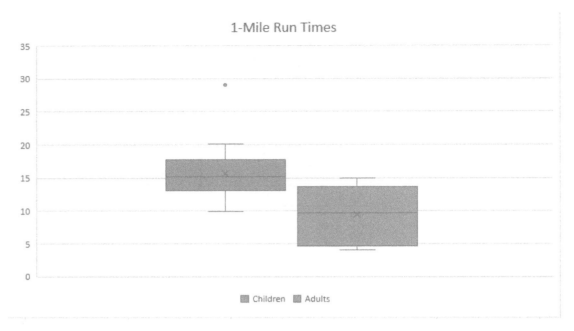

1-Mile Run Times

Children   Adults

The above image shows a box plot of the data table, generated in Excel. Even without further explanation, you can likely tell that the children completed the race on average slower than the adults. The blue box, which represents the children, is shorter than the orange box, indicating that the middle 50 percent of children completed the mile-long run in times that had less variation than that of the middle 50 percent of adults. To understand how this conclusion was arrived at, we'll take a look at all the elements of a box plot.

A box plot begins with the upper and lower hinge – the top and bottom of the box. The top represents the 75th percentile; the bottom represents the 25th percentile of the data. The line within the box represents the 50th percentile. Within the box are the 50 percent of data points between the 25th and 75th percentiles.

Each box plot receives upper and lower whiskers indicating the range of most of the other data within a set. In this case, Excel creates whiskers that extend to the top and bottom of a range barring any statistical outliers. Some statistical analysis software or methodologies use other methods to create the whiskers with very similar results.

Finally, since all plot points must be represented on a box plot graph, outliers are indicated with dots. You'll see a blue dot above the children's box, representing the data point of 29 minutes. That particular point is a statistical outlier; Six Sigma teams who note outliers on box plots should consider the data that is shown as an outlier. If an explanation can be found for the outlier, it can be ignored. For example, if the child who took 29 minutes to complete the mile was much younger than the other children or was walking with an injury, the data point is explained and can be excluded from further analysis.

In addition to calling out outliers, box plots let you compare two distributions graphically to see if, as in the above example, there are obvious differences between the data sets. Box plots are useful in comparing how various attributes impact a process. Six Sigma teams might compare process results for different operators, different times of day, different teams, or using different inputs. It's important when comparing data in this fashion to only alter one attribute or input; otherwise, you won't be able to tell what the cause of any difference between data sets was if a statistical difference does seem likely on a box plot.

Use some information for a work process you are familiar with, or use the sample data provided, to create box plots in Excel following the steps provided below.

A department manager believes that the staff on her teams would be more productive if they were able to work with two computer monitors. Because outfitting an entire department with dual monitors would be costly, the manager's boss requires some proof that her assumption is correct. The manager equips a few stations with dual monitors and lets different team members work at the stations. She records the amount of work done within hourly increments at stations that have dual monitors as well as stations that have single monitors. Her data is featured in the table below.

One Monitor	Two Monitors
9	10
8	4
4	9
7	7
2	8
6	7
1	9
8	9
5	14
4	10
3	12
7	7

9	9
5	4
1	9
5	7
6	8
7	14
4	13
2	10
9	12
5	12
4	8
8	6
2	10

Create a box plot of the information in the manager's data table.

1. Copy the data from the table above into Excel.
2. Highlight all of the data cells, including the header row.
3. Click Insert > Statistic Chart > More Statistical Charts

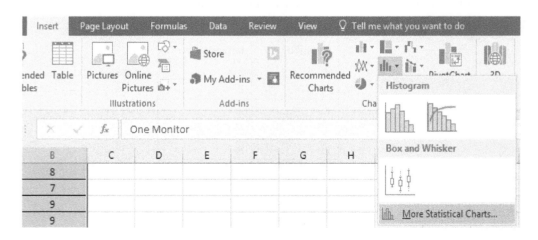

4. Select Box and Whisker and click OK.

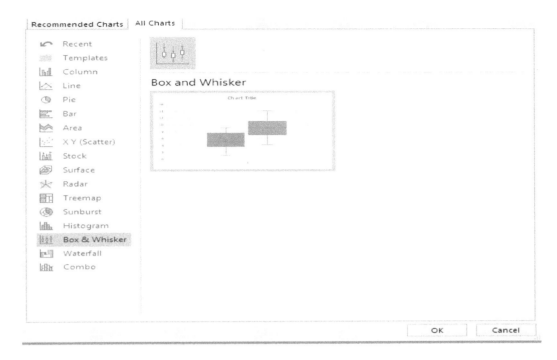

5. Using normal Excel chart editing functions, edit the title and data labels of your chart as desired.

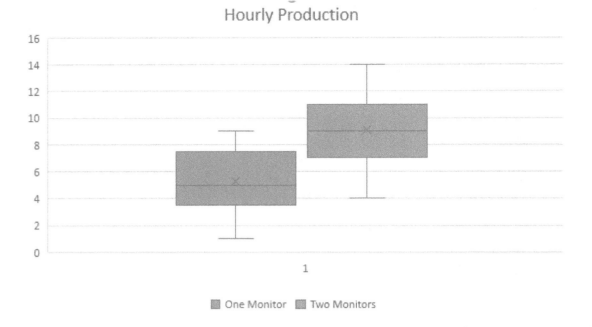

Hourly Production

■ One Monitor ■ Two Monitors

While a Six Sigma Black Belt would be able to back up the conclusion with hypothesis testing or other analytics, the manager might get her request for monitors approved with nothing more than this box plot. It's easy to see that the second monitor *did* increase production capability for staff. Another thing worth noting is that the distributions for each of the boxes and whiskers is similar, which is somewhat expected. High producers are still going to produce the most, and low producers are still going to produce less than high produces, even if everyone is producing slightly more with the new set-up.

Note that the two examples used in this chapter used data sets that were different enough to be visually noticeable on a box plot. This isn't always the case, which is why box plots and other graphical representations are often only the starting point for analysis.

Statistical Analysis

Because statistical analysis is covered in several future units, this section lists some common statistical analysis tools with definitions.

Hypothesis Testing

Hypothesis testing lets Six Sigma experts draw conclusions about the population based on statistical analysis performed on a sample. Because the conclusions are based on samples and not the entire population, there is always some risk of error. You might have seen or heard poll results given with a plus/minus in the result: "60 percent, plus or minus 2 percentage points, would vote for the candidate today." That plus/minus is the value for the error risk.

In statistical analysis, the risk that a sample doesn't offer a good representation of the population is known as the alpha-risk and the beta-risk. Using information about the sample and alpha and beta risks, statisticians calculate what is called the p-value. The p-value is a probability estimate that tells statisticians how likely an assumption or conclusion drawn on sample data will be incorrect.

Statistical software removes a lot of the manual calculations from the process of setting up and running hypothesis tests. With Minitab, for example, Six Sigma experts can conduct hypothesis tests on prepared data with a few mouse clicks. They do have to know which types of hypothesis tests to use in which situations.

Correlation and Regression Analysis

Regression and correlation analysis helps Six Sigma experts understand how variables within a process might be related. Regression analysis helps teams define the relationship between one independent variable – possibly an input – and one dependent variable – possibly an output. Does the temperature in the oven have a relationship to whether the cake is baked correctly, and how close are the two things related? Does the number of hours a person works have an impact on his or her productivity – can the team show a correlation between lower production as employees approach the end of a shift? These are the types of questions that regression analysis can answer.

To work with regression analysis, both of the variables being studied have to be in numerical format. To conduct a regression analysis regarding the relationship between oven temperature and whether a cake is baked correctly, a Six Sigma team baked cakes at varying temperatures and rated them numerically on "doneness." A rating of 1 indicated the cake hardly cooked at all; a rating of 5 indicated a perfectly baked cake. At 10, the cake was completely burned. The temperatures and corresponding ratings are seen in the data table below.

Oven Temperature	Doneness of Cake
200	1
225	1.2
250	2.2
275	2.4
300	4
325	5
350	5.2
375	6.2
400	8
425	8.9
450	9.5
475	10

Using this data, the team creates a scatter diagram with a trend line, as seen below.

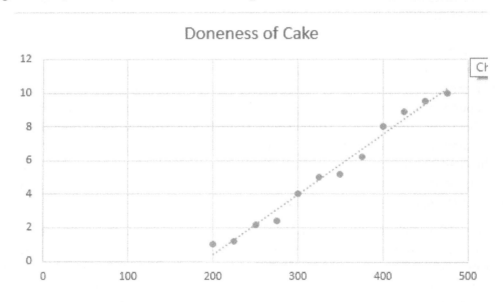

Just looking at this graph, you can tell that a relationship does exist. The data plots are gathered tightly around the trend line, which indicates that as temperature rises so does the doneness of the cake.

Design of Experiments

Correlation and regression analysis doesn't always provide the information a team needs to determine relationships between variables, especially when those relationships are complex, or multiple variables are present. Because the analyze phase sets the stage for the improve phase, teams have to be as certain as possible in their analytical conclusions before they decide on solutions for implementation. A design of experiments can provide the more granular details and analysis required for that level of certainty.

Design of experiments, or DoE, is performed via statistical analysis software such as Minitab. Teams can set up experiments for one factor or multiple factors.

Analyze Tollgate Checklist

- o Primary root causes have been identified.
- o Team has prioritized root causes.
- o Champion or sponsor agrees with team priorities moving into the improve phase.
- o Where possible, root cause assumptions are backed by statistical data.
- o Relationships between variables within a process are understood.
- o Where possible, variable relationships have been confirmed with statistical analysis.

CHAPTER 15:
IMPROVE

During the improve phase of a DMAIC project, Six Sigma teams brainstorm possible solutions for the root causes identified in the analyze phase and rank those solutions according to costs, how effective the solution would be, and how likely the solution could be implemented. Analytical rankings are used to prioritize and select solutions for implementation. Teams pilot solutions through beta tests or small roll outs, collect data on the solution, and verify that the solution is working as expected via statistical analysis. Once the team is confident that the solution works to address the problem, it plans and implements a full rollout of the solution.

Solutions Selection Matrix

A solutions selection matrix is an analytical tool that lets teams propose and rank solutions for any of the root causes identified in the analyze phase. While teams can work simultaneously on multiple solutions if multiple prioritized root causes were found, Black Belt and other team leaders must remain cognizant of timelines, resources, scope, and the purpose of the project. If a single solution provides enough positive impact to reach project goals, then other solutions might be saved for future improvement projects. If one solution would reach results, but another solution would be especially easy to implement and provide additional positive results, the team is likely to decide to implement both.

A solutions selection matrix can be created in Excel, and teams should work on the document together in a brainstorming capacity. It's a good idea to include the entire team as well as relevant subject matter experts and stakeholders during solutions brainstorming. This ensures the solutions the team comes up with are more likely to be a realistic fit for the process and business; once solutions are selected using the matrix, teams will also likely have to get sponsor, champion, or leadership council support before a partial or full implementation is possible. This is especially true where solutions require expenditure or will impact processes and people outside of the project's scope.

An example solutions selection matrix is pictured below.

Problem Statement	Validated Root Cause	Potential Solutions	Practical Method	Effectiveness	Feasibility	Cost-Benefit	Overall	Take action?

The matrix is completed by:

1. Entering the problem statement in the first column. This should be the final problem statement that was arrived at during the measure phase if the team decided that the statement should be altered after gathering data. Otherwise, this can be the problem statement from the define phase.

2. Entering a priority validated root cause from the analyze phase. If the team is going to attempt to solve more than one root cause during the improve phase, it should create a solutions selection matrix for each root cause.

3. Brainstorming potential solutions in column three. During the brainstorming process, teams should not question or attempt to analyze solutions, but should record any solution suggested that seems at all viable. The only solutions that might be ignored are those that are clearly out of scope or impossible, but the Black Belt leading the brainstorming exercise will have to use his or her own discernment about such suggestions.

4. Noting, at a very high level, the practical methods by which a solution could be implemented. In one example used in the analyze chapter, a commercial bakery had a problem that was caused by lack of baking instructions. In this case, the Six Sigma team might propose that staff be provided with proper instructions. The method by which that solution occurs is written documentation and training.

5. Rating solutions. After a list of possible solutions and practical methods is created, the team rates each possibility on effectiveness, feasibility, and cost-benefit. Each category is given a rating between 1 and 10.

    a. Effectiveness is the measure of how well a solution will eliminate a root cause for a problem, with 1 being not effective and 10 being highly effective.

b. Feasibility is the measure of effort required to implement the improvement, with 1 being not feasible because of the effort or resources required and 10 being highly feasible.

c. Cost-benefit is an estimated measure of how the costs of a project compare to the savings expected. This rating is not a formal cost benefit analysis, but is a high-level estimation. If savings are expected to outweigh the costs associated with a project, the team ranks the solution as high. Otherwise, the team ranks the solution low.

6. The scores for effectiveness, feasibility, and cost-benefit are multiplied to calculate an overall score. The overall score can be used to prioritize solutions and select the solution that features the best overall effectiveness, feasibility, and cost-benefit rating.

Consider a possible solutions selection matrix created regarding the medical claims denial example used in the analyze chapter.

Problem Statement	Validated Root Cause	Potential Solutions	Practical Method	Effectiveness	Feasibility	Cost-Benefit	Overall	Take action?
The Florida medical facility is experiencing a high rate of claims denials.	Claims are not being filed in a timely manner due to a need to chase documentation for the claim.	Require reception staff to collect all necessary patient demographics during the office visit.	Program system to require entry of certain data elements during patient check in	5	7	7	245	Yes
		Require patient to sign up for email and portal access to communicate about need for additional information	Require email address as part of the admission procedure	3	1	5	15	No
		Require clinical staff to input all information, including codes, during clinical visit.	Program system to mandate entry of claims components during clinical notes process	7	3	3	63	No
		Create follow-up claims billing team who prioritizes claims that are missing information.	Assign specific follow-up duties to on or more team members and create workflow to manage claims	10	7	7	490	Yes

During the analyze chapter, a Pareto analysis indicated that timely filing issues were a root cause for high claims denials. In the solutions selection matrix above, a team has identified and prioritized four possible solutions after discovering that claims were not filed on time because claims billing staff didn't have all the proper information in time.

The first solution is to require the front desk to collect as much information as possible. The team gave this solution a mid-range rating for effectiveness because it doesn't address the fact that clinical information can still be missing from the claim. But, the process would be effective at gathering demographic information and would not require large expense or effort to implement, so the team rated it high for the other categories.

Next, the team considered creating and requiring a patient email or portal system so billing staff could communicate quickly with patients when information was missing. Because not all patients have email and many would be unlikely to use such a system, the team ranked this solution as low for feasibility and effectiveness.

The third solution considered by the team was requiring clinicians to include all information necessary for billing as they charted during the visit with the patient. The team thought this solution would be fairly effective, but that clinicians would be unlikely to take the time to be so thorough when dealing with patient issues. The solution might also slow physician visits, resulting in a negative impact to revenue.

Finally, the team considered a solution that put certain staff members in charge of claims with missing information. Because those staff members could concentrate on missing claims and would work through a new workflow built by the team, they would be more likely to file claims on time. Overall, the team ranked this solution highest, but they decided to implement both solutions one and four because solution one required so little effort and would actually help drive the success of solution four.

Cost Benefit Analysis

When teams include the appropriate individuals in the process, a solutions selection matrix is very adept at identifying the best possible solutions for implementation. Leadership councils and executive sponsors often want more information about the costs and benefits expected for a solution, though, so teams should be prepared to create a cost benefit analysis. Black Belts often have many of the elements required for such an analysis after the measure and analyze phases, but teams might also need to work with accounting, finance, or business planning departments to gain accurate financial details required.

The goal of a cost benefits analysis is to compare the costs of implementing a solution with the monetary benefits expected from the solution. Costs include expenses such as software development or purchase, equipment purchase, building development or renovation, additional labor or hiring, training expenses, additional supplies, and any losses associated with disruption as the solution is implemented. Benefits might include an increase in product margin, increase in revenue, cost savings or avoidance, and intangible benefits such as increase to staff morale or customer retention.

Six Sigma teams usually aren't in a position to handle detailed cost benefit analysis such as might be completed by a certified accountant, but they can create an idea of cost benefit relationships via the payback method of analysis. This is the simplest way to approach such an analysis and provides leadership with an estimated time before a project "pays off."

Payback, or Pay Off, Analysis

To conduct a payback analysis, Six Sigma teams must have an estimated cost for the project as well as the estimated financial benefit per year. Remember, financial benefits don't just include increases in revenue. Cost savings, new customers, or mitigation of customer loss can all be considered as contributing to benefits each year. The team also needs to understand the estimated operating costs of an improvement for each year.

The formula for this analysis is:

(Cost of implementing solution) / (Annual financial benefits – annual costs)

If a project costs $50,000 to implement and $2,000 per year in extra labor, and the team expects the project to generate $15,000 in financial benefits each year, then the calculation is:

$50,000 / ($15,000 - $2,000)

$50,000/$13,000

Or, approximately 3.84 years until the project pays for itself.

Obviously, organizational leaders are looking for payback calculations that are as short as possible, but if the solution will solve a major problem or set a foundation for extraordinary success in the future, a longer payback time doesn't necessarily keep a solution off the table.

Net Present Value

A more concise way of calculating cost benefits is known as the Net Present Value, or NPV. NPV adjusts benefits and costs as time passes because cash flow in the future is not as valuable as current cash flow due to inflation and other economic factors. The discount rate for various endeavors can be calculated using expected return, interest rates, or inflation rates. Often, corporate finance departments can provide Six Sigma teams with a discount rate used for NPV in the company. A very basic NPV model is shown below.

	This year	First Year	Second Year	Third Year Total
Benefits				
Increased revenue		$10,000	$20,000	$30,000
Cost Savings		$5,000	$10,000	$15,000
Costs				
Capital	-$20,000			-$20,000
Equipment	-$15,000			-$15,000
Training	-$5,000			-$5,000
Labor		-$2,000	-$2,000	-$2,000
Total Benefits – Cost Annual	-$50,000	$13,000	$27,000	$3,000
NPV (Discounted 5 percent)		$12,350	$25,650	**$2,850**

In this model, the team spent $50,000 implementing a solution and expects a $2,000 labor expense associated with the solution each year. The estimated benefits from the solution are recorded for the first two years, and all of the benefits and costs are added up for a third-year view. The NPV is discounted by 5 percent, and the final number is seen in the bottom right cell: $2,850. The goal is a positive NPV, so this project fits that goal.

Piloting a Solution

Once a solution is selected and work done to bring it into production at a minimal level, the Six Sigma team is ready for a pilot. A pilot is a limited trial of a solution in a live environment. No matter how much analysis was completed or how well test cases were run, teams can't know for certain how a solution will behave in the "wild." The live production environment will always have variables that teams can't account for, particularly when people are involved in the process.

Benefits of a limited pilot include:

- Use of resources are limited, which reduces waste if the solution turns out to be incorrect or not effective in resolving the problem
- Confirmation that expected results occur
- Allows troubleshooting of a new solution on a smaller scale to minimize disruption during full transition
- Lets employees outside of the Six Sigma team provide feedback on the solution and implementation to make the final rollout more successful

Teams don't have to pilot every change they make. Simple or small changes can be made without piloting as long as teams document the changes well and measure results for verification. When changes are large in scope, could cause expensive or expansive consequences, or would be difficult to reverse, teams should begin with a pilot. The same is true for any solution that might be expensive to implement at a full scale.

Pilots can occur on a limited scale or for a limited time. Limited scale pilots incorporate a specific region, team, group of people, or machinery. Limited time pilots implement a temporary change; at the end of a scheduled time, the team makes a decision about whether the change should be made permanent.

Pilots can occur with either processes or products. Process pilots might feature testing specific locations, testing results with some customers, working with some employees to test new processes, or conducting dry runs of a process without impact to the end-user.

Product pilots are conducted using test markets, product models, or alpha and beta testing of the product with certain end-users.

To create a pilot, a Six Sigma team must first select the audience for the pilot. Internal process pilots can be performed by a select team or a select few employees. External product pilots can be performed using a subset of customers. For the best pilot results, avoid biasing results by selecting the best possible performers or customers who are most likely to work hard to ensure a product succeeds. When the solution is implemented on a full scale, it will be used by everyone, so you want to ensure it works for everyone.

When possible, pilot at a very small level and then expand the pilot to a larger audience. This is the premise behind alpha and beta testing. A very small set of loyal customers tests the product first, because you know they will provide feedback. Next, an expanded set of customers tests the product after teams have made changes associated with feedback from the first group of users. Finally, if the limited tests are successful, teams choose to roll out the product to the entire audience.

Analyze Pilot and Test Results

Six Sigma experts can use all the tools associated with the analyze phase to test whether solutions have a positive impact during testing or pilot programs. Hypothesis testing can be used to compare data from before the solution to data after the solution, determining if there is a statistically significant and positive change. Graphical analysis can be very helpful in demonstrating for executive leaders how a solution has positively impacted a problem by reducing defects, improving production or efficiency, or reducing costs.

Planning Implementation

Once solutions have been verified through tests and analysis, teams can begin the work of implementing changes on a large scale. Teams should create and work from an action plan during this vital and active stage of the DMAIC process to ensure that no plans or requirements fall through the cracks. During the active part of the improve phase, the project leader will likely delegate numerous activities to members of the team, and the team will also rely on input and assistance from those outside of the Six Sigma team. Keeping an action plan document helps everyone on the team see where they are in the process, what they are responsible for, and what date work must be completed by.

If the Six Sigma team is working with a project manager, he or she is likely responsible for action plan documentation and follow-up. Teams can also use a basic spreadsheet or Word document, which should be saved in a common location, to keep track of what work is to be done and who will do it.

Because every project is unique, improve action plans are also unique. Most action plans will contain common tasks such as documentation, training, and transition.

Documentation

First, the Six Sigma team should have documented all of its work so far during the DMAIC process. If asked, the Black Belt or designated team member should be able to present analysis in the form of data tables, statistical calculations and explanations, and graphical analysis. All brainstorming activities and diagrams should be saved in a central file location where all team members can view them and appropriate team members can edit them as needed. Access to these documents helps team members work efficiently on additional documentation required for implementation.

Almost any organization will require new processes or changes to processes to be recorded in standard operating procedures. Depending on the organizational structure of a business, Six Sigma teams might be responsible for drafting such documents or they might need to work with knowledge management resources to create SOPs in keeping with corporate branding and templates. Teams might also create general communications letting other staff members know about the upcoming changes and the reasons for those changes as well as general reference documents such as cheat sheets and Frequently Asked Questions.

Training

Strong documentation is key to the next part of implementing improvements, which is staff training. Six Sigma teams usually aren't in charge of complete staff training on any improvement they make. Instead, teams begin the training process by working with training subject matter experts or delegates in the department impacted by the upcoming changes. The Six Sigma team trains these individuals, who then go on to train other individuals who will be impacted by the process. At some point, the process training should be integrated into regular organizational training by trainers or knowledge management departments.

Transition

During the improve phase of a DMAIC project, teams should begin to consider the need to transition a process back to the business and traditional process owner. Transition is part of the control phase, but teams should move from improve to control with a good understanding of how the process should be measured and monitored. Strong documentation and training during the improve phase helps cement the success of the control phase.

Improve Tollgate Checklist

- o Solutions were reviewed and prioritized.
- o One or two top solutions were selected for action.
- o Solutions were implemented on a limited basis.
- o Data from limited trials was analyzed and solutions appear to work as expected.
- o Cost-benefits analysis was performed.
- o Sponsor, champion, or executive steering committee signed off on implementing the solution completely.
- o All team members agree the solution should be implemented.
- o The solution is fully documented through SOPs and training materials.
- o Critical staff received training on the solution and are prepared to pass that training on to others.

CHAPTER 16:
CONTROL

The last stage of a DMAIC project is control. During the control phase, teams build monitors that let them ensure the process continues to work successfully after changes are implemented across the regular business process. At the same time, Six Sigma teams work to transition the process back to the process owner.

Up until this point in the DMAIC process, Six Sigma teams have worked with statistical analysis tools, and a Black Belt or other Six Sigma expert has been present to walk team members through analysis and interpretation. While many organizations train process owners and other employees in Six Sigma fundamentals, it isn't always true that a process owner and his or her team will be familiar with the statistical controls that Six Sigma experts have been using. Because of that, appropriate documentation via a control plan and education regarding tools such as control charts might be necessary to ensure business teams can maintain a process and identify when it is out of control and needs remediation.

Revise FMEA

At this time, Six Sigma teams might want to revisit the FMEA tool originally introduced in chapter 13. Six Sigma teams initially use the Failure Modes and Effect Analysis to identify potential failures in a process and causes of those failures. In chapter 13, we discussed how the FMEA listed potential failure points and ranked them according to severity, occurrence, and detection, calculating a total risk priority number.

At the end of the improve phase or beginning of the control phase, Six Sigma teams should revisit the FMEA, noting what recommended actions were completed and recalculating risk priority numbers for the improved process. There are two reasons for revisiting the FMEA. First, the team is able to see that positive and significant changes have occurred because of the solutions adapted during the improve phase. For any root cause that matched a solution implemented, the team would hope to see a smaller risk priority number.

Second, an updated FMEA helps the team identify the next problem or root cause that might be addressed. Remember, Six Sigma is a continuous improvement initiative. The team might have implemented a solution and met an improvement goal, but further

234

improvements can always be made. Control is a time to review the process and suggest possible improvements for future projects.

Create a Control Plan

To facilitate continued success, Six Sigma teams should create a written control plan for the process owner. The purpose of a control plan is to help the process owner and business team track and respond to key performance indicators so that the process remains improved. The control plan should be a concise, easy-to-reference document that tells the business team when to monitor, how to monitor, what range of data is acceptable to the monitor, and how to respond with corrective action if the range measured is not acceptable.

Control plans can be spreadsheets, specialized digital documents, or hard-copy documents posted at a work station. Common elements of a control plan include:

- Company, division, or department name
- Name of person who created the plan
- Date the plan was created
- Name of the person who last edited the plan
- Date the plan was last edited
- Project and/or process name or identifier
- Process owner
- List of process steps where control action is required
- CTQ or metric associated with each action required
- Limit specifications, or the acceptable range of measurements
- The unit of measurement
- The method of measurement
- The necessary sample size
- The frequency of measurement
- The person responsible for measurement
- Where the information is recorded
- Correction actions
- Associated policy and procedure documents

In discussing quality in chapter 8, we introduced the example of a company that makes chocolate bars and noted that the amount of sugar in the chocolate bar recipe was critical to the customer's experience with the end product. If a Six Sigma team were tasked with improving customer satisfaction with a new chocolate bar product, they might have implemented a solution that ensures the proper amount of sugar is added to the mixture at the right temperature to incorporate the ingredient appropriately.

A control plan for the new chocolate bar solution might look something like the document below.

Company: XYZ Sweets	**Control Plan Created by:** Joe Black Belt	
Process: Sugar addition, raw goods mixture	**Control Plan Created on:** Jan. 4, 2012	
Process Owner: Sue Processor		
Process Step	Addition of sugar to batch	Heating of batch
CTQ/Metric	Total amount added to batch	Mean temperature during mixing
Limit specification	LSL: 4.90 cups USL: 5.10 cups	LSL: 105 F USL: 110 F
Unit of measurement	Cups	Degrees F
Method of measurement	6-cup sugar test bowl	Read integrated digital thermometer on mixing machine
Sample Size	One batch	3 reading, 2 minutes apart, during mixing
Frequency	Every 2 hours	Every 2 hours
Employee	Mixer operator	Mixer Operator
Record data in	Mix operation log spreadsheet	Mix operation log spreadsheet

Corrective action	Manually measure correct amount for current batch to allow for processing, calibrate sugar disbursement machine following SOP 100.54, test sugar disbursement for first batch after calibration to ensure problem is resolved. Report issue to supervisor.	Turn off machine, waste inappropriately heated batch, and report temperature calibration issue to maintenance.

The above example control plan provides instructions for two specific steps in the process with easy-to-understand measurement and monitor requirements. To reduce the chance of errors, the Six Sigma team has even specified a special measuring tool for measuring the sugar in the test batch so that every operator performing the monitor measures using the same tool.

At the end of the control document, the team provides steps for corrective action. The first step can be corrected by the operator, who has the ability to calibrate the machine him or herself. The temperature calibration in this case can't be performed by the operator, which means the process has to be stopped so that someone can attend to the issue. Note that it is always preferable, when possible, to build corrective action at the process level, such as was done with the sugar measurement. This minimizes downtime, puts employees more in control of the processes they own, and helps employees stay involved with the quality process.

The control plan above assumes that manual measurements must be taken or recorded. Optimally, Six Sigma teams should look for ways to automate measurements, which means data can be continuously gathered and converted into statistical process controls such as control charts. Automated data gathering doesn't mean a control plan isn't necessary, it just means that a control plan won't include instructions for gathering the data. Instead, employees and process owners can be instructed to review automated data or control charts and take action if necessary.

You'll also note that the specification requirements given above are provided with LSL and USL. LSL is the lower specification limit and the USL is the upper specification limit. These are the upper and lower limits of the acceptable range.

Visual Management

In addition to providing a control plan, Six Sigma teams can implement specific visual controls in a workplace to help business teams maintain a controlled process. Some of these tools were covered in chapter 4 on Lean process management, including 5S. Other visual controls teams might implement include signs, posted matrixes and instructions, auditing boards that let teams keep track of individual or group performance over time, color coding, and safety signals.

Standard operating procedures can often be distilled to visual representations on posters. A coffee shop, for example, might provide employees with a visual representation of what ingredients are used to create various complex drink flavors. Such a poster ensures that employees can prepare drinks quickly while reducing errors in ingredient inclusion.

Other SOP visualizations might include safety procedures in a medical environment, such as visual reminders for hand washing and short pictorial representations for how to operate equipment such as hospital beds. In an office environment, pictorial instructions are found on copy machines, where pictures indicate how paper should be loaded and visual gifs are often displayed on LED screens to help employees remove jammed paper. These are some examples that Six Sigma teams can follow when creating documents that will help business staff accept ownership of an improved process and maintain the improvements made.

SPC Charts

One of the most common methods Six Sigma teams use to monitor a process is the control chart. A number of types of control charts exist, and Six Sigma experts must choose the right control chart for the type of data and analytical purpose.

Now, we'll cover the visual tests that let a Six Sigma team or process owner know that a process is out of control.

A basic control chart has the following elements:

- A line chart of data with plot points for specific data points
- An x-bar line representing the average of the data points

- Lines above and below the x-bar line representing 1, 2, and 3 standard deviations from the median in either direction
- An upper control limit (UCL) line at 3 standard deviations above the median
- A lower control limit (LCL) line at 3 standard deviations below the median

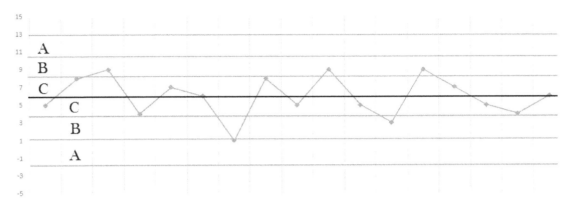

Above is an example of a control chart. The middle line, which is black, is the x-bar line. The x-bar line is bounded by green lines on both sides, indicating 1 and 2 standard deviations away from the mid-line. Those lines are bounded by orange lines on either side: at the top, the upper control limit, and on bottom, the lower control limit. Between the various lines are areas of the control chart, designated as C, B, and A going in either direction. These distinct areas are important for understanding if a process might be out of control. They are also called Zones 1, 2, and 3.

A control chart is best displayed using an automated reporting system or dashboard, where process owners or responsible employees can view it as needed. If automated data collection and control charting is not possible, then a business analyst can be tasked with collecting data and presenting it in this format periodically, though periodic graphical analysis is less likely to catch a problem of control within a process.

Statistical Process Control Tests: Control Charts

Eight tests exist that can quickly tell someone viewing a control chart if a process is out of control.

- **Test one:** A single point on the control chart appears outside of the upper or lower control limits. If this occurs, process owners should take immediate action, because it is evidence of a major problem within a process. While there is a very remote possibility that shifts outside of three standard deviations can occur randomly, the likelihood is only 3 in 1,000.

- **Test two:** Nine points in a row appear on one side of the center line. This indicates that a change occurred in the process; if the process owner knows what change caused the shift and it was intentional change, nothing needs to be done and the control chart will right itself over time with the new data. Otherwise, the process owner should investigate the process.
- **Test three:** Six points on the control chart increase or decrease in a row, indicating the process is becoming less or more efficient or is generating fewer or more errors. Process owners should investigate unless there is a known reason for the trend.
- **Test four:** Fourteen points on the control chart in a row alternate moving up and down. This could indicate variation in machines, employees, shifts, or over correction.
- **Test five:** Two out of three points in a row on the control chart are in the upper A section or in the lower A section. This might indicate some type of special cause creating sudden high variation.
- **Test six:** Four out of five points in a row on the control chart are located in the upper B section (or beyond) or the lower B section (or beyond). This can indicate a problem of major causation or a shift problem similar to that of test four.
- **Test seven:** Fifteen points in a row are located within the C section above or below the centerline. This can indicate that control limits are no longer relevant to the process; if a team has improved variation of a process, they should recalculate control limits to new parameters. Alternatively, this might occur temporarily when short-term variation is high or low relative to the rest of the points on a control chart.
- **Test eight:** Eight points in a row on the control chart are located on either side of the center line, but none are located in the C section above or below the line. This could indicate an issue of mixed resources or processes; a team might think they are measuring a single process when they are actually measuring two process, for example. Alternatively, it could indicate a major difference in processing for two employees or teams.

When it's possible to create control charts and display current data on a regular basis, these charts make a good addition to a control plan. Individuals don't have to be well-versed in

SIX SIGMA: A COMPLETE STEP-BY-STEP GUIDE

statistical process control to learn about the eight tests, and business teams with the benefit of control charts can spend more time working on production or correcting issues and less time collecting and documenting measurements.

Control Versus Capability

It's important to note the distinction between a controlled process and one that is capable of meeting customer requirements. We touched on this concept in unit 1: controlled processes don't have a lot of variation. Capable processes don't have a lot of variation *and* the outputs center around a customer requirement. This is why both control limits and specification limits are important.

Consider the example used earlier in this chapter about sugar in the chocolate mix. The specification limits ranged from 4.9 to 5.1 cups of sugar in each batch. It's possible for a control chart to show that the process is in control if the measurements range from 3.5 to 3.6 cups of sugar per batch, but the process owner should know that those measurements aren't going to contribute to a product that meets critical to customer quality requirements.

To understand how a process is performing against specification limits, Six Sigma teams can calculate sigma level and process capability.

Sigma Level

Sigma level is the number of standard deviations between the current process center, as measured by the median, and the nearest specification limit (not control limit.) The equation for sigma level is the smaller of the following calculations:

$$\frac{USL - \bar{x}}{\sigma} \quad or \quad \frac{LSL - \bar{x}}{\sigma}$$

For example, if a process has an USL of 5 and a LSL of 3, a standard deviation of .25 and a median of 4.2, then you would calculate from the USL, since the median is closer to the USL.

$$\frac{5 - 4.2}{.25} = 3.2 = \text{sigma level}$$

Process Capability

Process capability is calculated by dividing the sigma level by 3. In the case of the example, the capability is 1.06.

Process capability is denoted as C_{pk}. A process capability of 1.33 is equal to a sigma level of 4, which is what most experts agree is the minimal level at which most customers will be satisfied. Under statistical process control, many organizations aim for a process capability of 2.0 with minimal acceptable process capability at 1.5.

Team Celebration and Reflection

When Six Sigma teams deem improvements and the related process to be capable and in control, and they've passed those processes back to business and process owner control, they should take time to celebrate and reflect on the outcome of the project. This is usually done following the final tollgate review with a sponsor or champion, and can be a quick meeting to close loose ends, recognize the work done by the team, and discuss lessons learned within the process.

The celebration and reflection meeting is also a great time for team members to bring up ideas for possible improvement projects. While improvements – and the related problems and causes – are still fresh on the team's minds, they can effectively brainstorm ideas for next steps. As with any brainstorming session, no idea should be automatically held off the table because it seems silly, would be too hard to implement, is too costly, or seems too big. Not all of the ideas will become future projects, but the team's input provides valuable information that the Black Belt can later share with Six Sigma leadership panels.

Control Tollgate Checklist

- The team has calculated the performance and capability of the new process
- The team has written a control plan and communicated it to the process owner
- The team has created a monitor for the process, either through procedures for manual data collection or automated generation of control charts
- The team has provided the process owner and business team with all tools and information required to maintain improvements
- The sponsor, champion, or executive leadership has been informed about the state of the improvements
- The team met to reflect on the project and generate a list of ideas for future improvements

UNIT 4:
BEGINNER STATISTICS

CHAPTER 17:
INTERMEDIATE GRAPHICAL ANALYSIS

Graphical analysis is a critical part of the Six Sigma approach. Whenever data or ideas can be displayed in a visual format, obvious data trends can be quickly identified and communicated. Visual analysis is extremely helpful when presenting ideas to auxiliary staff or executives, who might not be trained in intermediate or advanced statistics. The Black Belt or other Six Sigma experts have the ability to tell the same story that statistics tell, but in a format that can be understood by anyone. Visual depictions are tools that make it easier for Six Sigma professionals or sponsors to retell the story to others, which can be helpful for training, building cultural buy-in for a process change, or even resource requests.

Throughout the first three units of this book, we've discussed a number of graphical analysis tools, including:

- Pareto charts in chapters 5 and 14
- Run charts in chapter 13
- Box plots in chapter 14
- Introduction to control charts in chapter 16
- Introduction to scatter diagrams in chapter 14

In this chapter, we'll discuss additional graphical analysis tools, including bar charts and pie charts. We'll also look again at scatter diagrams and how to create them in Excel. In Chapter 16, you learned about the components of an X-bar control chart and how to tell if a control chart indicates a process might be out of control. In this chapter, we'll walk through the steps for manually creating an X-bar control chart in Excel. Finally, you'll learn how to install a data analysis add-in for various versions of Excel. The add-in provides functionality that will become relevant in the next few chapters.

Additional Graphical Analysis Tools

As with many other areas of the Six Sigma methodology, it can be easy to go overboard when dealing with graphical analysis – particularly when presenting information to others. With so many tools at your disposal, it's tempting to pick the graph that is new, exciting, or more complex. Often, though, that means spending non-value added time creating one visual tool when an easier tool would do the job. If you recall from chapter 4, this would be an instance of over-processing to avoid.

Consider the two charts below to understand when over-processing might be occurring with regard to graphical analysis.

Both charts are a graphical representation of the same information. The first is a simple bar chart that was created within a few clicks in Excel. The second is a Pareto chart, also created in Excel but requiring many more clicks of the mouse. In this particular case, a Pareto chart is not necessary to convey the required information. The data is diverse enough that anyone can see from looking at the bar chart that sales person E accounts for a lot of the errors. In this particular case, a Pareto chart is overselling the conclusion and doesn't need to be created if extra work is required.

In this example, it's possible that a visual portrayal of the data isn't required at all: the conclusion is obvious. Looking at the raw data below, you can quickly see that employee E has triple the errors as the next-highest employee. Even when the raw data provides for easy analysis, however, many Six Sigma experts do take the time to create a graphical representation for the purpose of presentations. A graph is more visually appealing and quicker to read than a data table.

Employee	Sales Errors
A	10
B	5
C	2
D	9
E	34
F	7
G	3

The simplest graphical analysis isn't always the best choice, especially when data elements are not so obvious to note. More complex analysis might be required to discover outliers, relationships, and trends. Even when conclusions about data seem obvious, they aren't always correct. This is especially true when dealing with the relationship or correlation between factors in a process.

As a Six Sigma expert, it takes time to be able to quickly choose which type of graphical analysis will best represent the data at hand. It's also important to note that the best choice for graphical analysis relies equally on the questions being asked as much as it does on the data itself. In the example above, the basic bar chart is a good choice for a team that wants to know where errors might be coming from. If the team was comparing errors to shift times being worked, the bar chart would not be helpful.

While it's true that you don't want to waste time and space presenting data in a way that is not helpful – or could be considered muda of over-production – the same isn't always true when dealing with analysis. At the analysis stage of a DMAIC project, Black Belts and other Six Sigma experts often work with numerous graphical analysis tools as they attempt to understand data. The need to view data in various ways is one reason statistical analysis software is helpful: such software takes some of the manual work out of creating these charts and graphs. Trial-and-error work with all types of Six Sigma analysis tools also helps you learn to identify which tools fit each situation best.

In this section, we'll discuss some tools that haven't been introduced so far, covering benefits, limitations, and how to create the tools in Excel without statistical analysis software when necessary.

Bar Charts

One of the biggest benefits of bar charts is that they are recognizable and easy to read. Almost any employee in a company can glean information from a properly formatted bar chart without instruction or guidance, making them a great choice for general use presentations and training materials. Bar charts are also easy to create, so they are a preferred method of illustration in presentations and reports. Other benefits include:

- The ability to summarize large data sets in a simple visual format
- The ability to clarify trends
- The fact that most people can easily estimate important values on a well-formatted bar chart
- The ability to visually check data and identify areas where data might be skewed
- The ability to easily display data sets that range above and below zero on the same chart

Bar charts typically require nominal or ordinal data – data that is classified according to qualitative information. When displaying nominal data, it's often beneficial to create a Pareto-style chart so the reader can see instantly how the population relates to the categories. Ordinal data usually involves its own logical order for presentation. For example, if individuals are asked to rank satisfaction with a product as very satisfied, somewhat satisfied, neutral, unsatisfied, and very unsatisfied, then you usually would not want to change the order of that presentation on a bar chart.

Bar charts are not without limitations. Depending on what is being presented, additional narrative might be required to explain the chart. Bar charts also often fail to reveal key information about trends that aren't part of the specific design of the chart, and they rarely on their own provide detailed data about causes or patterns in data. Finally, it's easy to manipulate colors, order, and layout of a bar chart to influence the message that your audience takes away. Six Sigma experts should always choose the best format for displaying fundamental truths, but should never format a chart to create an impression that might not be in keeping with the statistical data behind the graphical representation.

Create a Bar Chart in Excel

Create your own bar charts in Excel by starting with data tables of relevant nominal or ordinal data. Copy the data table below into Excel to practice bar chart creation, or use data relevant to your own processes or projects. The sample data table provides the total number of phone calls experienced by a regional customer service call-center team for each hour in a particular day.

Hour	Phone calls
8:00 AM	78
9:00 AM	89
10:00 AM	107
11:00 AM	118
12:00 PM	149
1:00 PM	147
2:00 PM	105
3:00 PM	90
4:00 PM	97
5:00 PM	85
6:00 PM	178
7:00 PM	198
8:00 PM	145
9:00 PM	57

1. Highlight the columns that contain the data you want to chart as well as the labels for that data. In this case, the data is the number of calls and the labels are the hours.

	A	B
1	Hour	Phone calls
2	8:00 AM	78
3	9:00 AM	89
4	10:00 AM	107
5	11:00 AM	118
6	12:00 PM	149
7	1:00 PM	147
8	2:00 PM	105
9	3:00 PM	90
10	4:00 PM	97
11	5:00 PM	85
12	6:00 PM	178
13	7:00 PM	198
14	8:00 PM	145
15	9:00 PM	57

2. Select Insert > Chart > Bar Chart

3. For this example, the simplest form of bar chart is appropriate.
4. Use Excel formatting tools as desired to customize the chart title, colors, and labels.

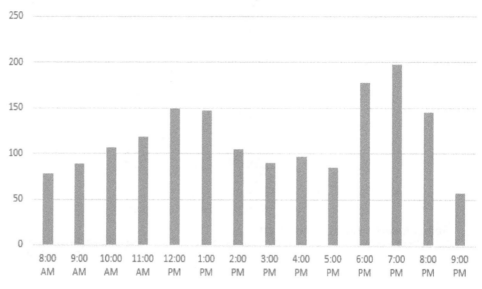

Most versions of Excel offer several types of bar charts, and you can experiment with these various formats to see how they display your data. Some notes about common formats are included below.

Column versus Bar

Technically, what is commonly referred to as a bar chart – and what we've been calling a bar chart here – is a column chart. The visual columns representing each data category rise vertically. A literal bar chart displays the same information horizontally. Most versions of Excel let you choose between the two displays. The information from the example data table is presented below in a horizontal bar chart.

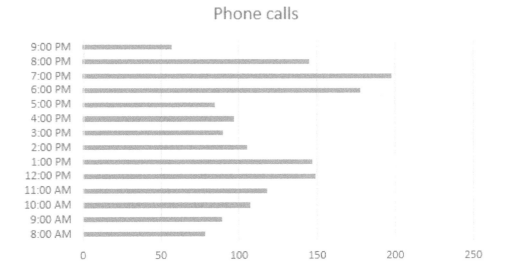

3-D Bar and Column Charts

The charts displayed so far in this chapter are all 2-dimensional. Excel can also help you create 3-dimensional charts to add visual appeal to a presentation. 3-D charts are helpful if you are presenting a number of similar-looking charts in a row, as it helps to differentiate between information in your presentation. It might also be helpful to create more visually appealing charts simply to capture audience attention more fully. Here's an example of the same data used above in a 3-D chart.

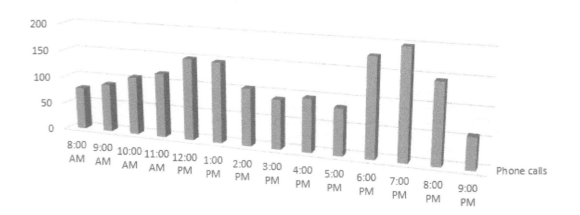

Stacked Bar Charts

Stacked bar charts let you display the total nominal or ordinal data for each category while also breaking that information into color coded categories. For example, if the Six Sigma team analyzing phone calls per hour wanted to display data that included how many calls were handled by separate teams within a department, the bar chart might look something like the image below.

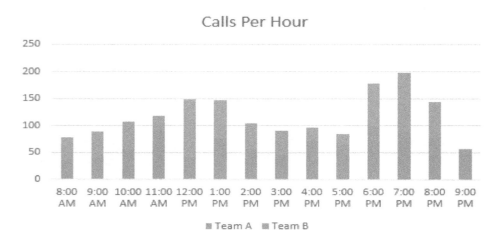

Create a Stacked Bar Chart

To create a stacked bar chart, you must have ordinal or nominal data that is broken into categories. The categories must be the same for each data set so that the total of the sub-category numbers equals the total of the main category. For example, if you have three bags of marbles, you might have data that says:

Bag	Number of marbles
1	10
2	3
3	15

Upon further analysis, you realize you have marbles in three colors: red, blue, and yellow.

	Bag 1	Bag 2	Bag 3
Red	7	1	5
Yellow	3	1	8
Blue	0	1	2

Bag 1 doesn't include any blue marbles, but you must include blue as a category for Bag 1 because it is a category in the other two bags. You simply put a 0 in that data field. You'll note that the totals of the subcategories under each bag add up to the amount of marbles in each bag. Following these guidelines – including all subcategories for each section *and* ensuring the subcategories total correctly – helps you create accurate stacked bar charts.

Examine the data table below, which displays the breakdown of calls by teams in the call center.

Hour	Phone calls	Team A	Team B
8:00 AM	78	35	43
9:00 AM	89	40	49
10:00 AM	107	57	50
11:00 AM	118	90	28
12:00 PM	149	42	107
1:00 PM	147	77	70
2:00 PM	105	57	48
3:00 PM	90	45	45
4:00 PM	97	72	25
5:00 PM	85	64	21
6:00 PM	178	98	80
7:00 PM	198	89	109
8:00 PM	145	77	68
9:00 PM	57	54	3

1. Highlight the cells containing the data you want to include in your stacked bar chart as well as the cells containing the data labels.

Hour	Phone calls	Team A	Team B
8:00 AM	78	35	43
9:00 AM	89	40	49
10:00 AM	107	57	50
11:00 AM	118	90	28
12:00 PM	149	42	107
1:00 PM	147	77	70
2:00 PM	105	57	48
3:00 PM	90	45	45
4:00 PM	97	72	25
5:00 PM	85	64	21
6:00 PM	178	98	80
7:00 PM	198	89	109
8:00 PM	145	77	68
9:00 PM	57	54	3

2. Select Insert > Charts > Bar Charts > Stacked Bar Chart

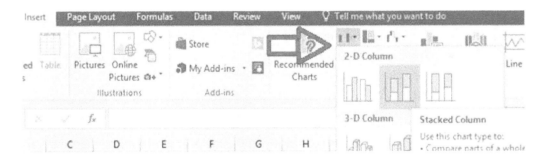

3. Use Excel's format options to edit titles, colors, and data labels as desired.

Pie Charts

The pie chart is another visual tool that almost any employee in a business environment will be familiar with, making it a good choice for displaying certain types of information. Ordinal and nominal information can also be displayed in a pie chart with the main purpose of visually representing how each category relates to the whole. Conventional wisdom says to use a pie chart when the numbers you are charting add up to 100, but this doesn't have to be the case. Excel converts values to percentages to create pie charts. Consider the pie chart below, which graphs the numbers 8, 5, and 4. Excel considers each of these numbers against the total "pie" of 17. The blue section, which represents 47%, corresponds to the raw data 8/17.

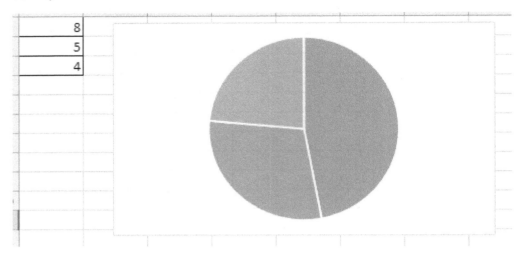

Benefits of pie charts include:

- The ability to summarize large amounts of specific data types in a visual format.
- Simplicity; the pie chart is one of the simplest types of graphs
- The ability to identify obvious problems with data or calculations
- Pie charts usually require very little extra explanation when labeled correctly
- Pie charts display the relevance of subset data within a total data set

The fact that pie charts are used constantly in business environments is both an advantage and disadvantage for Six Sigma teams and experts. When data can be depicted in a pie chart, the Six Sigma expert usually has to create less narrative to get a potential point across. At the same time, pie charts don't always carry the weight that a more advanced statistical representation might because business employees are so used to seeing them. Other disadvantages of pie charts include the fact that they can be manipulated in much the same way as bar charts, they usually fail to easily display changes over time, and it can be difficult to visualize exact values when presented with a pie chart.

Create a Pie Chart in Excel

Practice creating a pie chart in Excel using the following data table, which records how many minutes are spent on average for each step of a process. You can also use data relevant to your own process or project to create a practice pie chart if desired.

Process Step	Minutes
A	14
B	18
C	41
D	64
E	12
F	4
G	3
H	7
I	23
J	18

1. Highlight the column of data you want to chart as well as the data labels. In the example, we are charting the number of minutes and the process numbers are the data labels.

Process Step	Minutes
1	14
2	18
3	41
4	64
5	12
6	4
7	3
8	7
9	23
10	18

2. Click Insert > Chart > Pie Chart

257

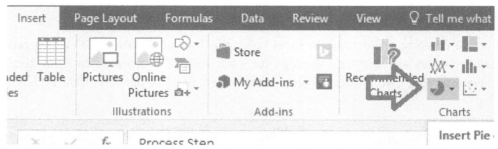

3. Use Excel's formatting tools to make changes to color, title, and labels as desired.

Minutes

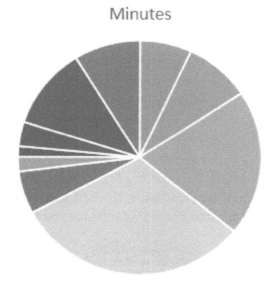

From the pie chart created for our sample data, we can see that approximately half of the total process time is related to only two steps in the 10-step process. We can also quickly see which steps take the longest on average and which are the shortest, although we can't draw any conclusions about actual time from only this chart.

As with bar charts, you can take advantage of Excel options for creating three-dimensional pie charts. A particularly helpful function is the Pie of Pie function in Excel, which lets you create an overall pie chart and carve out a second pie chart to delve deeper into certain areas of the larger structure. Consider a Pie of Pie chart below, which represents the same data from the pie chart above.

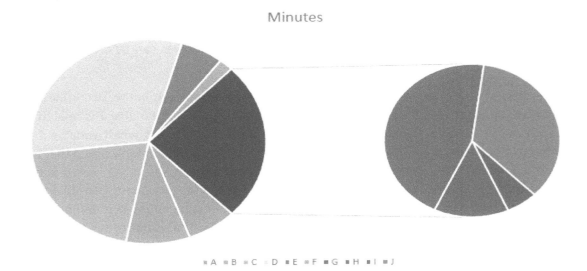

Minutes

■ A ■ B ■ C ■ D ■ E ■ F ■ G ■ H ■ I ■ J

The original pie chart depicted 10 steps. The illustration above shows a large pie chart with a secondary chart. The large pie chart appears to show 7 steps – but this pie chart shows the same information as the one above. However, four steps from the process are called out in a smaller chart so you can see how they relate to each other better. Those four steps combined make up the 7th, dark-blue pie piece in the larger pie. This makes it easier to pinpoint relevance of smaller data categories within the whole or to emphasize a certain area of the chart.

You do have to be careful, however, that the viewer doesn't assign relevance or importance based solely on the size of the pie pieces. The gray pie piece in the secondary chart above is bigger than some of the other pieces in the larger pie, but that doesn't mean that step takes longer. The smaller pie should be considered a large-scale view of a small piece of the overall graph. In this case, that small piece takes into account four of the steps.

X Y Scatter Diagrams

We introduced scatter diagrams very briefly in chapter 14, and we'll revisit them in depth in later chapters on correlation and regression modeling. In this section, we'll cover how to create a scatter diagram in Excel with any analysis add-on. In chapter 19, we'll use an add-on for Excel to conduct some statistical analysis while creating scatter diagrams.

Scatter diagrams are beneficial because they can help teams visually see the relationship between two factors in a process. Does temperature decrease over time? Does a person's productivity increase with his or her salary? These are examples of questions that might be answered by scatter diagrams, but it's important to realize that correlation as depicted on a scatter diagram doesn't necessarily mean causation. Two variables can be closely related without one causing changes in the other.

Scatter diagrams typically help teams see whether there is no correlation, weak correlation, or positive or negative correlation. Positive correlation occurs when variable 2 is related to an increase in variable 1, or vice versa. Negative correlation occurs when variable 2 is related to a decrease in variable 1, or vice versa. For example, it is commonly noted that the rate of crime and the average per-capita income of geographic areas in the United States are related. Areas that demonstrate higher crime rates often also demonstrate lower income statistics. The statement can be made the other direction: areas that demonstrate lower income statistics often demonstrate higher crime rates. That is not to say that either of these things necessarily causes the other.

Drawbacks of scatter diagrams are that they are not as familiar to business employees as bar, pie, or even line charts. There is also a risk that individuals who don't have an understanding of statistical analysis will mistake correlation for causation, which can lead to incorrect decisions. Black Belts and other Six Sigma experts must be cognizant of these risks so they can appropriately explain scatter diagrams and provide further explanation when necessary.

Create a Scatter Diagram in Excel

Use the data table below, which includes the average number of errors per hour a process creates as output is increased per hour to create a scatter diagram in Excel. Copy the information from the table below into Excel, or use data from your own process or project if desired.

Parts Per Hour	Defects
100	3
150	4
200	5
250	5
300	7
350	7
400	9
450	8

500	10

1. Highlight the data you want to chart. To create a scatter diagram, you will need to highlight two sets of data that you want to compare.

Parts Per Hour	Defects
100	3
150	4
200	5
250	5
300	7
350	7
400	9
450	8
500	10

1. Select Insert > Chart > Scatter

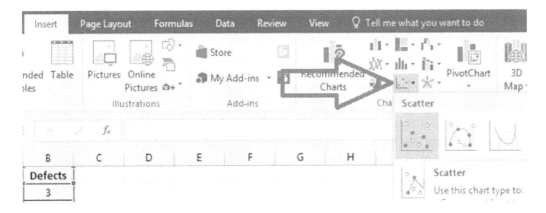

2. Use Excel's formatting functions to edit colors, titles, and labels as desired.

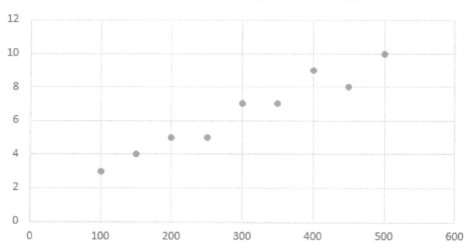

Defects as Production Increases

From the scatter diagram created, we can see that the two variables – production volume and errors – appear to be related in some manner. While it's a good bet that increased production actually *causes* increased errors, you can't simply assume causation from this graph. This assumption could be further tested using more advanced statistical techniques.

It should be noted that, even when correlation seems obvious on a scatter diagram, it isn't always the case. Six Sigma experts should always test correlation assumptions to ensure they are correct statistically before presenting a scatter diagram to others as an illustration of a relationship. We'll cover statistical regression and correlation tests in chapter 19.

Creating an X-Bar Control Chart without Statistical Software

The X-bar control chart plots the mean of a sample over time – or the mean of samples taken over time, in the case of an active process. X-bar control charts are one of the most frequently used control charts. Some control charts can also be created in Excel using these steps; more advanced control charts require statistical analysis software.

1. Create the following template in an empty Excel spreadsheet.

	A	B	C	D	E	F	G
1	X-Bar Data Points	UCL	LCL	Mean		Standard Deviation:	
2						Upper Control Limit (UCL)	
3						Lower Control Limit (LCL)	
4							
5						Process Mean	
6							
7							
8							
9							
10							
11							
12							
13							
14							
15							
16							

2. Enter your data points in column A.
3. In cell G1, enter the formula =STDEV(A2:A15)
   a. The cell references A2:A15 should be edited to correspond to your actual data list.
   b. This calculates the standard deviation of your data set.
4. In cell G5, enter the formula =AVERAGE(A2:A15)
   a. The cell references A2:A15 should be edited to correspond to your actual data list.
   b. This calculates the mean of your data set.
5. In cell G2, enter the formula: =G5+3*(G1)
   a. This calculates an upper control limit that is three standard deviations above the mean.
6. In cell G3, enter the formula: =G5-3*(G1)
   a. This calculates a lower control limit that is three standard deviations below the mean.
7. In the UCL column (B), direct Excel to create a column of numbers where every number is equal to the upper control limit by copying =$G$2 into each cell in a row that has an X-bar data point in column A.
8. In the LCL column (C), direct Excel to create a column of numbers where every number is equal to the lower control limit by copying =$G$3 into each cell in a row that has an X-bar data point in column A.

9. In the Mean column, direct Excel to create a column of numbers where every number is equal to the mean by copying =$G$5 into each cell in a row that has an X-bar data point in column A.

(Practice steps 1 through 9 with the following data.)

X-Bar Data Points
24.1
25.2
24.7
28.3
27.1
26.4
25.4
21.4
24.5
23.5
27.5
29.5
24.5
26.8

The result should be a spreadsheet that looks just like the one below.

	A	B	C	D	E	F	G
1	X-Bar Data Points	UCL	LCL	Mean		Standard Deviation:	2.115003962
2	24.1	31.98073	19.2907	25.63571		Upper Control Limit (UCL)	31.98072617
3	25.2	31.98073	19.2907	25.63571		Lower Control Limit (LCL)	19.2907024
4	24.7	31.98073	19.2907	25.63571			
5	28.3	31.98073	19.2907	25.63571		Process Mean	25.63571429
6	27.1	31.98073	19.2907	25.63571			
7	26.4	31.98073	19.2907	25.63571			
8	25.4	31.98073	19.2907	25.63571			
9	21.4	31.98073	19.2907	25.63571			
10	24.5	31.98073	19.2907	25.63571			
11	23.5	31.98073	19.2907	25.63571			
12	27.5	31.98073	19.2907	25.63571			
13	29.5	31.98073	19.2907	25.63571			
14	24.5	31.98073	19.2907	25.63571			
15	26.8	31.98073	19.2907	25.63571			
16							

10. Create a control chart by highlighting the data in columns A through D.

	A	B	C	D
1	X-Bar Data Points	UCL	LCL	Mean
2	24.1	31.98073	19.2907	25.63571
3	25.2	31.98073	19.2907	25.63571
4	24.7	31.98073	19.2907	25.63571
5	28.3	31.98073	19.2907	25.63571
6	27.1	31.98073	19.2907	25.63571
7	26.4	31.98073	19.2907	25.63571
8	25.4	31.98073	19.2907	25.63571
9	21.4	31.98073	19.2907	25.63571
10	24.5	31.98073	19.2907	25.63571
11	23.5	31.98073	19.2907	25.63571
12	27.5	31.98073	19.2907	25.63571
13	29.5	31.98073	19.2907	25.63571
14	24.5	31.98073	19.2907	25.63571
15	26.8	31.98073	19.2907	25.63571
16				
17				

11. Select Insert > Charts > Line Chart > 2-D Line Chart with Markers

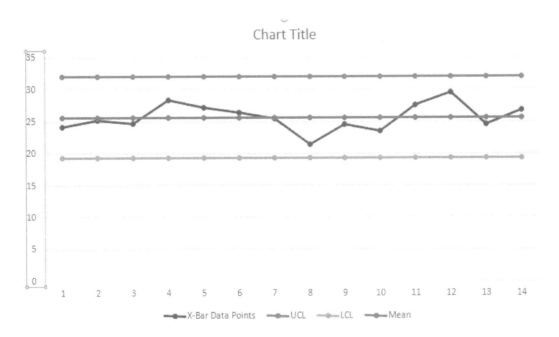

12. Right click on the data labels for the Y axis and select "Format Axis."

13. Alter the bounds for the axis to remove excess white space in your control chart. In this case, we'll change bounds from 0 to 35 to 15 to 35.

14. Format the chart as desired for color, titles, and data labels. You now have a very basic control chart.

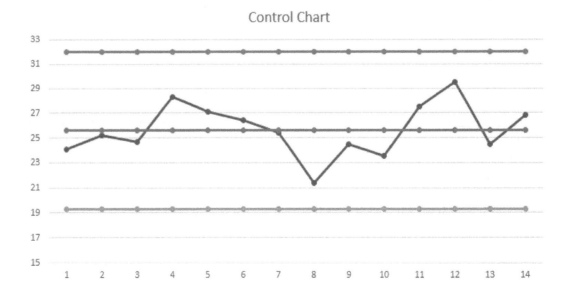

One thing you'll note missing from this control chart is the lines that denote one and two standard deviations above and below the mean. In chapter 16, you learned that those lines help you apply the tests that determine if a process is in control or not. You can easily add those lines by following the steps below.

Add Standard Deviation Lines

1. Add calculations to your spreadsheet for:
   a. The mean plus one standard deviation
   b. The mean plus two standard deviations
   c. The mean minus one standard deviation
   d. The mean minus two standard deviations
2. Add four data columns, one for each of the calculations in step one. Copy the numbers from each of the calculations down the columns as you did with the upper and lower control limits and the mean in the original instructions above.
3. The spreadsheet should now appear similar to the image below.

	A	B	C	D	E	F	G	H	I	J	K
1	X-Bar Data Points	UCL	LCL	Mean	1 SD	2SD	Minus 1 SD	Minus 2 SD		Standard Deviation:	2.115003962
2	24.1	31.98073	19.2907	25.63571	27.75072	29.86572	23.52071032	21.4057064		Upper Control Limit (UCL)	31.98072617
3	25.2	31.98073	19.2907	25.63571	27.75072	29.86572	23.52071032	21.4057064		Lower Control Limit (LCL)	19.2907024
4	24.7	31.98073	19.2907	25.63571	27.75072	29.86572	23.52071032	21.4057064			
5	28.3	31.98073	19.2907	25.63571	27.75072	29.86572	23.52071032	21.4057064		Process Mean	25.63571429
6	27.1	31.98073	19.2907	25.63571	27.75072	29.86572	23.52071032	21.4057064			
7	26.4	31.98073	19.2907	25.63571	27.75072	29.86572	23.52071032	21.4057064			
8	25.4	31.98073	19.2907	25.63571	27.75072	29.86572	23.52071032	21.4057064		1 SD Above	27.75071825
9	21.4	31.98073	19.2907	25.63571	27.75072	29.86572	23.52071032	21.4057064		2 SD Above	29.86572221
10	24.5	31.98073	19.2907	25.63571	27.75072	29.86572	23.52071032	21.4057064		1 SD Below	23.52071032
11	23.5	31.98073	19.2907	25.63571	27.75072	29.86572	23.52071032	21.4057064		2 SD Below	21.40570636
12	27.5	31.98073	19.2907	25.63571	27.75072	29.86572	23.52071032	21.4057064			
13	29.5	31.98073	19.2907	25.63571	27.75072	29.86572	23.52071032	21.4057064			
14	24.5	31.98073	19.2907	25.63571	27.75072	29.86572	23.52071032	21.4057064			
15	26.8	31.98073	19.2907	25.63571	27.75072	29.86572	23.52071032	21.4057064			

4. Highlight all of the information in columns A through H.
5. Select Insert > Charts > Line Chart > 2-D Line Chart with Markers.
6. Change the Y-Axis to an appropriate range.
7. Edit the background standard deviation lines to be less intrusive by clicking on each and first selecting the gradient line option.

8. Click on the line again and select "Marker." Select none to remove the markers for the background lines.

9. Edit the final chart as desired with titles and labels.

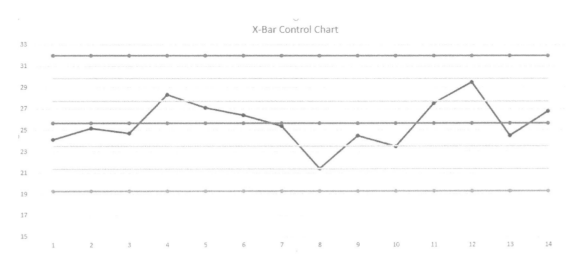

This process might seem very time consuming, but it only takes a few minutes once you are well-versed in the elements of a control chart. It's a good idea to know how to create control charts in Excel, because Six Sigma experts can't always rely on access to statistical analysis software.

Adding Free Data Analysis Tools to Excel

You *can* complete these calculations by hand, but that can be time consuming and require extremely advanced statistical skill sets. We will start with manual calculations because it helps to understand the reasoning behind an analysis. But we'll also rely heavily on tools that complete most of the calculations. Not only does statistical analysis software minimize the time it takes to conduct such analysis, but it also reduces the chance of calculation errors and increases the accuracy of analysis and conclusions offered by Six Sigma experts.

For lessons covered in the next few chapters, you can rely on the free data analysis tool available from Microsoft for Excel. To add this free tool in Excel 2013 and higher, follow the steps below.

1. Select File

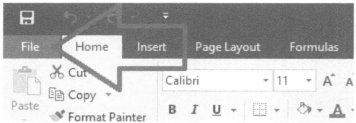

2. Select options

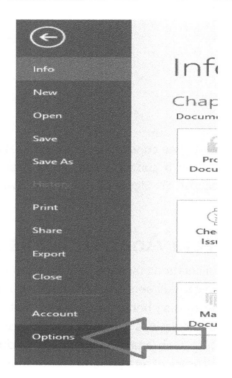

3. Select Add-ins

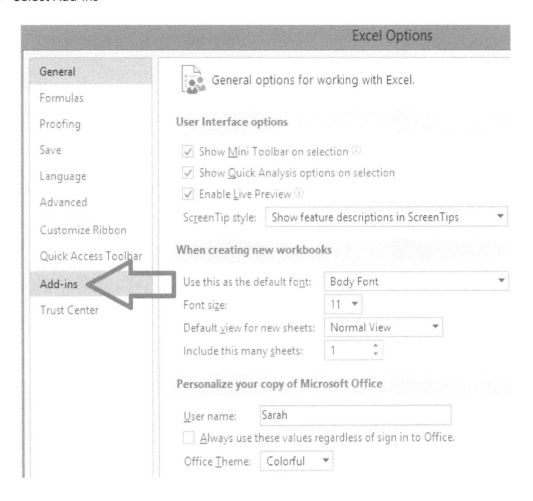

4. Locate the Analysis ToolPak under inactive application add-ins. Note: if the Analysis ToolPak is located under Active Application Add-ins, then it is already active and you don't need to take any of the next steps.

5. At the bottom of the dialogue box, ensure that "Excel Add-ins" is listed in the Manage box, and click "Go".

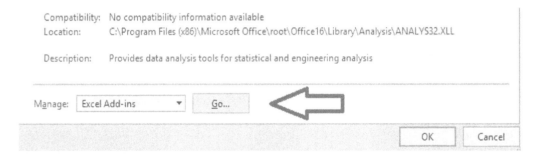

6. In the new dialogue box, ensure the option for Analysis ToolPak is checked.

7. Click OK
8. Check that the Analysis ToolPak was installed by selecting "Data" from the Excel menu bar and looking for the Data Analysis option.

If the Analysis ToolPak doesn't appear as an Add-In option, that means it wasn't installed when your version of Excel was installed. If you are using Excel that was installed from a disk, you'll need to locate your software CDs and either reinstall the software or complete a custom install of just the Analysis ToolPak file.

Note that there are two files with the Analysis ToolPak name. The file called Analysis ToolPak – VBA is not the file that provides analytical capability.

The Analysis ToolPak is also available in earlier versions of Excel. In 2003 and earlier versions of Excel, you'll find the Add-in menu item under Tools. In 2007, the Add-in option is found by selecting the Office button and then Excel options. In 2010, select File, Options, and Manage Add-ins.

CHAPTER 18:
NORMAL PROBABILITY
DISTRIBUTIONS

Now that you've downloaded the Analysis ToolPak in chapter 17, you can begin learning more detailed statistical analysis. In this chapter, we'll discuss how and when to use a normal probability curve to draw inferential statistics. Now is a good time to know the difference between descriptive statistics and inferential statistics.

Descriptive statistics

Descriptive statistics are numbers used to describe a set of data. Given a set of data about the employees in a company, for example, someone might say, "Over 50 percent of the employees work in sales or marketing departments," or, "86 percent of the employees live in the same zip code that the office is located in." These are descriptive statistics because they simply discuss the nature of the data at hand. Averages, means, and even standard deviations associated with that data are all descriptive in nature.

Inferential statistics

Inferential statistics involve calculations and resulting numbers that draw more general conclusions from data. For example, if you have data about a sample of 150 employees in a city – not all the employees from a single business, but random employees from different companies – you might be able to use inferential statistics to draw conclusions about all the working individuals in that city based on the data in your sample.

Descriptive statistics can relate to population data or sample data. Inferential statistics are used to draw conclusions about the population from sample data. If you randomly select 20 people from an overall population and record their height, then the mean of the recorded heights is a descriptive statistic about the sample size. Descriptive statistics about the sample are used in calculations for inferential statistics about a population.

Probability distributions

Probability is the likelihood that a certain event or outcome will occur given a specific set of data or a specific action. If you flip a coin one time, the probability of it coming up heads is 1 in 2, or 50 percent.

When discussing basic probability, we talk about outcomes and events. The outcome is the result of one trial: you flip the coin once or you randomly select a single item from the sample. The event is a specific outcome or outcomes. The coin coming up heads is an event. A person measuring 5 feet tall is an event if you are talking about selecting from a population or sample.

Basic probability can be calculated by the formula:

$$P = \frac{\# \ of \ events \ defined \ as \ the \ outcome}{\# \ of \ total \ events}$$

In the case of the coin, there are two possible events, or outcomes, that can occur when you flip it. Only one of those events is coming up heads. Therefore, ½ = .5, or 50 percent.

In the case of rolling a six-sided die, there are six possible events. You can roll a 1, 2, 3, 4, 5, or 6. The probability of rolling a 5 is 1/6, or .167. The probability of rolling either a 4 or a 5, however, is 2/6, or .33.

While probability measurements can be expressed as a percentage, they are calculated and usually communicated in statistics as a decimal point. Since probabilities are presented as fractions, the lowest probability possible is 0 and the highest is 1. A probability of 0 means an impossible event; a probability of 1 means a certain event.

Basic Probability Practice

Twenty marbles are placed in a bag. They are all the same size, but are different colors as follows:

- 3 red
- 5 black
- 8 blue
- 4 green

What is the probability that a green marble would be pulled from the bag?

4 / 20 = 0.2

What is the probability a blue or a black marble would be pulled from the bag?

13 / 20 = 0.65

What is the probability a yellow marble would be pulled from the bag?

0 / 20 = 0

Note: *This is an impossible task, because there are no yellow marbles in the bag.*

Applying Basic Probability Concepts to Six Sigma Analysis

In a Six Sigma setting, you aren't dealing with marbles and bags, but the ideas of probability are somewhat similar. If a process produces 100 products an hour and two of those products are defective, the probability of receiving a defective product within that hour is 2/100, or 0.02. However, it's rare that a team or business unit would review all 100 products that were produced that hour to know that 2 out of 100 are defective. That information is also only useful for stating probabilities with relation to that particular hour of output, given that the sample wouldn't be random.

Instead, Six Sigma experts randomly sample the population of all outputs of a process for a certain amount of time. They create descriptive statistics about that sample and use the descriptive statistics to further study and understand the nature of the data they are working with. Once they know the nature of the data, they can work with probability distributions and curves to determine probability via calculations and statistical analysis. In this chapter, we'll discuss how to work with what is called normal probability distributions.

Histograms

Before moving forward with probability distributions, it's important to understand histograms. Histograms are another graphical analysis tool. Technically, histograms are bar charts where each bar, or "bin," corresponds to a data range. Data points within a sample or population are divided between the bins and are graphed accordingly.

Histograms are used to analyze continuous or variable data that is finite in nature or comes from population sampling. Histograms help Six Sigma experts understand how the spread, or distribution, of the data is shaped and where the center of that data might be. The center is the average or middle of the data spread, though the mean or median values aren't always located at the center of a histogram. A histogram also shows the range of the data – the variation between the highest value of the data set and the lowest value of the data set. Finally, the histogram's shape provides information about where the data is concentrated.

Consider the two histograms below. In the first, the data elements are concentrated toward the center. The histogram approximates what is called the bell curve, or normal curve. This shape is likely to indicate that the data used to create the histogram is normal data, which will be discussed further later in this chapter.

The second histogram depicts data that is concentrated at either end of the range. When two specific concentrations, or humps, are noted on a histogram, this is called bi-modal distribution. Often, when you see this shape of data, it means that you are measuring two processes that you believe are a single process. For example, if two different people are performing a piece of work, they might have different outcomes that result in two different humps on the histogram. If bi-modal data *does* come from a single process, then the data is not normal.

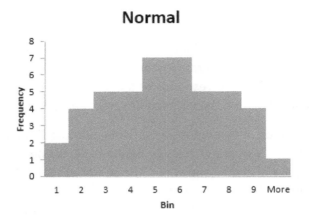

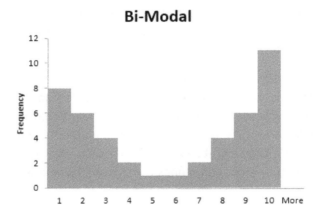

Histograms can also have several other common shapes, especially when presenting non-normal data or data that has an error or issue. If the histogram appears very random, as in the first example below, then it's possible an error lies within the data measurement process. The measurement might not be adequate to capture the true picture of the process, or the definition of the operation and how to collect data might be at fault. The same is true if the histogram depicts an almost even distribution of data elements among bins.

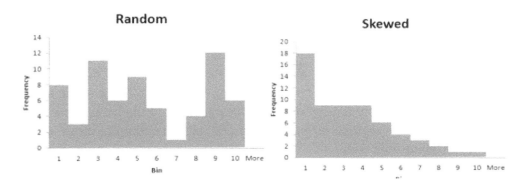

A skewed distribution, seen in the second diagram above, features data that is clustered at only one end of the graph. Skewed histograms are common with certain types of data, particularly when data "falls off" at a natural cut-off time. For example, in a call center, you might measure the time it takes representatives to complete a certain type of phone call. A natural end-point for that data is 0 – it will always take more than 0 seconds to complete a phone call. sually, it will take more than a few seconds, so you won't have many data points in the lower end of the range. Perhaps this particular phone call follows a script and the majority of the calls end at the 7 to 8-minute mark. A histogram for length of calls might look something like the chart below.

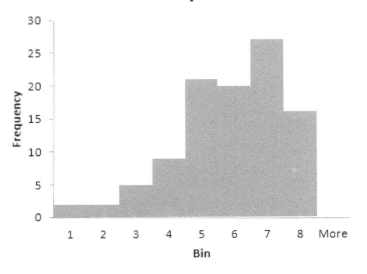

Consider the basic example below to understand histograms further.

A local distribution company wants to understand more about how well delivery drivers are meeting estimated arrival times. The team pulls a random sample of deliveries from a week's worth of information and considers two data points for each delivery: the estimated time of delivery and the actual time of delivery. They subtracted the actual time from the estimated time to determine how far off one way or the other the deliveries were. The result was the following data table.

Estimate	Actual	Difference in minutes
8:00 AM	7:55 AM	-5
8:30 AM	8:20 AM	-10
8:50 AM	9:07 AM	17
9:15 AM	9:23 AM	8
9:45 AM	9:46 AM	1
10:05 AM	10:03 AM	-2
10:30 AM	10:33 AM	3
10:55 AM	11:05 AM	10
11:30 AM	11:27 AM	-3
12:45 PM	12:32 PM	-13
1:30 PM	1:35 PM	5
1:45 PM	1:57 PM	12
2:20 PM	3:01 PM	41
3:00 PM	3:48 PM	48
3:30 PM	3:05 PM	-25

SIX SIGMA: A COMPLETE STEP-BY-STEP GUIDE

8:50 AM	8:45 AM	-5
9:15 AM	9:58 AM	43
9:45 AM	10:21 AM	36
10:05 AM	10:09 AM	4
10:30 AM	10:03 AM	-27
1:45 PM	1:46 PM	1
2:20 PM	2:54 PM	34
3:00 PM	3:04 PM	4
3:30 PM	3:23 PM	-7
11:30 AM	11:16 AM	-14

To create a histogram, the team sorted the selection by difference in minutes and discovered the range as -27 to 48. The team decided to create a histogram from -30 to 50 with a bin size of 10. The resulting data is as follows:

Bin	Frequency
-30	0
-20	2
-10	3
0	5
10	8
20	2
30	0
40	2
50	3

To create the above table, the team simply counted how many data points fell in each bin. The data points -27 and -25 fell into the bin -20 (to -29); that is 2 data points. Eight data points fell into the 10 bin. When charted on a bar chart, this information creates a histogram.

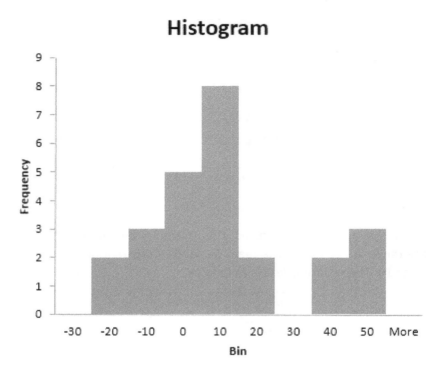

When dealing with histograms, the number of bins used is important. If you have too few bins, the graph doesn't provide any relevant information. If you have too many bins for the data set in question, you also lose informative functionality and your graph, rather than appearing as a rough curve, becomes something that looks like a comb. Usually, the more data you have, the more bins you can include on your histogram.

Consider the following four histograms that all represent the same set of data. The data features 150 random numbers ranging from 38.62 to 62.89.

Histogram with 7 Bins

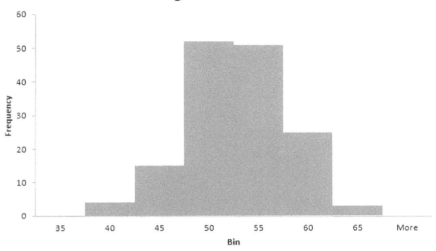

Histogram with 16 Bins

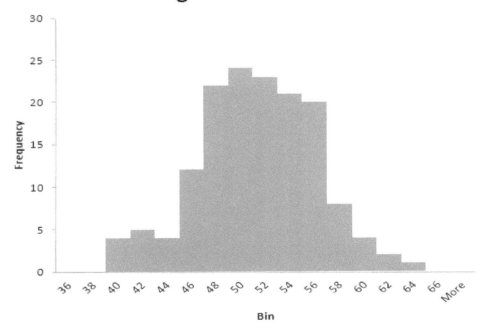

NORMAL PROBABILITY DISTRIBUTIONS

Histogram with 29 bins

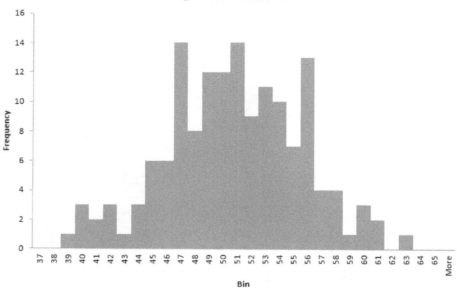

Histogram with 57 Bins

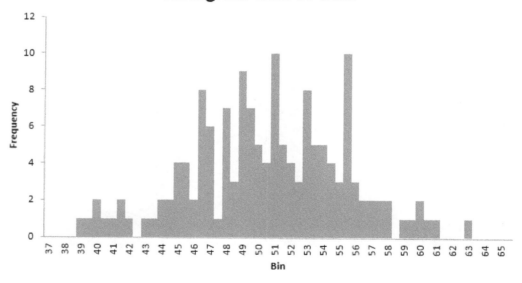

The bin sizes get progressively smaller as the number of bins increase. In the first chart, bin sizes are 5; in the last chart, bin sizes are 0.5. For the purposes of understanding what type of data is represented in this histogram, the second or third charts are probably the most relevant. We'll cover determining data type from a histogram and associated statistics later in this chapter.

Creating a Histogram in Excel

Before moving on with probability distributions, we'll look at creating histograms in Excel using the Analysis ToolPak that was discussed in the last chapter.

1. Open Excel and copy the following data table into a blank workbook.

56.1
38.2
47.1
48.1
60.1
45.8
33.4
49.2
53.1
41.8
19.2
49.3
49.0
61.8
42.4
53.2

61.6
20.8
55.2
57.5
48.8
28.9
33.8
53.2
58.0
47.3
51.4
61.5
58.9
60.4
30.7
52.5
40.7
44.8
54.6
61.6
31.0
52.7
47.5

26.3
71.3
61.8
51.9
43.9
50.0
47.4
61.9
51.8
50.4
61.0

2. Copy the following bin designations into the second column in the same worksheet.

10
15
20
25
30
35
40
45
50
55

| 60 |
| 65 |
| 70 |
| 75 |

3. Select Data > Data Analysis

4. Select Histogram and click OK.

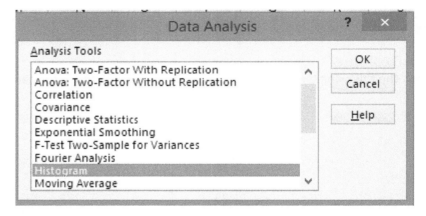

5. Click in the Input Range box, and then highlight the cells for the input range (the 50 data cells you copied from above).
6. Click in the Bin Range box, and then highlight the cells that include the bin data you copied from above.
7. Check the New Worksheet Ply: option.
8. Check the Chart Output option.
9. Ensure that your Histogram dialog box appears as below.

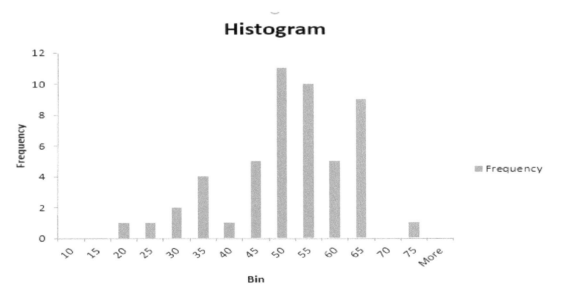

10. Click OK.

Excel automatically generates a bin and frequency table as well as a histogram graph in a new worksheet. The histogram design defaults to a standard bar graph, but you can create the look of the histograms previously shown by changing one setting on the design.

1. Click on the histogram.
2. Select Design from the top menu.

3. Under Quick Layout, choose the layout where the bars are stacked next to each other rather than with space between them.

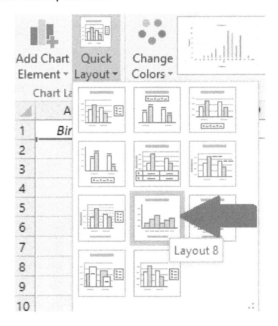

Your result should look like the graph below.

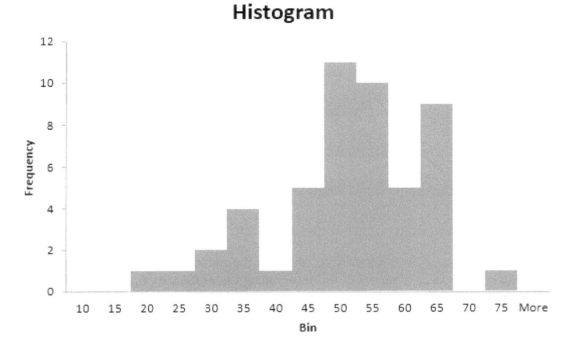

Experiment with your own data, creating histograms with various bin sizes to begin to develop an understanding of how data converts to this type of chart.

Normal Distributions

Normal distribution, also called Gaussian distribution, is probably the most important distribution related to continuous data from a statistical analysis standpoint. A normal, or Gaussian, distribution is depicted below.

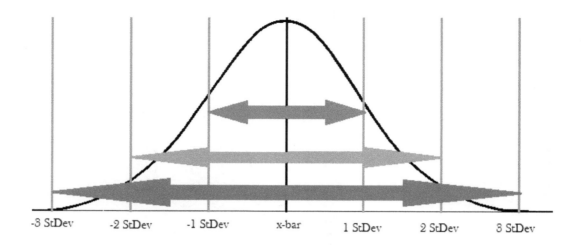

Normal data is shaped symmetrically surrounding the mean, represented above by the x-bar line. A normal curve is beneficial for determining the probability that a given data point in a population will fall inside a certain range within the distribution.

In a perfect normal distribution, 68.26 percent of all data points fall within plus or minus one standard deviation from the mean; this area is represented by the red arrow on the visual above. The blue arrow, which covers plus or minus two standard deviations from the mean, indicates the area under the curve that includes 95.46 percent of the data points. The purple area, which covers plus and minus three standard deviations from the mean, indicates the portion of the curve that covers 99.73 percent of the data. Less than 1 percent of data will fall under the curve outside of three standard deviations on either side.

Distributions – even normal distributions – vary a bit. To determine the exact probabilities of various data points, advanced statistics are required; Excel and other programs perform the calculations for you, making it easier to conduct analysis. Before we discuss probability calculations using Excel, we'll look at determining whether your data is normal in the first place.

Testing whether data is normal is critical to many steps in statistical analysis, because the results of many tests can be invalid if you don't account for the data you are working with. The most basic form of many of these tests are designed to work with normal data.

Normality Testing in Excel: Chi-Squared Goodness-of-Fit Test

We've touched on how visual inspection can help you determine whether data is normal or not. The histogram below, taken from earlier in the chapter, presents what seems to be obviously normal data. Data points converge around the center, and the histogram is roughly symmetrical in nature.

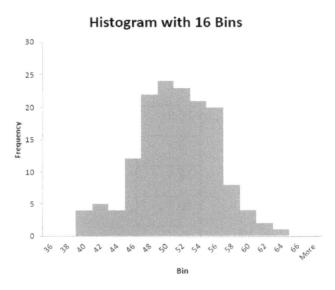

But what about this histogram, which is the one created in the practice exercise in the section on creating histograms in Excel?

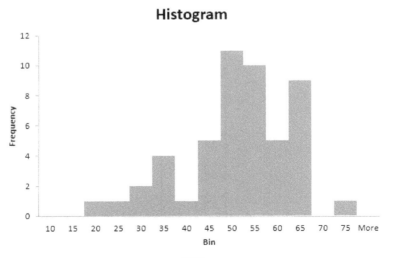

NORMAL PROBABILITY DISTRIBUTIONS

The histogram above is an example of a chart that doesn't fall neatly into any of the histogram shapes previously discussed. It seems to have elements of the normal curve, but it could also be skewed data. This is why we perform statistical tests to determine normality.

You'll usually begin exploring probability data by following the instructions in the previous section to create a histogram for the data. For the example of the normality test, we'll use the same data from the section above, which is:

19.2
20.8
26.3
28.9
30.7
31
33.4
33.8
38.2
40.7
41.8
42.4
43.9
44.8
45.8
47.1
47.3

47.4
47.5
48.1
48.8
49
49.2
49.3
50
50.4
51.4
51.8
51.9
52.5
52.7
53.1
53.2
53.2
54.6
55.2
56.1
57.5
58

58.9
60.1
60.4
61
61.5
61.6
61.6
61.8
61.8
61.9
71.3

Creating a histogram using the Analysis ToolPak generates a chart and a data table, as seen below.

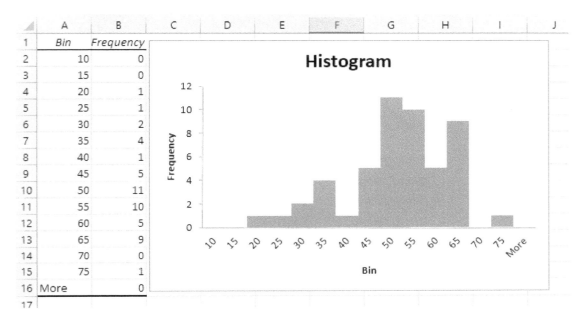

	A	B
1	Bin	Frequency
2	10	0
3	15	0
4	20	1
5	25	1
6	30	2
7	35	4
8	40	1
9	45	5
10	50	11
11	55	10
12	60	5
13	65	9
14	70	0
15	75	1
16	More	0
17		

Calculate descriptive statistics for the data.

Use the Descriptive Statistics option in the Analysis ToolPak to quickly generate descriptive statistics for your data set.

1. Select Data > Data Analysis > Descriptive Statistics
2. Click OK
3. Click in the Input Range box and select your input range using the mouse.

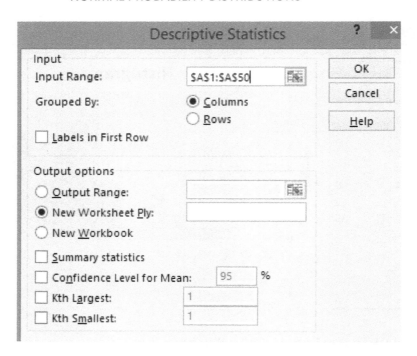

4. In this case, the data is grouped by columns. In most statistical analysis, that will be the case, but if you have data grouped by rows, you should change the Grouped By selection.

5. Select to output information in a new worksheet.

6. Ensure at least the Summary statistics box is checked. You can also check the Confidence level for mean and the Kth largest and smallest boxes, though that information isn't required in the Chi-Squared Goodness-of-Fit test, which is the test we are running to test for normality of the data. If you check these extra boxes, Excel will simply provide you with additional information that we won't be using at this time.

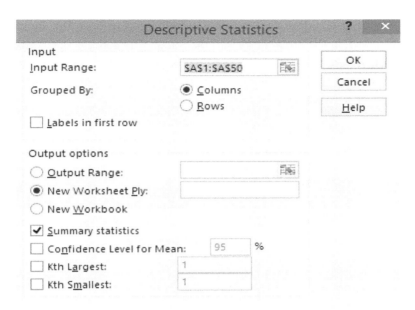

7. Click OK.
8. Excel returns descriptive summary statistics for your data set.

	A	B
1	*Column1*	
2		
3	Mean	48.778
4	Standard Error	1.618427783
5	Median	50.2
6	Mode	53.2
7	Standard Deviation	11.4440126
8	Sample Variance	130.9654245
9	Kurtosis	0.353568183
10	Skewness	-0.780565708
11	Range	52.1
12	Minimum	19.2
13	Maximum	71.3
14	Sum	2438.9
15	Count	50

For the Chi-Squared Goodness-of-Fit test, you will need to note the sample size (or count), the same standard deviation, and the sample mean. The sample size is the number of items in the data set, which was 50 for this example. If you don't remember what the sample size was, you can refer to the count listed in the descriptive statistics. The other two figures are taken from the descriptive statistics above:

- Sample mean: 48.778
- Sample standard deviation: 11.444

Set up the hypothesis.

The Chi-Squared Goodness-of-Fit test is actually a hypothesis test. That means you are testing the data with regard to a null hypothesis and an alternative hypothesis. The two hypotheses for the Chi-Squared Goodness-of-Fit test are:

- Null hypothesis: The data is normal.
- Alternative hypothesis: The data is not normal.

If one is not true, then the other is. In statistical terms, we talk in terms of accepting or rejecting the null hypothesis. If we reject the null, we accept the alternative.

Understand the Chi-Squared Goodness-of-Fit test premise.

Basically, the Chi-Squared Goodness-of-Fit test takes the number of samples in each bin on the histogram and compares that to the number of samples you might expect to find in each bin given a normal curve. Using the actual number of samples in each bin and the expected number of samples, we can calculate what is called the Chi-Square Statistic in Excel. That number then lets us calculate a p-Value. In this case, it is the size of the p-Value that lets us decide whether to accept or reject the hypothesis that the data is normal.

For the purpose of the Chi-Squared Goodness-of-Fit test in this situation, if the p-Value is greater than 0.05, we will accept the null hypothesis that the data is normally distributed.

The Observed Bins

Having created a histogram via the Analysis ToolPak, you already have access to the observed bin distribution. That information is housed in the data table Excel creates to make the histogram.

Bin	Frequency
10	0
15	0
20	1
25	1
30	2
35	4
40	1
45	5
50	11
55	10
60	5
65	9
70	0
75	1
More	0

The Expected Bins

We can use statistics related to the normal curve to calculate how we might expect bins to behave given the median and standard deviation of our sample.

To give you an idea of what is going on with the statistical calculations involved in determining expected size of bins, consider the graphic below.

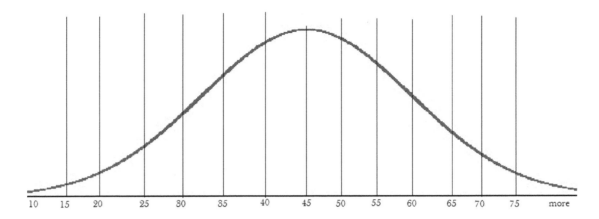

This graphic roughly depicts the bins from our histogram drawn on the normal curve. Because mathematical formulations exist for determining the area under a curve, it's possible to determine the area under the curve within a specific bin. Ultimately, that is done by calculating the total area and subtracting portions.

We begin with a calculation known as the Cumulative Distribution Function, or CDF. The CDF measures the total area under a curve to the left of the point we are measuring from. For example, the total area under the curve above that is to the left of 45 is 50 percent. Once we know the CDF at each border of our bins, it's a matter of subtraction to calculate the CDF for each individual bin. For example, the CDF for the bin located between 40 and 45 would equal the CDF of 45 minus the CDF of 40.

One problem with this rough depiction is that the curve drawn above centers on 45, and we know from Excel that our mean is 48.778. We'll use that number in our calculations to account for the slight shift.

Excel can calculate CDF with the formula:

=NORMDIST(x value, Sample Mean, Sample Standard Deviation, TRUE)

Set up the tables for calculating the CDF of each bin by copying the bin designations onto the descriptive statistics worksheet that Excel previously created for you and creating two columns, one for total CDF and one for bin CDF. Use the image below as an example.

	A	B	C	D	E	F
1	*Column1*			Bins (x)	CDF to Left	Bin Only
2				10		
3	Mean	48.778		15		
4	Standard Error	1.618427783		20		
5	Median	50.2		25		
6	Mode	53.2		30		
7	Standard Deviation	11.4440126		35		
8	Sample Variance	130.9654245		40		
9	Kurtosis	0.353568183		45		
10	Skewness	-0.780565708		50		
11	Range	52.1		55		
12	Minimum	19.2		60		
13	Maximum	71.3		65		
14	Sum	2438.9		70		
15	Count	50		75		
16						

Enter the formula for calculating CDF into column E, referencing the same mean and standard deviation for each row and using the numbers in D as X.

	A	B	C	D	E	F
1	*Column1*			Bins (x)	CDF to Left	Bin Only
2				10	=NORMDIST(D2,B3,B7,TRUE)	
3	Mean	48.778		15		
4	Standard Error	1.618427783		20		
5	Median	50.2		25		
6	Mode	53.2		30		
7	Standard Deviation	11.4440126		35		
8	Sample Variance	130.9654245		40		
9	Kurtosis	0.353568183		45		
10	Skewness	-0.780565708		50		
11	Range	52.1		55		
12	Minimum	19.2		60		
13	Maximum	71.3		65		
14	Sum	2438.9		70		
15	Count	50		75		
16						

NORMAL PROBABILITY DISTRIBUTIONS

	Column1			Bins (x)	CDF to Left		Bin Only
				10		0.000351384	
				15		0.001580727	
Mean	48.778			20		0.005957067	
Standard Error	1.618427783			25		0.018865379	
Median	50.2			30		0.050413444	
Mode	53.2			35		0.114304773	
Standard Deviation	11.4440126			40		0.221529268	
Sample Variance	130.9654245			45		0.37065126	
Kurtosis	0.353568183			50		0.542518532	
Skewness	-0.780565708			55		0.706672736	
Range	52.1			60		0.83660501	
Minimum	19.2			65		0.921833034	
Maximum	71.3			70		0.968160416	
Sum	2438.9			75		0.989027809	
Count	50						

For the first row – in our case, the bin marked 10 -- the bin-only area is equal to the CDF because there is nothing left of the bin's upper limit. For all other rows, the bin-only area is the CDF minus the CDF for the bin designation above. So, you would enter =E2 in the first data row for column F. The second data row would be calculated as E3-E2; the next would be E4-E3, and so forth. The result is the percentage of the curve in each bin.

	Column1			Bins (x)	CDF to Left		Bin Only
				10		0.000351384	0.000351384
				15		0.001580727	0.001229343
Mean	48.778			20		0.005957067	0.00437634
Standard Error	1.618427783			25		0.018865379	0.012908312
Median	50.2			30		0.050413444	0.031548065
Mode	53.2			35		0.114304773	0.063891328
Standard Deviation	11.4440126			40		0.221529268	0.107224495
Sample Variance	130.9654245			45		0.37065126	0.149121993
Kurtosis	0.353568183			50		0.542518532	0.171867271
Skewness	-0.780565708			55		0.706672736	0.164154205
Range	52.1			60		0.83660501	0.129932273
Minimum	19.2			65		0.921833034	0.085228025
Maximum	71.3			70		0.968160416	0.046327381
Sum	2438.9			75		0.989027809	0.020867393
Count	50						

Calculating the expected number of samples in each bin is as easy as multiplying the percentages of each bin by the sample size. Again, you can see from the descriptive statistics that the count for this set of data was 50.

Bins (x)	CDF to Left		Bin Only	Expected Number	
10		0.000351384	0.000351384	=F2*50	
15		0.001580727	0.001229343		
20		0.005957067	0.00437634		

304

	A	B	C	D	E	F	G
1		*Column1*		Bins (x)	CDF to Left	Bin Only	Expected Number
2				10		0.000351384	0.000351384	0.017569213
3	Mean	48.778		15		0.001580727	0.001229343	0.061467129
4	Standard Error	1.618427783		20		0.005957067	0.00437634	0.218817013
5	Median	50.2		25		0.018865379	0.012908312	0.645415598
6	Mode	53.2		30		0.050413444	0.031548065	1.577403261
7	Standard Deviation	11.4440126		35		0.114304773	0.063891328	3.194566424
8	Sample Variance	130.9654245		40		0.221529268	0.107224495	5.361224739
9	Kurtosis	0.353568183		45		0.37065126	0.149121993	7.456099635
10	Skewness	-0.780565708		50		0.542518532	0.171867271	8.593363571
11	Range	52.1		55		0.706672736	0.164154205	8.207710239
12	Minimum	19.2		60		0.83660501	0.129932273	6.496613655
13	Maximum	71.3		65		0.921833034	0.085228025	4.261401231
14	Sum	2438.9		70		0.968160416	0.046327381	2.316369071
15	Count	50		75		0.989027809	0.020867393	1.043369664

To calculate the Chi-Squared statistic, you'll use both the expected number of items in each bin and the actual or observed number. Copy the observed numbers over from your histogram worksheet.

D	E	F	G	H
Bins (x)	CDF to Left	Bin Only	Expected Number	Observed
10	0.000351384	0.000351384	0.017569213	0
15	0.001580727	0.001229343	0.061467129	0
20	0.005957067	0.00437634	0.218817013	1
25	0.018865379	0.012908312	0.645415598	1
30	0.050413444	0.031548065	1.577403261	2
35	0.114304773	0.063891328	3.194566424	4
40	0.221529268	0.107224495	5.361224739	1
45	0.37065126	0.149121993	7.456099635	5
50	0.542518532	0.171867271	8.593363571	11
55	0.706672736	0.164154205	8.207710239	10
60	0.83660501	0.129932273	6.496613655	5
65	0.921833034	0.085228025	4.261401231	9
70	0.968160416	0.046327381	2.316369071	0
75	0.989027809	0.020867393	1.043369664	1

Apply the following formula to each row:

$$(\text{expected} - \text{observed})^2 / \text{expected}$$

Calculate the final numbers for each row as desired in Excel.

	G	H	I	J
	Expected Number	Observed	(Exp - Obs)^2	Divided by Exp
4	0.017569213	0	0.000308677	0.017569213
3	0.061467129	0	0.003778208	0.061467129
4	0.218817013	1	0.610246859	2.78884558
2	0.645415598	1	0.125730098	0.194804864
5	1.577403261	2	0.178588004	0.113216454
8	3.194566424	4	0.648723246	0.203070827
5	5.361224739	1	19.02028123	3.547749283
3	7.456099635	5	6.032425418	0.809059121
1	8.593363571	11	5.791898901	0.673996725
5	8.207710239	10	3.212302586	0.391376217
3	6.496613655	5	2.239852434	0.3447723
5	4.261401231	9	22.45431829	5.26923354
1	2.316369071	0	5.365565674	2.316369071
3	1.043369664	1	0.001880928	0.001802743

Add up the final numbers to get the Chi-Squared statistic, denoted by X^2. For our example, X^2 is 16.7333.

To use the Chi-Squared statistic to find the p-Value, we also need one more item for the Excel formula to work: we need what is called the degrees of freedom.

Degrees of freedom = #bins − 1 - #calculated parameters

We have 14 bins. The parameters we used to arrive at the Chi-Squared statistic that we calculated from our sample were the mean and standard deviation: two parameters. For our example:

Degrees of freedom = 14 − 1 − 2 = 11

Now that we have both the degrees of freedom (df), and the Chi-Squared value, we can use Excel to calculate the p-Value. Simply enter the formula below, inputting the correct values.

In the case of our example, the resulting p-Value is 0.116. Because the p-Value is greater than 0.05, we accept the null hypothesis. Our data is normal.

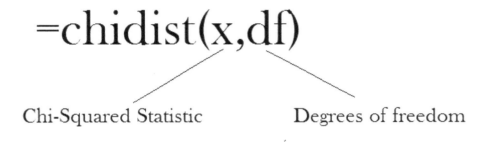

$=\text{chidist}(x, df)$

Chi-Squared Statistic   Degrees of freedom

Normal Probabilities

Once you verify that your data is normal, you can use many statistical tests to draw conclusions about the data and the population as a whole from your sample. One of the things you can do is use Excel's normal probability functions to draw conclusions about data.

For example, let's assume that the data we've been working with throughout this chapter is a sample selection of the weights of boxes in a delivery channel. The 50 samples were taken from the same shipping center over the course of a week and were randomly selected. Given that we know the data is normal, what is the probability that any package selected from the distribution center will weigh over 50 pounds?

Excel provides the following formula:

=NORMDIST(x, mean, standard_dev, cumulative)

When using this formula:

- X = the value you are testing
- Mean = sample mean from the descriptive statistics
- Standard_dev = sample standard deviation from the descriptive statistics
- Cumulative = FALSE if you want to test the probability of the exact occurrence; TRUE if you want to test the probability of any value left of x on the curve (or, in most cases, less than x)

Entering the formula in Excel for our data set with a FALSE cumulative tells us there is a 3.47 percent chance of a randomly selected box weighing 50 pounds. This is a *real* and important piece of information that might be beneficial to a Six Sigma team.

Entering the formula in Excel for our data set with a TRUE cumulative tells us there is a 54.25 percent chance of a randomly selected box weighing less than 50 pounds. Subtracting from 100 percent leaves a 45.75 percent chance that a box will weigh over 50 pounds.

Why might this be important? In this particular case, a shipping manager might be working to hire shipping reps. Because there is a strong likelihood that the employees will handle boxes over 50 pounds, the manager knows to include that requirement in job descriptions. Or, a Six Sigma team might be working on a process to increase production in a warehouse; the knowledge that many of the boxes are heavy enough to require special handling is relevant to how the team approaches the process.

Six Sigma teams can use Excel to generate a lot of information about the data. Excel also provides a formula for the inverse of the above calculation. What if the team wanted to know about the weight of the heaviest 80 percent of boxes in the shipping center?

The formula is:

=NORMINV(probability, mean, standard_dev)

Probability must be entered as a decimal point, not a percent. In the case of 0.8 in our example data set, all of the boxes in the heaviest 80 percent are above 58.40 pounds.

Because we are drawing statistical conclusions from samples, there is some error inherent in the process. Error is usually calculated for in advanced analysis.

How to apply statistical data and conclusions to a business or project approach is covered in depth in the next unit, where we'll look at how these concepts can generate real information that is applicable to business processes.

CHAPTER 19:
CORRELATION AND REGRESSION

Correlation and regression are statistical concepts that help Six Sigma teams understand whether two factors within a process are related. You can use these tools to calculate whether an input is related to an output in some way or even whether two inputs might be related. The concept of correlation and regression was introduced in chapter 14 in the section on scatter diagrams. In this chapter, you'll learn how to calculate the correlation coefficient in Excel, and what that number means, as well as how to create linear regression models in Excel to test relationships between a dependent and independent variable.

It's worth covering a point made in chapter 14 again. Strong correlation or regression between two variables *does not* indicate a causal relationship. Even when strong regression is found between a dependent and independent variable, it doesn't mean that the dependent result is *caused* by the independent variable. This is a critical concept to understand, because attributing causation because correlation is strong can mean making poor decisions regarding a process. A team might decide to alter or remove one element because it has a strong correlation to an output; they might then be surprised that the output doesn't change because it wasn't in a causal relationship with the input in question.

Why work with correlation and regression at all?

Correlation and regression is still important to understand, because it helps teams understand more about processes, analyze how elements of a process are related, and make predictions about a process. When two elements are strongly related along a linear line – or even along a curve – teams can create equations linking the two elements. This lets Six Sigma teams predict how the dependent element will perform if a change is made in the independent variable.

Before moving forward, it should be noted that the analysis tools in this chapter don't assume normal data in all cases, but it is possible that very abnormal data can skew results. Before analyzing data, Six Sigma experts should always understand what type of data they are working with.

Correlation

Typically, when talking about correlation, we mean the linear association that exists between two variables. In chapter 14, we introduced the concept that correlation can be strong or weak; it can also be positive or negative.

Positive Correlation: One variable increase as another variable increases.

Negative Correlation: One variable decreases as another variable increases.

Correlation can sometimes be roughly approximated by viewing a graphical analysis of data in the form of a scatter diagram or X/Y plot. The steps for creating such diagrams were covered in chapter 17. To understand how various types of correlation might appear graphically, consider the example scatter diagrams below.

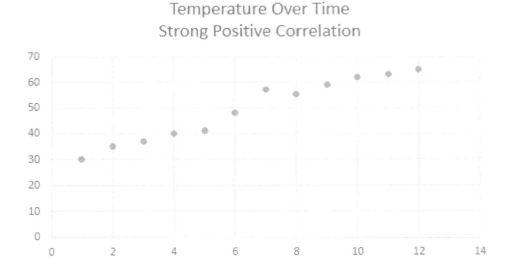

In the scatter diagram above, temperature has a strong positive correlation to time. This means that temperature in the process has a tendency to increase as time increases. The relationship is strong, because you could draw a best fit line, as seen in the image to the left, and it would touch almost every data point with minimal deviation of data points from the line.

Temperature Over Time
Strong Positive Correlation

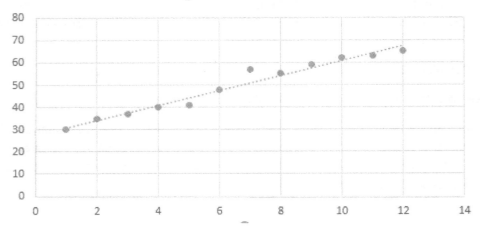

Temperature Over Time
Strong Negative Correlation

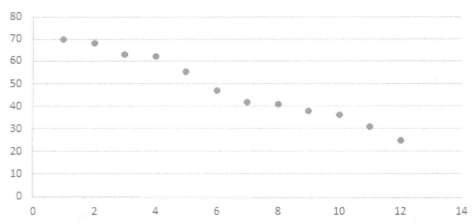

The diagram above features a strong negative correlation. This means that temperature in the process has a tendency to decrease as time increases. Again, you can draw a best fit line through the points of data and all of them remain very close to the trend line, as seen in the graph to the right.

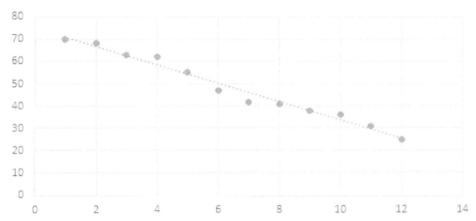

In contrast, the graph to the left represents a set of data where correlation might be present, but it is weaker than either of the two examples above. Weak correlation is represented on a scatter diagram where a trend line does seem to exist and where roughly the same number of data points that don't touch the line are located above or below. Typically, the data points located above and below the trend lines are somewhat symmetrical, meaning that one side doesn't feature points that are extremely far away from the line as compared to points on the other side, but this isn't always the case. Weak correlation can be easy to see, as in this case, or more difficult to see on a graph, warranting the use of statistical analysis to make a strong case for correlation.

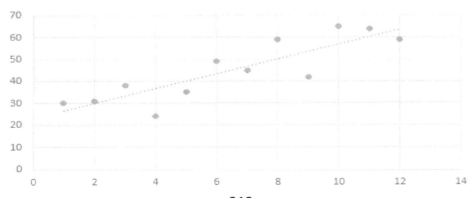

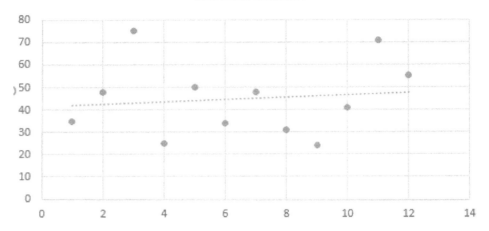

The graph above shows a scatter diagram that indicates no or almost no correlation between time and temperature in a process. The data points are scattered randomly over the graph, and the trend line is almost horizontal. A horizontal trend line is usually an indication of a lack of correlation.

The Correlation Coefficient

Images aren't always accurate, especially when correlation is weak. And in some cases, an image capturing a small sample of data could show correlation or no correlation when correlation did exist in the overall sample or data set. Graphical analysis is useful to gain an idea about data relationships – and very useful for illustrating relationships to others – but statistical analysis helps teams understand relationships with more certainty.

For the purpose of correlation, the statistical calculation we are concerned with is known as the correlation coefficient, or R value. The correlation coefficient is a number between -1 and 1. As the correlation coefficient approaches either -1 or 1, a relationship between two variables is considered more likely or stronger.

- If the correlation coefficient is equal to 1, then the relationship is certain: all the data points on the set are found *on* the positive trend line.
- The same is true for a correlation coefficient that is equal to -1, except that all the data points are found *on* the negative trend line.
- A correlation coefficient equal to 0 means there is certainly no relationship between the variables, and there is no trend line.

314

- Most of the time, when you calculate correlation coefficients, the number will be between 0 and 1 or 0 and -1.

Calculating Correlation Coefficient in Excel: Two Methods

Correlation coefficients are calculated using several formulas. One of the most common formulas used in basic statistics is Pearson's correlation coefficient formula, which is shown below:

$$r = \frac{n(\Sigma xy) - (\Sigma x)(\Sigma y)}{\sqrt{[n\Sigma x^2 - (\Sigma x)^2][n\Sigma y^2 - (\Sigma y)^2]}}$$

Another calculation uses the sum of squares. The formula is shown below.

$$R = \frac{SS_{xy}}{\sqrt{SS_{xx}SS_{yy}}}$$

Where:

$$SS_{xx} = \Sigma(x_i - \bar{x})^2$$
$$SS_{yy} = \Sigma(y_i - \bar{y})^2$$
$$SS_{xy} = \Sigma(x_i - \bar{x})(y_i - \bar{y})$$

of these formulas rely on the specific (x,y) data arrived at by combining data pairs. For example, consider the following data set:

Months on Job	Average Production
2	10
2	11
3	12
3	11
3	13
4	11
4	15
4	15
5	16
5	15
5	18

If average production is considered the Y axis and months on the job the X axis, paired points of this data set would be written as:

- 2, 10
- 2, 11
- 3, 12
- 3, 11
- And so forth

Those numbers can then be included in the equations above; the sigma symbol (which looks like an E) indicates summing. In Pearson's equation, you sum all of the (x*y) and subtract the (sum of all x)*(sum of all y) to arrive at the top number, for example.

It is possible to calculate the correlation coefficient using one of these formulas, but luckily today's technology provides digital methods for automatically calculating the number. You can use statistical analysis software or graphing calculators to arrive at the correlation coefficient given data about two variables in a process. In this section, we'll look at two quick ways of determining correlation coefficients using Excel.

For both exercises below, we'll use the following data table. Copy the data table into a blank Excel worksheet.

Time	Temperature A	Temperature B	Temperature C	Temperature D
1	30	70	35	30
2	35	68	48	31
3	37	63	75	38
4	40	62	25	24
5	41	55	50	35
6	48	47	34	49
7	57	42	48	45
8	55	41	31	59
9	59	38	24	42
10	62	36	41	65
11	63	31	71	64
12	65	25	55	59

CORREL Formula

One of the easiest ways to calculate the correlation coefficient for two sets of possibly related data is to use Excel's CORREL formula. Follow the steps below to calculate the correlation coefficient between time and Temperature A.

1. In any cell in the worksheet where you copied the data table above, the formula =CORREL

CORRELATION AND REGRESSION

▲	A	B	C	D
1	Time	Temperature A	Temperatur B	Temperatɪ
2	1	30	70	
3	2	35	68	
4	3	37	63	
5	4	40	62	
6	5	41	55	
7	6	48	47	
8	7	57	42	
9	8	55	41	
10	9	59	38	
11	10	62	36	
12	11	63	31	
13	12	65	25	
14				
15				
16	R (time and Temp A)	=CORREL(		
17		CORREL(**array1**, array2)		
18				

2. Array 1 is the set of cells containing data for time. Array 2 is the set of cells containing data for Temperature A. You can select these cell ranges with your mouse, separating them with a comma in your formula. The end result should appear as follows.

13	12	65	25
14			
15			
16	R (time and Temp A)	=CORREL(A2:A13,B2:B13)	
17			
18			

3. Hit enter.
4. Excel will calculate the correlation coefficient. In this case, it is 0.981167422

The correlation coefficient calculated above is for the data set that created the very first scatter diagram for this chapter. If you recall, the scatter diagram appeared to show that

318

the data had a very strong positive correlation; a correlation coefficient (or R value) of 0.98 is certainly in line with that assessment.

Let's calculate the correlation coefficient for time and temperature C from the data table above. Repeat the steps above, but change your Array 2 range to reference the data set for temperature C.

12	11	63	31
13	12	65	25
14			
15			
16	R (time and Temp A)	0.981167422	
17			
18	R (time and Temp C)	=CORREL(A2:A13,D2:D13)	

The R value for time and temperature C is calculated as 0.107, which is much closer to zero. This data set created the scatter diagram above that appeared to have no correlation. The R value corresponds with the conclusions drawn from the scatter diagram. *In most applications, correlation is considered to occur at some level if the R value is 0.4 or more or -0.4 or less.*

Data Analysis ToolPak

You can also use the Analysis ToolPak to calculate correlation coefficients. Follow the steps below to calculate the R value for time and Temperature B.

1. Format your spreadsheet so that the Time and Temperature B columns are next to each other.
2. Select Data and then Data Analysis from the top menu.

3. Highlight Correlation and select OK.

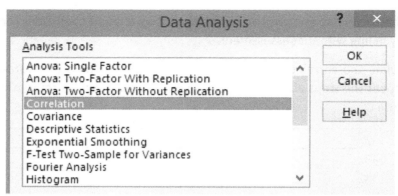

4. Click in the input box and select the inputs for the correlation analysis. Select the data from both the time and temperature B columns.

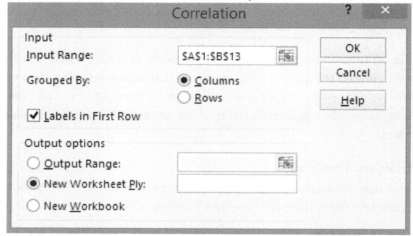

5. Note that your data is grouped by columns. If you selected the header rows in the input range, check the box for "labels in the first row."
6. Opt to output in a new worksheet.
7. Click OK.
8. Excel will calculate the correlation coefficient.

▲	A	B	C
1		Time	Temperatur B
2	Time	1	
3	Temperat	-0.98978	1
4			
5			
6			

In the above example, the R value shows a very strong negative correlation between time and temperature. This data set is the same set used to make the negative correlation scatter diagram above, so the R value is consistent with that graphical analysis.

Repeat the steps above to find the correlation coefficient of time and temperature D.

▲	A	B	C
1		Time	Temperature D
2	Time	1	
3	Temperat	0.860624	1
4			

The R value returned shows a weaker positive correlation than in our first calculation using the CORREL function, but we would still consider these data correlated. The data for temperature D is the same data that created the third scatter diagram in the graphical analysis portion of this chapter.

Linear Regression Analysis

Once you know your data has a linear correlation, you can conduct further analysis through regression testing. Regression lets you create a linear model that helps you predict how one variable might behave given changes in the other variable. Note again that the changes aren't necessarily an indication of cause – only that the variables are intertwined in some way.

When working with regression, we talk about the coefficient of determination, or the r^2 value. The r^2 value is, literally, the square of R, or the square of the correlation coefficient.

So, from our last example in the correlation coefficient section, R = 0.860624. The r^2 value in this case would be 0.74.

The r^2 value is a number between 0 and 1. The number tells us about the strength of the linear relationship between two variables – x and y. While the R value tells us how likely it is that two values are related in some way, the r^2 value tells us how much the fluctuation in one variable (the dependent variable, or y) is related to changes in another variable (the independent variable, or x).

In the example used above, r^2 is 0.74. That means that approximately 74 percent of the variation in the temperature is related to the change in time; the other 26 percent variation in temperature is unexplained.

Regression analysis lets us create a best fit line and equation for our data, and the r^2 value tells us how confident we can be in using that line to make predictions about data.

Analyzing Regression Using the Data Analysis ToolPak

To understand how regression works, consider the same data set used in the correlation coefficient examples above:

Time	Temperature A	Temperature B	Temperature C	Temperature D
1	30	70	35	30
2	35	68	48	31
3	37	63	75	38
4	40	62	25	24
5	41	55	50	35
6	48	47	34	49
7	57	42	48	45
8	55	41	31	59
9	59	38	24	42
10	62	36	41	65
11	63	31	71	64
12	65	25	55	59

If you recall, the correlation between time and temperature A was strong. We'll look at that relationship on a regression model using the Analysis ToolPak in Excel.

Creating the Regression Worksheet

Begin by creating a regression worksheet using the data. Follow the steps below.

1. Copy the data table into a new worksheet in Excel.
2. Select Data and then Data Analysis from the top menu.

3. Select Regression and click OK.

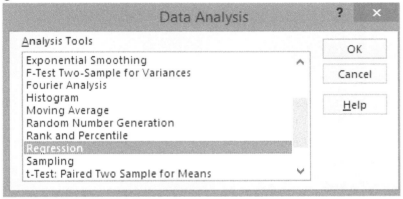

4. Select Temperate A as your Y input range and Time as your X input range.

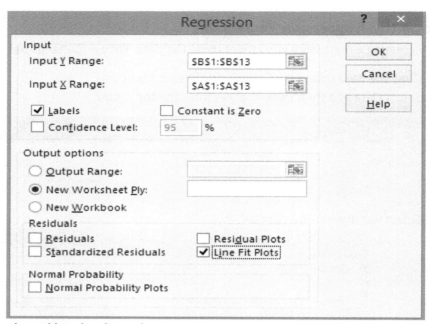

5. If you selected header data when inputting ranges, check that labels are included.
6. Check the box for new worksheet.
7. Check the box for line fit plots.
8. Click OK.

Excel generates a new workbook with a number of statistical outputs. The relevant values for the purpose of this chapter are found under "Multiple R" and "R Square."

	A	B	C	D	E	F
	SUMMARY OUTPUT					
	Regression Statistics					
	Multiple R	0.981167				
	R Square	0.96269				
	Adjusted R Square	0.958958				
	Standard Error	2.493675				
	Observations	12				
0	ANOVA					
1		*df*	*SS*	*MS*	*F*	*gnifica*
2	Regression	1	1604.483	1604.483	258.0211	1.81E
3	Residual	10	62.18415	6.218415		
4	Total	11	1666.667			
5						
6		*Coefficients*	*andard Err*	*t Stat*	*P-value*	*Lower*
7	Intercept	27.56061	1.534751	17.95771	6.13E-09	24.14
8	Time	3.34965	0.208532	16.06304	1.81E-08	2.885
9						

The Multiple R value is the correlation coefficient. You can see that the coefficient in this case matches the correlation coefficient calculated for this data set in the last section. The r^2 value for this data set is 0.96, which means almost all the variation in temperature in this data set is related to a change in time.

Because you selected the line fit plots box when creating your regression analysis, Excel has also generated a scatter diagram and a best fit plot.

Time Line Fit Plot

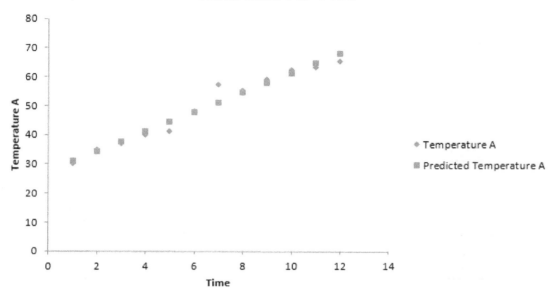

The chart shows all of the actual data points in blue and predicted data points along a best fit line in orange. Those data points are calculated by Excel using a formula created from the data. You can display the formula by making design changes to the graph. Follow the steps below to display the formula.

1. Click on the graph in Excel.
2. Select Design.
3. Select Add Chart Element.

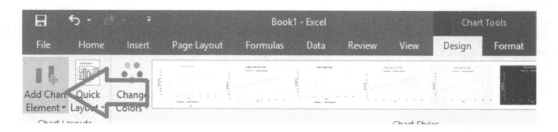

4. Select Trendline, More Trendline Options.

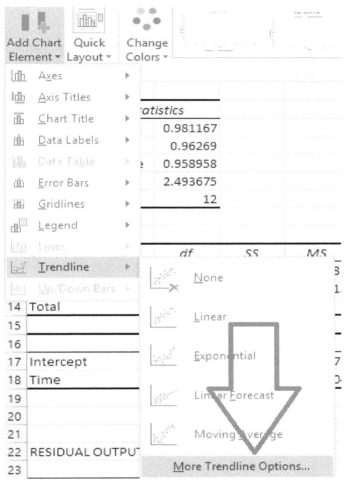

5. Select the option for the predicted trend line and click OK.

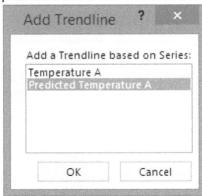

6. Click the box to display the equation on the chart.

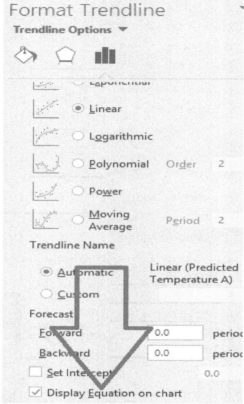

7. Note the trend equation on the graph.

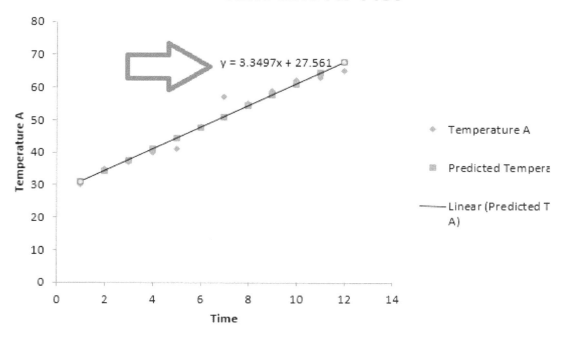

Time Line Fit Plot

In this case, the equation is y = 3.3497x + 27.561.

The r^2 value, if you recall, is 0.96, which means that our linear equation is going to be very good at determining the approximate temperature in our process as a relation to time.

At 5 minutes, for example, our equation predicts that the temperature is 44.30.

$$Y = 3.3497(5) + 27.561$$

At 25 minutes, our equation predicts that the temperature is 111.30.

Regression test with low correlation

To see how regression tests might look with low correlation, repeat the steps above with the data for temperature C.

◢	A	B	C
1	SUMMARY OUTPUT		
2			
3	*Regression Statistics*		
4	Multiple R	0.107776	
5	R Square	0.011616	
6	Adjusted R Square	-0.08722	
7	Standard Error	17.19736	
8	Observations	12	

Again, the correlation coefficient is very low. The r^2 value is also very low; according to this model, only about 1 percent of the variation in temperature is related to time.

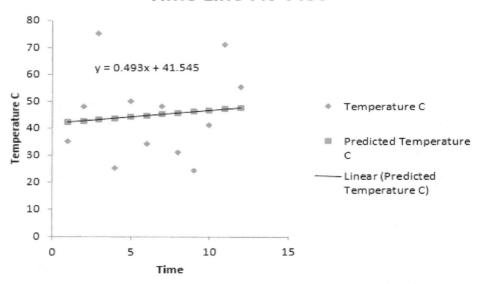

If you format it to do so, Excel will create a predicted line and a linear trend equation. Given the extremely low r^2 value, though, you know that this equation is not useful in making any real predictions about the temperature for a given time. You only have to look at the graph to see this is true. For a time around 3, the equation predicts a temperature of just over 40. The actual temperature, however, was 75. And that number doesn't just reflect an outlier that might point to a problem of data collection or a temporary process issue; the data throughout the chart is skewed far away from the line.

Using Correlation and Regression in Six Sigma

Correlation and regression are useful tools, usually deployed by teams in the measure, analyze, or improve stages of a DMAIC project. The tools don't apply to all data and are not useful in all situations where they might apply. One of the things that a Six Sigma expert develops over time is the ability to decide which tools might be relevant given certain data and situations. Because Excel and other statistical analysis software make it easy for Six Sigma experts and teams to "play" with data in various graphical and statistical analysis, there is no harm in creating correlation or regression analyses for data to explore connections between variables. This is true as long as you are careful about what conclusions you draw. When in doubt, it's always best to back conclusions up with multiple types of statistical analysis.

Continuous and ratio data

Both correlation and regression work with continuous or ratio data, and both sets of variables have to be quantitative in nature. For example, you can't have x variables that are the names of people and y variables that are the number of outputs.

Suzy	10
Jim	11
Rhonda	15
Misha	14
Aisha	13

The above chart is an example of the type of data that would not apply to regression and correlation analysis, but *might* be analyzed using tools such as Pareto charts or pie charts.

Correlation requires two quantifiable data elements. Regression requires data that can be written as function:

$$y = f(x)$$

Some examples of data that can be written as a function include:

- Distance
    - Y, the distance, is function of time, speed, acceleration, etc.
- Hardness of a substance
    - Y, the hardness, is a function of temperature, alloy, etc.
- Experienced (feels like) temperature
    - Y, the temperature it feels like, is a function of the actual temperature, wind, humidity, etc.
- BMI (body mass index)
    - Y, the BMI, is a function of height and weight

Why use correlation and regression?

Correlation and regression can be applied by Six Sigma experts at a number of points in a DMAIC process. During the analyze phase, teams can use these tools to help verify relationships between inputs or to help bolster understanding of root cause analysis. While correlation and regression don't prove causation, they don't negate causation either. A strong correlation doesn't prove causation, but if a team already believes causation is a factor, then a strong regression model helps validate that assumption. This is especially true if a team couples regression modeling with trial-and-error hypothesis testing.

For example, a Six Sigma team might conduct brainstorming and fishbone diagrams, coming to the conclusion that a certain input, A, is causing variation in an output, B. The team's Six Sigma experts conduct regression testing, which shows that variation in B is definitely related strongly to variation in A. The team can remove A from the process – or alter A in some way – and measure the process again. The team can then use hypothesis testingto determine if their changes created a statistical difference in the output.

An even more important function of regression in the DMAIC process is determining optimum input values so teams have a goal for control. Consider the example data used throughout this chapter. What if the team exploring this sample data was working with a process that involved mixing ingredients at a specific temperature range to create certain results? If the continuous time a mixing machine runs causes temperature fluctuations, those fluctuations would create variation in the final product. If the team discovered that the temperature range 40 to 50 degrees correlated to the most optimal product output, then the team could use the equation provided by the regression model to determine at what time range the mixing machine should be operated.

Consider the data for Temperature A again:

Time	Temperature A
1	30
2	35
3	37
4	40
5	41
6	48
7	57
8	55
9	59
10	62
11	63
12	65

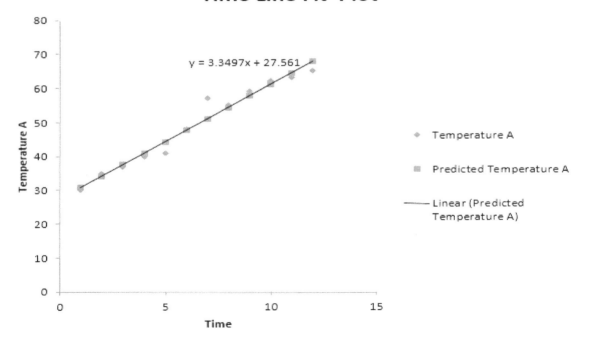

This data had both a strong correlation coefficient and a strong r^2 value, which means the team can rely on the equation for the best fit line.

In this case, to find the time values relating to a range between 40 and 50 degrees, the team would solve for x when y = 40 and when y = 50.

$40 = 3.3497x + 27.561$

$40 - 27.561 = 3.3497x$

$12.439 = 3.3497x$

3.71 = x when y = 40

$50 = 3.3497x + 27.561$

$50 - 27.561 = 3.3497x$

$22.439 = 3.3497x$

6.69 = x when y = 50

Using these results, the team decides that mixing must be done when the machine has been on between 3.71 and 6.69 minutes. They create a change in the process that involves starting the mixing procedure after the machine has warmed up for 4 minutes.

UNIT 5: INTERMEDIATE STATISTICS

CHAPTER 20: NON-NORMAL PROBABILITY DISTRIBUTIONS

In chapter 18, we discussed the normal probability curve, which is also called the Gaussian distribution. While it's true that the normal probability curve is the most important and commonly used distribution in statistics and by Six Sigma teams, it's also true that every set of data is not going to fall along the normal probability distribution. This chapter covers non-normal probability distributions, how to recognize some of the more common distributions through graphical analysis, and some information about using statistical analysis with such distributions.

Some of the simpler statistical calculations for non-normal probability distributions are included in this chapter, along with details for how to handle those calculations manually. Calculations for all of the distributions mentioned are not included, because they can be very complex and almost no one handles these calculations manually. In unit 6, we'll cover how to calculate probabilities using a wide variety of distributions in Minitab.

Reviewing Normal Probability Distributions

Before moving forward, it's important to revisit some of the fundamental information about the normal curve covered in chapter 18. First, remember that the normal distribution is related to *continuous data*. This means that your data is associated with random variables that can take the form of any of an infinite number of points along an interval. Temperature over time is a continuous type of data. Yes, you might never see the temperature of a room fall below 40 degrees F, but within a range such as 40 degrees and 80 degrees are an infinite number of continuous data points if you measured to a high enough degree of accuracy.

Remember that **discrete data** is not continuous in nature. Discrete data is typically about categorical occurrences. In some cases, discrete data can be converted to continuous data to allow Six Sigma teams to use more statistical analysis tools when working with the information. When that isn't possible, however, you cannot use the normal curve or related statistical analysis on discrete data. Discrete data usually involves either a binomial distribution or a Poisson distribution; both will be covered later in this chapter.

Anatomy of a Normal Curve

The normal curve, when presented in graphical format or on a histogram, is typically symmetrical in nature. The data elements tend to concentrate along the center of the curve, with elements fanning out slowly on either side as the curve drops ever toward zero.

While a visual inspection of data through graphical analysis can help determine if data might be normal, there are several continuous distribution curves that look a lot like normal curves. That's why we apply statistical tests, such as the Chi-Squared Goodness-of-Fit Test discussed in chapter 18, to determine whether data is actually normal. Don't confuse the Chi-Squared Goodness-of-Fit Test with the Chi-Squared distribution, which makes an appearance later in this chapter. One is a statistical test and the other is a probability distribution.

The normal curve:

- Is symmetrical
- Is most commonly required for inferential statistics
- Is described statistically using both the mean and standard deviation
    - The curve centers on the mean
    - The number of standard deviations away from the mean changes the probability of the amount of data under the curve

Non-Normal Continuous Distributions

Exponential Distribution

The exponential distribution creates a histogram or trend line that is exponential in nature. It decreases exponentially as you travel across the x-axis. See the image below for an example.

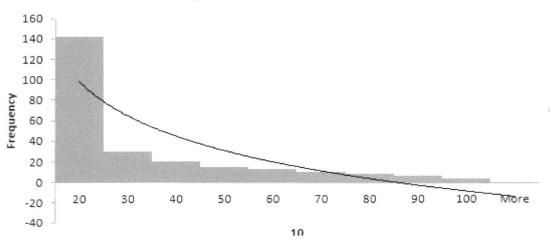

In an exponential distribution, the data is not organized around the mean as in the normal probability curve, but at one end of the x-axis. The data used to create the histogram above had a mean of 24.79 but a median of 16. Often, when working with non-normal data, the median is a more applicable data point than the mean for graphical analysis. If you locate the median on the x-axis of an exponential histogram, you know that 50 percent of the other data points fall before it and 50 percent after it.

Exponential distributions are often used when working with data sets that include arrival times, the average or mean time between failures in a process, wait-line theories, or the distance – in time or space – between interesting points of occurrence in data, processes, or experiments. The exponential distribution is particularly valuable when working with certain Poisson distributions. If you recall, Poisson distributions are discrete rather than continuous, which means Six Sigma teams are limited in what statistical tools can be used to analyze the data. However, the exponential distribution can often be used to describe the rate of change within the data that is distributed in a Poisson distribution, providing a method for creating continuous data that can be analyzed.

The exponential curve:

- Never appears symmetrical
- Is described statistically by the mean of the data and a value known as lambda

Here is another graphical representation of an exponential distribution generated in Minitab, which is a statistical analysis software.

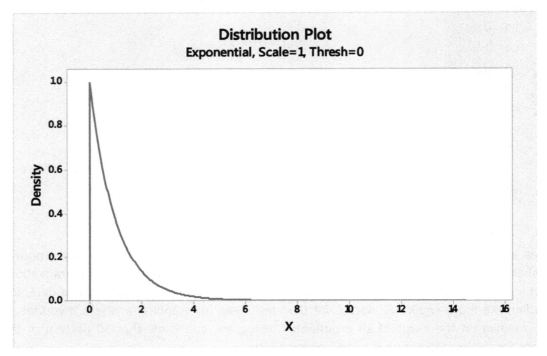

As with the normal distribution, you *can* run a statistical test in Excel to determine if your data is exponential. The test is basically the same Chi-Squared Goodness-of-Fit test we used in chapter 18. The same idea is used: you first predict the number of data points you would find in each bin in a perfect exponential curve given the statistical data regarding your set. You then compare the actual breakdown of your data against expected numbers to find the Chi-Squared value, which is used to evaluate your hypothesis that the data is exponential.

Because we are going to introduce using Minitab for statistical analysis functions in the next few units, and because Minitab handles Chi-Squared Goodness-of-Fit testing and many other statistical calculations automatically, we won't cover detailed steps for testing each type of data distribution in Excel. Because most of the tests that can be performed using the free Analysis ToolPak in Excel require normally distributed data, the steps for testing for normal data in Excel in chapter 18 should be sufficient for much of your Excel-only based work.

Lognormal Distribution

At first, the lognormal distribution might appear to be an exponential distribution, but on a graphical analysis, it is obviously constrained by zero. The lognormal distribution on a histogram is asymmetrical, with the trend line appearing more as a wave that moves across the page. The location and size of the wave varies with each data set, and the shape can even be very different from the one below.

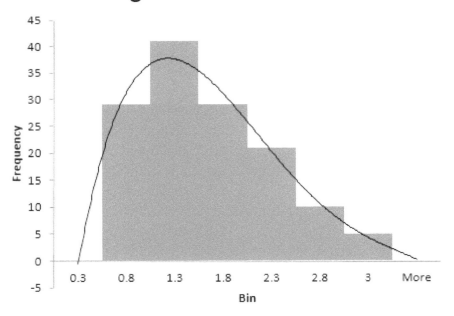

Lognormal distributions are often used when working with data sets that describe time durations, such as the time a process or machine is down, or distribution of assets or wealth among the population. Anytime data has a positive skew, which means it the tail of the data is to the right, then a lognormal distribution might be possible. Consider the example of wealth within a population. If we only consider the amount of income each household within a population reports, almost no household will report an income of zero, and it's impossible to have an income of less than zero. (Yes, you can have a net worth that is negative, and you can have a cash flow that is negative if you consider income and expenses, but for our example, we're only discussing income.)

Now, in a random sample of income from across a large population – a city, for example -- data is likely to be lognormal. As you move further right in the bins on a histogram – representing increasing dollar figures of income – there are fewer households that will fall into each bin. As you reach the highest dollar bins, you'll likely see the fewest households represented on a histogram. While the effect is similar to the positive exponential distribution seen above, there are some differences. The lognormal distribution of the wealth doesn't typically begin with the highest number of data points in the first bin; more often, you'll see a small number of or no data points in the first bin, followed by a quick rise to a median point, and then a sloping trail to the right.

The lognormal distribution:

- Typically describes a data set with values in large ranges
- Can be described with both mean and standard deviation
- Always has a positive skew

Here is another image of a lognormal distribution, generated from Minitab.

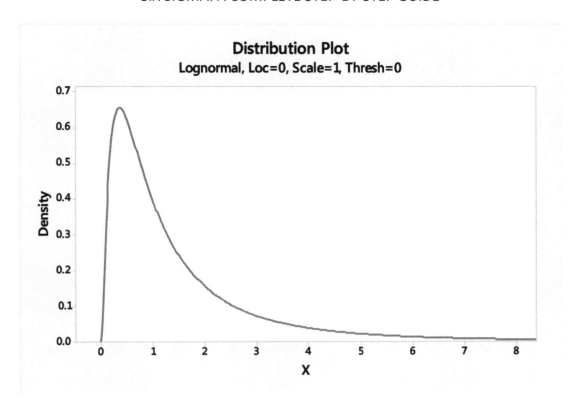

Weibull Distribution

Just to make things more confusing, probabilities can fall into families of distributions, such as the Weibull distributions. Data that fits a Weibull distribution *might also* fit another distribution, including all of those discussed previously in this chapter. Note that Weibull distributions relate to continuous data, so the data would not likely fit a discrete data distribution.

Look at the Weibull distributions below, which were created in Minitab. Do these images look familiar?

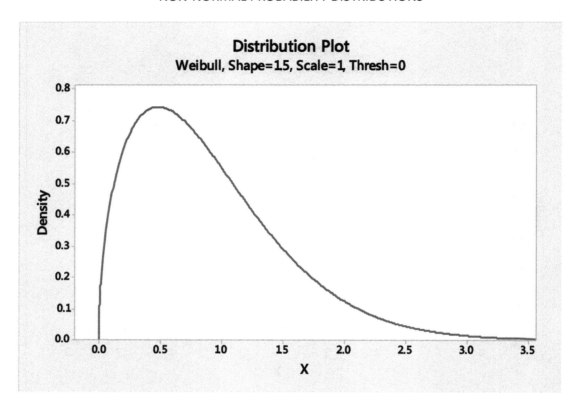

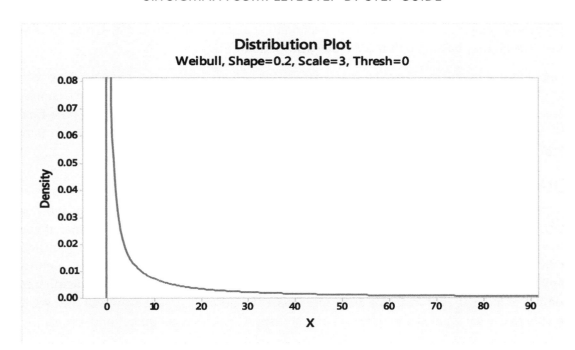

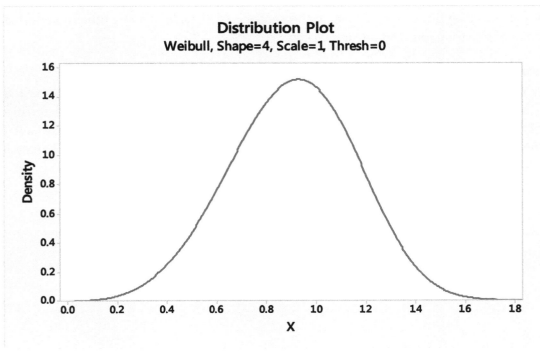

The curves appear to fit the lognormal, exponential, and normal distributions, respectively, even though they each also fit the Weibull distribution.

Weibull distributions can describe many data types and are often used when working with reliability applications and failure probabilities that change or vary with time. For example, the chance that a plasma screen will be damaged by burn-in increases both over the time the screen is used *and* over the time that a single still image is displayed on a screen. Data associated with such a concern might feature a Weibull distribution.

Other Types of Continuous Distributions

As previously stated, you will commonly work with normal distributions when applying statistical analysis. Even if the underlying distribution of your data set is not normal, if you have a large, random sample of continuous data, you are usually able to perform statistical analyses that are reserved for normal data thanks to the **Central Limit Theorem**. The Central Limit Theorem states that the distribution of the mean of a large, identically distributed number of independent variables will approximate the normal curve. Because of this, you'll be able to use software like Minitab to apply statistical analysis to a number of data sets.

It's still a good idea to be able to recognize common continuous distributions that are not normal, including those listed above. In this section, we'll highlight a few other non-normal continuous distributions and provide images.

Cauchy Distribution

In a graphical representation, the Cauchy distribution often looks like an elongated normal curve with a tighter peak. While the Cauchy distribution does share some characteristics with the normal curve, the data itself is not normal. In fact, the distribution doesn't have a defined mean or variance, which makes it not useful for many common statistical analysis tools used in Six Sigma.

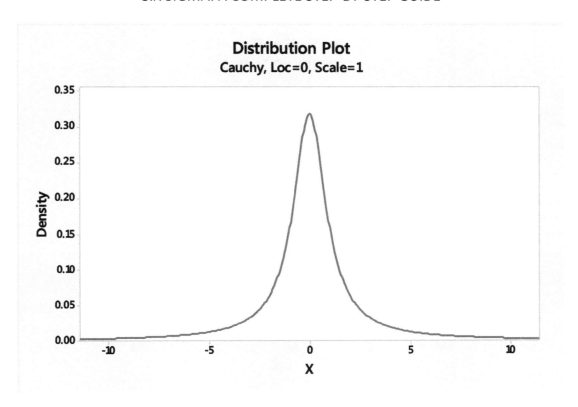

Logistic Distribution

The logistic distribution also appears to approximate the normal curve, and is, in fact, used in some science and math functions to approximate other symmetrical distributions. This is because the CDF of a logistic distribution is more consistently calculable. Remember that the CDF is the cumulative density function and calculates the probability that a given data point is less than or equal to X, where X is any point on the x-axis of a probability curve.

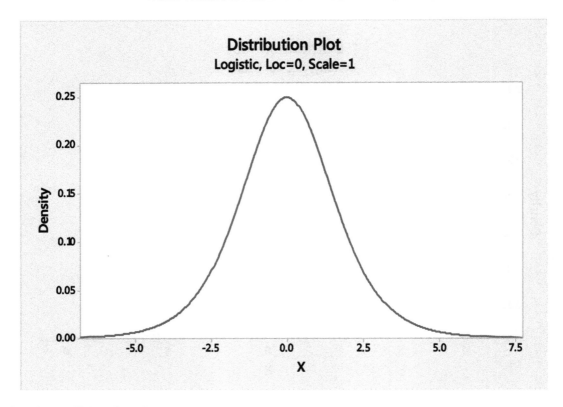

Laplace Distribution

The Laplace Distribution is often referred to as the bilateral exponential distribution or the double-exponential distribution. You can see from the image below, the Laplace distribution does seem to pair exponential distributions back to back.

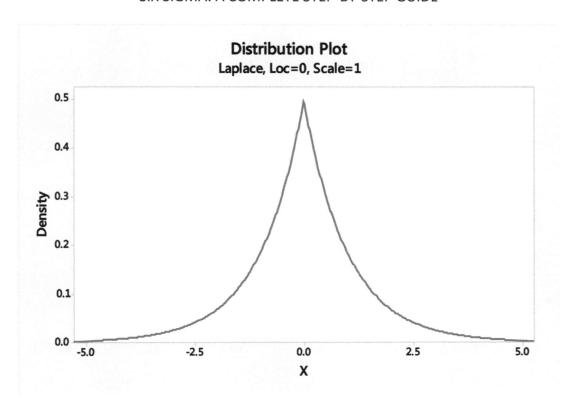

Uniform Distribution

A uniform distribution occurs when data points are divided evenly among bins. Exact uniform distributions are almost never going to occur in randomly-sampled data, which means Six Sigma teams that see such distributions in data should check the authenticity of the data. Uniformity often points to an error of measurement, problem with the measurement system, a non-random sample, or an issue with a process.

In some very specific cases, uniform distributions *could* point to success. For example, in a manufacturing plant, one machine might make dowels that are used later in the manufacturing process. If the dowels must measure 4 inches for functionality later, and a random sampling of dowels across all time buckets for the machine show 4-inch dowels being made, then uniformity equals success.

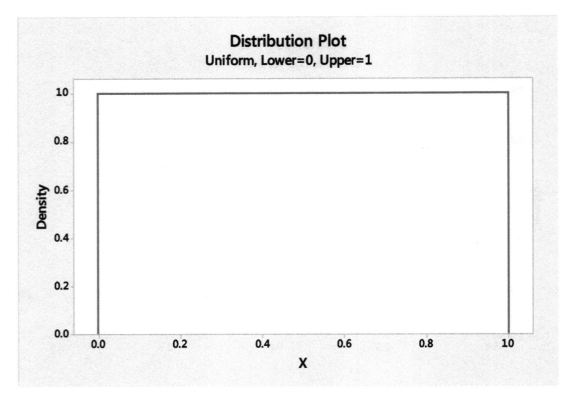

Beta Distribution

Like Weibull distributions, Beta distributions can take on a number of shapes, two of which are pictured below. Beta distributions are considered extremely flexible, and can become stand-ins for other distributions given certain statistical parameters.

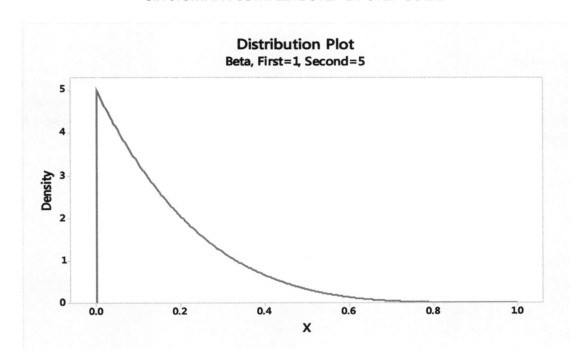

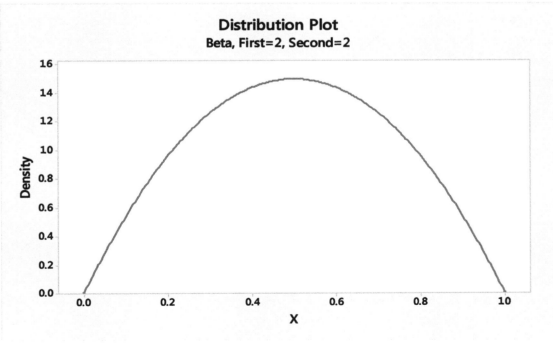

Gamma

Gamma distributions are similar to Beta and Weibull distributions, in that they take on a number of shapes. In fact, some distributions that aren't covered in this chapter are actually just more specific forms of the Gamma distribution. Gamma distributions are, however, always skewed to the right.

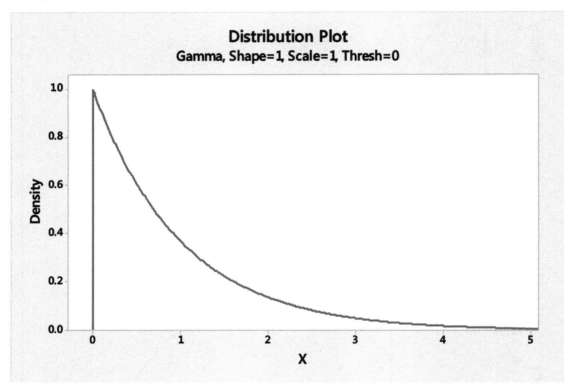

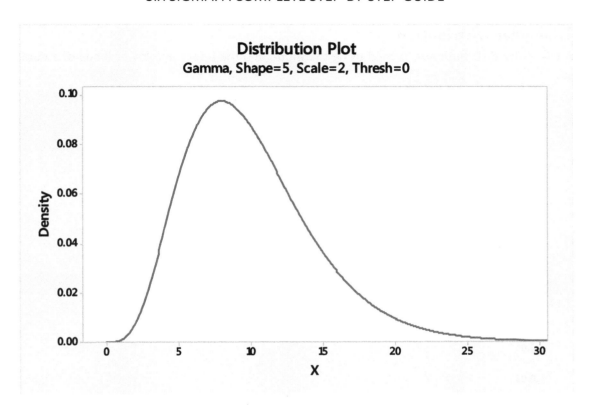

Triangular Distribution

A triangular distribution is formed using the mode and the upper and lower limits of a data set.

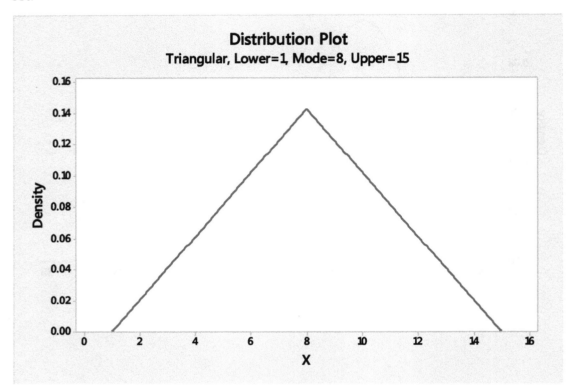

Non-Normal Discrete Distributions

Binomial Distribution

A binomial distribution is used when you are dealing with discrete data and there are only two outcomes for each trial or sample. In short, binomial distributions relate to attribute data: Yes or no, pass or fail, one or the other.

A binomial distribution assumes that the outcome of any given trial is independent of the outcome of another trial. If you flip a coin, it will either be heads or tails. If you flip it again, it again will be heads or tails, with a 50 percent probability for either outcome. It doesn't matter what happened with the first flip of the coin.

In most cases when considering attribute outcomes, the probability is not distributed evenly between the two events, as it is with a coin flip. Instead, there is a probability of success (notated as p) and a probability of failure (notated as $1 - p$). For example, if a machine making parts creates defects in 5 percent of the parts, then you have two outcomes for each part made. Either the part will be defective, or it will not be defective.

For this example, p (the outcome that the part will be defective) equals 0.05, and $1 - p$ (the outcome that the part will not be defective) is 0.95. If you select one random part, the chance of getting a defective part is 0.05.

(It's worth noting before moving on the seeming discrepancy in the above two paragraphs. First, we said that the probability of success was notated as p. Then, we said that the probability of pulling a defective part is p, or 0.05. In business terms, pulling a defective part would not be deemed a success. However, *in statistical terms,* we are not talking about the quality nature of the outcome. We are talking about whether an outcome will successfully match the definition we have created. In this case, whether the outcome will be defective.)

The Binomial distribution of the data described above on a histogram might appear as follows:

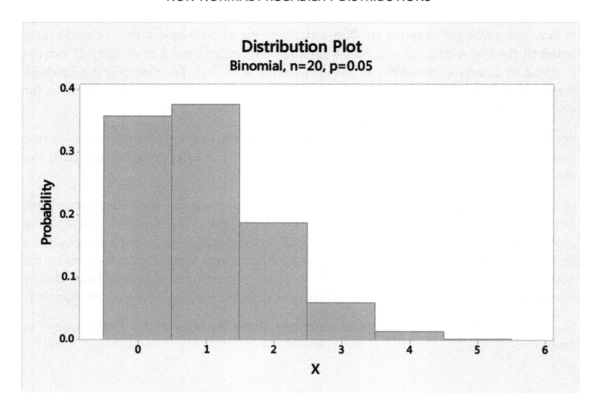

When you are dealing with binomial data sets, you can use the Binomial Distribution Probability Function to determine the probability of the number of successes you will have within a given number of trials *given the sample data* you have. The answers generated by the Binomial Distribution Probability Function correlate to the histogram generated by Minitab given the same information.

To understand what we mean by this, let's consider the example of the coin toss again. For this example, imagine a coin is tossed 10 times, and we consider heads to be success. The chance of success (heads) for each coin flip is 0.5. Given that information, Minitab creates the histogram below.

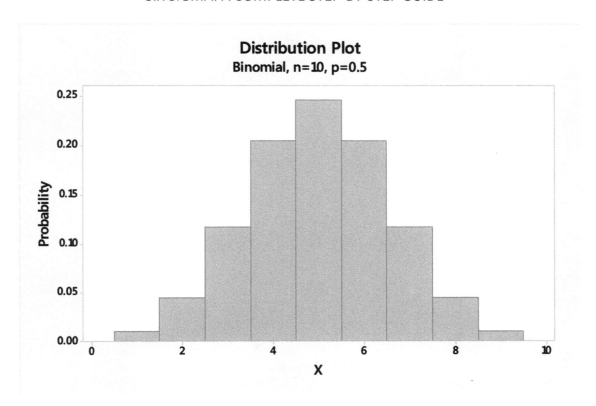

This graph shows us that, if we toss the coin 10 times, the chance of getting 1 success in all those 10 tosses is very small – as is the chance of getting 9 successes. The chance of getting 5 successes out of 10 is much higher – but not actually 50 percent.

To apply this concept to a real-world situation, let's look again at our machine process, which produces defective parts at a rate of 0.05. Again, the histogram below illustrates the data that might occur if we took 20 random samples from the process.

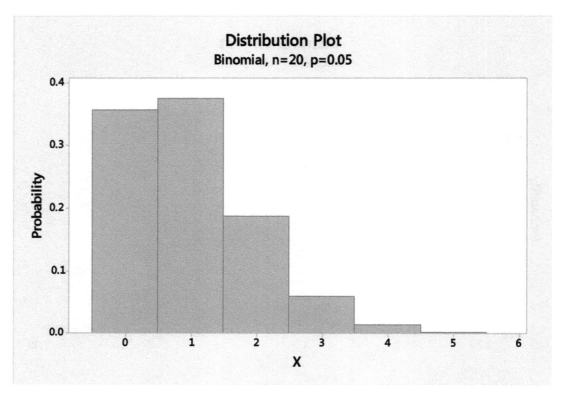

The probability that we will have 0 successes (defective parts) in our sample of 20 is a bit over 0.35. The probability that we will have 1 defective part is a bit higher, but the chance that we'll have five defective parts in 20 is very, very small. The probability of more than 5 defective parts in our batch of 20 is almost nonexistent.

What does this tell a real-world Six Sigma team? Imagine a quality control team took 20 random samples from this process every day. For two weeks straight, the quality team records no defects within those samples. If the Six Sigma team believes a process generates 0.05 defective parts, then a lack of defective parts in the samples shows that (1) something has changed to improve the performance of the process, (2) the measurement system is defective, or (3) the samples are not actually random.

If you increase the number of trials to 100, the binomial distribution remains.

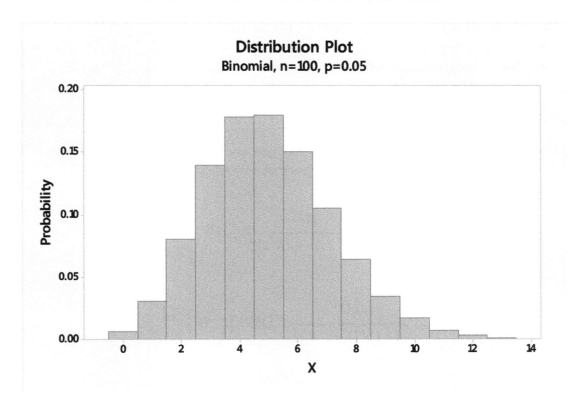

Here, you can see that the greatest likelihood for this process is that, within 100 samples, 4 or 5 will be defective. It is unlikely, given a defect rate of 0.05, that a random sample of 100 would ever have more than 11 or 12 defective parts.

What we have done graphically, you can also do mathematically using the Binomial Distribution Probability Function. The equation is provided below.

$$p(x) = \frac{n!}{x!\,(n-x)!} p^x q^{n-x}$$

For this formula:

- x is equal to the number of successes desired
- n is equal to the number of trials

- p is equal to the probability of success in each trial
- q is equal to 1 – p
- The exclamation point indicates a factorial.
  - 3! = 3x2x1 = 6
  - 4! = 4x3x2x1 = 24
  - 5! = 5x4x3x2x1 = 120

Using the Binomial Distribution Probability Function, we can calculate the probability that 20 trials will yield 4 defective parts in a process that delivers 0.05 defective parts.

$$p(x) = \frac{n!}{x!\,(n-x)!} p^x q^{n-x}$$

$$p(x) = \frac{20!}{4!\,(20-4)!} (.05^4)(.95^{20-4})$$

$$p(x) = \frac{2432902008176640000}{24(20922789888000)} (.05^4)(.95^{16})$$

$$p(x) = \frac{2432902008176640000}{502146957312000} (0.00000625)(0.440127)$$

$$p(x) = (4845)(0.00000625)(0.440127)$$

$$p(x) = 0.013$$

The probability of pulling 4 defective parts is very low, as was shown on the distribution graph.

What are some reasons this type of calculation might matter in the business world or for Six Sigma teams?

Consider a company that sells chocolates. If 20 chocolates come in each box, what is the chance that a customer might receive defective product in his or her box? What is the chance that a customer might receive more than one defective chocolate? Teams can calculate these probabilities after sampling data to determine how often a process generates defective product.

What if a Six Sigma team randomly samples the chocolate process and determines that the process operates at a 4-sigma level. Remember from Unit 1 that at 4 sigma, a process generates 6,210 defects per million opportunities. Let's assume that means 6,210 defective chocolates per million created, or a chance of a chocolate being defective equal to 0.00621.

In a box of 20 chocolates, with p = 0.00621, Minitab generates the following binomial histogram.

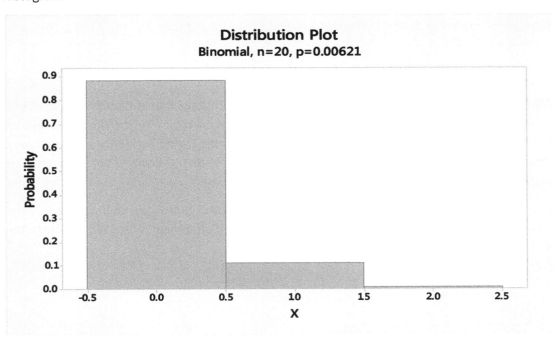

From the above histogram, you can see that the likelihood of a box having no defective chocolates is approximately 88 percent. The likelihood of a box having one defective chocolate is approximately 10 percent. The likelihood of a box having two or more defective chocolates is almost nonexistent.

What does this mean for the business? It depends on the goals of the business or the Six Sigma project. If the Six Sigma team was tasked with improving customer satisfaction or decreasing the rate of return of chocolate boxes, then a 10 percent probability of a defective chocolate in a box might be something the team wants to address. However, if customer satisfaction is strong and return costs are low, then the potential complaints or returns associated with a small number of boxes might be acceptable to the business – particularly if a Six Sigma team discovers that reducing the error rate would cost well over the amount that it costs to handle the errors.

By applying the binomial distribution in this manner to pass/fail, yes/no, or defect/no defect, Six Sigma teams can calculate data that is useful in a variety of real-world situations. The ability to tie costs to defects makes it even more possible to evaluate this type of information using binomial probability, because teams can speak in terms of the probability that different processes or outcomes will cost varying amounts of money – or save varying amounts of money – both of which are metrics company leadership will be interested in hearing.

Poisson Distribution

The Poisson distribution is often used when dealing with data that is distributed randomly within time, distance, or other unit of measurement. For example, the distribution might be relevant when dealing with calls per hour in a call center, traffic accidents per week on a specific block or street, or number of defects in a batch. In fact, the word "per" in a metric is a good indication that the Poisson distribution might be useful.

As you can see from the graph before, the Poisson distribution can look a little like the normal curve, but it is not symmetrical. This curve, based off a mean of 4, tails slightly to the right.

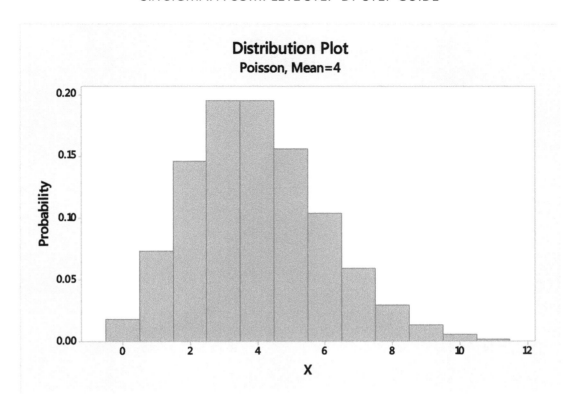

This graph of a Poisson distribution with a mean of 42 looks even more like the normal curve. If you look very close, however, and count the bins to the left and right of the mean, you see that the curve tails very slightly to the right. This is a good example of why statistical analysis is needed in addition to graphical analysis when working with data. Data can approximate the normal curve on a graph without being normal.

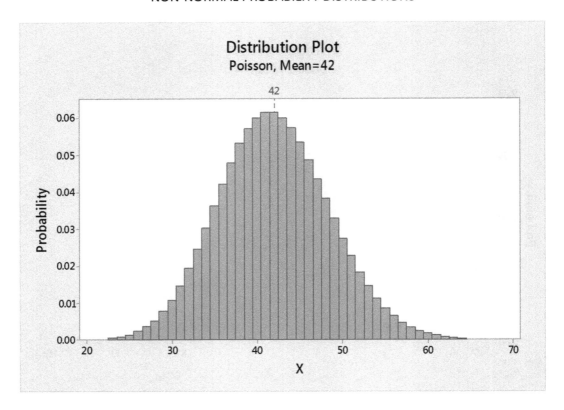

One interesting thing to note about the Poisson distribution is that it relates closely to the exponential distribution. Remember, the Poisson distribution is discrete, not continuous. The distribution is an analysis of how many of one thing occurs per another. For example, consider the number of errors in a data entry employee's work each hour.

Errors Per Hour
5
8
5
5
4
7
4
12
3
6
9
9
7
3
6
5
7
6
4
5
5
2
4
7
6

Here is the histogram of the above data:

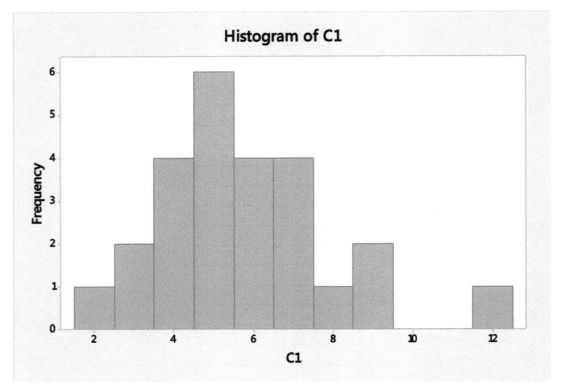

Histogram of C1

The data isn't continuous. Instead, it is categorical. How many errors does the employee make in hour 1, hour 2, hour 3, and so forth. However, if the process is following a Poisson distribution, then the time between each event in the process when looked at continuously yields an exponential distribution. Understanding this relationship can help Six Sigma teams convert Poisson distributions to exponential distributions when necessary for statistical analysis. The use of this conversion within a Six Sigma environment is not likely to be common for most teams, but could be useful in special applications – some of which we'll cover in the industry-specific sections at the end of this book.

The Poisson distribution might be applicable when the following statements can be used to describe your data:

- Data describes events that occur at a random interval measurement – the word "per" is usually involved.

- The sample size (number of intervals) is at least 16. If you are measuring per hour, you have at least 16 hours' worth of data. If you are measuring per foot, you have at least 16 feet of data.
- You know that the population size is 10 times the size of the sample or bigger. If you are measuring worker productivity, for example, you can't take the first 16 hours the worker is on the job.
- Event occurrences are independent of each other. In our data-entry example, if we are counting each unnecessary keystroke as an error, we might count the backspace. However, the backspace is dependent on the person making another error. If the person types "b" when he or she meant "n," that's one error. If we count the backspace as error 2, then the errors are not independent.
- The probability of occurrences is less than 0.1. Consider the data-entry example above. When using a 10-key number pad, the average rate of entry for employees in the United States is approximately 8,000 per hour. If an employee is making 8 – 12 errors an hour, the probability of an error for each keystroke is well below 0.1.
- The rate of occurrence per interval is constant. The average number of phone calls per hour is 50; the average number of errors per hour is 6.

If data fits the Poisson distribution, you can use an equation to determine the probability of certain events.

The Poisson equation is:

$$P(x) = \frac{e^{-\mu}\mu^{x}}{x!}$$

Within the Poisson equation:

- e equals the Poisson constant, which is 2.71828
- μ is the mean or average of the process
- X is the specific case or data point; remember that the exclamation point indicates a factorial.

For example, if a Six Sigma team was working to improve processes in a call center, they might have gathered data that indicates the average number of people on hold for a customer service representative at any given time is 10. Given that information and a Poisson distribution when considering number of holds per increments of time, the team can use the Poisson equation to calculate probabilities related to various call scenarios.

What is the probability that there are 15 callers on hold at a given time?

$$P(x) = \frac{e^{-\mu}\mu^x}{x!}$$

$$P(x) = \frac{2.71828^{-10}10^{15}}{15!}$$

$$P(x) = \frac{2.71828^{-10}10^{15}}{1307674368000}$$

$$P(x) = \frac{2.71828^{-10}1,000,000,000,000,000}{1,307,674,368,000}$$

$$P(x) = \frac{45,400,235,147.3734}{1,307,674,368,000}$$

$$P(x) = 0.034$$

The probability of having exactly 15 callers on hold at a given time in the call center is 0.034, or approximately 3.4 percent.

That number in itself isn't extremely helpful to a business or Six Sigma team unless there is a specific protocol or process problem that occurs *only* when call holds hit exactly 15. It's not an extremely likely scenario. However, what if a Six Sigma team has noted that when the number of callers on hold hits 15 or above, a regularly staffed call center team is unlikely to catch up, resulting in continued high hold times and volumes. Knowing this, the team might inform the process owner that when hold numbers hit 15, it's time to move some resources from other areas to answering calls.

But how does a process owner or Six Sigma team plan appropriately? Do other resources need to constantly be on hand? Is the probability of this situation occurring high or low?

To answer the question, you can use the Poisson equation to find the probability of there being 0, 1, 2, 3, 4, 5, 6, 7, 8, 9, 10, 11, 12, 13, and 14 callers on hold at any given time. Because the probability of all possible outcomes totals to 1, you would subtract the sum of all those probabilities from 1 to determine the probability of the number of holds being 15 or more.

Mathematically, the concept is written as:

$$P(x \geqq 15) = 1 - P(0) + P(1) + P(2) + P(3) + P(4) + P(5) + P(6) + P(7) + P(8) + P(9) + P(10) + P(11) + P(12) + P(13) + P(14)$$

To manually calculate the above probability, you would have to use the Poisson equation for each P(x) listed above. You can also use statistical analysis software, such as Minitab, to make the calculations for you. We'll cover how to handle such analysis in Minitab in later chapters. For now, though, consider the chart below, which shows the probability of each x.

0	0.0000454
1	0.0004540
2	0.0022700
3	0.0075667
4	0.0189166

5	0.0378333
6	0.0630555
7	0.0900792
8	0.112599
9	0.125110
10	0.125110
11	0.113736
12	0.0947803
13	0.0729079
14	0.0520771

Summing the probabilities for each X provides a total probability that x will be less than 15 of 0.916541.

Alternatively, you can use statistical software to determine the cumulative probability – the area under the curve to the left of a certain point. The cumulative probabilities of x being less than or equal to 14 is 0.916541.

Therefore, the probability of x being 15 or greater is 1 – 0.916541, or 0.083459.

The probability that there are 15 or more callers on hold at any given time is about 0.083, or just over 8 percent. Given this probability, call center leadership can make a more educated decision about whether they want to pay for more staff or take a risk at hitting the higher call volume and having to play catch up for the rest of the shift.

Teams can use the Poisson distribution and calculations in this manner to understand the probabilities of different events occurring. They can also tie financial data to such events to make even better data-driven decisions.

Other Types of Discrete Distributions

Geometric Distribution

The geometric distribution is used when there are two outcomes for a trial, trials are independent, and there is a waiting time before the first occurrence. As with the binomial distribution, the outcome of each trial must be independent. A real-world use of the geometric distribution might include the number of inspections that occur before finding a defective part or the number of resumes or applications a recruiter reviews before finding the first candidate that meets minimal job requirements.

An example of the geometric distribution is seen below.

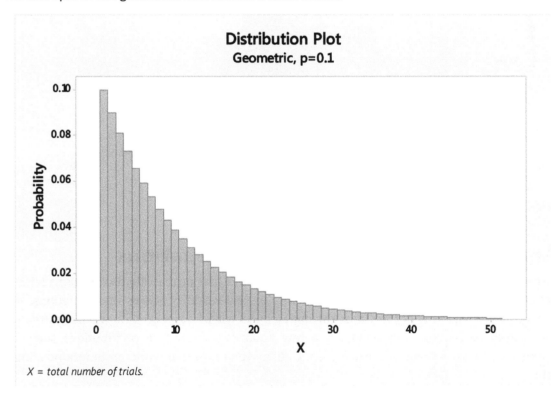

X = total number of trials.

Negative Binomial

The negative binomial distribution is also used with attribute data – fail/pass and other situations where there are only two outcomes for each trial. Again, the outcomes must be independent of each other; the probability of an occurrence must be the same across each trial, just as with the binomial distribution. The negative binomial distribution is often used when teams are trying to determine the probability of a certain number of passes or fails before reaching the sth pass or fail.

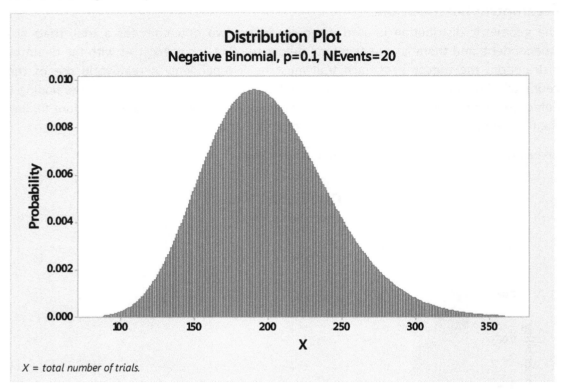

X = total number of trials.

Applying Data to Real-World Situations

Throughout this chapter, we've touched on some ways that probability distributions let Six Sigma teams apply raw data about processes to real-world concerns and situations. As previously stated, many of the statistical analyses you will perform on data will be related to the normal curve. But understanding a few equations related to distributions such as Binomial or Poisson helps you expand your ability to create real-world assumptions about data.

When you can determine the probability for certain events or data points, you can make educated decisions about a process. What is the probability that a cost-heavy event will occur? Is the cost associated with an event enough to create a reason for working to reduce the likelihood of that event? If the probability of a low-cost defect is high, are the total expenses associated with that defect likely to be higher than the total expenses associated with a high-cost defect that has an extremely low probability? These are just some of the questions that teams can use statistics and probability distributions to answer

CHAPTER 21:
HYPOTHESIS TESTING

Hypothesis tests are statistical tools used to draw conclusions based on data. With a basic understanding of the process and process performance, as well as real-time data – or as close to real-time data as possible – Six Sigma teams can draw statistical conclusions that are extremely accurate if they (1) ensure that the measurement systems are good, (2) have the right sample size, and (3) know how to set up the right type of hypothesis test.

Measurement systems analysis was discussed in Chapter 13. In this chapter, we'll talk about different types of hypothesis tests, how to set them up, and how to read the results. In Chapter 22, we'll cover how to choose the right sample size for various data types and hypothesis tests, and in the chapters on Minitab, you'll find a step-by-step guide for running tests in the software program. You can also run some tests in Excel using the Analysis Toolpak you previously downloaded.

Hypothesis Test Basics

Hypothesis tests cover three broad categories:

- Testing whether the data you have fits a data model. In Chapter 18, we conducted a hypothesis test to determine whether data fit the normal curve. We used the Chi-Squared Goodness-of-Fit Test, but ultimately, it was a hypothesis test.
- Comparing a statistic to a hypothesis about the data or population.
- Answering the question whether something changed within the data, often after a team has modified an input or other part of the process. In the case of most Six Sigma projects, the team probably wants to find out whether the process or outcome is improved.

While the type of hypothesis test you use depends on the answers you are seeking and the type of data you have, all of the tests follow essentially the same guidelines:

- You begin with a statistic or criteria that you usually compute from your sample data

- You create a null hypothesis and an alternate hypothesis, in keeping with the type of test you are dealing with
    - Remember, in chapter 18 when we ran the Chi-Squared Goodness-of-Fit Test:
        - The null hypothesis was that the data was normal
        - The alternate hypothesis was that the data was not normal
- The statistic or criteria is compared against a reference criteria or distribution
- How the calculated statistic compares to the reference criteria determines whether you accept the null hypothesis or reject the null hypothesis in favor of the alternative hypothesis

Hypothesis tests are a large part of inferential statistics, where we draw conclusions about the overall process or population by analyzing the sample data and measurements. When stating hypotheses, we are not making statements about the sample. We are making statements about the population or entire process.

A hypothesis is "the population mean is 5."

We don't need to make a hypothesis about the sample mean – we can calculate the sample mean.

Null Versus Alternative

Hypothesis tests have two main parts: the null hypothesis and the alternative hypothesis.

The null hypothesis is abbreviated as H_0 and is usually a statement about the data that reflects no effect or no difference. In chapter 18, we hypothesized that our data was normal. In effect, we were saying "there is no statistical difference between the distribution of our data and the distribution of data on a normal curve."

The alternative hypothesis is abbreviated as H_a and is usually a statement that is likely to be true if the null hypothesis is not true. In chapter 18, the alternative hypothesis was "there *is* a statistical difference between the distribution of our data and the distribution of data on a normal curve." In short, if we reject the null hypothesis, we accept the alternative hypothesis – in this case, that our data is not normal.

Typically, the null hypothesis is an equal statement of some type. The mean of the new process is equal to the mean of the new process. The distribution of the data is equal to the normal curve.

The alternative hypothesis is typically written as a not equals, a greater than, or a less than statement. The mean of the new process is greater than the mean of the old process. The distribution of the data is not equal to the normal curve. How you write the alternative hypothesis depends on the question you are asking and the type of hypothesis test you are running.

The Risk of Hypothesis Testing Error

Anytime you draw inferences about a population from sample data, there is at least some likelihood of error. With hypothesis testing, errors come in two types.

- **Type I Error:** The null hypothesis is rejected when it is actually true.
  - Also called producer risk
  - The probability of the risk is measured by alpha, where α is a probability between 0 and 1.
- **Type II Error**: The null hypothesis is accepted when it is actually false.
  - Also called the consumer risk
  - The probability of the risk is measured by beta, where β is a probability between 0 and 1.

To describe the risk – and set up our hypothesis test for what we deem to be an acceptable risk, a confidence level must be picked. The most common confidence level used is 95 percent, or $\alpha = 0.05$. Typically, the confidence level is set with the Type I error in mind, so you use alpha for the confidence level. The value of β then contributes to the sample size requirements and the power; sample size will be covered in the next chapter. Additional information about alpha and beta values is covered in the section in this chapter on running individual hypothesis tests.

A school administrator believes that the students in a certain classroom are being impacted by some environmental issue with that room. The administrator wants to see if the students in that room perform statistically lower on tests than the students throughout the school; she has already noted that different classes in that room are taught by other teachers who also teach in the other rooms, which means she has ruled out a teacher influence.

The administrator gathers data. The rate of failure for classes taught in any other classroom is 20 percent. Out of 142 students who have a class in the classroom in question, 38 are failing that particular class.

The hypothesis test would be written out with both a real-world statement and a statistical statement for both the null and alternative hypothesis.

Selecting the Right Hypothesis Test

To determine which hypothesis test to run, you must know:

- Which type of data you have (continuous/variable or discrete/attribute)
- The number of levels of interest for the input in question (1, 2, or more than two)
- Distribution of data (normal or non-normal)
- What you are testing (means, medians, variance, count, or proportions)

In this chapter, the hypothesis tests that are covered deal with 1 or 2 levels of interest.

In the following section, we'll introduce various types of hypothesis tests. Then, we'll walk through running some of these tests using statistical software.

Hypothesis Tests for Discrete Data

1-Proportion Test

- Used when there is only one factor for x
- Used when there is one level of interest for x (the input)
  - Typically, there is one set of data (the sample) and a target
- Used when comparing proportions (percentage, rates) between samples and a target
- Test is available in Minitab
  - Requires samples in columns *or* summary of data to include number of events, number of trials, and hypothesized proportion

The hypothesis test is set up as:

$$H_0 : P_{sample} = P_{target}$$

$$H_a : P_{sample} \neq P_{target}$$

Note that in the above set-up, the alternative hypothesis is set in a default to "not-equal." Minitab allows you to adjust the alternative hypothesis to a greater than or less than scenario if desired.

Example of the 1-Proportion Test:

- H_0: There is no difference in the failure rate between the classes taught in the specific classroom and those taught elsewhere.

  - $P_{classroom} = P_{elsewhere}$
  - $P_{classroom} = 0.2$
- H_a: The rate of failure is greater for those classes taught in the specific classroom.
  - $P_{classroom} > P_{elsewhere}$
  - $P_{classroom} > 0.2$

2 Proportion Test
- Used when there is only one factor for x
- Used when there are 2 levels of interest for x (the input)
  - Typically, there are two sets of data regarding the input and you are comparing those two sets of data
- Used when comparing proportions (percentage, rates) between samples or between samples and a target
- Test is available in Minitab
  - Requires samples in columns

The hypothesis test is set up as:

$$H_0 : P_1 = P_2$$

$$H_a : P_1 \neq P_2$$

Note that in the above set-up, the alternative hypothesis is set in a default to "not-equal." Minitab allows you to adjust the alternative hypothesis to a greater than or less than scenario if desired.

Example of the 2-Proportion Test:

Reconsider the example above about the school administrator and the classroom. Perhaps the school administrator determines that students in that classroom *do* in fact perform statistically differently from students in other classrooms. The administrator makes a decision to move the students in that classroom to another classroom. She then gathers data about test performance in the new classroom.

Now, the administrator has two sets of test performance data for the same students. The only variable that has changed is the classroom location. She wants to know, is there a difference between performance in the old room versus the new room?

- H_0: There is no difference in the failure rate between the old room and the new room.
  - $P_{old} = P_{new}$

- H_a: The rate of failure is less in the new classroom.

  - $P_{old} > P_{new}$

Hypothesis Tests for Continuous Normal Data
1-Sample T Test (or Paired T Test)
- Used when comparing means
- Typically used when dealing with smaller samples or when standard deviation is known.
  - When dealing with larger samples or when standard deviation is not known, use the 1-Sample Z-Test.
- 1-Sample T Test compares the mean of a sample to a target mean
- Paired T Test compares the mean of a sample against the mean of another sample for the same factor of X. Usually, the first sample is the baseline and the second sample is taken after a change is made; the test is run to see if the change made a difference.
- 1-Sample T Test is available in Minitab
  - Requires standard deviation, mean, and sample size as well as the target, or hypothesized mean.
- Paired T Test is available in Minitab and Excel's Analysis TookPak

The hypothesis test is set up as:

$$H_0 : \mu_1 = \mu_2$$

$$H_a : \mu_1 \neq \mu_2$$

Note that in the above set-up, the alternative hypothesis is set in a default to "not-equal." Minitab allows you to adjust the alternative hypothesis to a greater than or less than scenario if desired.

Example of the 1-Sample T Test

An agriculture company growing corn produced an average of 168 bushels of corn per acre each year for five years. The company made a change to its seeding process in an attempt to increase the yield of its fields. The harvest following the seed change resulted in an average of 175 bushels of corn per acre each year. Did the seeding change result in a statistically different outcome in yield per acre?

- H_0: There is no difference between the outcome after the seeding change and the outcome before it.
  - $\mu_{old} = \mu_{new}$
- H_a: The seeding change resulted in an increase in the average amount yielded per field.
  - $\mu_{old} < \mu_{new}$

Chi Square Test (or 1-Variance Test)
- Used when comparing standard deviation or variance
- Compares the standard deviation or variance between two samples of the same x factor (usually one sample is taken after a change to the process has been made) or compares the standard deviation or variance to a target or hypothesized statistic.
- Is available in Minitab
  - Requires sample data in two columns or summary data to include sample size with either sample standard deviation or sample variance *and* a hypothesized standard deviation or variance.

The hypothesis test is set up as:

$$H_0 : \vartheta_1 = \vartheta_2$$

$$H_a : \vartheta_1 \neq \vartheta_2$$

Note that in the above set-up, the alternative hypothesis is set in a default to "not-equal." Minitab allows you to adjust the alternative hypothesis to a greater than or less than scenario if desired.

Example of the Chi-Square Test (or 1-Variance Test)

A manufacturing plant makes the wheels that are put on dolly carts. The plant provides three sizes of wheels to a partner plant, which makes the dolly itself and uses the wheels to complete the process. The partner plant makes a complaint: The smallest wheels coming from the factory have enough variation in size to cause stability problems with the final product, resulting in defective dollies or wasted wheel parts.

The wheel-making plant launches a Six Sigma improvement project to reduce the variation of the size in the smallest wheels. The team measures for a baseline and finds that the standard deviation in the size of the wheels is 0.0409. The team makes changes to the process and measures again to compare the new standard deviation to the old.

- H_0: There is no difference between the standard deviations; the changes did nothing to statistically reduce the variation in the process.
    - $\vartheta_{new} = 0.0409$
- H_a: The improvements reduced the standard deviation in the process.
    - $\vartheta_{new} < 0.0409$

2-Sample T Test
- Used when comparing means
- Compares the means between two samples of the different x factors
- Is available in Minitab and Excel
    - Requires sample data in two columns or summary data to include sample size, sample mean, and standard deviation for both samples
- Requires you to note whether equal variances between the two samples are assumed or not

The 2-Sample T Test might seem like the 1-Sample T Test, because in the 1-Sample T Test, we discussed how you might compare a sample from before a change to a sample from after a change. However, the 2-Sample T Test is slightly different, because you are comparing two samples from different populations. For example, you might compare the mean body temperature for children who didn't receive the influenza vaccine to mean body temperature for children who *did* receive the vaccine. This is different than comparing mean body temperature for the same group of children from last year, when they didn't receive the vaccine, to this year, when they did receive the vaccine. The first example would use the 2-Sample T Test; the second (year-over-year) example would use the 1-Sample T Test.

The hypothesis test is set up as:

$$H_0 : \mu_1 = \mu_2$$

$$H_a : \mu_1 \neq \mu_2$$

Note that in the above set-up, the alternative hypothesis is set in a default to "not-equal." Minitab allows you to adjust the alternative hypothesis to a greater than or less than scenario if desired.

Example of the 2-Sample T Test

Two attorneys practicing in the same law firm are turning in very different amounts of billable hours, even though the partners note that the two lawyers have similar caseloads. One partner hypothesized that Attorney A's legal staff is taking too long to handle some tasks; because the firm bills at a certain time for administrative-style tasks regardless of how long those tasks take, if legal staff is taking too long for such tasks, they are spending time on work that can't be billed for.

To test the theory, data is gathered about the time legal staff spends on tasks. Specifically, a team looks at time spent on three tasks for which the legal staff is allowed to bill 15 minutes each: certain types of simple administrative phone, copying, or filing tasks.

- H_0: There is no difference between the average time Attorney A's staff takes and the average time Attorney B's staff takes for such tasks.
  - $H_0 : \mu_{AttorneyA} = \mu_{AttorneyB}$

- H_a: Attorney B's staff takes, on average, less time for these tasks.
  - $H_a : \mu_{\text{AttorneyA}} > \mu_{\text{AttorneyB}}$

Hypothesis Tests for Continuous Non-Normal Data

Chi-Square Test

The Chi-Square Test, which was described in the above section, can also be used to compare standard deviation between a sample and a hypothesized standard deviation when data is not normal.

One Sample Wilcox

- Used when comparing medians
- Compares the medians between a sample and a hypothesized sample *or* a new sample to a previous sample before changes were made
- Is available in Minitab
  - Requires sample data in a column and hypothesized mean
- Typically used when data is somewhat symmetrical; otherwise, you can use the 1-Sample Sign test in Minitab for the same thing

The hypothesis test is set up as:

$$H_0 : M1 = Mt$$

$$H_a : M1 \neq Mt$$

Note that in the above set-up, the alternative hypothesis is set in a default to "not-equal." Minitab allows you to adjust the alternative hypothesis to a greater than or less than scenario if desired.

Example of the One-Sample Wilcox

A real estate company wants to enter a high-dollar market, so they want to build some regional websites that cater to homebuyers looking for larger homes. Specifically, they want to cater to homebuyers who are purchasing homes with 4 or more bedrooms. Before the company can build websites and begin marketing, it needs to find neighborhoods where homes for sale typically have 4 or more bedrooms.

The real estate company gathers information about the median number of bedrooms in homes in a specific area.

- H_0: The median number of bedrooms is equal to 3.
  - $H_0 : Mbedrooms = 3$
- H_a: The median number of bedrooms is greater than 3 (4 or more).
  - $H_a : Mbedrooms > 3$

Mann-Whitney Test

- Used when comparing medians
- Compares the medians between samples of two factors of x
- Is available in Minitab
  - Requires sample data in columns

The hypothesis test is set up as:

$$H_0 : M1 = M2$$

$$H_a : M1 \neq M2$$

Note that in the above set-up, the alternative hypothesis is set in a default to "not-equal." Minitab allows you to adjust the alternative hypothesis to a greater than or less than scenario if desired.

Example of the Mann-Whitney Test

Consider the real estate company example above again. Now, imagine that the real estate company has limited resources, so they can only launch a campaign for one neighborhood at a time. To maximize potential results of their first campaign, the company wants to choose the neighborhood with the highest number of bedrooms in the highest number of homes.

The company gathers information about homes in two neighborhoods. They then compare the samples to determine whether one sample has a statistically higher median number of bedrooms.

- H_0: The median number of bedrooms in neighborhood A is equal to the median number of bedrooms in neighborhood B.
  - $H_0 : MbedroomsA = MbedroomsB$

- H_a: The median number of bedrooms in neighborhood A is higher than that in neighborhood B.
  - $H_a : MbedroomsA > MbedroomsB$

Why Run Hypothesis Tests?

At this point, a common question about hypothesis tests comes up: Why go through the trouble to run statistical tests to determine if things are different?

Consider the example problem presented for the 1-Sample T Test:

An agriculture company growing corn produced an average of 168 bushels of corn per acre each year for five years. The company made a change to its seeding process in an attempt to increase the yield of its fields. The harvest following the seed change resulted in an average of 175 bushels of corn per acre each year. Did the seeding change result in a statistically different outcome in yield per acre?

The question is: Is the mean corn yield per acre statistically higher following the seed change? Just looking at the numbers presented in this problem, we can see that the mean following the seed change is 175. When you compare that to 168, it is obviously higher. Why would we go through the trouble of setting up and running a hypothesis test?

When introducing the normal curve in chapter 18, we noted that it's not always enough to see that a histogram appears to be symmetric and following the normal curve. Raw data can be deceptive, which is why we ran the Chi-Squared Goodness-of-Fit test in Excel to ensure the data was normal. The same principle is true when comparing statistics from samples. Yes, 175 is higher than 168. But in the case of the corn yield – is it *statistically different*?

Six Sigma teams can't just answer the question "Is this number different?" They must answer the question "Is this number so statistically different that we can take action on this information?" Statistically different doesn't have to do with scale. In one process, the difference between 10 and 23 might not be statistically different. In another, the difference between 10 and 10.5 might be statistically different.

Running Hypothesis Tests

To run a hypothesis test, you typically follow the same series of steps:

1. State the null and alternative hypotheses. The null hypothesis is always written from the perspective that no change or difference occurs or is present. The alternative hypothesis is always written from the perspective that a change or difference is present – either not equal, greater than, or less than.
2. Set the confidence level for alpha. Usually, the confidence level is set at 95 percent for alpha, but other common settings are 99 and 99.9 percent. A confidence level of 95 percent means an alpha value of 0.05; a confidence interval level of 99 percent means an alpha value of 0.01; a confidence interval of 99.9 percent means an alpha value of 0.001.
3. Decide which hypothesis test you are going to use. Use the information in the above section to find the appropriate test based on:
    a. The type of data you have
    b. The statistic you are dealing with (mean, variation, etc.)
    c. How many sets of data you have (level of interest in x)
    d. Remember, testing more than two sets of data is covered in Unit 7 on Design of Experiments and ANOVA
4. Decide whether your sample size is fixed or whether you can select a sample sized based on your beta setting. Setting sample size is covered in Chapter 22.
5. Run the test in Minitab. Specific steps for each hypothesis test – as well as other Minitab functions – are covered in Unit 6.
6. Interpret the p-value against your alpha setting, which tells you whether or not to reject the null hypothesis.
7. Translate the statistical analysis into real-world, business-relevant language.

For each statistical test, the calculations – handled automatically for us in Minitab or other software programs – return several values. Some calculations, such as the Chi-Squared tests, return specific statistics. In the case of the Chi-Squared tests, that statistic is the Chi-Squared value. These statistics can be valuable in applications and analyses, but for the purpose of hypothesis testing, we are primarily concerned with the p-value. The p-value is returned for each test, and we compare the p-value to the alpha value we set before we ran the test.

If the p-value returned for a test is *less than* the alpha value you set, then you reject the null hypothesis and accept the alternative hypothesis. If the p-value returned is *more than* the alpha value you set, then you fail to reject the null hypothesis and you do reject the alternative hypothesis.

Above, we talked about setting a confidence interval for alpha. If the confidence interval is 95 percent, then the alpha value is 0.05. Given a p-value of 0.02, we would reject the null hypothesis and accept the alternative. Given a p-value of 0.13, we would fail to reject the null hypothesis and *would* reject the alternative.

Hypothesis Test Examples

We'll go through the steps for setting up and evaluating hypothesis tests using some of the example tests from the section above.

1-Proportion Test

Problem: A school administrator believes that the students in a certain classroom are being impacted by some environmental issue with that room. The administrator wants to see if the students in that room perform statistically lower on tests than the students throughout the school; she has already noted that different classes in that room are taught by other teachers.

The administrator gathers data. The rate of failure for classes taught in any other classroom is 20 percent. Out of 142 students who have a class in the classroom in question, 38 are failing that particular class.

Step 1: State Null and Alternative Hypothesis

H_0: There is no difference between the failure rate of students in the classroom and those in other classrooms.

H_a: The failure rate of students in the classroom is statistically higher than the failure rate of students in other classrooms.

Step 2: Set Confidence Level

Unless otherwise stated in this book, the confidence level will always be 95 percent, or alpha = 0.05.

Step 3: Select Appropriate Test

Our data takes the form of pass/fail, which is attribute or discrete data. We have one set of data that we are comparing to the hypothesized rate of failure of 20 percent. Given that information, the 1-Proportion Test is the appropriate test.

Step 4: Select Sample Size

In this case, we aren't worried about sample size because we have been provided with the data. Since Six Sigma teams usually gather their own data, they need to worry about the proper sample size. How to determine sample size is covered in the next chapter.

Step 5: Run the Test and Analyze P-Value

The test is run in Minitab with the following information:

- Number of trials: 142 (there are 142 students)
- Number of events: 38 (there are 38 students meeting the event parameter "fail")
- Hypothesized proportion: 0.20 (20 percent of students in other classrooms meet the event parameter "fail")
- Alternative hypothesis: proportion > hypothesized proportion (we are testing whether the fail rate of students within the classroom is higher than the 20 percent fail rate of those outside the classroom)

Given all of the information above, Minitab returns a p-value of 0.031.

Test and CI for One Proportion

```
Test of p = 0.2 vs p > 0.2


                                                  Exact
Sample    X    N   Sample p   95% Lower Bound   P-Value
1        38  142   0.267606          0.207083     0.031
```

Since the p-value is less than the alpha value of 0.05, we reject the null hypothesis and accept the alternative. *Yes, the rate of failure is statistically higher for students in the classroom.*

1-Sample T Test

Problem: An agriculture company growing corn produced an average of 168 bushels of corn per acre each year for five years. The company made a change to its seeding process in an attempt to increase the yield of its fields. The harvest following the seed change resulted in an average of 175 bushels of corn per acre each year over 500 acres of fields. The standard deviation is 2.2 bushels. Did the seeding change result in a statistically different outcome in yield per acre?

Step 1: State Null and Alternative Hypothesis

H_0: There is no difference in the mean yield after the seed change as compared to before the seed change.

H_a: Following the seed change, the acres produce a statistically higher mean yield of corn.

Step 2: Set Confidence Level

Again, we set the confidence level for alpha at 95 percent, so alpha is 0.05.

Step 3: Select Appropriate Test

We are testing the mean of a sample against a hypothesized (or historic, or population) mean. Assume for the purpose of this example that our data is normal. The correct test would be the 1-Sample T Test *or* the Z Test if we didn't have the standard deviation.

Step 4: Select Sample Size

In this case, we aren't worried about sample size because we have been provided with the data. Since Six Sigma teams usually gather their own data, they need to worry about the proper sample size. How to determine sample size is covered in the next chapter.

Step 5: Run the Test and Analyze P-Value

The test is run in Minitab with the following information:

- Sample size: 500 (there were 500 acres of corn fields)
- Sample mean: 175 (following the seed change, the 500 acres yielded an average of 175 bushels)
- Standard deviation: 2.2 (provided in our problem)
- Hypothesized mean: 168 (prior to the seed change, the average yield was 168 bushels)

- Alternative hypothesis: mean > hypothesized mean (we are testing whether the average yield after the seed change is statistically higher than the yield prior to the seed change).

Given all of the information above, Minitab returns a p-value of 0.000.

One-Sample T

```
Test of μ = 168 vs > 168


   N     Mean   StDev   SE Mean   95% Lower Bound       T       P
 500   175.000  2.200    0.098            174.838   71.15   0.000
```

Since the p-value is less than the alpha value of 0.05, we reject the null hypothesis and accept the alternative. *Yes, the mean yield is statistically higher following the seed change.* It should be noted that the p-value in this case is exceptionally low. For our purposes, it is zero. That means there is only a very tiny chance of a Type 1 hypothesis testing error in this case. Why is this important? When making a decision that involves resources of money, leadership is always happy to hear that analysts are especially confident in their conclusions.

2-Sample T Test

Problem: Two attorneys practicing in the same law firm are turning in very different amounts of billable hours, even though the partners note that the two lawyers have similar caseloads. One partner hypothesizes that Attorney A's legal staff is taking too long to handle some tasks; because the firm bills at a certain time for administrative-style tasks regardless of how long those tasks take, if legal staff is taking too long for such tasks, they are spending time on work that can't be billed for.

To test the theory, data is gathered about the time legal staff spends on tasks. Specifically, a team looks at time spent on three tasks for which the legal staff is allowed to bill 15 minutes each: certain types of simple administrative phone, copying, or filing tasks. The following data is collected.

Minutes Spent on Quarter-Hour Tasks	
Attorney A's Team	Attorney B's Team
10	8
8	7
15	10
16	12
17	18
5	6
8	9
16	12
12	11
11	11
8	9
9	8
15	14
17	15
22	16
25	12
30	19
2	8
9	12
4	6
5	8
7	11
8	12
12	13
13	15
15	17
16	13
18	15
19	15
20	12
22	21

25	32
15	18
14	11

Step 1: State Null and Alternative Hypothesis

H_0: There is no difference in the average time it takes Attorney A's team to handle quarter-hour tasks as compared to the time it takes Attorney B's team.

H_a: Attorney A's team takes on average longer to perform quarter-hour tasks than Attorney B's team.

Step 2: Set Confidence Level

Again, we set the confidence level for alpha at 95 percent, so alpha is 0.05.

Step 3: Select Appropriate Test

We are testing the mean of one sample against the mean of another. For this problem, we will assume the data was tested to be normal. The data is time, so it is continuous. The appropriate test is the 2-Sample T test.

Step 4: Select Sample Size

In this case, we aren't worried about sample size because we have been provided with the data. Since Six Sigma teams usually gather their own data, they need to worry about the proper sample size. How to determine sample size is covered in the next chapter.

Step 5: Run the Test and Analyze P-Value

The test is run in Minitab by indicating the two columns with the same data in it and setting the alternative hypothesis to greater than.

Given all of the information above, Minitab return a p-value of 0.255

Two-Sample T-Test and CI: A, B

```
Two-sample T for A vs B

     N    Mean   StDev   SE Mean
A   34   13.76    6.56       1.1
B   34   12.82    5.07      0.87


Difference = μ (A) - μ (B)
Estimate for difference:  0.94
95% lower bound for difference:  -1.43
T-Test of difference = 0 (vs >): T-Value = 0.66  P-Value = 0.255  DF = 62
```

Since the p-value is greater than the alpha value of 0.05, we *fail to* reject the null hypothesis and we do reject the alternative. *The average time spent on the quarter-hour tasks is not statistically different* for each team. Minitab also calculates the means for us: Attorney A's team spends an average of 13.76 minutes on each task while Attorney B's team spends an average of 12.82 minutes on each task. Both teams, in fact, spend less time on the tasks than they can bill for the tasks, which means neither team is technically wasting any time.

One Sample Wilcox

Problem: A real estate company wants to enter a high-dollar market, so they want to build some regional websites that cater to homebuyers looking for larger homes. Specifically, they want to cater to homebuyers who are purchasing homes with 4 or more bedrooms. Before the company can build websites and begin marketing, it needs to find neighborhoods where homes for sale typically have 4 or more bedrooms.

The real estate company gathers information about the number of bedrooms in homes in a neighborhood. That data is presented below.

Number of Bedrooms
4
4
4
4
4
5
5
5

5
5
5
5
5
5
5
3
3
3
3
3
3
3
3
3
6
6
6
6
6
6
6
6
7
7
5
5
5
5
4
4
4
4

3
3
3
2
2
2
2
1
1
1

Step 1: State Null and Alternative Hypothesis

H_0: The median number of bedrooms is equal to 3.

H_a: The median number of bedrooms is greater than 3.

Step 2: Set Confidence Level

Again, we set the confidence level for alpha at 95 percent, so alpha is 0.05.

Step 3: Select Appropriate Test

We are testing the median of a sample against a hypothesized median. We only have one factor for X, so we will use the One Sample Wilcox.

Step 4: Select Sample Size

In this case, we aren't worried about sample size because we have been provided with the data. Since Six Sigma teams usually gather their own data, they need to worry about the proper sample size. How to determine sample size is covered in the next chapter.

Step 5: Run the Test and Analyze P-Value

The test is run in Minitab by indicating the column where the sample data resides, notating a hypothesized median of 3, and setting the alternative hypothesis to greater than 3.

Given all of the information above, Minitab returns a p-value of 0.000.

Wilcoxon Signed Rank Test: Bedrooms

```
Test of median = 3.000 versus median > 3.000

                N for   Wilcoxon            Estimated
          N    Test   Statistic      P       Median
Bedrooms  52    40       726.0   0.000       4.000
```

Since the p-value is less than the alpha value of 0.05, we reject the null hypothesis and accept the alternative. *Yes, the median number of bedrooms for homes in the neighborhood is 4 or more.*

Hypothesis Testing in Analyze, Improve, and Control

For Six Sigma teams, hypothesis testing is an activity typically found in the latter three phases of a DMAIC project, and most specifically in Analyze or Improve. During Analyze, teams might use hypothesis testing to help determine if certain inputs or factors could be a root cause. Given historical data, teams who can separate factors within a process can use that data to run a hypothesis test. For example, a team might believe that one employee is responsible for defects in a process. By comparing defect rates when that employee is on shift to defect rates when the employee is not working, teams can draw conclusions from data.

During Improve, hypothesis tests are often used to validate solutions that are being tested in beta environments or in small batches. The team compares the results of that solution with previous data about the process to determine whether the solution has created a statistically different result – and whether that result is what the team wanted.

Because hypothesis tests can begin to sound very mathematical, it's important to start with a business-friendly statement and end with a business-relevant statement regarding the conclusions. Chapter 24 covers some tips for converting various Six Sigma and statistical conclusions to business-friendly presentations and knowledge, which is especially helpful when a Six Sigma team is proposing changes based on statistical analysis. The ability to convert that analysis into business-friendly language helps teams explain to decision-makers why a change is likely to help.

A Review of Hypothesis Testing Terms

This chapter introduced a lot of new statistical terms, many of which will come up again in future chapters. Before moving to the next chapter, take a few minutes to review the terms that came up in this chapter.

Null Hypothesis: The assumed hypothesis; the statement that nothing has changed or no statistical difference exists. This is like the innocent verdict in a criminal court: it is assumed unless evidence tells us otherwise.

Alternative Hypothesis: The statement that something has changed or is statistically different – can be framed as not equal, greater than, or less than. If evidence means rejecting the null hypothesis, then the alternative hypothesis is assumed to be true.

Alpha: The measurement of the risk of a Type I error – the error that occurs if the null hypothesis is rejected when it was actually true.

Beta – The measurement of the risk of a Type II error – the error that occurs if the null hypothesis is *not* rejected when it was actually false.

Test Statistic – A standard value that is used to calculate the p-value to determine whether to reject the null hypothesis. For example, in the T test, the value is "t". We didn't calculate or discuss these values in detail, but they are shown in Minitab's output screen and can be valuable for more advanced statistical calculations. When using Minitab for hypothesis testing, the p-value is automatically generated.

P-Value: The number typically used to compare to the alpha value to determine whether or not to reject the null hypothesis. The null hypothesis is rejected if the p-value is less than the alpha value.

CHAPTER 22:
SAMPLE SIZE

Accuracy in inferential statistics requires that you have the right sample size. A retail company with thousands of customers would never make a major product decision based on feedback from five people, and Six Sigma teams should never make decisions based on statistical analysis when the sample size is not big enough to create an acceptable margin of error.

To understand the importance of sample size, we'll first review some important notes about sampling as related to inferential statistics.

Six Sigma teams take samples because they want to determine information about a population. With some exceptions, it is very difficult, very expensive, or impossible to run statistical calculations on the *entire* population of data. However, when we sample the population and draw inferences from those samples about means, proportions, or variances, there is always some risk of error. Some level of uncertainty will always exist when we draw conclusions about a population from sample data. In many cases, a larger sample size helps reduce the uncertainty of our conclusions.

The uncertainty associated with sampling is defined by something called the Confidence Interval, which is also called the margin of error in some applications. You've likely read or seen survey or poll results reported with a margin of error: The fans are 93 percent in favor of the new team colors, +/- 2 percent. The margin of error in that particularly survey was 2 percent, or 0.02.

In chapter 21, we discussed hypothesis testing and we set our alpha value at 0.05, which means we were at least 95 percent confident in choosing to reject or not reject the null hypothesis. We can make our hypothesis tests even more accurate by defining power and sample size for our data – particularly when we are pulling the data ourselves and can choose how many samples to take.

Download Minitab

Minitab is one of several advanced statistical analysis software program available, and it is a software that is commonly used by Six Sigma experts. For this chapter, we will work extensively in Minitab to perform calculations and analyses.

Screenshots are included for all of the analysis completed in Minitab going forward. If you would like to follow along or experiment with your own data in Minitab, you can download a trial version of the program from www.minitab.com. As of early 2016, the free trial is offered for 30 days. If you are part of an organization that uses Six Sigma for process improvement, you might also be able to gain access to Minitab through your employer.

A Review of Hypothesis Testing Errors

The concept of hypothesis testing errors is key to selecting sample sizes for various hypothesis testing. The two types of errors were introduced in Chapter 21, but warrant a quick review before moving on with sample size calculations.

Type I Error

A Type I error occurs when you reject the null hypothesis during a hypothesis test when, in fact, the null hypothesis is true. You might reject the null hypothesis that the mean of the sample is statistically the same as the hypothesized mean, deciding instead that the sample mean is statistically greater than the hypothesized mean. If the sample mean is, in fact, statistically the same as the hypothesized mean, you have a Type I error.

Type I error risks are denoted by alpha.

As stated in chapter 21, the Type I error is also called the producer risk. In a manufacturing environment, if the null hypothesis is true but it is rejected due to a Type I error, then material that is within specification (material that is statistically the same as the target) will be rejected. This is a producer risk – it causes waste, extra cost, and lower employee morale.

Type II Error

A Type II error occurs when you accept the null hypothesis when it is, in fact, not true. If you accept the hypothesis that the sample mean is statistically the same as the hypothesized mean when, in fact, the sample mean is statistically greater than the hypothesized mean, then you have a Type II error.

Type II error risks are denoted by beta.

As stated in chapter 21, the Type II error is also called the consumer risk. In a manufacturing environment, if the null hypothesis is false but it is accepted anyway due to a Type II error, then material that is *not* within specification (material that is *not* statistically the same as the target) is accepted. That means product that doesn't meet target is passed onto the consumer. That is a consumer risk – it could cause returns, unsatisfied customers, poor brand reputation.

The appropriate sample size can reduce the risk of either type of error.

What Information is Required for Choosing Sample Size?

To perform sample size calculations – or have Minitab perform them for you – certain information and assumptions are required.

Alpha	The alpha level you set – remember, the default in Minitab is typically set at 0.05
Beta	The beta level can be set by the experimenter and a sample size calculated from that number. If the sample size is fixed, then the experimenter usually sets alpha and calculates the beta risk from the sample size.
Delta	The practical difference the experimenter wants to detect using the test.
Standard deviation	The estimated population standard deviation.
Type of Data	Discrete or continuous?

Type of Test	Which hypothesis test are you using (see Chapter 21 for selecting the right test)

Before you can move onto calculating sample size, some practical considerations must be made with regard to alpha, beta, and delta. In our review of Type I and Type II errors, we covered the difference between producer and consumer risks, but that breakdown doesn't work in all organizations or with all hypothesis tests.

Because the outcome of your hypothesis tests are going to be used to make real-world decisions, you have to truly understand what the test and its outcomes means for the business, employee, and consumer. That real-world understanding helps you set appropriate Alpha and Beta values.

Questions to Ask About Alpha, Beta, and Delta Values

In most cases, you can set the alpha value at 0.05. However, in specific experiments, accuracy is extremely important. In medical or drug trials, for example, alpha values could be set to 0.99 or 0.999, making it very unlikely that a researcher would accept an alternative hypothesis (that a drug caused a change, for example) if it was not correct.

When selecting alpha, Six Sigma teams should ask:

- What are the costs associated with an unnecessary change if the team makes a mistake in rejecting the null hypothesis?
    - o In a manufacturing environment, what are the costs with rejecting materials that actually fit specifications?
    - o In a non-manufacturing environment, what are the costs associated with accepting the hypothesis that change did occur?
        - Are there dangers or costs associated with concluding that a statistical change occurred? What are they?

When selecting a beta value, Six Sigma teams should ask:

- What is the potential costs of a Type II error if the team makes a mistake in *not* rejecting the null hypothesis?
    - o What is the potential damage or cost if defective materials are passed to the customer? If a defective spoon is passed along, the ultimate cost might be minimal compared to a defective piece of medical equipment or car engine.

o Are there costs associated with lost time or resources in correcting a problem that comes from a Type II error?

When selecting a value for delta, Six Sigma teams should ask:

- How small does the difference have to be before it becomes practically insignificant to the customer? In a pizza restaurant, for example, a customer who orders a 14-inch pizza is going to care if he or she receives a 12-inch pizza. If the pizza that is delivered measures 13.9 inches, the customer is unlikely to care.
- What is the smallest delta that provides the best chance at exposing all benefits or information *but* is not so small as to be unfeasible. Working at smaller delta values means larger sample sizes or smaller measurement requirements, which take time to gather.
- Ultimately, Six Sigma teams should ask themselves: what margin of error is tolerable in results? The type of test you are running, the decisions you are making, and the processes you are dealing with help you make this determination.

The delta, or critical difference, should always be based on business needs. It is helpful in Minitab to express the delta in terms of sigma, or standard deviation. We want to detect differences of .5 σ or 2 σ, for example.

Guidelines for Setting Various Numbers When Calculating Sample Size

While values for various factors in sample size calculations should be guided by the business needs and purposes of the test, here are some guidelines Six Sigma teams can follow for baseline values or if no other information or needs are present.

When Testing Means for Continuous Data

If you have some information about the population, including standard deviation:

- Set alpha at 0.05.
- Set beta at 0.10 or 0.20 (which will give you a power of 0.90 or 0.80 – a power of 0.90 is less likely to produce a Type II error than a power of 0.80, but it will also require a much larger sample size in most cases).
- Set delta with absolute values as required by business needs or, more often in Minitab, as a function of standard deviation (.5 σ, 1 σ, and 2 σ.)

When Testing Variance for Continuous Data

- Set alpha at 0.05.
- Set beta at 0.10 or 0.20 (which will give you a power of 0.90 or 0.80 – a power of 0.90 is less likely to produce a Type II error than a power of 0.80, but it will also require a much larger sample size in most cases).
- Set delta greater than 1 and according to business needs, or, more often in Minitab, as a function of standard deviation (.5 σ, 1 σ, and 2 σ.)

When Testing Proportions for Discrete/Binomial Data

If you have some information about the population, including standard deviation:

- Set alpha at 0.05.
- Set beta at 0.10 or 0.20 (which will give you a power of 0.90 or 0.80 – a power of 0.90 is less likely to produce a Type II error than a power of 0.80, but it will also require a much larger sample size in most cases).
- Set delta logically according to business needs, or, more often in Minitab, as a function of standard deviation (.5 σ, 1 σ, and 2 σ.)

Note: General sampling on an unknown population, also called survey sampling, requires a different approach to sample-size calculation. Typically, you begin by setting alpha to 0.05, beta to 0.5, and delta to a proportion in keeping with a standard deviation of 1. This provides an initial sample size so you can better understand the population, but you might have to do additional sampling based on the statistics calculated from your first sample.

Sample Size Calculations: Choosing the Right Method

Just as there were numerous hypothesis tests to cover a range of data types and questions, there are numerous sample size calculations – all of which can be performed in Minitab. Review the list below to determine what type of calculation to perform when determining sample size for various hypothesis tests.

1-Sample T Test Sample Size Calculation

- Means testing
- Comparing to a target value
- You already have sample statistics about the population

1-Sample Z Test Sample Size Calculation

- Means testing
- Comparing to a target
- You do not have sample statistics about the population (standard deviation is not known)

2-Sample T Test Sample Size Calculation

- Means testing
- Comparing means from two sets of data

2-Sample Variance Test Sample Size Calculation

- Variance testing
- Comparing variance from two sets of data

1-Sample Variance Test Sample Size Calculation

- Variance testing
- Comparing variance of one data set to a target

1-Sample Proportion Test Sample Size Calculation

- Proportion testing (rate, x per y)
- Comparing rate of one data set to a target

2-Sample Proportion Test Sample Size Calculation

- Proportion testing (rate, x per y)
- Comparing rate from two sets of data

Analysis of Variance (ANOVA) Sample Size Calculation

- Means testing
- More than 2 sets of data
- Only one factor for x

Design of Experiment (DOE) Sample Size Calculation

- Means testing
- More than 2 sets of data

- More than one factor for x

Running and Analyzing Sample Size Tests in Minitab

To understand more about running and analyzing sample size tests in Minitab, we'll walk through the process for most of the test types above.

To find the Power and Sample Size calculation tools in Minitab, select Stat > Power and Sample Size

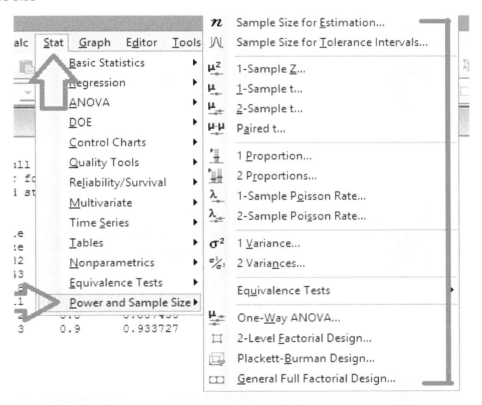

First, let's look at the 1-Sample Z power and sample size calculation. Remember, you would use this calculation in conducting survey sampling for means testing, especially if you don't know the standard deviation for the process or population. This calculation provides you with a "jumping off point" – a sample size that provides you some relevant information that is as accurate as you define and that you can use as a basis for future sampling.

Selecting the 1-Sample Z calculation from the menu brings up the following dialogue box.

Minitab lets you calculate sample sizes or back into power values if a sample size is fixed, which is why it asks you to fill in only two of the three first values.

Because we don't yet know much about our data, we leave sample size blank and provide several parameters for differences and power values for Minitab. This causes Minitab to provide a number of answers – one for each difference and power value combination – so we can make a more viable decision about sample size.

In this case, we've set the differences at .5 σ, 1 σ, and 2 σ. We've set power values at 0.8 and 0.9 (or, beta to either 0.2 or 0.1 respectively). Standard deviation for this first pass is assumed to be 1; if we had information about standard deviation, we could run a more precise calculation or use the 1-Sample T Test calculation.

If you click options, you can change the confidence level or alternative hypothesis (to a greater or less than scenario).

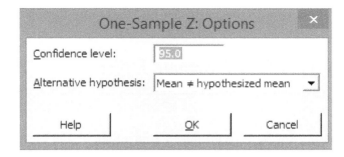

In this case, we're leaving the options as is.

After we click OK on the Power and Sample Size box, Minitab returns the following information.

Power and Sample Size

```
1-Sample Z Test

Testing mean = null (versus ≠ null)
Calculating power for mean = null + difference
α = 0.05   Assumed standard deviation = 1


             Sample  Target
Difference     Size   Power   Actual Power
      0.5        32     0.8       0.807430
      0.5        43     0.9       0.906375
      1.0         8     0.8       0.807430
      1.0        11     0.9       0.912556
      2.0         2     0.8       0.807430
      2.0         3     0.9       0.933727
```

The data table returned by Minitab shows us the required sample size for each difference and target power. You can see that for the lowest difference and highest target power, the sample size required is only 43. But to determine a difference of 1 σ at a target power of 0.9, you only need 11 in the sample size.

Here, the team has to make a business-centric decision. Perhaps samples are easy and inexpensive to capture, so the team selects the maximum sample size. But if each sample takes an hour to obtain and costs the company $26, then the team might make the call to select a smaller sample size.

Again, it is important to note with this particular test that more sampling might be required to draw further conclusions.

Sample Calculations for a 1-Sample T Test

To see the 1-Sample T Test sample calculation in action, let's revisit a problem from Chapter 21.

An agriculture company growing corn produced an average of 168 bushels of corn per acre each year for five years. The standard deviation is 2.2 bushels. The company made a change to its seeding process in an attempt to increase the yield of its fields. Did the seeding change result in a statistically different outcome in yield per acre?

How many acres would the company need to sample to determine if the new process made a difference? This could help the company know how many acres to plant with the new seed process.

To generate data for this problem, select the 1-Sample T calculation from the Power and Sample Size menu in Minitab.

For this calculation, enter the differences as a multiple of standard deviation, the power values as desired, and the standard deviation provided in the data.

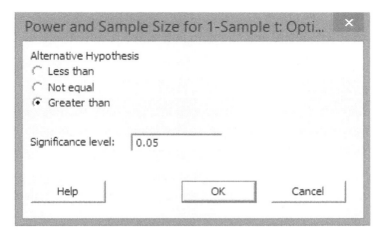

Change the alternative hypothesis to greater than. The company wants to determine whether the yield of the new process is greater than the average yield of the old process.

After you click OK, and then OK again, Minitab generates the following set of information.

Power and Sample Size

```
1-Sample t Test

Testing mean = null (versus > null)
Calculating power for mean = null + difference
α = 0.05  Assumed standard deviation = 2.2


              Sample  Target
Difference     Size   Power   Actual Power
       0.5      122    0.8        0.802721
       0.5      168    0.9        0.901296
       1.0       32    0.8        0.807760
       1.0       43    0.9        0.900995
       2.0        9    0.8        0.800109
       2.0       12    0.9        0.903589
```

We can see from the above table that the company would have to plant 168 acres to achieve a target power of 0.9 and be able to discern differences of 0.5 standard deviations. That's a lot of acreage to plant with an experimental seeding process. The company might weigh its options and resources and decide, instead, to plant 43 or 32 acres. By planting 43 acres, the company can detect differences as low as one standard deviation at 0.9 target power. Given that the standard deviation is assumed to be 2.2 bushels, that is still a relatively small detection range, and the company saves a ton of money by planting over 100 fewer acres for the test.

Backing into target power

What if the agriculture company didn't have a choice regarding the number of acres it could plant for a test? Finances, resources, or corporate leadership might collude to decide that the test could be run on a total of 18 acres – and only 18 acres.

Minitab can take the information about the test and calculate the target power. The test is run the same way, but sample size is entered and power values are left blank.

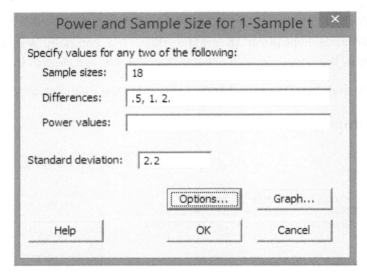

Power and Sample Size

```
1-Sample t Test

Testing mean = null (versus > null)
Calculating power for mean = null + difference
α = 0.05  Assumed standard deviation = 2.2
```

	Sample	
Difference	Size	Power
0.5	18	0.236131
1.0	18	0.581637
2.0	18	0.979934

You can see from the above data that, given a sample size of 18, the power for detecting a difference of 0.5 σ is fairly small. Remember, Power = 1 – beta. In this case, beta (the risk of making a Type II error) is over 0.75.

However, for detecting a difference of 2 σ – approximately 4.4 in this case – the power is extremely high. The team in this case would likely conclude that planting on the 18 sample acres would provide an appropriate sample for running the hypothesis test.

Sample Calculations for a 1-Sample Proportion Test

Proportion tests are a bit different for two major reasons:

- Proportion tests are run using attribute data. Attribute data almost always requires a larger sample size for accurate results than continuous data does.
- Because you are dealing with attributes – and rates – you don't need to provide any information about population parameters such as sigma levels or standard deviation.

To calculate the sample size required for accurate 1-Sample Proportion hypothesis testing, you simply set alpha and beta and enter the proportions for both the null and alternative hypothesis.

Let's consider a real-world example to better understand the calculations in Minitab.

A grocery store chain discovers it has a problem with prices being entered correctly into the system when product is placed in the store or prices are updated. In population sampling, the store found that approximately 8 percent of the prices are entered incorrectly. The store provided ½ of the employees who do pricing entry with new scanners to attempt to mitigate the problem. Before the store commits to a full-time lease on the new equipment for all employees, it wants to confirm that the new scanners bring the error-rate down by 5 percent – to 3 percent or less.

SAMPLE SIZE

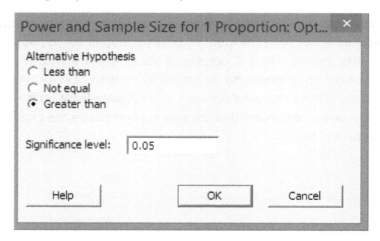

Select the 1-Proportion calculation from the Power and Sample Size menu in Minitab. The comparison proportion is entered as 1 − the probability of failure for a single trial. In this case, 1 − 0.03, since the company wants to reduce the error rate to 3 percent.

The hypothesized proportion is entered as 1 − the probability of a failure for a single trial, or 1 − 0.08, since the original process had an 8 percent failure rate.

Under options, select "greater than" as the alternative hypothesis.

Click OK and then OK, and Minitab generates the information seen below.

Power and Sample Size

```
Test for One Proportion

Testing p = 0.92 (versus > 0.92)
α = 0.05


             Sample  Target
Comparison p   Size   Power  Actual Power
       0.97    140     0.8      0.802942
       0.97    177     0.9      0.900362
```

To run a valid 1-Proportion test, the company needs to gather between 140 and 177 data samples.

Sample Size Calculations for a 2-Sample T Test

Consider again the 2-Sample T test problem from the last chapter:

Two attorneys practicing in the same law firm are turning in very different amounts of billable hours, even though the partners note that the two lawyers have similar caseloads. One partner hypothesizes that Attorney A's legal staff is taking too long to handle some tasks; because the firm bills at a certain time for administrative-style tasks regardless of how long those tasks take, if legal staff is taking too long for such tasks, they are spending time on work that can't be billed for.

To test the theory, data is gathered about the time legal staff spends on tasks. Specifically, a team looks at time spent on three tasks for which the legal staff is allowed to bill 15 minutes each: certain types of simple administrative phone, copying, or filing tasks. The following data is collected.

Minutes Spent on Quarter-Hour Tasks	
Attorney A's Team	Attorney B's Team
10	8
8	7
15	10
16	12
17	18

SAMPLE SIZE

5	6
8	9
16	12
12	11
11	11
8	9
9	8
15	14
17	15
22	16
25	12
30	19
2	8
9	12
4	6
5	8
7	11
8	12
12	13
13	15
15	17
16	13
18	15
19	15
20	12
22	21
25	32
15	18
14	11

For the purposes of this problem, the firm team collected a sample of 34 data elements from each team. But is that enough to provide a strong conclusion in the 2-Sample T Test?

First, let's look at the sample size calculations given what we know of the data in question. The standard deviation of the data is 5.83, and we want to test whether the mean for

Attorney A's team is greater than the mean for Attorney B's team. We would set up a 2-Sample T Test in Minitab as pictured below.

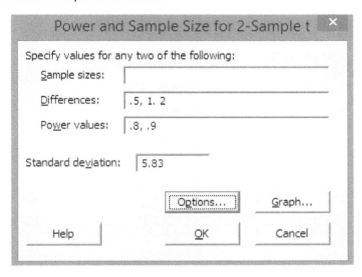

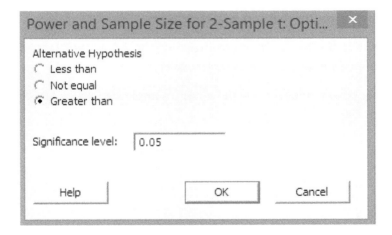

Minitab generates the following information:

Power and Sample Size

```
2-Sample t Test

Testing mean 1 = mean 2 (versus >)
Calculating power for mean 1 = mean 2 + difference
α = 0.05  Assumed standard deviation = 5.83


             Sample  Target
Difference    Size   Power   Actual Power
      0.5     1682    0.8       0.800045
      0.5     2330    0.9       0.900079
      1.0      421    0.8       0.800038
      1.0      583    0.9       0.900075
      2.0      106    0.8       0.800820
      2.0      147    0.9       0.901369

The sample size is for each group.
```

You can see above, the minimal sample size – for each group – that Minitab calculates is 106, and that is for a difference of 2 with target power of 0.8. While a 2-Sample T test *can* be run on the data set provided above – and we did, in fact, run that test in chapter 21 – the likelihood of a type II error for that test was fairly high.

Just how high was the likelihood for an error running the 2-Sample T test with a sample size of 34 for each group? Minitab can tell us that answer.

Instead of entering power values in the power and sample size dialog box, enter the sample size of 34 and click OK.

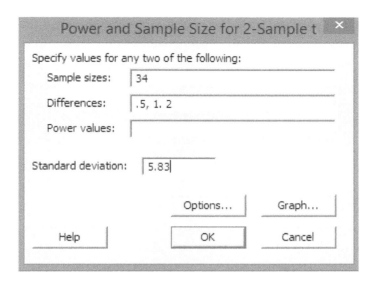

Power and Sample Size

```
2-Sample t Test

Testing mean 1 = mean 2 (versus >)
Calculating power for mean 1 = mean 2 + difference
α = 0.05  Assumed standard deviation = 5.83


              Sample
Difference     Size      Power
       0.5       34   0.097685
       1.0       34   0.172364
       2.0       34   0.403259
```

The highest power for a sample size of 34 given this data is 0.40, which means a beta of 0.60 – more than 50 percent chance of a Type II error in the hypothesis test. In this particular case, before the firm makes any decisions, they should gather a larger sample of data.

A Reminder Regarding Random Samples

Before moving on from sample size calculations, it's worth noting again the importance of random sampling. Even if you perform a calculation to determine an appropriate sample size – and you choose to ere on the side of caution by sampling at the largest count size returned by Minitab – you can draw the wrong inferences because the sample was not random.

CHAPTER 23:
ADVANCED CONTROL CHARTS

The concept of control charts was introduced in the DMAIC chapter on control. Chapter 17 provided instructions for creating a specific type of control chart – the x-bar chart – in Excel if you don't have access to other statistical software. If you remember that section, you'll remember it took many steps and some basic graphical formatting to create a full-fledged x-bar control chart. That's not something a Six Sigma expert wants to go through every time leadership wants to see an update on a process, and certainly not something day-to-day analysts want to do for regular reporting.

Luckily, Minitab offers more automated x-bar control charting. The statistical software also offers easy access to other types of control charting. After the chapters on hypothesis testing and sample size calculations, it should come as no surprise that there are many types of control charts, each of which are useful in monitoring different types of data and processes. In this chapter, we'll look at the different types of control charts and when to use them before defining terms for each type of chart and walking through creating the charts in Minitab.

Common Control Chart Types and When to Use Them

X-bar & R Chart

- Data is variable (continuous)
- Data can be grouped into subgroups, letting you chart the mean of each group
    - o Production mean per hour
    - o Average answer speed of phones per hour
    - o Average number of customers each day
    - o Defects per hour
- Data count in each subgroup is less than 8 (although you can use the x-bar & R chart for subgroup sizes up to 100 in Minitab)
- Presents two charts
    - o The x-bar control chart plots the mean of each subgroup
    - o The R chart plots the range

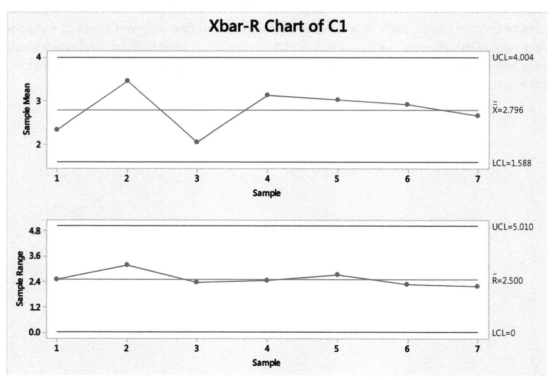

X-bar & S Chart

- Data is variable (continuous)
- Data can be grouped into subgroups, letting you chart the mean of each group
- Data count in each subgroup is more than 8
- Sigma can be easily calculated (otherwise, use x-bar &R)
- Presents two charts
    - The x-bar control chart plots the mean of each subgroup
    - The S chart plots the standard deviation

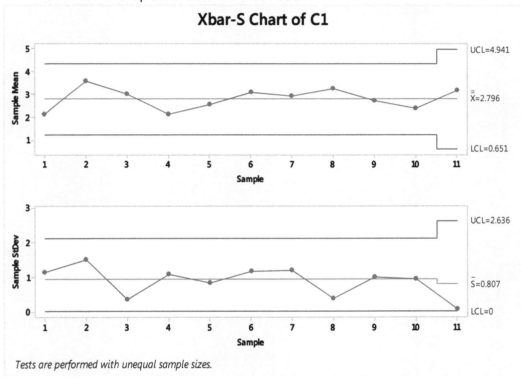

Tests are performed with unequal sample sizes.

I-MR Chart

- Data is variable (continuous)
- Data cannot be easily grouped into reasonable subgroups, so you must track individual data points instead of subgroup means
    - Data is very difficult or expensive to obtain
    - Production is very slow, so waiting for enough data to create subgroups would take too much time (for example, tracking data about surgeries performed in a small outpatient facility)
    - Products have a low cycle time

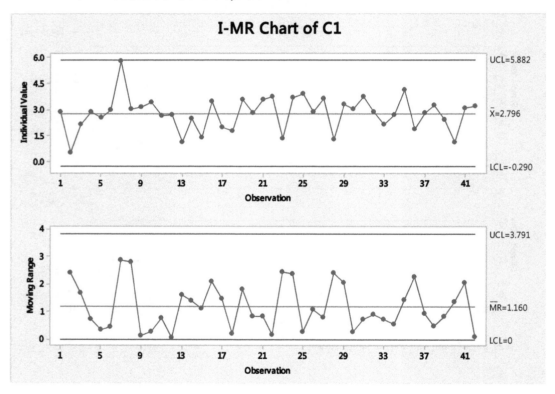

P-Chart

- Data is discrete
- Data is presented as a percent (percent defective) rather than a count
- Doesn't require a constant sample/subgroup size
- Plots the proportion of units that are nonconforming (are defective, don't meet specifications)
- Use when:
    - it is impossible, very time-consuming, or not financially feasible to measure or analyze numerical measurements
    - sample or subgroup sizes are not equal, so the percent of defect is more important that the number of defects per group (as you can't compare numbers in a smaller group with numbers in a larger group accurately)
    - data is rate-based because it comes from a binomial or attribute process: the measurement or process is pass/fail, go/no go, etc. You can't plot 1 or 0 on a control chart, but you can plot the percent of 1 or 0 in each sample.

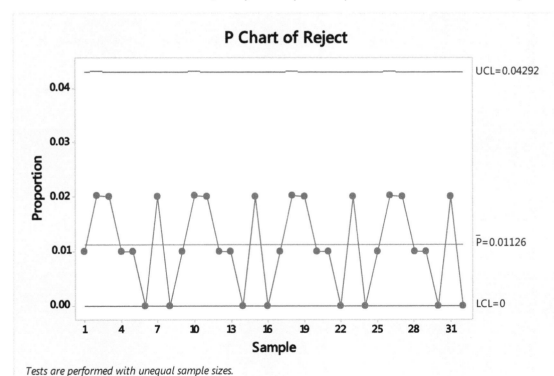

Tests are performed with unequal sample sizes.

NP-Chart

- Data is discrete
- Data is presented as a percent (percent defective) rather than a count
- Does require a constant sample size to be of use; other than this, you can use it for anything that you would use a p-chart for
- Plots the *number* of units that are nonconforming in each sample size

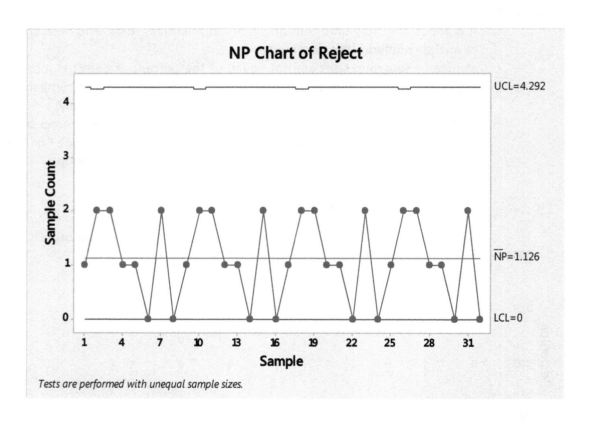

U-Chart

- Data is discrete
- Data is presented as a count (number of defects)
- Doesn't require a constant sample/subgroup size
- Plots the number of defects *per unit*
- Use when data is about the defects themselves, not the overall defective product

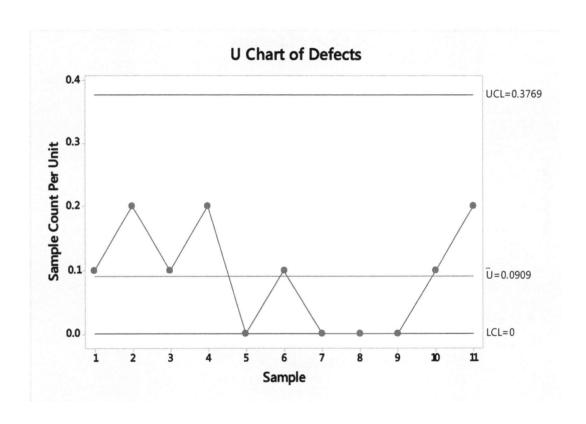

C-Chart
- Data is discrete
- Data is presented as a count (number of defects)
- Does require a constant sample/subgroup size
- Plots the number of defects *per sample*
- Use when data is about the defects themselves, not the overall defective product

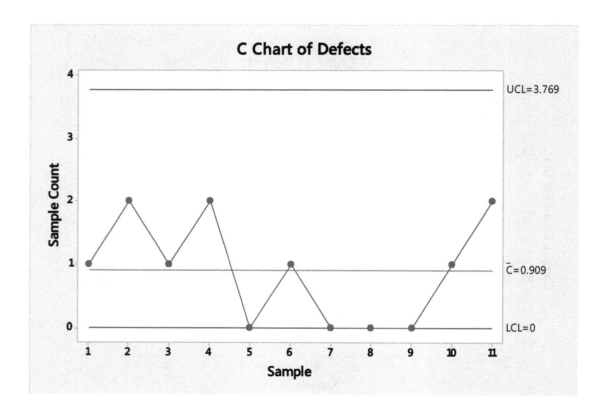

Creating and Reading Control Charts in Minitab
X-Bar & R Charts or X-Bar & S Charts
To better understand the X-Bar & R Chart process in Minitab, consider a real-world scenario. A call center is tracking the number of calls on hold. The calls center randomly

records the number of calls on hold at a given moment five times each hour. That data is presented below for a 10-hour shift.

Hour	Calls On Hold
1	14
1	12
1	15
1	11
1	10
2	25
2	10
2	13
2	15
2	9
3	15
3	10
3	13
3	10
3	11
4	12
4	13
4	10
4	15
4	15
5	9
5	11
5	13
5	8
5	16
6	15
6	13
6	11
6	13
6	12

ADVANCED CONTROL CHARTS

7	10
7	10
7	12
7	11
7	10
8	13
8	13
8	9
8	12
8	6
9	12
9	15
9	14
9	11
9	12
10	15
10	14
10	14
10	8
10	9

Copy this information into Minitab if you are following along with the analysis on your own. If you aren't sure how to use Minitab's basic data entry or navigation functions, see chapter 25 for additional information.

All of the control charts are found under Stat > Control Charts

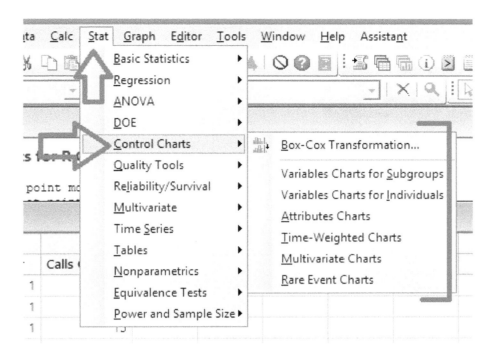

Select Stat > Control Charts > Variables for Subgroups > Xbar- R

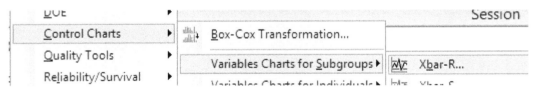

Click into the box under "All observations for a chart are in one column."

ADVANCED CONTROL CHARTS

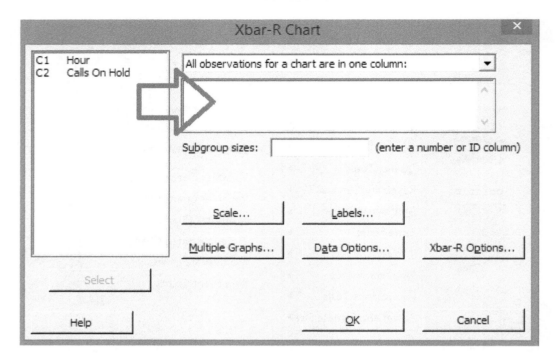

Click on "Calls on Hold" and click "Select"

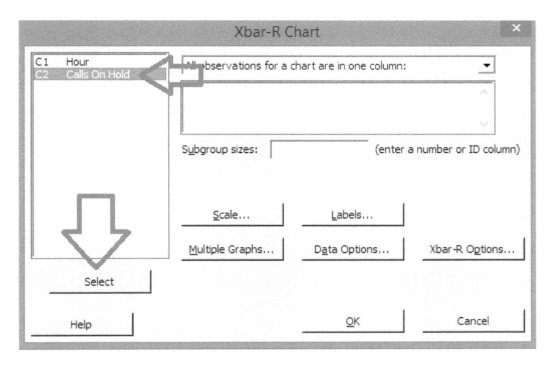

Since the data was sampled 5 times per hour, enter "5" in the subgroup size. Then click "Xbar-R Options".

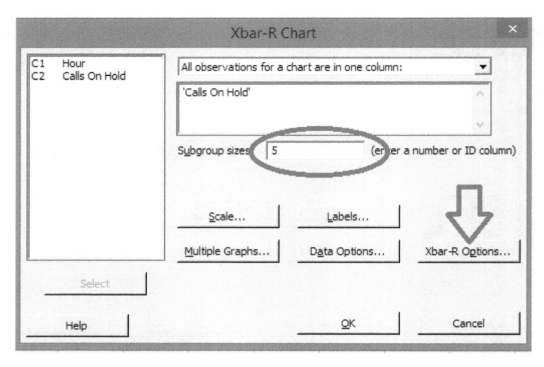

In the Xbar-R Options dialogue box, click "Tests"

In the drop down menu on the Tests tab, select "Perform all tests for special causes."

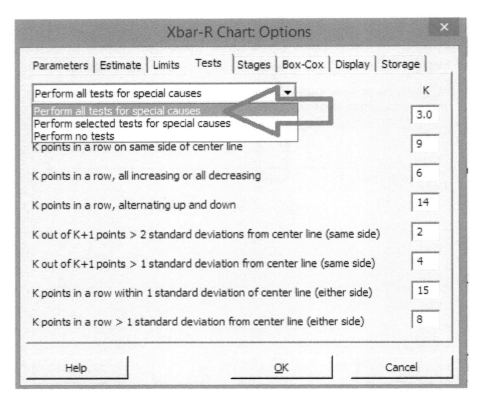

This option tells Minitab to perform the control tests covered in chapter 16. If a data point or series of data points on the control chart fails any of these tests, Minitab will highlight them in red, making it easy for Six Sigma experts to tell if a process might be out of control.

Click OK on the options dialogue box.

Click OK on the Xbar-R chart dialogue box.

Minitab generates a chart and a text description for any failed control tests.

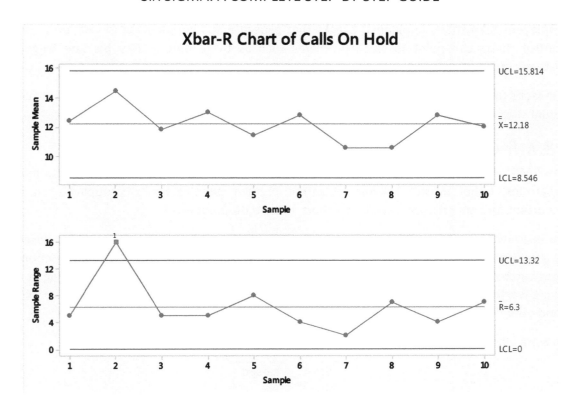

Test Results for R Chart of Calls On Hold

```
TEST 1. One point more than 3.00 standard deviations from center line.
Test Failed at points:  2
```

You can see above, the control chart for the range failed at point 2 – one point is beyond 3 standard deviations from the center line. All other points are within control parameters, and the sample mean (x-bar) chart is also within control. That means that the average number of calls on hold within each hour was controlled. However, without hour 2, the specific data points ranged much more than in other hours, which means one or more samples collected was very high.

Someone viewing this chart would not likely consider the process to be completely out of control, but they would want to investigate the samples for hour 2. What happened to make a drastic change in the range? Was a number recorded incorrectly? Did several employees take short, unplanned breaks that caused a sudden increase in calls on hold? Control charts can point to small problems such as these before they become bigger, systemic problems.

The steps for creating an X-bar & S chart are the same as those described above, except you would start with Stat > Control Charts > Variables for Subgroups > Xbar- S

I & MR Chart

The I-MR (individual and moving range) chart is used when you aren't grouping data into subgroups. Either it isn't feasible to gather enough samples for subgrouping or it is important for some reason to view the chart at the data-point level.

For example, a medium-sized car dealership wants to measure the number of sales closed on a daily basis. Most car dealers aren't closing hundreds of sales a day, so tracking per hour or in batch sizes won't provide much information for data in a single month. If looking at a year's worth of data, the dealership might subgroup by week; otherwise, the I-MR chart is a good option.

To work along with this example, copy the sales data below into Minitab.

Sales closed daily
19
17
17
17
20
23
22
18
19
19
18
20
21
19
24

16
15
21
21
20
19
20

Select Stat > Control Charts > Variables for Individuals > I-MR

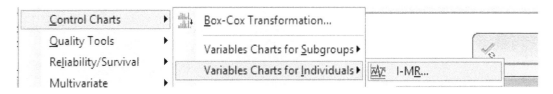

Complete steps similar to the steps completed for the X-bar & R chart:

1. Click in the box under "variables."
2. Click on "Sales closed daily" in the list of columns and click select.
3. Click on I-MR Options
4. Click on Tests
5. In the drop down box, select "Perform all tests for special causes."
6. Click OK
7. Click OK

Minitab generates the I-MR chart and data about whether any test was failed.

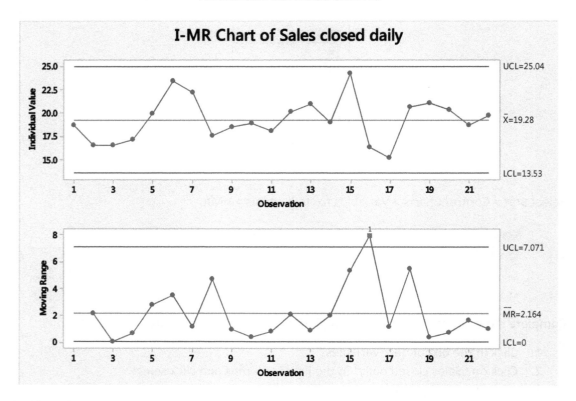

I-MR Chart of Sales closed daily
Test Results for MR Chart of Sales closed daily

```
TEST 1. One point more than 3.00 standard deviations from center line.
Test Failed at points:  16
```

In this particular case, the number of sales per month, which is depicted on the top individual chart, are within control. The moving range – how much change there is between the numbers for each day – is in control except for point 16. If you look at the data, you see that between point 16 and point 17, there is an 8-sale difference. This is the point with the biggest difference in day-to-day data points, which likely accounts for the test failure.

A car dealership or Six Sigma team working with this data would probably not be too concerned about that one point. When you consider it in practical terms, it could be that some sales that might have begun the day before didn't close, which bumped up the day's numbers artificially and caused the sudden wider-than-normal spread. In this case, the dealership or Six Sigma team would simply note the point and keep an eye on the control chart for similar test failures in the future that might indicate some type of pattern or problem with the process.

P-Chart

Remember, a p-Chart is used to track attribute, rate data. It's probably one of the most-used attribute-based control charts because rates are often easier to work with than actual attribute data, particularly because you don't have to worry about ensuring the same sample or subgroup size. You can also combine multiple types of defects in the same report, because p-charts are typically concerned with whether the product, part, or test passed or failed — not with the specifics about the defects that caused the pass or fail.

The type of data that is reported at a management level also tends to be complemented by the p-Chart characteristics. Executive leadership often want to know audit results, first-run yields, scrap rates, or defect rates, all of which can be illustrated with p-Charts.

Proportion data is usually one of the first available to Six Sigma teams — even before a Six Sigma team is associated with a process, many business operators and managers capture pass/fail type data. This means that a Six Sigma team might be able to create a first baseline control chart from proportion data and see rates improve as process improvements are made.

To understand how to create a p-Chart in Minitab, consider the following real-world scenario. A professional printing company discovers a possible problem with a printing process used to print business cards. Customer are reporting high rates of defects. The company begins monitoring the process more closely, reviewing 100 samples daily to determine if there are any defects on each printed card. The results are recorded in the data table below.

Copy this data into Minitab if you are following along with creating control charts.

Samples	Defects
100	5
100	2
100	1
100	0
100	0
100	2
100	1
100	0
100	6
100	0
100	7
100	0
100	9
100	0
100	0
100	1
100	2
100	0
100	7
100	0

To create a p-Chart given this data, begin by going to Stat > Control Charts > Attribute Charts > P

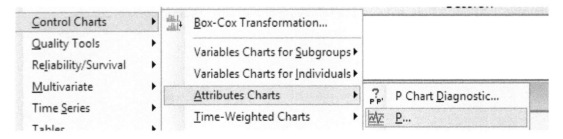

Follow the steps below to enter data in the dialogue box, as pictured below the steps.

1. Click in the box under Variables.
2. Click on "Defects" in the left column.
3. Click Select under the left column to select "Defects" into the Variables box.
4. Click on the box next to "Subgroup sizes".
5. Click on "Samples" in the left column.
6. Click Select under the left column to select "Samples" into the Subgroup box.
7. Click P-Chart Options.

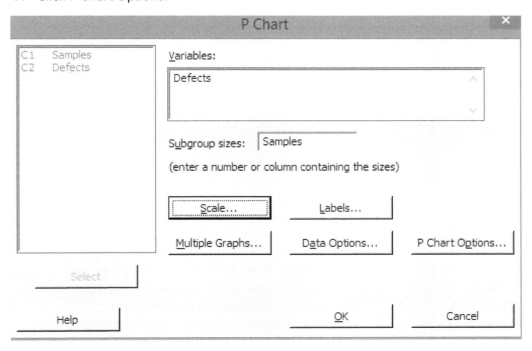

8. Click Tests
9. In the drop down box, select "Perform all tests for special causes"

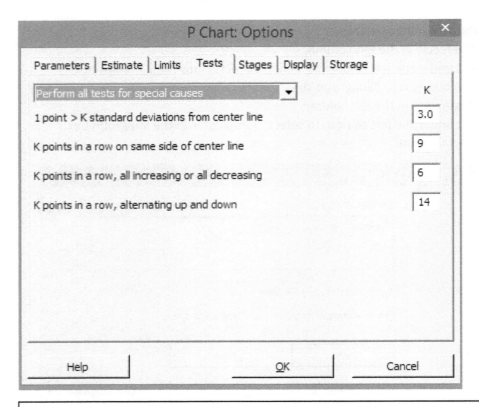

Note that there are fewer tests for special causes listed than there were for the previous control charts created. That is because there are fewer control tests for attribute data. It's been stated several times throughout this book that continuous, or variable, data is typically better for statistical analysis than attribute data, and this is one example of a reason for that.

10. Click OK.
11. Click OK.

Minitab generates the control chart of defect rates along with the test results from the control tests.

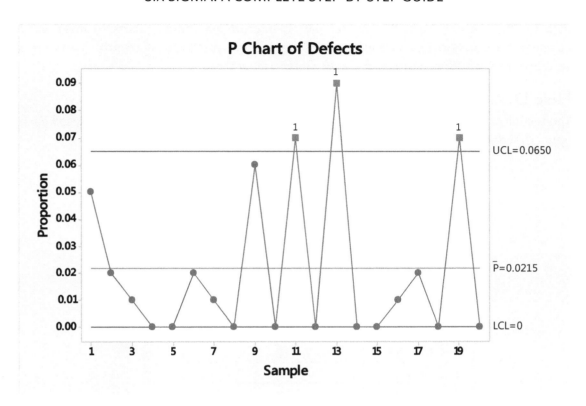

Test Results for P Chart of Defects

```
TEST 1. One point more than 3.00 standard deviations from center line.
Test Failed at points:  11, 13, 19
```

In this case, there is likely a problem of control within the process, given the failure of three points. The process owner or Six Sigma team associated with this process would want to investigate both the samples and the process to find out if there is an ongoing process problem or a sample-specific issue here.

The steps for creating other attribute control charts, including np, u, and c charts, are the same as those for creating the p-chart.

Practice Interpreting Control Charts

With Minitab, creating control charts simply requires following the steps outlined above and some practice determining which control chart is correct for the situation and setting up data for the control chart. The harder part is interpreting control charts to make valid business decisions or recommendations. In this section, you'll review control charts for a variety of real-world scenarios and practice interpreting them.

Help Desk Ticket Process

The technical support desk in an office tracks the number of tickets opened and closed each hour. That data is found in the table below.

Incoming Tickets	Complete Tickets
10	8
12	10
15	12
7	9
2	5
8	9
9	8
11	12
1	2
16	14
18	17
5	6
8	7
14	13
7	6
6	7
17	12
8	10
5	6

Management wants to know whether the help desk process is performing well given only this information. A Six Sigma expert can do a few things to provide a preliminary answer to management.

First, you might create an I-MR chart for the Complete Tasks data. Why use an I-MR chart? We don't have enough data to create an X-bar chart, because we would only have a few subgroups.

The I-MR chart is shown below, and you can see that there are no control failures for either the moving range or the number of tickets closed per hour.

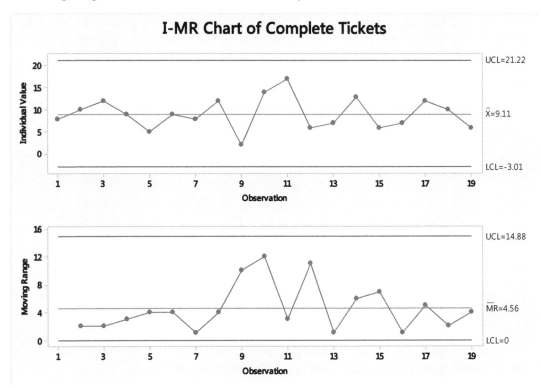

Someone might point out, though, that a control chart of the number of tickets completed only tells us there isn't a great deal of deviation in the amount of work completed each hour, and this is true. This control chart does not actually take into account the amount of work that came in each hour and whether the help desk was clearing that work.

So, a Six Sigma expert might add another column to the data. This column keeps a running total of how many tickets at that point of the day remain open.

Incoming Tickets	Complete Tickets	Tickets Left Unresolved
10	8	2
12	10	4
15	12	7
7	9	5
2	5	2
8	9	1
9	8	2
11	12	1
1	2	0
16	14	2
18	17	3
5	6	2
8	7	3
14	13	4
7	6	5
6	7	4
17	12	9
8	10	7
5	6	6

Creating an I-MR chart of this figure yields very different results.

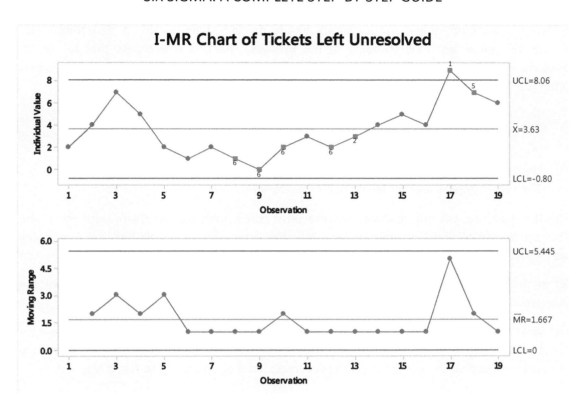

Test Results for I Chart of Tickets Left Unresolved

```
TEST 1. One point more than 3.00 standard deviations from center line.
Test Failed at points:  17

TEST 2. 9 points in a row on same side of center line.
Test Failed at points:  13

TEST 5. 2 out of 3 points more than 2 standard deviations from center line
(on one side of
     CL).
Test Failed at points:  18

TEST 6. 4 out of 5 points more than 1 standard deviation from center line
(on one side of
     CL).
Test Failed at points:  8, 9, 10, 12
```

Numerous tests are failed at numerous points on the chart. Is this a bad thing? Not necessarily, given an understanding of the process. The first five points that fail do so because they are below the centerline. That means the process was leaving fewer tickets open per hour than might be expected. Several reasons could exist for such results:

- The team was just especially efficient at closing tickets those hours.
- The team received tickets that were abnormally easy to deal with and close during those hours.
- The team closed tickets without really resolving them.
- The team simply received fewer tickets to work on.

The first two reasons are positive, and the third could point to a problem with the team. The last reason could be positive or negative: Were there fewer tickets because everything was working better than normal, or was there a problem with the ticketing software?

All of these questions are worth looking into – they not only tell the team whether the process is possibly out of control, but they also provide valuable business information.

The next two points that are out of control on this chart are due to upward trend – something a help desk manager would not want to see. He or she would want to continue monitoring this chart to see if the process corrects itself or continues to trend upward.

Running a Hypothesis Test

Given all of this information, a Six Sigma expert might even run a hypothesis test to go along with any control charts. He or she might run a 2-Sample T test to determine whether the team is closing on average the same number of tickets that are being opened. If the answer is yes, then the help desk is probably performing well. If the answer is no, then the team might ask "how many tickets on average is the help desk not closing?"

The results of running the 2-Sample T test in Minitab are seen below.

Two-Sample T-Test and CI: Incoming Tickets, Complete Tickets

```
Two-sample T for Incoming Tickets vs Complete Tickets

                    N   Mean  StDev  SE Mean
Incoming Tickets   19   9.42   4.89      1.1
Complete Tickets   19   9.11   3.62     0.83


Difference = μ (Incoming Tickets) - μ (Complete Tickets)
Estimate for difference:  0.32
95% CI for difference:  (-2.52, 3.16)
T-Test of difference = 0 (vs ≠): T-Value = 0.23   P-Value = 0.822 | DF = 33
```

Granted, with a sample size of 19, the chance of a Type II error is relatively high, but the p-Value is also very strong in favor of accepting the null hypothesis that the mean is statistically the same between the data for opened tickets and closing tickets. Given this information, the Six Sigma team might accumulate more data before running another test to verify these results.

Yarn Skeins

At a company that produces yarn skeins for retail sales, each 244-yard skein features a certain color or color pattern. The company allows slight defects in dye at a rate of 10 per 244-yard yarn length before the skein is considered defective overall.

A team has been tasked with controlling the quality of this process. This team reviews 10 lengths of sampled yarn each day before it is wound into a skein to determine the number of defects. Over several days, the team gathers data and creates a control chart to indicate whether its process is in control.

The team generates the following data table.

Skein Sampled	Defects Found
10	8
10	2
10	12
10	15
10	22
10	6
10	8
10	14
10	9
10	23
10	24
10	26
10	10
10	7
10	5
10	12
10	15
10	18
10	19
10	14
10	27

Because all the sample sizes are the same and the team is concerned with the number of defects, it chooses to create a c-chart in Minitab.

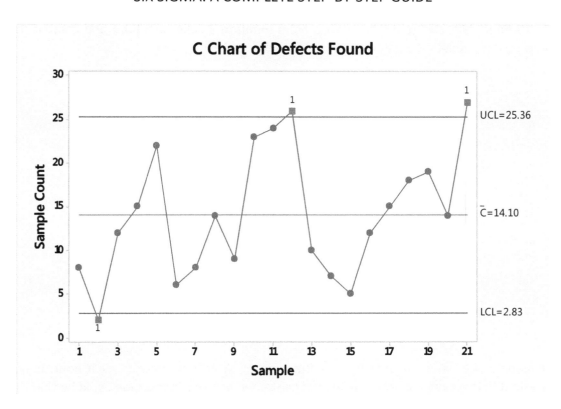

Test Results for C Chart of Defects Found

```
TEST 1. One point more than 3.00 standard deviations from center line.
Test Failed at points:  2, 12, 21
```

Based on three points that fail the control tests, this process is not completely in control and should be reviewed.

Call-Center Compliance

A banking call center monitors its employees for compliance with numerous federal regulations as well as internal policies and procedures. The monitoring comes from a quality assurance team who randomly listens to phone calls and records information about errors that team members might make when on the phone. Team members can make more than one error on each phone call; for example, a team member might forget to let the caller know the call is being recorded *and* not provide the caller with the right information.

In a 10-hour shift, the quality assurance team monitored calls each hour and created the following data table.

Hour	Calls Monitored	Errors
1	15	3
2	13	5
3	18	4
4	10	0
5	12	2
6	9	2
7	11	4
8	12	5
9	8	0
10	7	1

The sample size, which is indicated by the number of calls monitored each hour, is not consistent in this example. Reasons for inconsistent subgroups in this case could be that the number of calls received each hour vary and the quality assurance team only reviews a certain portion of calls. It could also be that some calls take longer – and thus take longer to review. Regardless of the reason for inconsistent subgroup sizes, it leads us to choose the u-Chart, which is concerned with the number of errors per unit. In this case, that would be calculated by dividing errors by calls monitored, creating rate or proportion data so that the actual sample size isn't as important.

When plugging data into Minitab to create this control chart, Errors are the Variables and Calls Monitored are the Subgroup size.

Minitab generates the following control chart.

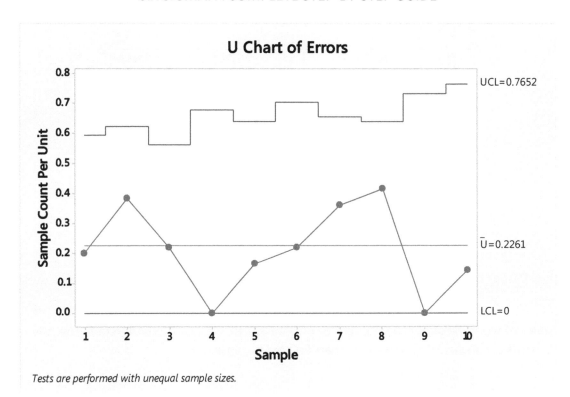

Tests are performed with unequal sample sizes.

You can see that no tests are failed, which indicates the process is in control. You'll also note that the upper control limit seems to stair-step all over the place. This is because each sample was a different size, so each upper control limit is calculated at a different value.

What if call center management was especially concerned with a specific error?

If call center management was concerned with PCI-compliance (compliance with the regulations for the payment card industry), they might want to dig into the data to see information about the number of errors related to PCI-compliance. They might ask the quality assurance team to check a box when reviewing a call to denote whether the call was compliant with PCI standards or not.

The new data table is seen below.

Hour	Calls Monitored	Errors	PCI Non-compliance
1	15	3	1
2	13	5	0
3	18	4	1
4	10	0	0
5	12	2	1
6	9	2	1
7	11	4	2
8	12	5	2
9	8	0	0
10	7	1	1

Instead of worrying about the number of errors per call, we want to understand the rate of PCI errors occurring. We can use a p-chart for that purpose.

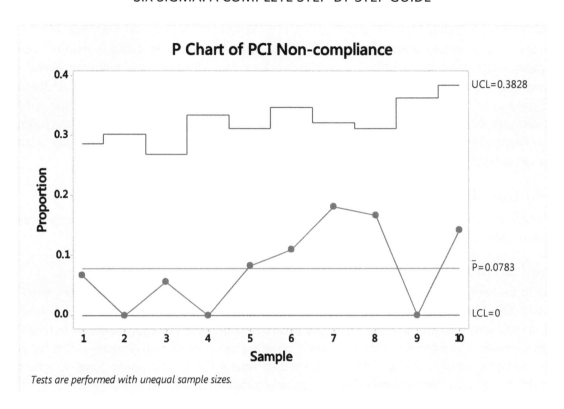

Tests are performed with unequal sample sizes.

This chart is a great illustration of how an in-control process can still be a problematic process. This process is in control, but four of the last five points are above the 0.10 proportion mark. That means that out of 10 samples, four had a fail rate of 10 percent or more when it comes to PCI compliance.

In the banking world, PCI compliance issues can cost a great deal of money, which means banking call centers will want to see PCI compliance error rates as close to zero as possible. The process owner for this call center is likely to take action to reduce the mean proportion of this process, even though it is in control.

Common Cause versus Special Cause Variation

When selecting the control tests in Minitab, you'll note that we selected to perform all tests for special causes. This lets Minitab know to perform all the tests for special cause variation – special cause variation is that which is caused by something outside of the normal expectations within a process.

Any process is going to have some amount of variation. The normal variation within a process – the variation that is caused by the process itself – is called common cause variation. For example, a phone operator working at a call center is going to make an occasional speaking or typing error while performing job duties. That variation is accounted for on a control chart. However, an operator who is working too many hours, has a bad headset, or is new on the job might make more than the normal amount of errors. That abnormality is likely to show up on a control chart and it is explained by the special causes such as a malfunctioning headset.

Additional Minitab Control Charts

Minitab offers a variety of other control charts. We have covered the most commonly used control charts in this chapter, but highlight a few others briefly below.

The I & MR Chart (Within/Between)

Not to be confused with the aforementioned I-MR (Individual Moving Range) chart, the I & MR (Within/Between) chart provides a three-way chart that indicates variation within a group and between groups. You might use this chart when the variation between batches is high compared to variation within batches or when variation is not randomly distributed. For example, when working with a process that spans shifts, you might have subgroups within shift groups, and differences might appear between the shifts.

You can find this chart under Stat > Control Charts > Variables for Subgroups

Exponentially Weighted Moving Average

The EWMA chart delivers an individual and moving range graph. This chart is rarely used in common statistical analysis, as it is difficult to work with. Most often, the EWMA chart is used when dealing with automatic data systems.

Cumulative Sum

The CUSUM chart deals with the cumulative sums of the deviations of each sample as they relate to a target value. CUSUM is very adept at detecting a small shift from a target, particularly in a process that is in control. Like the EWMA, CUSUM is not a commonly used control chart for most business environments.

CHAPTER 24:
APPLYING STATISTICS TO BUSINESS APPLICATIONS THROUGH SIX SIGMA

You aren't done with statistics yet but, it's a good idea to take a break from the numbers and analysis to revisit some fundamental concepts of Six Sigma.

Throughout Unit 4 and 5, we've worked extensively with data and analysis, and it can be easy to get wrapped up in the numbers without remembering the business need. In fact, the more you learn about statistical analysis, the easier it is to get caught up in the challenge of the analysis and forget that the business is relying on you for answers about its own challenges. In this chapter, we'll cover some obstacles you might run into when communicating your statistical findings to business employees and leaders. We'll also talk about the importance of including statistics in business presentations and some tips for integrating statistics within those presentations.

Common Challenges When Presenting Statistical Analysis

Here is the first, and perhaps biggest, challenge faced by Six Sigma experts when delivering information from statistical analysis: Most people don't care. Truly, unless your sponsor is a Six Sigma expert too or your leadership committee is well-versed in Six Sigma methods, the people you are presenting to don't care about which hypothesis test you used or what your Chi-Squared statistic or p-value was. That isn't to say that business leaders and others don't care about the conclusions or results of your analysis, and they certainly care about the results of the project as a whole. But you have to find a way to present your information in a way that ties in with what they care about and doesn't rely solely on statistical concepts and language.

A second challenge is that general business staff and leaders are unlikely to have the same understanding of statistical analysis as a Six Sigma expert does. The Six Sigma presenter is then tasked with presenting data when the backup for the data might not be understood. As a Six Sigma expert, you have to be able to explain *why* the team chose to move in a certain direction or *how* you know a process has improved, and not everyone is simply going to take your word that the p-Value was appropriate for the decision you made.

A third challenge when presenting your analysis is that you can easily become distracted or derailed by the statistics without getting your business point across. This can happen for one of two reasons. First, if your sponsor or another member of your audience is knowledgeable about Six Sigma and statistical analysis, he or she might begin asking statistical questions instead of business questions. Why did you use the 1-Proportion test? How did you choose the sample size? Do you really think a beta of 0.2 is sufficient, or should you have gone with a beta of 0.1?

Some statistical questions might very well be valid. How *did* you choose the sample size? That might be something relevant to cover in a presentation so that the audience understands what assumptions were made by the team and what risks were considered acceptable. On the other hand, if you've already done the analysis and made decisions based on sample size and hypothesis testing, then it's a moot point on whether the power was set correctly. One way to keep this type of derailment from occurring is to keep a sponsor with Six Sigma knowledge in the loop throughout the project; that way, he or she can provide input on such things in real time if desired.

The other reason you might get lost in statistics when you are supposed to be presenting business-relevant information is because your audience *doesn't* understand the statistics, leading to the presentation becoming a statistics lesson. It's important to walk the line between educating the audience on necessary information regarding the Six Sigma process and providing an in-depth discussion of statistical analysis. For example, you probably should ensure your audience understands what standard deviation is and why it's important. You probably *don't* need to explain all the types of hypothesis tests – or even, in some cases, that you used a hypothesis test at all.

A final challenge in presenting statistical data is in a tendency to include too much information or too many examples. You have a box plot, a bar graph, a pie chart, a hypothesis test, and several calculations based on probability distributions. They all look good to you. They all say a little something different about the data. They should *all* go in the presentation, right? Wrong – too many ways of illustrating the data overwhelms the audience. It's also likely that the majority of people within the business won't see the nuances in the data that a trained Six Sigma expert does, which means from their perspective, you're simply showing the same data over and over. It's not an effective use of presentation space or meeting time.

Why Include Some Statistics?

Even with all the challenges discussed above, you shouldn't leave statistics out of your presentation altogether. Whether you are presenting findings at a Measure or Analyze tollgate review or you are presenting for final approval on improvements, statistics are what provides your conclusions or results credibility. Incorporating your data into a presentation can be difficult, but we've provided some tips for doing so in the next section.

Tips for Creating Business-Friendly Presentations

If it's important to include statistics for credibility, but many people in your business audience are likely not to follow the intricacies of the actual analysis, what do you do? This is actually where some of the biggest benefits of Six Sigma's statistical process control come in. If you are working in a true Six Sigma environment, then you are never working only with the numbers. Remember from Unit 1 that Six Sigma is *more* concerned with the business – and its goals and success – than it is with the data and the analysis. In fact, the analysis and data is only relevant in so much that it can be used as a tool to make or measure improvements to business processes.

Because of this, the Six Sigma team should already be rooted in business terms and phrases. Consider the act of drafting the problem statement, which we covered in chapter 5. The problem statement combines statistical concepts with business goals and needs – and it is a good reference point for anyone presenting Six Sigma information throughout and following a DMAIC project. If you aren't sure if something should be included in a presentation, then ask yourself: does it relate to the problem statement or a solution for the problem statement? If not, then it's probably not necessary to communicate or present in a general business environment. As you work with data and statistics, you might be surprised by how your interest in the numbers grow. While interest in the numbers can lead you to valuable discoveries and conclusions, you do need to avoid the temptation to include data or conclusions in a presentation simply because you think they are interesting or "cool."

Other ways you can create viable business presentations when dealing with statistics and analysis include tailoring presentation to the audience, creating a story-style narrative, keeping things short and simple, integrating appropriate pictures, and avoiding misuse of technology, presentation, or statistical tools.

Understand the Target Audience

When presenting or communicating about a Six Sigma project or statistical analysis, tailor the information to reflect your audience's level of concern and knowledge. For example, consider a Six Sigma Black Belt who is presenting during an Improve tollgate review meeting. The Black Belt is presenting to a leadership team, which includes the project sponsor. At least two members of the leadership team are also Black Belts – perhaps one is even a Master Black belt.

Given this scenario, the audience is both invested in the information and capable of understanding many of the statistical concepts behind the decisions made by the Six Sigma team during the project. That doesn't mean you should automatically include all of your data in the presentation – your audience is also busy. But it does mean you should anticipate at least a few questions about methodology or statistical analysis, and you can incorporate a few technical terms or results into your presentation without worrying about having to explain them.

When dealing with this type of audience, it's often a good idea to create a presentation appendix. You can put your analysis, data tables, and even specific Minitab results in the appendix, where they can be quickly displayed if a specific question calls for it. In situations that involve high costs or high risks, leadership teams are more likely to want to see the background analysis because they need to fully understand all assumptions and risks before making a decision on the recommended improvements.

In other situations, you might be called upon to present Six Sigma information or statistical findings to audiences that are less invested or who don't have any background with statistics. Examples include presenting to general management or presenting the reasons behind changes to the staff in a department impacted by a Six Sigma process improvement. When this happens, it can be helpful to rely on graphical representations of your analysis, particularly if the information you are trying to share is very apparent on a certain type of graph.

For example, a Six Sigma team in a government office has been task with improving the production of a workflow process that involves reviewing applications for financial aid. The team has made improvements to the process and now compares the average hourly production rate of the process before the changes with the current average hourly production rate. To do so, they complete a 2-Sample T Test to determine whether the new data has a higher average mean than the old data. The Minitab results are presented below.

Two-Sample T-Test and CI: C1, C2

```
Two-sample T for C1 vs C2

     N   Mean  StDev  SE Mean
C1  23   4.00   2.76     0.58
C2  23   6.35   3.11     0.65


Difference = μ (C1) - μ (C2)
Estimate for difference:  -2.348
95% upper bound for difference:  -0.889
T-Test of difference = 0 (vs <): T-Value = -2.70  P-Value = 0.005  DF = 43
```

Knowing what you do about hypothesis tests and p-values, you can see quickly that we reject the null hypothesis and accept the alternative. Yes, the mean averages of the process have changed. It is, according to our statistical analysis, a more productive process.

But can you just copy that Minitab data into a PowerPoint slide? Probably not – only a Six Sigma or statistical analysis expert is going to be able to make that connection between p-value and real-world conclusion.

Consider the graphical image below.

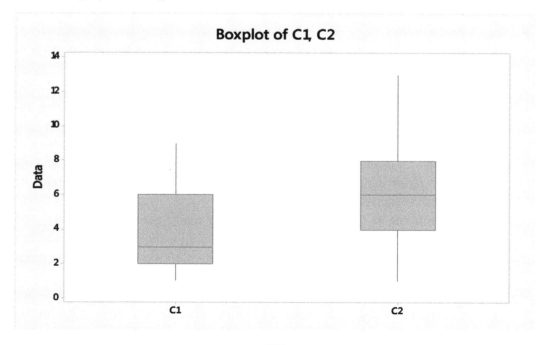

This is a box plot of the same data used to create the 2-Sample T Test above, but it provides a friendlier version of the data for most business employees. You can quickly see that the process C2 has a higher rate of production than the process C1 – even if you don't know anything about box and whisper plots.

It's not enough to understand how the target audience is likely to interact with data and statistical analysis. When creating a presentation about your project or statistical data, you also need to understand what the target audience wants to know and how they need to know it.

- High-level leadership typically wants to know whether the project was a success, how you know it was a success, what savings or gains can be expected, and how you are controlling the process to ensure the same issues don't arise again.
- Process owners and employees close to the process should know all of the above, though you might have to broaden discussions about costs and savings to leave out sensitive data that could be included in an executive-level presentation (such as assumptions about employee pay). Process owners and employees are also likely to want to know more details about the specific changes to the process – why were such changes implemented and how does it impact daily workflow? Where leadership might be satisfied with a high-level process map, for example, process owners want to see more granular maps.
- Audience members from disparate departments are likely to ask questions that make sense from their perspective, so know who will be in a tollgate or other type of presentation meeting, and be prepared to answer questions specific to their world.
  - Compliance staff asks about adherence to regulations. Did the team consider regulations when making decisions? What happens when compliance required a decision that seemed opposite of where the statistical inferences led the team? Did the team calculate risks and costs associated with compliance failures, which are often greater than other process failures?
  - Accounting or finance staff asks about budget, revenue, and savings. Does the team have a graph that shows results in a dollar format? What is the likelihood of saving over a certain amount? Can the team associate a dollar amount with various analysis, changes, or improvements?
  - Marketing, sales, and customer service staff are likely to ask about customer-facing and customer-centric information. How did the team gather the voice of the customer? What assumptions about the customer

did the team make? When making process changes or analyzing data, how did the team consider the customer?

You obviously can't create a presentation that answers every possible question about your process, project, or statistical analysis. The presentation would be enormous and take much too long to present. It's typically a good idea to keep a presentation under 10 to 20 minutes with plenty of time for questions, and your presentation time might be even more constrained depending on organizational business practices. So, you should always answer the biggest and most important questions about your improvements, project, or DMAIC stage in the presentation and be prepared for other types of questions in the question and answer session (this is where an appendix can be helpful).

Tell a Story with Text and Images

Use PowerPoint or another presentation program to combine your information in a way that tells a story that the audience can understand and care about. Keeping your audience and the purpose of your presentation in mind, attempt to tell an overall story across your entire presentation while presenting "miniature narratives" on each slide.

Consider the example slide below, which presents the 2-Sample T Test information we used previously in this chapter. The slide tells a story with the placement of information, the inclusion of a graphic, and the question-and answer format. This is an easy template that can be used in a majority of Six Sigma presentation slides, particularly when presenting statistical analysis or data.

- First, ask a question as the title of the slide. Create a concise question, but try to write a stand-alone question. The slide example doesn't do a great job of that: what changes, what process, and what hourly rates are being discussed? In the context of an entire presentation, this isn't a problem. However, you might want to pull a single slide out for an email communication or training document – and executive leaders tend to pull out one slide or graphical image to communicate information about a sponsored project. A better title for this slide might be "Did software changes to the Aid Application Review workflow increase hourly production rates?"
- Next, include an image that answers your question or provides additional information regarding the data or process. Pictures, graphs, and maps break up long blocks of text in a presentation, making it easier for the audience to digest. By presenting data in a variety of formats on one slide, you also capture the interest and understanding of a wider audience. Graphical representations of data often get the point across quicker and can help you tell a complex data story in a small amount of time.

- It can be a good idea to include some basic statistical information, such as a business-friendly version of the null and alternative hypothesis. At the very least, everyone in the audience can understand that these two statements are what the team were evaluating, and only one of them can be true. Including the type of test run and the p-Value is optional, but can be a good idea both for the team's own reference and for informing sponsors or others who are also knowledgeable in Six Sigma.
- Finally, answer the question posed in the title in a short, text-based conclusion. The conclusion should align with any graphical representation or statistical test data included on the slide. You should avoid presenting contradicting data and conclusions on a single slide unless you have a specific reason for doing so and an explanation of why the contradiction is important.

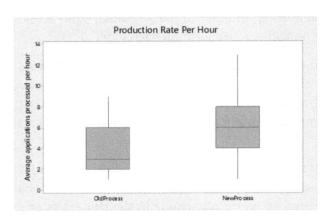

Not all questions require all elements of the above slide. Sometimes, it makes sense to provide the answer in concise text. For example, you might ask "What problem is the team trying to solve?" The right content for that slide would be the problem statement as written in the Define phase.

Sometimes, the only thing you need to include on the slide is a graph or chart. Consider the slide below.

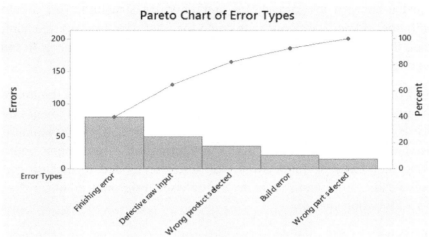

This slide asks what is causing defective orders to be sent out, and it answers the question with a Pareto chart. Even if someone is not familiar with the Pareto chart, it's fairly obvious given the labels and data that the issue creating the biggest number of defects is in product finishing. Someone who knows about Pareto charts could see within seconds that finishing errors and defective raw inputs account for over 60 percent of the errors; if you add "wrong product selected," you account for 80 percent of the errors.

Some Six Sigma tools, such as the Pareto chart, are easy to explain to audience members who don't have a pre-existing understanding of data analysis or Six Sigma. Given a minute or two of presentation time, you could sufficiently explain how the above chart answers the slide's question, and this is one reason Pareto (and other bar-type charts) are popular in such presentations.

Be Clear and Concise

No matter how you are presenting your data, make sure each slide – and each element on the slide – is clear and concise. This means writing in active language as much as possible, avoiding long text explanation, and ensuring everything is spelled correctly and that you didn't use the wrong word by accident. When including statistics in a presentation, it can be easy to make an incorrect word choice that changes the meaning of your entire statement. Simply saying "greater than" when you meant "less than" or "decrease" when you meant "increase" can skew the information you are providing or make it confusing to your audience.

Clarity isn't just a concern in word choice and sentence structure. You should also be concerned with how elements on your slide come together. Don't put so much information on a single slide that words or images become unintelligible to the audience. In some cases, you might need to ask a question and answer it over a series of slides.

Be cognizant of the fact that a projected slide image is never as clear as the image on your computer. Because of this, you should always avoid layering light font or images over a light background or layer dark font or images over a dark background. Don't minimize fonts to something as small as 12-point just to fit all the information -- remember, your audience could be sitting feet away or yards away. You also don't need to include every bit of information on a slide – the slide should act as the visual reference point for the audience while you add information verbally.

The text and images you add directly to the slide shouldn't be your only concern. You also need to make sure text and images within graphs are as clear and concise as possible. Consider the two boxplots below.

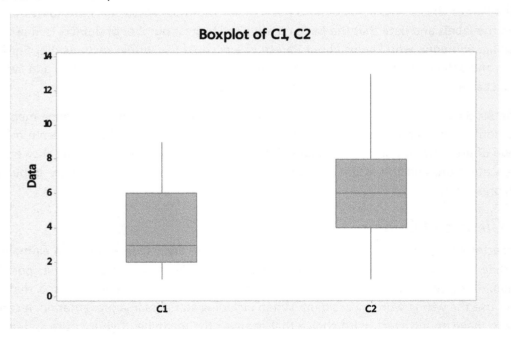

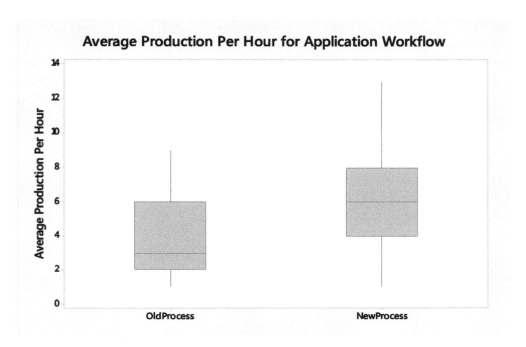

The first boxplot, on its own, doesn't provide much information to an audience. Someone who understands boxplots would simply be able to tell that two things were being charted and that the average of one was higher than the average of the other.

The second boxplot is the same as the first, but the title and data labels have been edited. Now, you can see that the graph provides information about the application workflow. Specifically, the graph is illustrating the average production rates per hour for that workflow, and the new workflow process seems to be more productive than the old one.

Creating graphical analyses that tell a small story all on their own – with the help of data labels and titles – is important. First, as the Six Sigma presenter, labels provide cues that help you verbally explain the slide or graph. After several slides with similar-looking graphs or charts, even you can get confused about what specific data you are talking about. Second, appropriate labels on such images let you reuse the image without the context of the presentation or slide. This means you waste less time and can reuse your work when communicating about your project or data – effectively reducing muda of rework. Finally, you don't have to worry as much about someone taking your data or analysis and misinterpreting it or getting the wrong idea from it. If graphs are properly labeled, then it is harder for someone seeing the information outside of your presentation to draw the wrong conclusions.

You can also edit colors of data on charts in both Minitab and Excel, making it even easier for an audience to draw appropriate conclusions from the illustration. Consider the Pareto chart below. This is the same Pareto chart shown earlier in this chapter, but in this version, the top three categories are presented in red. The color change emphasizes those categories, which account for 80 percent of the errors, making it easier for the audience to draw the conclusion that these are the issues that the team will concentrate on.

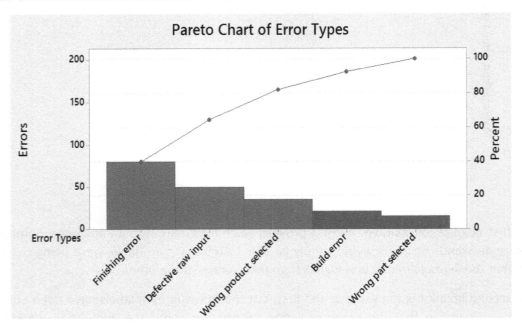

Don't Misuse Your Tools

A final tip for creating business-friendly presentations is: don't misuse the tools, knowledge, and resources you have for creating a presentations or communicating ideas.

Don't misuse PowerPoint, for example. Most audience members don't want to see a 100-slide presentation. Just because you can include it, doesn't mean you should. Likewise, try to avoid animating every aspect of your presentation. Yes, there is a time for fade-in or fly-in, but the time is *not* every single bullet point or image. Use animations sparingly – if at all – for impact about very important conclusions or elements of your presentation. For the most part, a strong Six Sigma presentation should rely on clarity and data over gimmicks and animations.

Don't misuse Minitab or your other statistical analysis software. It takes mere seconds to perform certain tests or create graphs in Minitab, as you'll see in the next Unit. Because of that, Six Sigma analysts and teams tend to accumulate a lot of versions of data. Treat Minitab graphs and analysis as you do PowerPoint animations. Use them as needed, but don't use them because they are there. One good rule is no more than one graph or chart per slide or data-related question. This forces you to choose the graph or chart that you feel most powerfully or appropriately illustrates your data. There are exceptions to this rule, and you might need to include two charts if one chart helps explain another or you are comparing information about data or multiple data sets.

Don't misuse your data analysis skills. Misuse of data analysis can come in two forms: either you make a data analysis error inadvertently or you force an analysis to fit a desired outcome or conclusion. The first step is more of an error than a misuse; you can avoid presenting such errors to others by double checking all conclusions and inferences and having someone else knowledgeable about Six Sigma review your analysis before you finalize a presentation. This is why many Six Sigma organizations have at least one Master Black Belt on staff – Black Belts and Green Belts can call on the Master Black Belt if they have analysis questions or simply want to confirm they are on the right track with analysis.

No one is infallible, and mistakes can happen. As a Six Sigma expert, however, you can never allow biases to force statistical conclusions that aren't supported by the data. And you certainly should never cloud analysis by presenting it in a way that makes it hard for your audience to see the appropriate conclusion because you want them to draw another conclusion. For example, the trick used above to highlight a certain part of the Pareto chart with color can be used inappropriately. You can draw attention to a certain part of a graph or bar chart with color, increasing the chance that the audience will conclude that the colored portion is of more relevance or more important than other data on the graph. While this is sometimes true, Six Sigma teams and presenters must be careful when using such tactics – only create this scenario when the data supports such an emphasis.

Another example of creating bias in a presentation comes when you present analysis information knowing the sample size was not big enough for strong conclusions, but you don't make that known when you present the information. This can result in leadership or others making decisions based on your data without understanding the risks that the conclusions might be wrong.

Similarly, if you run four types of test in Minitab and three support one conclusion while only a single test supports the conclusion the team originally wanted to present, you shouldn't present only the results of the single test. Before presenting anything, you should review each of the tests to understand why there is a difference in one; you should also ensure that the tests you are using are appropriate for the data, question, and sample size at hand. If you verify the statistics are all correct, then you usually go with the conclusion supported by the greater number of tests.

Don't Let the Presentation Drive the Project

Given the decision-making processes and requirements in a corporate business world, presentations are a requirement of the DMAIC process. Six Sigma teams and experts are going to have to present their findings at some point, so presentation skills are something you do need to work on.

That being said, it is important that you never let the need for a good presentation drive any part of the process. Six Sigma teams should never make decisions about data gathering, graphical analysis, process mapping, brainstorming, or any other Six Sigma function because they think it will be good or look good for the presentation. Instead, the presentation of information to the business must come *after* the work is done.

This truth is relevant any time you are presenting information to the business or business staff – not just when you are standing in front of a conference room with a PowerPoint behind you. For example, Black Belts often communicate with sponsors or business leaders regularly during the course of a DMAIC project. Perhaps the team provides a daily email or a weekend update to the sponsor; whatever the mode of communication is, all of the tips in this chapter are relevant.

UNIT 6:
ADVANCED CONTROL

CHAPTER 25:
INTRODUCTION TO MINITAB

If you've been following along in previous chapters through Minitab for sample size calculations and control charting, then you've probably already used some of the interfaces within Minitab. This entire unit provides a how-to for some of the more common Six Sigma statistical analysis tools used in Minitab. We are including Minitab because it is one of the most widely used programs for this type of application, because it is, overall, fairly user friendly, and because it is incredibly powerful for statistical analysis purposes.

In previous chapters, we walked through Excel calculations and analysis for some very basic problems. The steps involved sometimes became very complex. Consider the Chi-Squared Goodness-of-Fit Test performed in Excel in the chapter on normal probability distributions. The calculations *do* work, and you can always use them absent a statistical software program. However, by using Minitab, within a half-dozen mouse clicks you can arrive at the same answer about the normality of data that all those Excel calculations required. Not only do you save time, but you reduce the opportunities for a numerical or mathematical error.

If Minitab or other software is an option, why bother learning how to perform some of these statistical analyses by hand or in Excel? As stated in the above paragraph, you might not always have access to Minitab or a similar program. Even when you do have access, it's important to understand the fundamentals behind some of these calculations so you understand why Minitab provides the results that it does. Without that background, it's difficult to create the presentations and explanations discussed in chapter 24. Instead, you would simply be relying on Minitab to make decisions for you, which is never a good way to manage a Six Sigma project.

Remember: *Statistics don't lie, but math cannot evaluate non-numerical priorities.* Statistics can say something is a better option than another, but you – knowing the process, the goals, the resources, and the willingness of leadership to take risks or spend money – might decide against that option for good reason.

Overview of the Minitab Interface

Before getting into some specific Minitab capabilities, take a moment to understand the Minitab interface. At first glance, you might think this is just a spreadsheet, but the interface actually has three prominent windows.

When you first open Minitab, you'll likely see the session window on top and the worksheet window on bottom. The worksheet window looks and behaves a lot like a worksheet in Excel. You can have more than one worksheet window open in Minitab at a time, and you can save individual worksheets as part of a Minitab project.

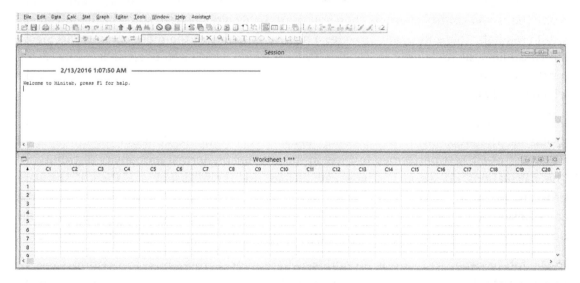

At the top of the worksheet window, you'll find the traditional Windows-based icons for minimizing, maximizing, and closing the worksheet. You can also use your mouse to grab the edges of the worksheet on all four sides to make it larger or smaller in the window as you wish.

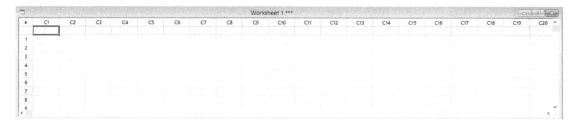

The worksheet is where you enter data that you are attempting to analyze. You can enter data by typing it in yourself, but you can also copy data into Minitab from numerous other spreadsheet programs, including Excel.

If you enter data into a column in Minitab, you can right click on that column to make format changes to the column or the data within the column.

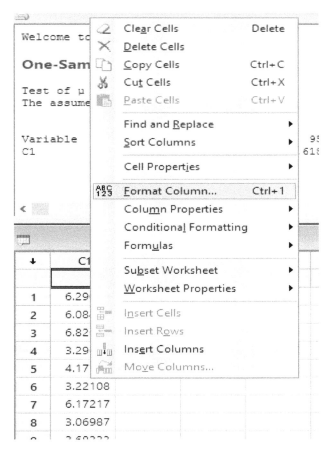

Clear, delete, copy, cut, find and replace, sort, insert, and conditional formatting all work very similar to the way these functions work in Excel. You might use these options when you are ordering and preparing data for analysis or if you have analyzed data and you want to create a more visually-pleasing format for a presentation. Minitab *is* more limited than Excel when it comes to formatting and presenting information, which is why Six Sigma experts often work simultaneously in both programs.

One of the more valuable cell/column functions is the "format columns" option. Clicking this option brings up the Format Column dialogue box.

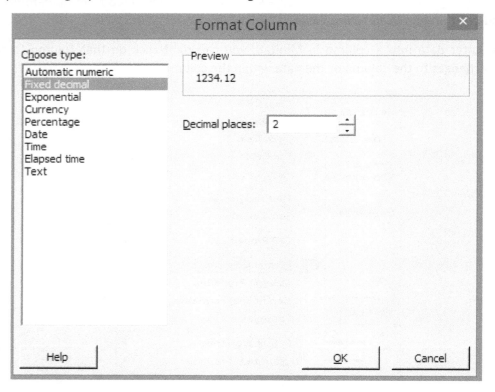

The dialogue box lets you format numbers within a column to match certain parameters. You can set Minitab to only display 2 decimal places, or set a column for percentage, currency, or time. This helps create uniform data and reduce the confusion of the display, especially since Minitab tends to default to a 3 or 4 decimal readout, which is not appropriate for every analysis. If you are analyzing the number of workers in a shift, for example, you probably don't want to consider 0.005 of a worker.

Like Excel, Minitab accepts both numerical and alpha-numerical entries. If any cell in a column features alpha-numerical text, Minitab notes that the cells in that column are text cells. You can't perform calculations on a column with a text cell included. The purpose of including text in Minitab would be to clarify subgroups or divisions of data and for use in automatically labeling some charts.

C2	C3-T	C4	C5
	Monday		
	Tuesday		
	Wednesday		
	Thursday		
	Friday		
	Saturday		

When you first open Minitab, the session window is located above the spreadsheet-style worksheet. The session window is critical to Minitab functionality because this is where all of the analysis and calculations are displayed. Below is an example of results in the session window. You can see that Minitab typically provides a bold header identifying what calculation or analysis was run, followed by a summary of the test or analysis and the results.

Here, for example, you see the results of a 1-Sample Z test. The null hypothesis is that the mean is equal to 5. The alternative is that the mean is not equal to 5. A standard deviation of 1 was assumed for this test.

Minitab provides several pieces of analysis, the most important in this case being the p-Value of 0.893. In this case, the p-Value is above 0.05, so we would fail to reject the null hypothesis.

```
                                                                    Session

Welcome to Minitab, press F1 for help.

One-Sample Z: C1

Test of μ = 5 vs ≠ 5
The assumed standard deviation = 1


Variable    N   Mean   StDev   SE Mean      95% CI          Z      P
C1         30   4.975  1.119    0.183    (4.618, 5.333)  -0.13  0.893

|
```

Throughout the next three chapters, we'll look repeatedly at the session window when learning to run and interpret various tests in Minitab.

Before moving onto the various menu options in Minitab, consider one more window in the interface. The window might be minimized at the bottom of the screen. Click to maximize this window for a moment.

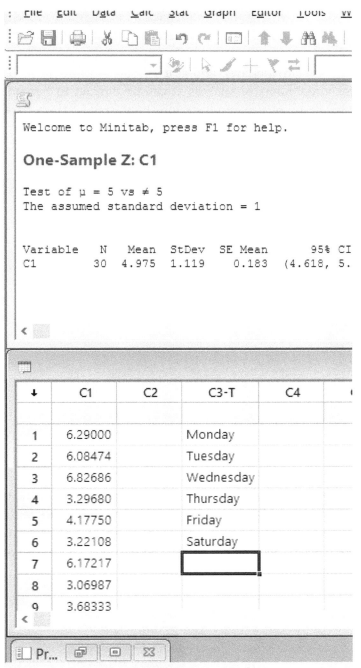

This is the project window, where you can manage all of the data, worksheets, charts, and graphs you create with Minitab. Minitab functions similar to Microsoft OneNote in this regard. You can create a project file. Within that file, you can store additional files, including workbooks, reports, session windows, and graphs. You can also view the history of your open session; after a few hours of analysis, it can be difficult to remember what various results are. In this window, you can find tests you already ran and click back to view them.

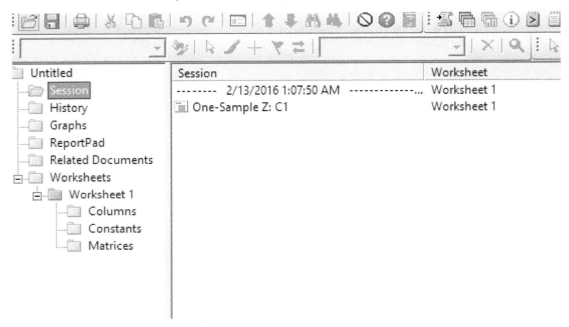

Overview of the Minitab Menu

Minitab has a fairly expansive menu bar, and we will not cover all of the options and icons within this unit. The file, edit, window, and help menu bar options are fairly self-explanatory and function in keeping with similar menu options in common software programs. If you are working in your own version of Minitab, you can experiment with those menu options and the variety of icons below the menu on your own.

For this unit, we'll concentrate on the menu options with statistical analysis functions: the Calc, Stat, and Graph menus.

The Calc Menu Option

In this chapter, we're going to look at three major capabilities found under the Calc menu option:

- Generate random data
- Calculate column or row statistics
- Calculate probabilities given various distributions

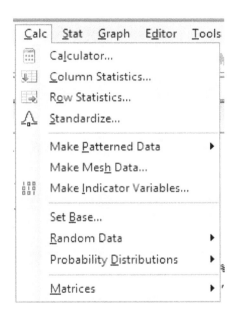

Random Data

The random data tool lets you generate random data that conforms to a certain probability distribution. This tool is helpful if you are testing different capabilities in Minitab or practicing Six Sigma statistical analysis without any of your own data to start with. It can also be helpful if you want to compare your own data to various types of distributions.

We're going to use the random data generation function to create some data that we can use for other functions within this chapter.

Click Calc > Random Data and then select a distribution you want to work with. For the purpose of this exercise, select the normal distribution.

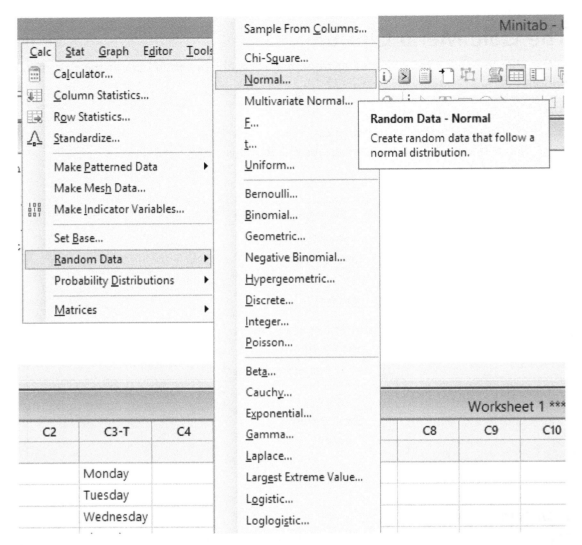

In the Normal Distribution dialogue box, type:

- 30 for the number of rows of data to generate. This will generate a sample size of 30. You can create a sample size of a few data points or hundreds of data points.
- C1 for the column you want to store data in. You can type the alpha-numeric name of any column or, if you already named some columns, you can select them from the list on the left.
- 5 for the mean. You can specific any mean when you generate random data on your own.

- 1.0 for the standard deviation. You can also specific any standard deviation when you generate random data on your own.

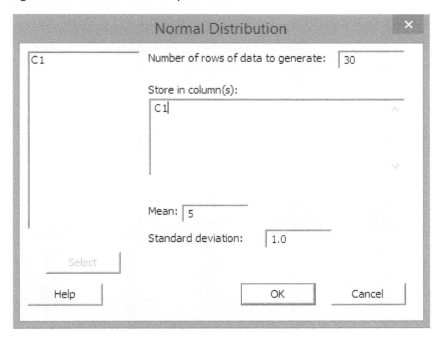

Once your dialogue box looks like the one pictured above, click OK.

Minitab populates column C1 with data that fits the parameters you set. You can try creating other types of data using this function, with various other parameters such as different means and standard deviations, to see how inputting different information changes the data that is returned.

Column and Row Statistics

Sometimes, you just need to know a specific statistic about your data quickly. The calculate Column or Row Statistics functions lets you calculate the sum, mean, standard deviation, min, max, range, median, sum of squares, or N total given data in a single column or row. You can only calculate one of these statistics at a time, though, which creates some limitations. In chapter 27, we'll cover another Minitab function that returns all major descriptive statistics at one time.

Using the random set of data created in the previous section, try out the column statistics function.

Click Calc > Column Statistics.

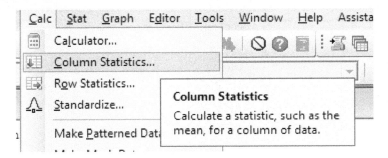

Click to select the mean.

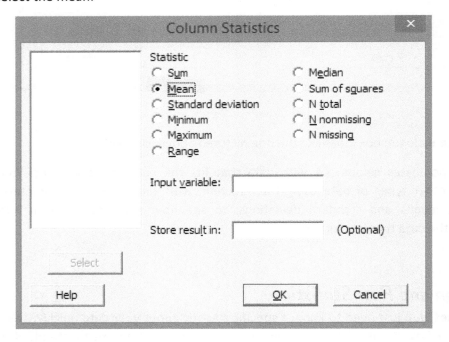

Click in the Input Variable box.

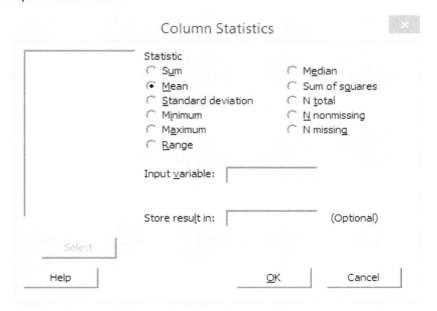

Without clicking in any other box first, click on the C1 listing in the large box to the left.

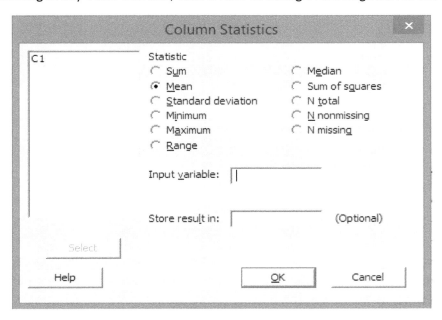

Click "Select" to select C1 into the Input Variable box. Note, you can also double click C1 to move it into the Input Variable box.

Note, many of Minitab's dialogue boxes follow a similar structure, with data columns listed in a box on the left. You have to select data by double clicking or by clicking the column name and clicking select.

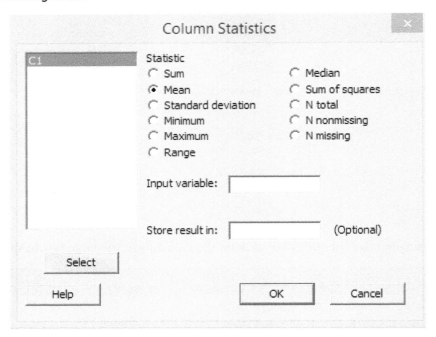

Click OK.

Minitab displays the mean of the data in the session window.

Mean of C1

Mean of C1 = 4.81277

Note, the mean of your data will not necessarily be the same as the value calculated above, since you generated random data that is likely somewhat different from the data that was used to calculate the example in this book.

Calculating statistics for row-based data is done in the exact same fashion, except that you would select a row name instead of a column name.

Probability Distributions

Take a moment to recall the chapters on both normal probability distributions and non-normal probability distributions. In both of those chapters, we demonstrated calculations that let us determine the probability of certain outcomes given a set of data and a certain probability distribution.

If you recall, we mentioned that some of these calculations can get fairly complex, and we only handled a few through manual calculations in those chapters. This is because software such as Minitab lets you calculate the PDF and CDF by entering a few pieces of information

---

Brief Review

PDF = Probability Density Function – the probability that a random variable, X, will occur in the data. In a given population of people, what is the probability that a randomly selected person will weigh 125 pounds?

CDF: Cumulative Density Function – the probability that a randomly selected data point will be less than or equal to a variable, x. In a given population of people, what is the probability that a randomly selected person will weigh *less than or equal to* 125 pounds?

---

about your data.

To understand how to calculate PDF and CDF in Minitab, let's look at a real-world example.

A Six Sigma team working to increase the process efficiency of a library checkout system randomly measured the length of time it takes for librarians to check out patrons. For this purpose, assume the data is normal. The mean time of the sample was 5.5 minutes. The standard deviation was 3.028 minutes. What is the probability that it takes exactly 5 minutes to check out a patron?

Begin the calculation by selection Calc > Probability Distributions > Normal

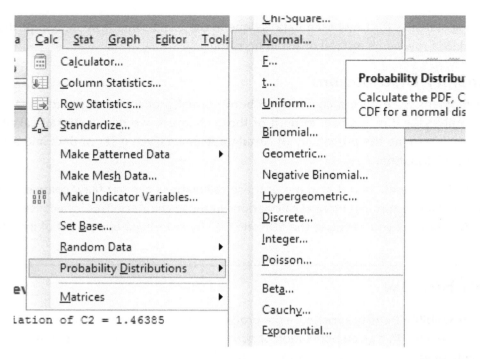

Select "probability density" to calculate the PDF, since you want to know the probability of an exact value.

Enter the data for the mean and standard deviation. Select "Input Constant," since you want to find the answer for a specific number, not for a list of numbers in a column in your worksheet.

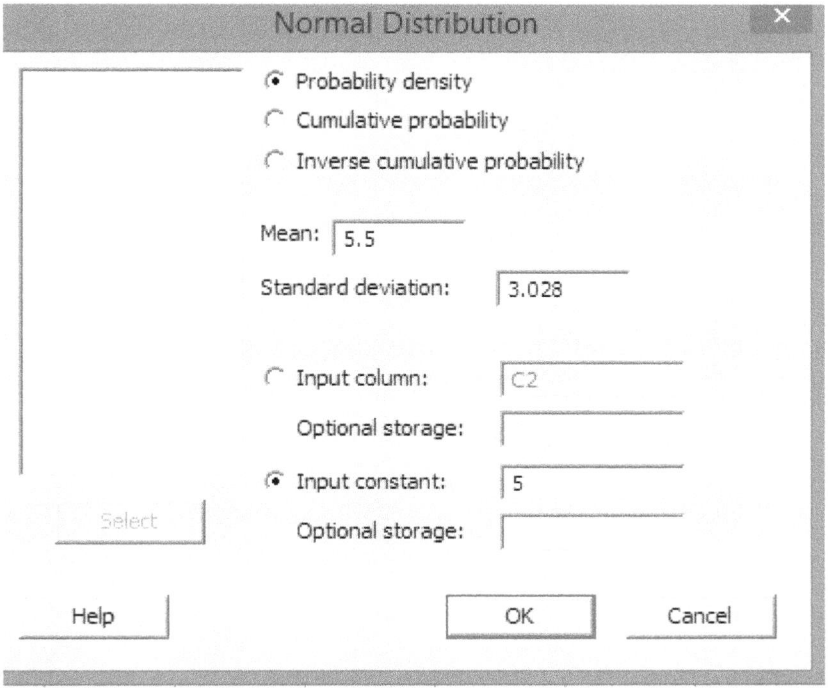

Normal Distribution ✕

○ Probability density
○ Cumulative probability
○ Inverse cumulative probability

Mean: 5.5

Standard deviation: 3.028

○ Input column: C2

Optional storage:

● Input constant: 5

Optional storage:

Select

Help   OK   Cancel

Once your dialog box looks like the one pictured above, click OK.

Probability Density Function

```
Normal with mean = 5.5 and standard deviation = 3.028

x     f( x )
5   0.129967
```

The PDF is calculated in Minitab's session window. There is a 0.129 probability of the time being exactly 5 minutes.

What if you wanted to find out what the probability was that the time would be 5 minutes or less?

Repeat the steps above, but choose cumulative probability instead.

Minitab's new answer is calculated and displayed in the session window.

Cumulative Distribution Function

```
Normal with mean = 5.5 and standard deviation = 3.028

x   P( X ≤ x )
5     0.434423
```

There is a 0.434 probability the time will be 5 minutes or less.

What is the probability that the time will be greater than 5 minutes? The total probability is 1, so:

$1 - 0.434 = 0.566$.

There is approximately 0.566 probability of the time being greater than 5 minutes.

Let's look at another example, this time using the box of chocolate scenario from chapter 20. In that scenario, a Six Sigma team was working with a process that produced boxes with 20 chocolates each. For each chocolate, there was a 0.05 probability of the chocolate being defective. What is the likelihood of getting a box of chocolates where 2 of those chocolates are defective?

This time, select Calc > Probability Distributions > Binomial.

Unlike the normal curve, the binomial distribution deals with number of trials and event probability. If you recall from chapter 20, when discussing binomial probabilities, we talk about the likelihood of one event or the other occurring for each trial.

For our chocolate boxes, there are effectively 20 trials in each box – each chocolate can be either defective or not defective. For each chocolate, there is a 0.05 probability that a defect will occur. This is the event probability. We can plug these two numbers into the Binomial Distribution dialog box and select the input constant "2" to determine the probability of getting a box with exactly 2 defective chocolates.

Click OK.

Probability Density Function

```
Binomial with n = 20 and p = 0.05

x    P( X = x )
2    0.188677
```

Minitab's answer is that there is a probability of 0.189 of getting exactly two defective chocolates.

What if we want to know the chance of getting over 5 defects? Repeat the steps above, but select "Cumulative probability" and enter 5 as the input constant.

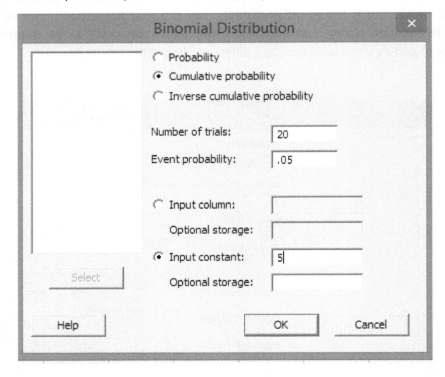

Click OK.

Cumulative Distribution Function

```
Binomial with n = 20 and p = 0.05

x   P( X ≤ x )
5     0.999671
```

Minitab returns an answer of 0.999, but remember that this is the cumulative probability. It is the probability of having 5 or less defects in the box. The probability of having more than 5 is:

$1 - 0.999$, or 0.001.

It's not a high probability at all.

Calculating Multiple Probabilities at Once

One of the reasons for using Minitab is that it lets you analyze data with utmost efficiency. While you can see that calculating a single probability or CDF is much faster than handling the math on your own, what if you wanted information about a set of numbers at one time? What if the chocolate team wanted to know the probability of getting 1, 2, 3, 4, 5, 6, 7, 8, and 9 defects?

First, enter all of these numbers in a column in Minitab.

Follow the steps above to choose the appropriate distribution. In this case, since we're dealing with the defect/no defect data, it's the binomial distribution.

Choose "Probability" and enter the information about trials and event probability. Instead of inputting a constant, select "input column." Select the column where you entered the numbers 1 through 9.

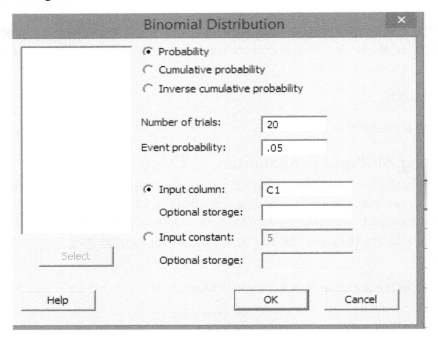

Click OK.

Minitab generates the probability for all the numbers you entered in the session window.

Probability Density Function

```
Binomial with n = 20 and p = 0.05

x     P( X = x )
1      0.377354
2      0.188677
3      0.059582
4      0.013328
5      0.002245
6      0.000295
7      0.000031|
8      0.000003
9      0.000000
```

Remember to Work with the Right Probability Distribution

Before calculating probabilities, make sure you have the right distribution. If you have data that follows a Binomial Distribution and you use Minitab to calculate answers based on the normal curve, your answers will be incorrect.

Use the Binomial Distribution when you are dealing with binomial data and a consistent event probability for every trial. Use the Normal Distribution when you are dealing with data that is normal or approximates the normal curve. Remember, the Central Limit Theorem says that, when dealing with continuous data, the larger the sample size, the closer it will approximately the normal curve.

You can run a quick graphical analysis to determine if data you are working with is normal.

To understand how to perform this analysis, copy the following data into Minitab.

6.319075
3.556859
3.452996
3.300786
4.340399
5.242524
2.542238
4.429293
7.757632
7.582288
4.692596
4.450197
6.454293
3.666121
5.243754
2.025502
4.189321
2.79723
3.397714
5.507707

Select Stat > Basic Statistics > Graphical Summary.

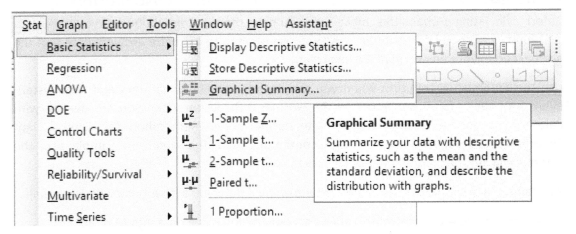

 For Variables, select the column where you copied the data from above. Leave the confidence level at 95.

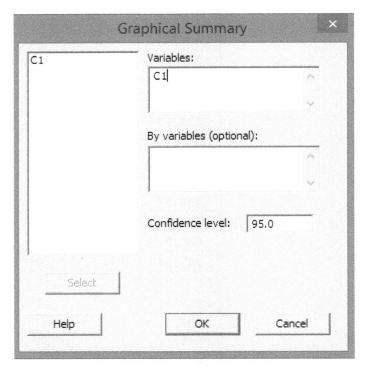

Click OK.

Minitab generates a graphical and statistical analysis of the data.

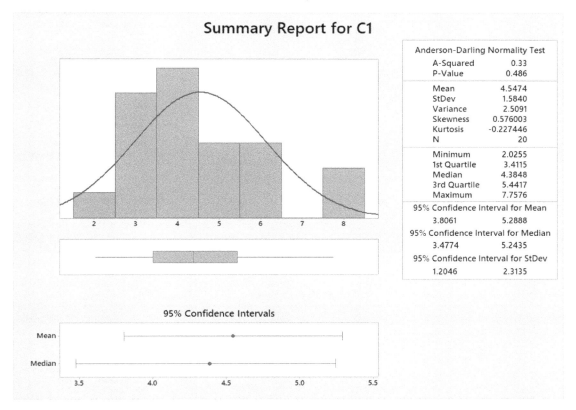

There are several things on this analysis that tell us the data is probably normal:

- The graphical analysis does somewhat appear to follow a normal curve. Because we only have 20 data points, though, it's difficult to come to a conclusion based solely on the image.
- The mean and median are fairly close, and the confidence interval of the mean is within the confidence interval of the median. This is another indication we could be dealing with a normal curve.
- Finally, the p-value for the Anderson-Darling Normality test is listed as 0.486. Since the p-value is higher than the alpha value (remember, we left the confidence level at 95, which means alpha is 0.05), we fail to reject the null hypothesis. The null hypothesis in a normality test is always that the data is normal.

Summary Report for C1

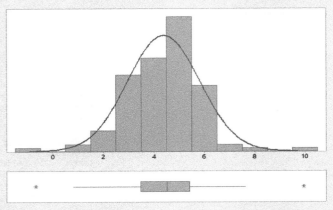

Anderson-Darling Normality Test	
A-Squared	0.53
P-Value	0.176
Mean	4.3948
StDev	1.4302
Variance	2.0455
Skewness	-0.02673
Kurtosis	2.14367
N	120
Minimum	-0.6780
1st Quartile	3.4745
Median	4.5212
3rd Quartile	5.4035
Maximum	9.9480

95% Confidence Interval for Mean
4.1362   4.6533
95% Confidence Interval for Median
4.2262   4.7776
95% Confidence Interval for StDev
1.2693   1.6382

95% Confidence Intervals

Summary Report for C2

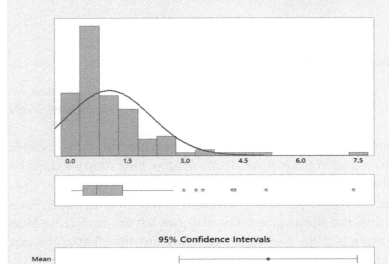

Anderson-Darling Normality Test	
A-Squared	7.97
P-Value	<0.005
Mean	1.0115
StDev	1.0871
Variance	1.1817
Skewness	2.6578
Kurtosis	10.1865
N	130
Minimum	0.0027
1st Quartile	0.3209
Median	0.6765
3rd Quartile	1.3484
Maximum	7.3700

95% Confidence Interval for Mean
0.8229   1.2001
95% Confidence Interval for Median
0.5964   0.8487
95% Confidence Interval for StDev
0.9691   1.2381

95% Confidence Intervals

CHAPTER 26:
GRAPHS AND QUALITY TOOLS IN MINITAB

One reason many Six Sigma experts use Minitab is the powerful and efficient graphical analysis interface it offers. As previously mentioned, with Minitab or similar software programs, you can quickly create graphs of various types to analyze your data. In the last chapter, you learned how to create a graphical analysis that included a histogram, a normality test, and several other pieces of information—all within a few mouse clicks. The same option is available in Minitab for scatterplots, histograms, boxplots, and dozens of other graphs.

Why is efficiency in graphing so important, and why isn't Excel enough? Excel *can* be enough for many graphical analysis needs, and you don't have to have access to a more advanced program such as Minitab to participate in a Six Sigma project. You can use Excel's charting functions and the Analysis Toolpak to conduct a lot of analysis and draw appropriate statistical conclusions. That said, Excel is usually too limited for most Black Belts – especially those who are leading projects.

First, as previously discussed, Excel's automated calculations are more limited than that of software built specifically for statistical analysis purposes. Can you do all of the calculations in Excel that Minitab does for you? Yes. But you can also do all of those calculations with a piece of paper, a basic calculator, and access to printed statistical tables. Either of those methods involves spending more time to come to the same conclusion, which, as you learned in the chapters on Lean, is muda or waste.

Second, Excel's charting capabilities suffer from the same efficiency problems. You have to do a lot of work to create some charts in Excel. If you are looking at multiple charts to analyze data, Minitab's faster output capability reduces the time spent creating charts and frees up time for analysis and consideration of data. This is helpful because, as mentioned in chapter 17, each chart provides a different perspective on data. You might look at four or five graphical representations of data – along with statistical analysis – before reaching a conclusion you are confident in.

Excel *does* offer some advantages when it comes to certain charts – specifically with regard to presenting data. It can be easier to customize formatting of bar and pie charts in Excel, for example, which means some Six Sigma experts analyze data in Minitab but use Excel to create some of the charts and graphs included in presentations. If you are working with team members who don't have access to Minitab and they need editable access to analysis and graph files, then you might also have to provide information in Excel for this reason.

This chapter will cover some of the commonly used graphs in Minitab.

The Graph Menu Option

The graph menu is found in the top menu bar in Minitab. Within the menu, you have access to over 20 graphical analysis options – with more detailed options for each type of graph. We won't cover all the types of graphs, but you can use your own data to explore some of the graphs we don't cover.

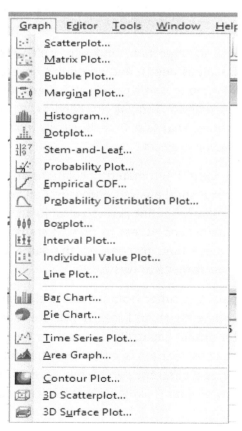

If you would like to explore graphing options alongside the steps presented in this chapter, begin by copying the information below into a new Minitab worksheet. Ensure both of the columns are marked by Minitab as containing numbers (meaning there is no "T" designation in the column header).

1	4.6
2	3.8
3	4.8
4	2.7
5	3.5
1	4.3
2	3.6
3	5.8
4	4.7
5	3.0
1	4.3
2	5.6
3	6.2
4	4.7
5	2.2
1	3.3
2	2.8
3	1.6
4	1.4
5	2.8

Scatter Plot

Scatter plots graph each data point on X-Y axis points and can help teams see how two inputs or data elements might be related. Scatter plots are often the first step in regression analysis, because you can tell quickly whether correlation is at all possible.

To create a scatter plot using the data from above, select Graph > Scatterplots > Simple and click okay.

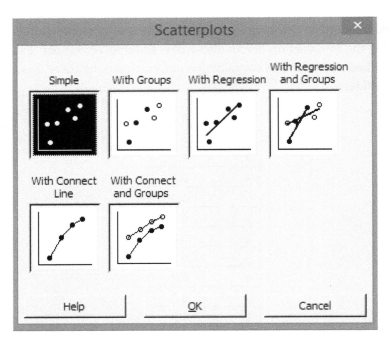

Click in the first row under Y-variables and select column C2. Click in the first row under X-variables and select column C1.

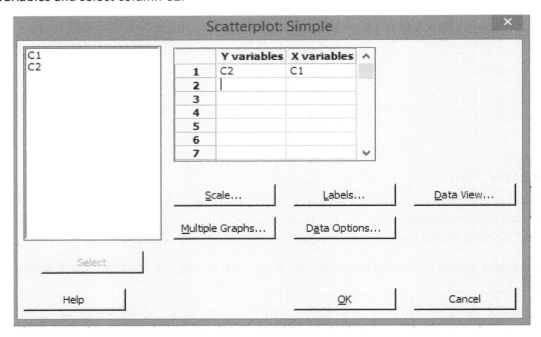

Click OK, and Minitab generates a scatterplot of the data. You can see that for x = 1, y values in our data range between 3 and 5. You can also see that there doesn't seem to be a relationship between the x and y values.

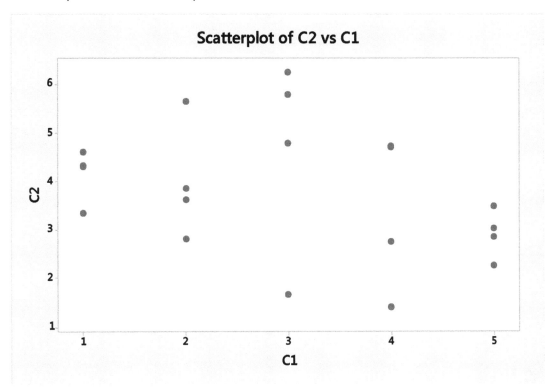

Now, copy the data below into columns C4 and C5 on the same worksheet.

1	1.5
2	2.2
3	3.3
4	4.2
5	5
1	0.9
2	2.3
3	3.7
4	3.9
5	4.5

1	1.2
2	2.1
3	3.1
4	4.2
5	5

Select Graph > Scatterplots > Simple.

Change the x and y references so that x is C4 and y is C5. Click OK, and Minitab generates the graph below. This graph is different from the one above – this data *does* appear to be correlated in some way.

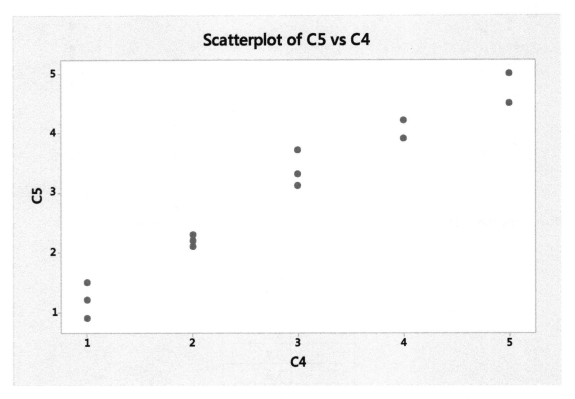

You can add a regression line to your scatterplot by selecting the "with regression" option in in the Scatterplots diagram.

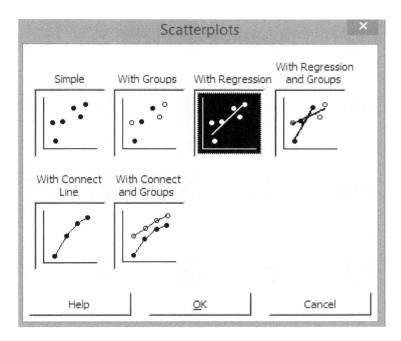

If it wasn't obvious just looking at the plotted dots, the line makes it even more noticeable that as x increases, y increases. Remember, this doesn't necessarily mean that x causes y, but it does seem that the two are correlated. Upon seeing such a result on a scatterplot, a Six Sigma expert might run a regression test to determine how likely a correlation is between the two factors. Running such analysis in Minitab will be covered in the next chapter.

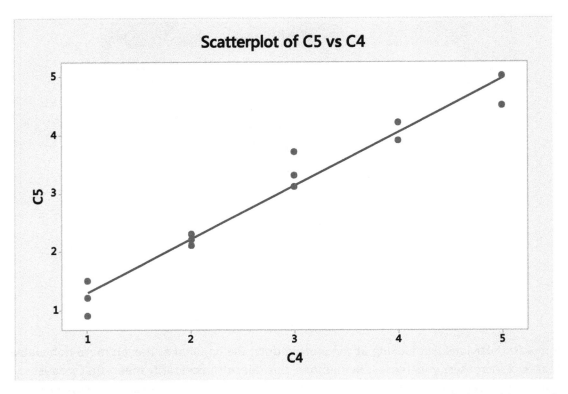

If a correlation is noted during a statistical analysis, the statistical proof alone (the math behind the conclusion) isn't likely to be of much help in a presentation. As discussed in chapter 24, you might want to include illustrations of the statistical analysis, which is another reason for using the scatterplot.

Histogram

Over the course of this book, we've worked with histograms several times. Histograms help Six Sigma experts understand the shape of the data, which also helps understand how data is distributed. You can create histograms in Minitab by selecting Graph > Histogram.

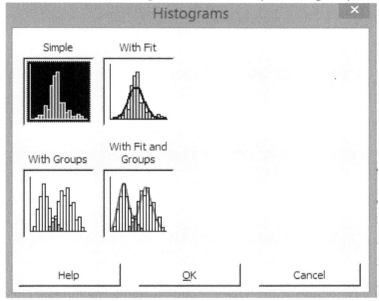

Choose the "Simple" option for a histogram with no other elements. If you're following along, select column C2 from your worksheet into the graph variables box and click OK.

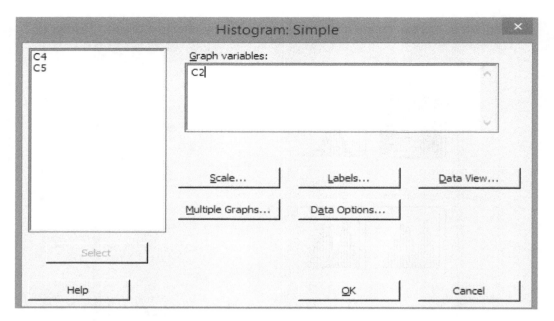

Minitab creates a histogram of the data in column C2. The column in question only has 20 data points, which can make it difficult to tell whether the data is distributed normally via a graphical analysis. Remember the lessons on sample size and the Central Limit Theorem. Smaller sample sizes don't always provide enough data to draw analytical conclusions, but as you increase the size of the data pool, most data does approach the normal curve.

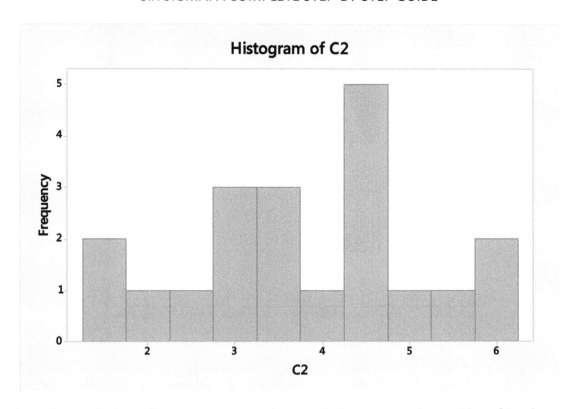

Sometimes, placing a fit curve over your data can help you get a better idea of its shape. Recreate the histogram of the data in column C2, but select "with fit" from the Histograms dialogue box.

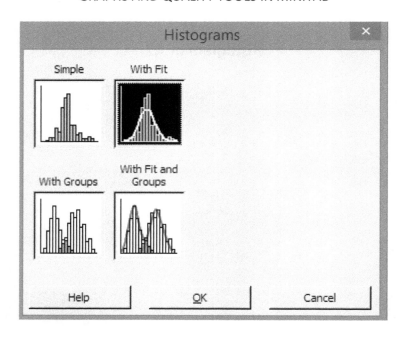

Minitab fits a normal curve over the histogram to help you visualize the distribution of your data. In this case, we might be tempted to say the data is somewhat normal. Only the one very tall column in the center throws off the overall symmetry of the graph. Still, there isn't enough information here to draw a conclusion.

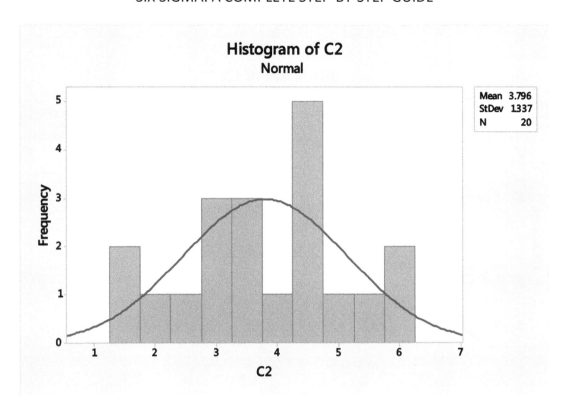

Create a histogram with fit curve of the data in column C1.

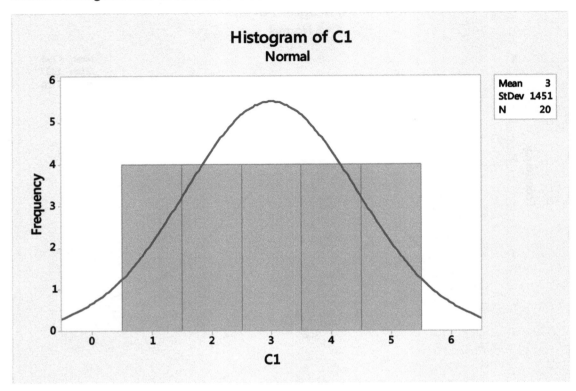

The result is obviously universally distributed data that doesn't fit the normal curve. In this case, you can more positively say that the data isn't normal.

Here's the graphical summary for the data in column C2 so we can double check our conclusions about normality. Remember, this summary is found under Stat > Basic Statistics > Graphical Summary.

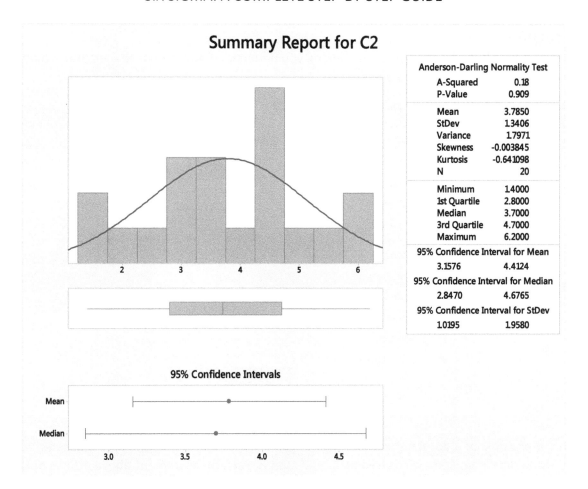

The p-value for the Anderson-Darling Normality test lets us fail to reject the null hypothesis that the data is normal. The other information on this summary all tends to lean toward a conclusion of normality too.

As you can see, the graphical summary provides the same information as the histogram graph *and* the extra information that lets Six Sigma experts make a better determination about data distribution. For that reason, you are more likely to run the graphical analysis for general understanding of your data. The histogram function is still valuable for analyzing certain pieces of information or for generating a single graph that you might want to include in a presentation or report.

Dotplot

A dotplot is similar to a histogram in helping you understand how data is shaped, but it plots individual data points along a single line.

Access the dotplot function via Graph > Dotplot.

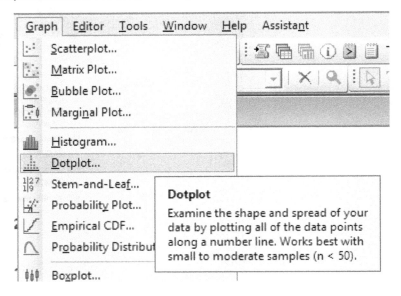

In the example of a dotplot graph below, you can see that four data points are measured as 9; three data points are measured as 5, 6, 7, and 8. Each measurement above 10 has only one data point related to it. The simple dotplot shown below is usually used for smaller sample sizes, and teams can even create rough dotplot sketches on white boards or paper during a meeting if they want a quick visual depiction of data for the discussion.

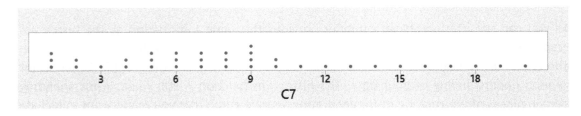

Draw a Dotplot

Use the data to the left to draw a small dotplot on a piece of scratch paper. Start with a line at the bottom with numeric labels along the line. For each time a number appears in the data table, create a dot above it on the line.

Data for Dot Plot

2	2
5	3
4	5
6	4
1	4
1	1
2	2
3	4

The dotplots created above are simple dotplots. They depict one Y (one measurement, one data set) over a single line. You can also depict single Y measurements with groups, separated or stacked. The concept is similar to a stacked bar graph, where you delineate the measurements via another variable or factor. For example, you might be creating a dotplot of amount of work done per hour. If you have all of the numbers per person recorded for a shift, you could group the information by person.

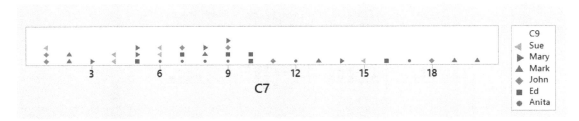

You can also work with more than one measurement, or Y, with simple, stacked, or grouped data. For example, you might have data for two shifts with employees in each shift.

The dotplot below shows the amount of work done each hour for two employees in each shift. You can immediately see that the employees in shift 2 seem to be doing more per hour than the employees in shift 1 – there are more data points located above the higher numbers in the graph for the second shift.

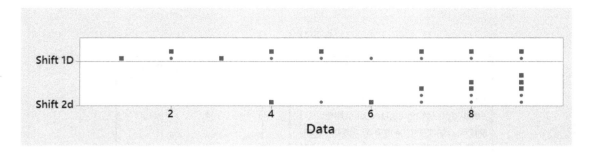

To select the type of dotplot you want to create, click on the appropriate image in the Dotplots box.

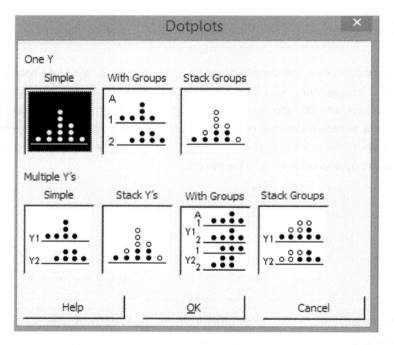

Select the appropriate columns for your dotplot chart data. Graph variables are always your data columns. Categorical variables for grouping are the columns with your categories listed, such as the names of people, the labels for shifts, or the time. If you are working with multiple Ys, you can select more than one data column into the graph variables box.

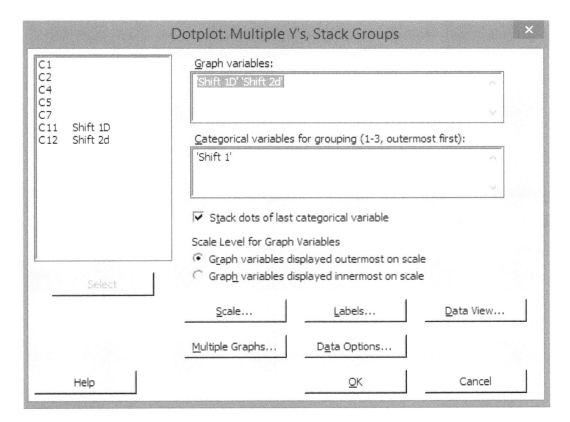

Boxplot

In chapter 17, you learned to create boxplots in Excel. Minitab creates box and whisker diagrams without all the editing you have to do in Excel. As with dotplots, you can also create boxplots with single sets of data, groups of data, and subgroups of data.

Group A	Group B	Group C
5	5	6
5	14	19
4	3	8
6	6	6
4	6	5
6	8	5
18	7	8
6	6	7

5	12	8
4	5	6
6	6	6
6	5	10
5	6	7
4	4	9
5	6	6

Copy the above data into Minitab to create some boxplots.

Select Graph > Boxplot > One Y Simple.

Select "Group A" into the Graph Variables box.

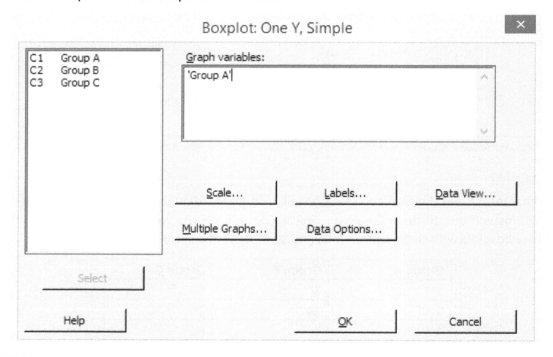

Click OK.

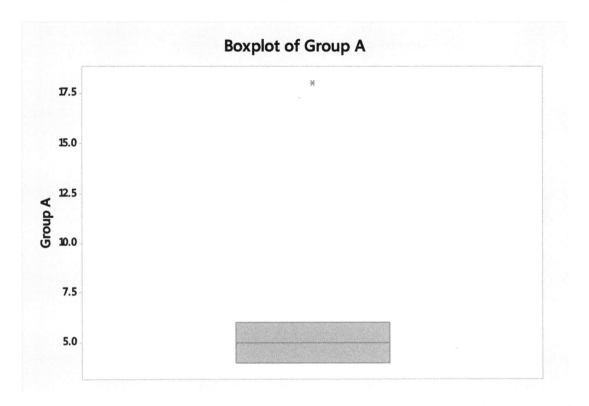

Minitab returns the boxplot of the data above. We can see that the data has a mean of about 5 and that there is an outlier of around 18 in the data. The outlier is indicated by the dot toward the top of the graph.

If you wanted to compare the three groups of data, you could graph them all at once.

Select Graph > Boxplot > Multiple Ys Simple.

Select all three data columns into the Graph Variables box.

Click OK.

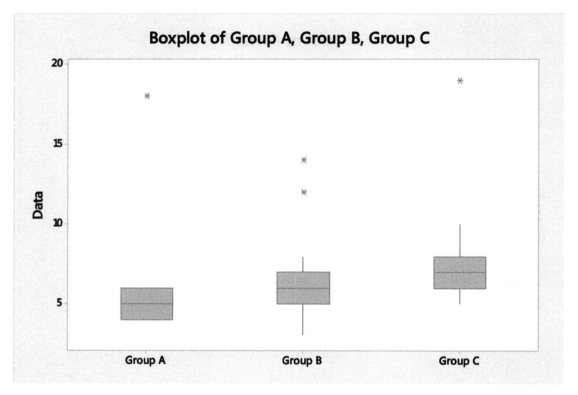

The above graph provides more information than a single boxplot for group A. You can see there are outliers in each group of data. You can also see that the mean of each group is progressively higher – the mean is denoted by the line in the center of each box. The boxes are roughly the same size, indicating that the standard deviation, or variance, within each data set is approximately the same.

What if your data was arranged differently than the table above, which has three groups of separate data? What if you have two columns of data, and the first column is the group indication and the second column is the measurement? The data for two groups might look something like the table below.

Group	Result
1	5
1	5
1	4
1	6
1	4
1	6
1	18
1	6
1	5
1	4
1	6
1	6
1	5
1	4
1	5
2	5
2	14
2	3
2	6
2	6
2	8
2	7
2	6
2	12
2	5
2	6
2	5
2	6
2	4
2	6

To create a boxplot for this type of data, select Graph > Boxplot > One Y with Groups.

Select the Result column into the Graph Variables box. Select the Group column into the Categorical Variables box. Note that you can only graph up to 4 categorical variables at once.

Click OK.

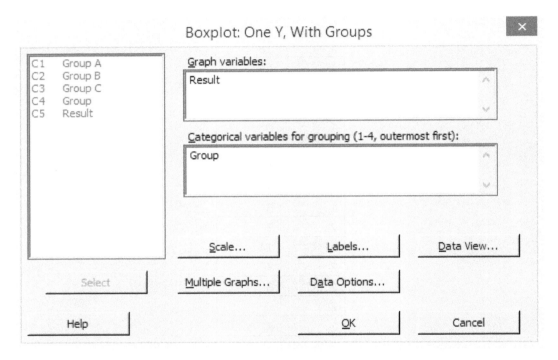

Minitab returns the boxplot below. It is similar to the boxplot returned for the three subgroups, although obviously there are only two groups here because there were only two different categories listed in our data table.

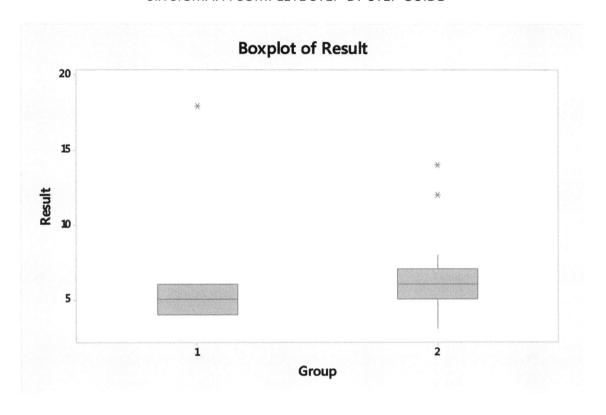

Interval Plot

Interval plots are helpful when you want to analyze the means or variance within a single group of data or between subgroups of data. The creation of interval plots in Minitab follows essentially the same steps as the creation of boxplots, and you can break interval plots into the same groups.

Using the first data table from the boxplot section above, in Minitab select Graph > Interval Plot > Multiple Ys Simple. Select all three of the data columns into the Graph Variables box. Click OK.

Minitab returns the interval plots below.

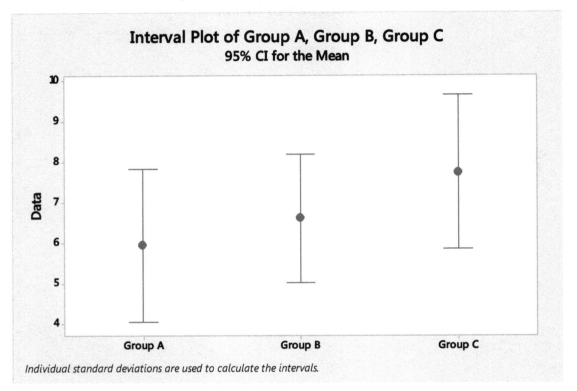

As with the similar boxplot, you can see that the mean for each group is slightly above the one before it. You can also see that the spread of the data is roughly the same for each group. What interval plots don't show are the outliers.

You can create interval plots for all of the data used in the boxplot examples just as you created the box plots. The only difference is that you select interval plots from the graph menu.

Bar Chart

Excel is a great tool for creating colorful, presentation-friendly bar and pie charts, but you can also quickly create such charts in Minitab for analysis purposes. Use the phone call per hour data below to create a bar chart in Minitab.

Hour	Phone calls
8:00 AM	78
9:00 AM	89
10:00 AM	107
11:00 AM	118
12:00 PM	149
1:00 PM	147
2:00 PM	105
3:00 PM	90
4:00 PM	97
5:00 PM	85
6:00 PM	178
7:00 PM	198
8:00 PM	145
9:00 PM	57

Select Graph > Bar Chart.

In the bars represent drop down menu, choose "values from a table."

Select Simple under one column of values.

Click OK.

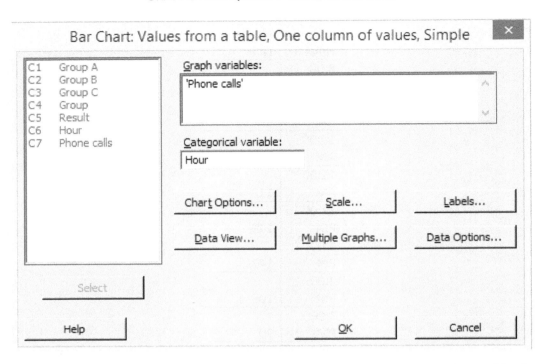

In the Bar Chart dialogue box, select the column "phone calls" into the graph variables box. You always select the column that has the data to be graphed here. Select the column "hour" into the categorical variables box. Always select the information that you want displayed along the x-axis here.

Minitab returns a simple bar chart, as seen below.

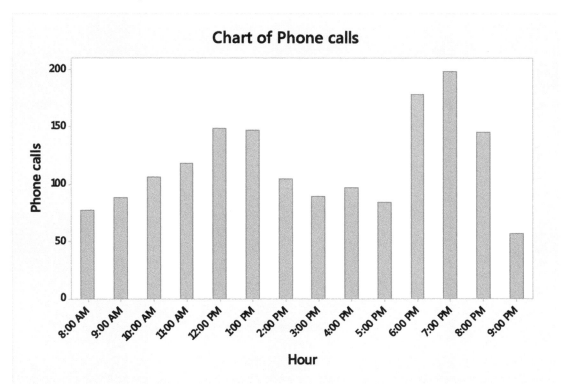

The options for creating bar charts in Minitab are similar to those in Excel: you can create stacked or grouped bar charts. But you can also create charts from data without having to perform the same calculations that you might have to do in Excel. For example, if you select "Counts of unique values" from the drop down menu in the bar chart box, then Minitab will count unique values for you. You can try this with the data table below, which lists the number of errors in 13 work samples.

Select Graph > Bar Chart. Select "Counts of unique values" in the Bars Represent drop down box. Select Simple and click OK.

Minitab counts the number of times each unique value – 1, 2, 3, or 4 – appears in the data and creates a bar chart of those counts.

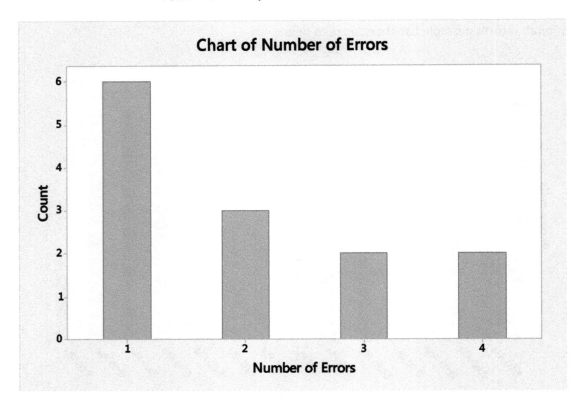

Minitab also offers some options for ordering data in your chart. Create the first chart of calls per hour again, but in the Bar Chart dialogue box, click "Chart Options."

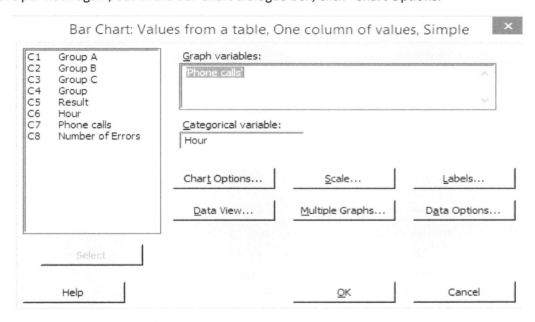

Select the option to order the bar chart by decreasing Y.

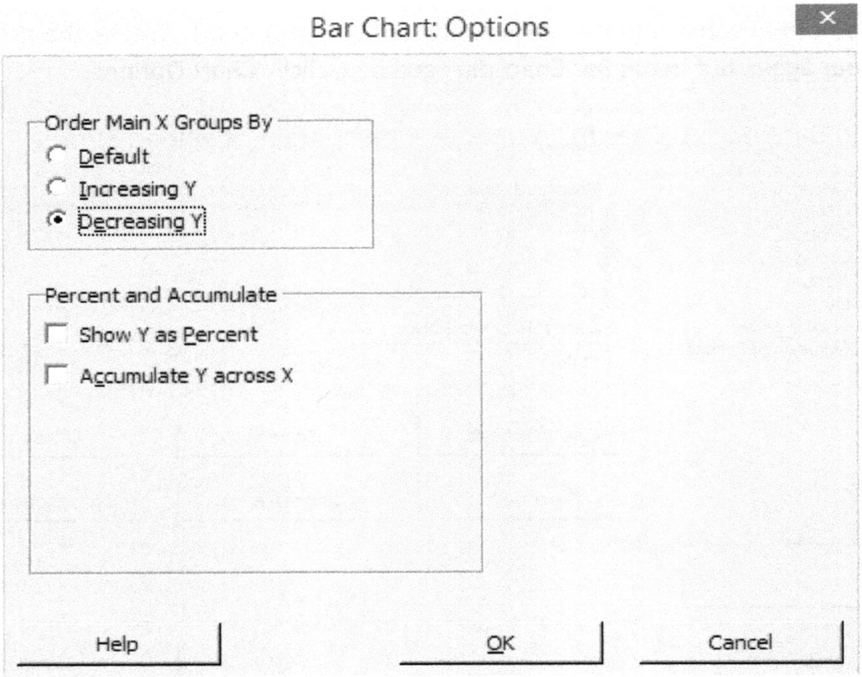

Bar Chart: Options

Order Main X Groups By
- ○ Default
- ○ Increasing Y
- ● Decreasing Y

Percent and Accumulate
- ☐ Show Y as Percent
- ☐ Accumulate Y across X

Help   OK   Cancel

Click OK. Click OK again.

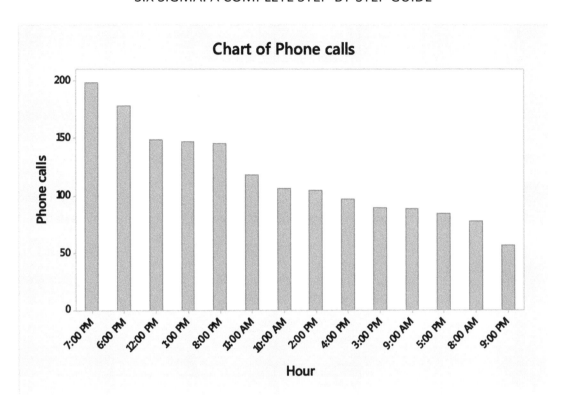

Minitab puts the x-axis data in order from biggest to smallest – as you might see in a Pareto chart. This is helpful to someone conducting analysis because you can get an idea of the highest and lowest values in a data set. Minitab also lets you order in the other way, show the information as a percent of the total, or accumulate the totals across the x-axis.

Pie Chart

Pie Charts in Minitab follow similar steps as bar charts. To create a pie chart, copy the data from the table below into Minitab.

Process Step	Minutes
A	14
B	18
C	41
D	64
E	12

F	4
G	3
H	7
I	23
J	18

Select Graph > Pie Chart.

Click the option for charting values from a table.

Select "Process Step" as the categorical variable and "Minutes" as the summary variables.

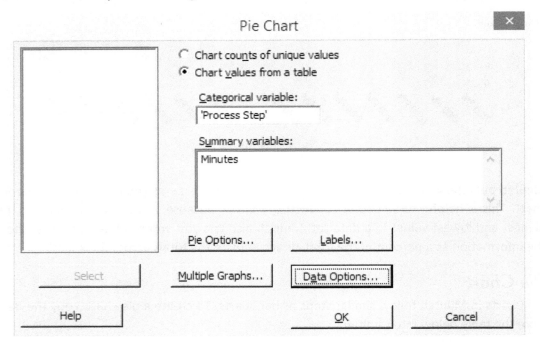

Click OK.

Minitab returns the pie chart below.

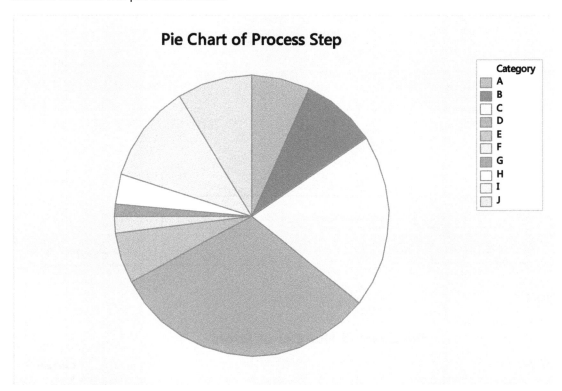

As with bar charts, you can choose to graph the counts of unique values. Use the number of errors data from the bar chart example to create a pie chart of counts of unique values.

Select Graph > Pie Chart.

Select the option for charting counts of unique variables.

Select "Number of Errors" as the categorical variable.

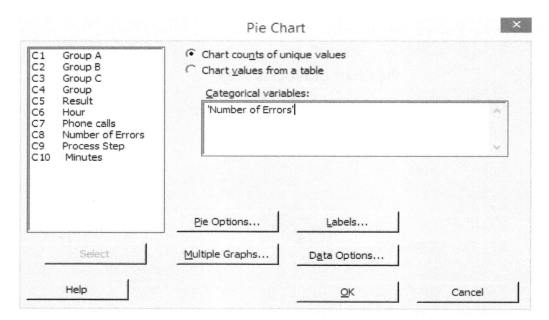

Click OK.

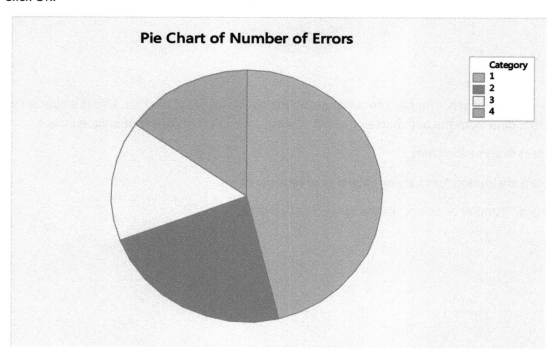

As with the bar chart example, Minitab counts the number of times each unique variable exists in the data and presents it in pie chart format.

Also similar to the bar chart, you can choose to have Minitab order the data in your pie chart. Recreate the pie chart for the first example in this section, which showed the number of errors at each process step.

Select Graph > Pie Chart.

Click the option for charting values from a table.

Select "Process Step" as the categorical variable and "Minutes" as the summary variables.

Click Pie Options.

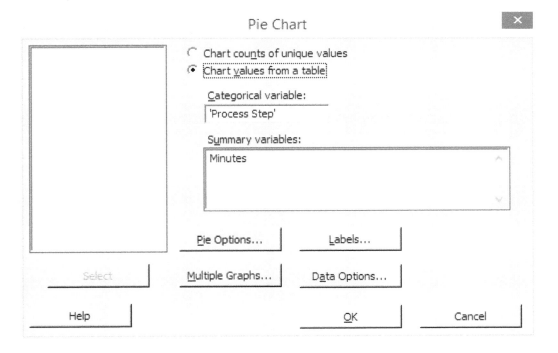

Choose to order the data by increasing volume.

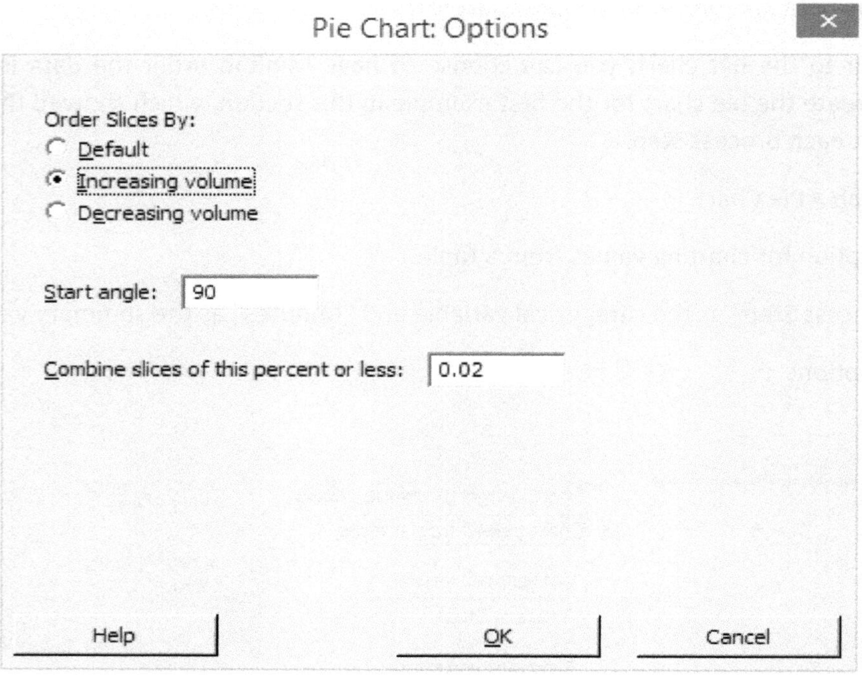

Pie Chart: Options ✕

Order Slices By:
- ○ Default
- ⦿ Increasing volume
- ○ Decreasing volume

Start angle: 90

Combine slices of this percent or less: 0.02

Help		OK		Cancel	

Click OK. Click OK again.

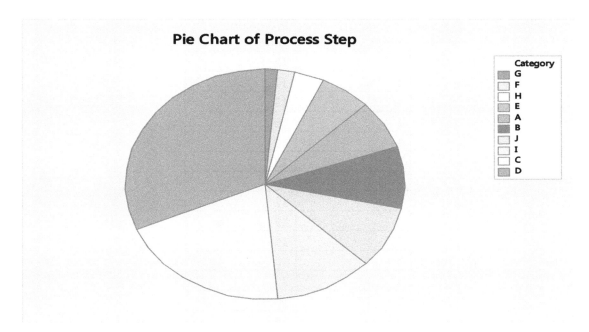

Pie Chart of Process Step

Category
G
F
H
E
A
B
J
I
C
D

Minitab returns a pie chart with data in order from smallest to largest going clockwise around the pie. When compared with the first pie chart of this data, this one is probably easier to read and draw conclusions from, because you can more easily compare the size of each section when they are ordered.

The Stat Menu: Quality Tools

Not all the graphs in Minitab are located under the Graph menu. You'll find control charts, run charts, and Pareto charts under the Stat menu. Creating control charts in Minitab was covered in Unit 5.

Run Chart

Remember that a run chart is a graphical representation of data elements over time. In Minitab, you can also create a run chart of subgroups means or medians over time. Create run charts using the data table below, which depicts the production time of various samples taken during specific hours of a shift. The quality team takes five samples each hour.

Hour	Production Time
1	12
1	11
1	13
1	18
1	16
2	13
2	10
2	12
2	19
2	15
3	10
3	7
3	10
3	18
3	14
4	10
4	15
4	12
4	14
4	18
5	11
5	9
5	8
5	14
5	12

In Minitab, select Stat > Quality Tools > Run Chart.

The data is arranged as a single column, where "production time" is the data to be graphed. Since the quality team samples 5 per hour, the subgroup size is 5.

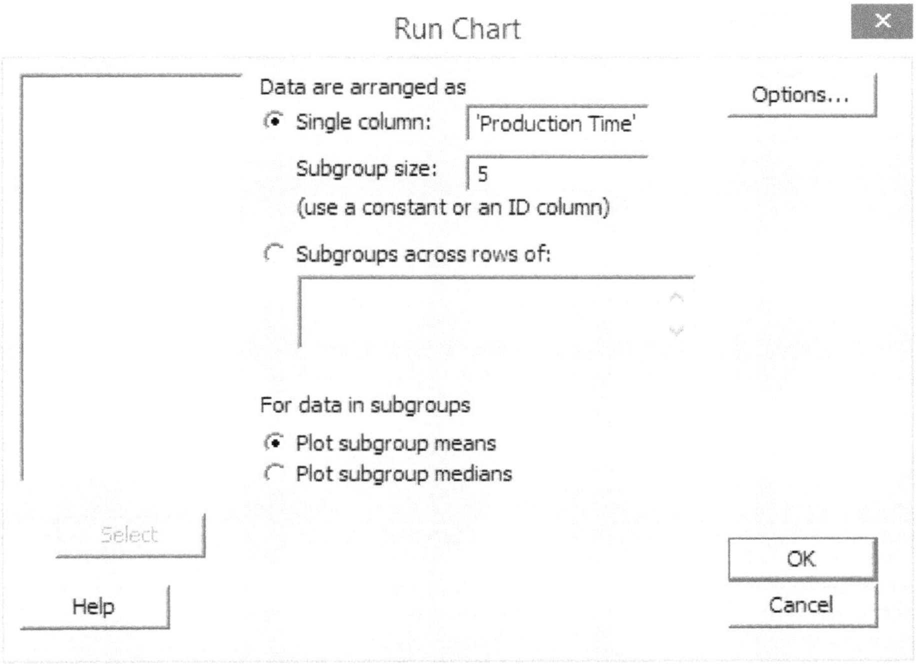

Run Chart

Data are arranged as

(•) Single column: 'Production Time'

Subgroup size: 5

(use a constant or an ID column)

( ) Subgroups across rows of:

For data in subgroups

(•) Plot subgroup means
( ) Plot subgroup medians

Options...

Select

Help

OK

Cancel

Click OK.

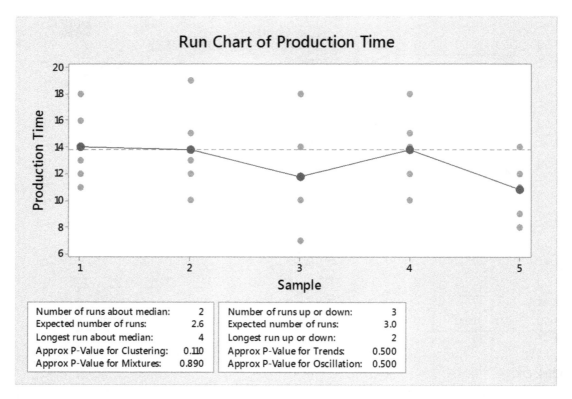

Graphed this way, Minitab plots the points of each subgroup on the graph in gray and then plots the mean in blue. The run line shown is for the mean of each subgroup. You can see that hours 1, 2, and 4 have roughly the same mean and hours 3 and 5 have lower means.

Alternatively, you can graph all of your data points on a single run chart.

In Minitab, select Stat > Quality Tools > Run Chart.

Select "subgroups across rows of".

Select the column for production time into the box.

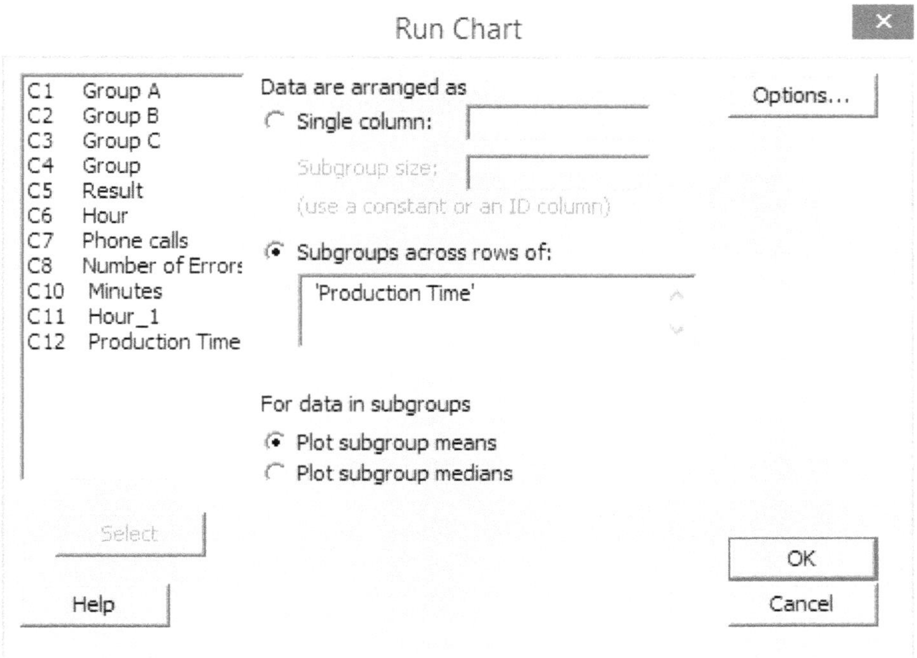

Run Chart

C1 Group A	Data are arranged as
C2 Group B	
C3 Group C	○ Single column:
C4 Group	
C5 Result	Subgroup size:
C6 Hour	(use a constant or an ID column)
C7 Phone calls	
C8 Number of Errors	● Subgroups across rows of:
C10 Minutes	'Production Time'
C11 Hour_1	
C12 Production Time	

Options...

For data in subgroups

● Plot subgroup means
○ Plot subgroup medians

Select

Help

OK

Cancel

Click OK.

Minitab returns a simple run chart of your data.

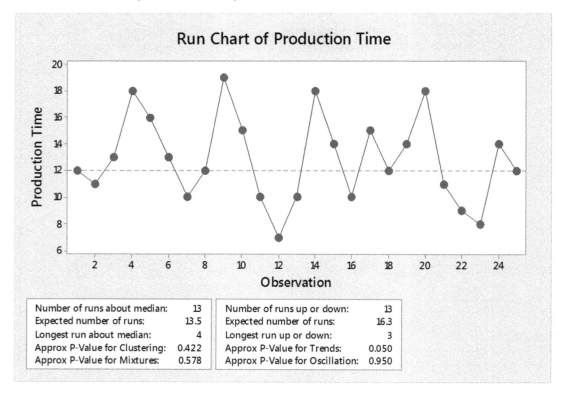

Pareto Chart

In chapter 14, we covered how to create Pareto charts in Excel, but you might recall that it took some data manipulation to get the chart in order, add trend lines, and create label percentages. In Excel, you had to have totals, or summaries, of the data. In chapter 14, one of the Pareto charts created was of claims denials per payer, and the data was presented as totals in a table.

With Minitab, you don't need totals in a table. You can create a Pareto chart with rawer data. In the data table below, a quality team reviewed 150 denied claims to determine the reason they were denied. You can copy and paste this data into Minitab if desired to create a Pareto chart.

Claim	Claim Denial Reason
1	Timely Filing
2	Timely Filing
3	Timely Filing
4	Timely Filing
5	Timely Filing
6	Timely Filing
7	Timely Filing
8	Timely Filing
9	Timely Filing
10	Timely Filing
11	Timely Filing
12	Timely Filing
13	Timely Filing
14	Missing Information
15	Missing Information
16	Missing Information
17	Missing Information
18	Missing Information
19	Missing Information
20	Missing Information
21	No Benefits
22	No Benefits
23	No Benefits
24	No Benefits
25	No Benefits
26	No Benefits
27	No Benefits
28	No Benefits
29	Lacking Medical Reason
30	Lacking Medical Reason
31	Lacking Medical Reason
32	Lacking Medical Reason
33	Lacking Medical Reason
34	Lacking Medical Reason
35	Lacking Medical Reason
36	Lacking Medical Reason
37	Lacking Medical Reason
38	Lacking Medical Reason
39	Lacking Medical Reason
40	Wrong Diagnosis Code
41	Wrong Diagnosis Code
42	Wrong Diagnosis Code
43	Duplicate Claim
44	Duplicate Claim
45	Duplicate Claim
46	Duplicate Claim
47	Duplicate Claim
48	Duplicate Claim
49	Duplicate Claim
50	Duplicate Claim
51	Duplicate Claim
52	Duplicate Claim
53	Duplicate Claim
54	Duplicate Claim
55	Duplicate Claim
56	Duplicate Claim
57	Duplicate Claim
58	Timely Filing
59	Timely Filing
60	Timely Filing
61	Timely Filing
62	Timely Filing
63	Timely Filing
64	Timely Filing
65	Timely Filing

66	Timely Filing		100	Duplicate Claim
67	Timely Filing		101	Duplicate Claim
68	Timely Filing		102	Duplicate Claim
69	Timely Filing		103	Duplicate Claim
70	Timely Filing		104	Duplicate Claim
71	Missing Information		105	Duplicate Claim
72	Missing Information		106	Duplicate Claim
73	Missing Information		107	Duplicate Claim
74	Missing Information		108	Duplicate Claim
75	Missing Information		109	Duplicate Claim
76	Missing Information		110	Duplicate Claim
77	Missing Information		111	Duplicate Claim
78	No Benefits		112	Duplicate Claim
79	No Benefits		113	Duplicate Claim
80	No Benefits		114	Duplicate Claim
81	No Benefits		115	Duplicate Claim
82	No Benefits		116	Duplicate Claim
83	No Benefits		117	Duplicate Claim
84	No Benefits		118	Duplicate Claim
85	No Benefits		119	Duplicate Claim
86	Lacking Medical Reason		120	Duplicate Claim
87	Lacking Medical Reason		121	Duplicate Claim
88	Lacking Medical Reason		122	Duplicate Claim
89	Lacking Medical Reason		123	Duplicate Claim
90	Lacking Medical Reason		124	Duplicate Claim
91	Lacking Medical Reason		125	Duplicate Claim
92	Lacking Medical Reason		126	Duplicate Claim
93	Lacking Medical Reason		127	Duplicate Claim
94	Lacking Medical Reason		128	Duplicate Claim
95	Lacking Medical Reason		129	Duplicate Claim
96	Lacking Medical Reason		130	Duplicate Claim
97	Wrong Diagnosis Code		131	Duplicate Claim
98	Wrong Diagnosis Code		132	Duplicate Claim
99	Wrong Diagnosis Code		133	Duplicate Claim

134	Duplicate Claim		143	Timely Filing
135	Duplicate Claim		144	Timely Filing
136	Duplicate Claim		145	Timely Filing
137	Duplicate Claim		146	Timely Filing
138	Duplicate Claim		147	Timely Filing
139	Duplicate Claim		148	Timely Filing
140	Duplicate Claim		149	Timely Filing
141	Duplicate Claim		150	Timely Filing
142	Timely Filing			

Select Stat > Quality Tools > Pareto Chart.

The defects or attributes being graphed are the claim denial reasons. There are no frequencies or variables by which this data is being graphed – you simply want to see how each type of denial impacts the overall denial count. It's worth noting that this is one of the few times in Minitab that you can graph non-numerical data.

It's also important to note that Minitab will separate defects or attributes by unique values, and it does differentiate by spelling, spacing, and capitalization. Therefore, "Timely Filing," "TimelyFiling," and "timely filing" would all be counted as separate attributes by the program. The Six Sigma expert has to ensure data is prepared appropriately and all categorical descriptions are the same before running a Pareto chart. One way to do this is to prepare data in Excel, where you can use the find and replace option to ensure all entries are corrected with regard to spacing or spelling.

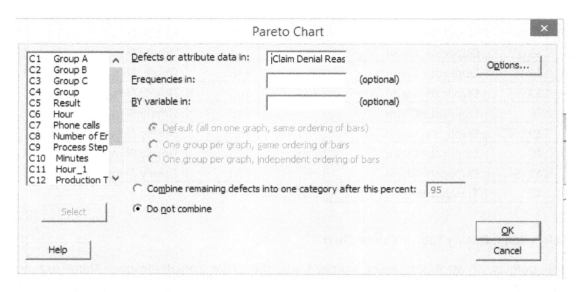

For this example, select "Do not combine" because there are only a handful of claims denial reasons in the data. If you have ten or more unique attributes, you might select the option to combine remaining defects after 95 or 90 percent. The defects that account for the final 5 or 10 percent would be displayed on the Pareto chart as "other."

Click OK.

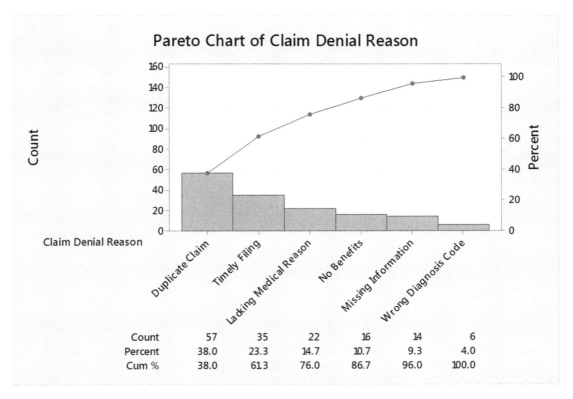

Count	57	35	22	16	14	6
Percent	38.0	23.3	14.7	10.7	9.3	4.0
Cum %	38.0	61.3	76.0	86.7	96.0	100.0

Minitab displays a Pareto chart with the bar chart, running percentage, and detailed count. From this chart, you can quickly see that approximately 80 percent of the denied claims are caused by the first three denial reasons.

Gage Studies

Another convenient tool in Minitab is the ability to generate Gage R & R worksheets and interpret the results of a Gage R & R study. Gage R & R studies were previously covered in chapter 13 on the Measure phase.

Create a Gage R & R worksheet by selecting Stat > Quality Tools > Gage Study > Create Gage R & R Study Worksheet.

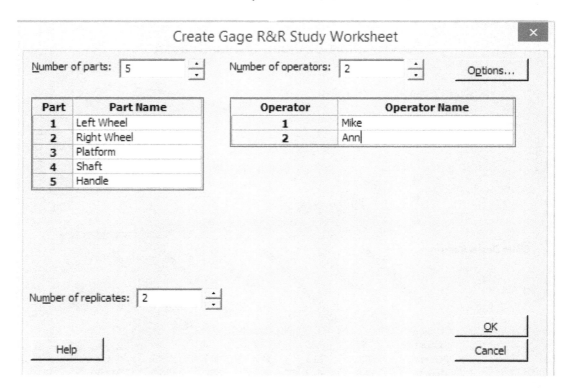

Minitab lets you input a variety of information to set up a randomly-ordered Gage R & R Study. In the example above, Mike and Ann are quality auditors reviewing dollies that come off a manufacturing line. In this study, each person is going to review five parts, and they will do so twice.

Minitab lets you select the number of parts to be reviewed, the number of reviewers or operators, and the number of replicates, or times the review or measurement is to be repeated. You can also click in the white space next to each part and operator number to name those items for clarity later.

Once you set the dialogue box up as above, click OK.

↓	C1	C2-T	C3-T	C4	C5
	RunOrder	Parts	Operators		
1	1	Handle	Mike		
2	2	Left Wheel	Mike		
3	3	Platform	Mike		
4	4	Right Wheel	Mike		
5	5	Shaft	Mike		
6	6	Right Wheel	Ann		
7	7	Handle	Ann		
8	8	Platform	Ann		
9	9	Shaft	Ann		
10	10	Left Wheel	Ann		
11	11	Left Wheel	Mike		
12	12	Platform	Mike		
13	13	Handle	Mike		
14	14	Shaft	Mike		
15	15	Right Wheel	Mike		
16	16	Shaft	Ann		
17	17	Platform	Ann		
18	18	Handle	Ann		
19	19	Right Wheel	Ann		
20	20	Left Wheel	Ann		
21					
22					

Minitab generates a worksheet for the Gage R & R Study. It randomizes how the parts are presented to each person for each replicate. Remember from chapter 13, this is a critical step in a measurement analysis, because it helps reduce the chance that the operator will remember the measurement they previously recorded.

Mike and Ann might then perform measurements on each of the parts. In this case, they are measuring the parts in inches to ensure they conform to a required range for quality. The Six Sigma expert running the Gage R & R is not concerned with whether the parts fit that range – he or she is concerned with whether the measurement system works. Can Ann and

Mike repeat the measurements consistently both within their own sets of data and when compared to each other?

The measurements are taken and entered into Minitab.

↓	C1	C2-T	C3-T	C4
	RunOrder	Parts	Operators	Measurement
1	1	Handle	Mike	5.5
2	2	Left Wheel	Mike	3.5
3	3	Platform	Mike	8.2
4	4	Right Wheel	Mike	3.4
5	5	Shaft	Mike	19.1
6	6	Right Wheel	Ann	3.5
7	7	Handle	Ann	5.5
8	8	Platform	Ann	8.3
9	9	Shaft	Ann	19.0
10	10	Left Wheel	Ann	3.5
11	11	Left Wheel	Mike	3.5
12	12	Platform	Mike	8.1
13	13	Handle	Mike	5.5
14	14	Shaft	Mike	19.0
15	15	Right Wheel	Mike	3.5
16	16	Shaft	Ann	19.0
17	17	Platform	Ann	8.2
18	18	Handle	Ann	5.5
19	19	Right Wheel	Ann	3.5
20	20	Left Wheel	Ann	3.5
21				

Since there is more than one operator and each is measuring all the parts, then the Gage R & R Study (Crossed) option is chosen to analyze the measurement system. You can see below, Minitab offers several options for Gage R & R studies, as well as information about when to use each.

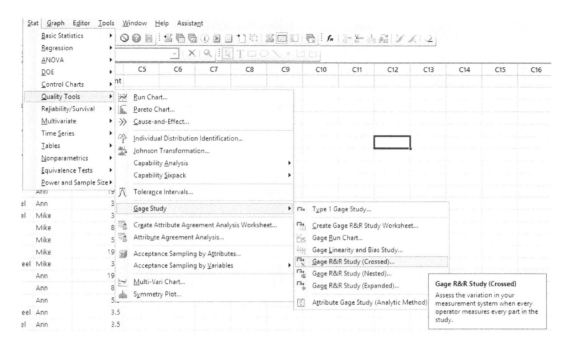

For this study, select "Parts" as the part numbers. Since you entered labels for the parts when setting up the worksheet, this is the column including those labels. Note that "Part numbers" are not always numbers. Select the operators column for operators and the column that includes the data measurements for "Measurement data." Leave everything else as shown and click OK.

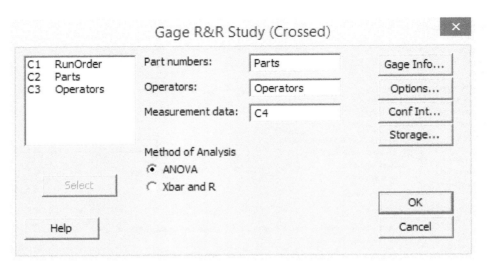

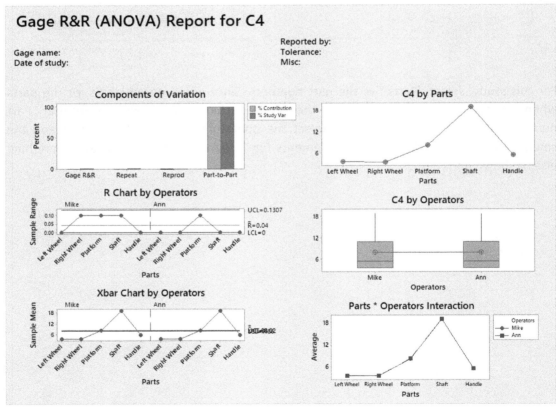

Minitab generates a series of graphical analysis to help determine whether the measurement system works. The two charts at the bottom show that each operator duplicates the results of the other operator fairly closely. The Xbar chart of each operator looks virtually the same, and the Parts Operators Interaction chart is so close, you can't even see Mike's blue square and line under Ann's red. The box plot of data also shows that the information for each operator is very similar – the mean appears to be the same, as is the spread of data.

The first graph details where variation shows up in the measurements. For both Mike and Ann, the variation came when comparing the measurement of one part in the first run to the measurement of the same part in the second run. Even with that slight variation between runs, however, the overall variation is very small and this Gage R & R indicates that the measurement system is working.

CHAPTER 27:
THE STAT MENU IN MINITAB

Chapter 21 introduced hypothesis testing and included information on how to select the right test and how to interpret the results of a test based on p-value. Chapter 19 covered correlation and regression and how to interpret the results of tests run in Excel. In this chapter, you'll learn how to run all these tests in Minitab.

Because interpreting test results and setting up hypothesis testing has been covered in detail in other chapters, this chapter simply offers some guidance for using Minitab to run the tests, including where to find the tests and how to enter information for various tests. Each individual test isn't covered in detail, since the entry of data for the various hypothesis tests is very similar.

Basic Statistics

Many of the tools used to run hypothesis tests are found under Basic Statistics in the Stat menu.

Run and Store Descriptive Statistics

Sometimes, you need to know the mean, standard deviation, or some other descriptive statistic about your data sample. When running many hypothesis tests, you need such data. Minitab's Descriptive Statistics function lets you run all of the most common statistics at one time, and you can store them in a worksheet for reference as you work on analysis.

Time	Temperature A
1	30
2	35
3	37
4	40
5	41
6	48
7	57
8	55

9	59
10	62
11	63
12	65

Copy the data above into Minitab.

Select Stat > Basic Statistics > Display Descriptive Statistics.

Select the temperature column as the variable.

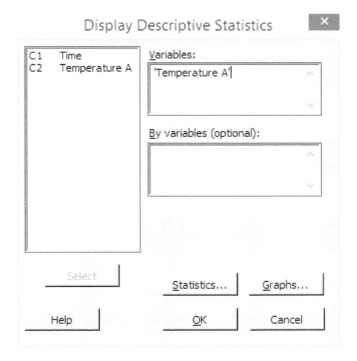

Click Statistics.

Check the box next to each statistic you would like to display.

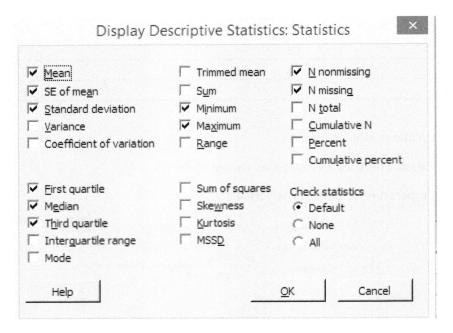

Click OK. Click OK again.

Minitab displays the statistics in the session window.

Descriptive Statistics: Temperature A

```
Variable         N  N*    Mean  SE Mean  StDev  Minimum      Q1  Median     Q3
Maximum
Temperature A   12   0   49.33     3.55  12.31    30.00   37.75   51.50  61.25
65.00
```

Complete the exact same series of steps, but choose Store Descriptive Statistics instead of Display Descriptive Statistics. Minitab will place the statistics in the workbook.

								Worksheet 2 ***
C2	C3	C4	C5	C6	C7	C8	C9	C10
›rature A	Mean1	StDev1	Variance1	Median1	Range1	N1		
30	49.3333	12.3091	151.515	51.5	35	12		
35								
27								

Regression Analysis

Use the data of temperature over time you copied above to run a regression analysis in Minitab. The question you want to answer is: Is there a correlation between the temperature and the time?

Select Stat > Regression > Fitted Line Plot.

Choose the temperature column as the response variable and the time column as the predictor variable.

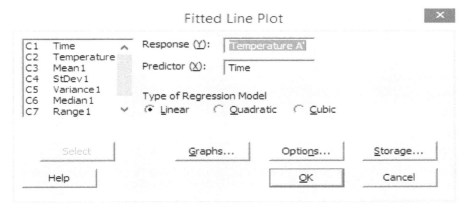

Click OK.

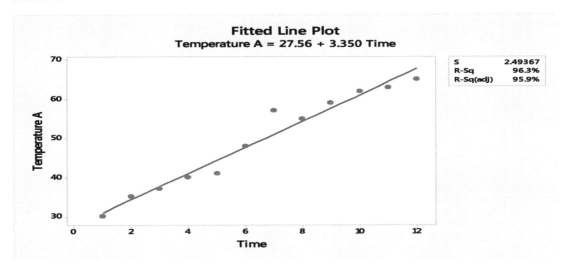

Minitab returns the fitted line plot along with R-squared values, which you can interpret following the information from chapter 19.

Statistical Tests

Most of the relevant hypothesis tests in Minitab are found either under Stat > Basic Statistics or Stat > Nonparametics.

The most relevant tests found under Stat > Basic Statistics are:

- 1 Sample Z
- 1 Sample t
- 2 Sample t
- Paired t
- 1 Proportion
- 2 Proportion
- 1 Variance
- 2 Variance
- Normality Test

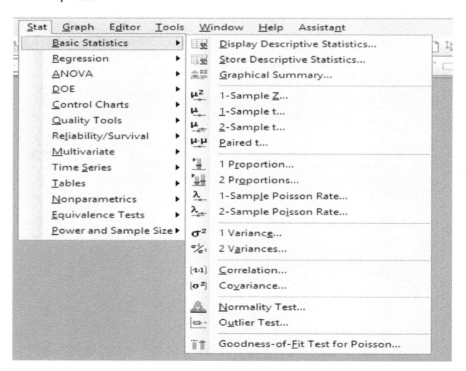

You might notice that the tests found under Basic Statistics tend to be the tests used for discrete or normally distributed continuous data. The test for nonnormally distributed continuous data can be found under Stat > Nonparametrics.

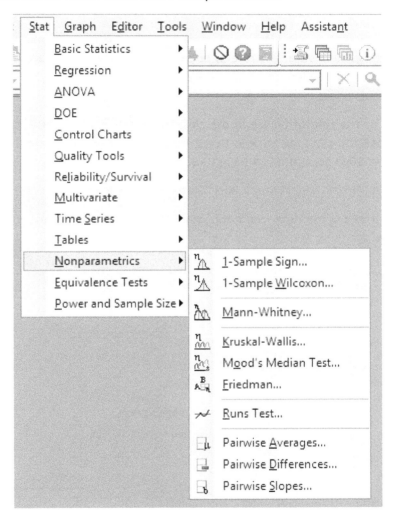

Running Hypothesis Tests

Example 1: 1 Proportion Test

Let's look at a few examples of hypothesis tests in Minitab. We'll look again at some of the problems discussed in the hypothesis testing chapter.

Problem: A school administrator believes that the students in a certain classroom are being impacted by some environmental issue with that room. The administrator wants to see if the students in that room perform statistically lower on tests than the students throughout the school; she has already noted that different classes in that room are taught by other teachers.

The administrator gathers data. The rate of failure for classes taught in any other classroom is 20 percent. Out of 142 students who have a class in the classroom in question, 38 are failing that particular class.

The question is, is the rate of failure in the classroom statistically greater than the rate in other classrooms? You can look back to the 1 Proportion section of chapter 21 to see how the null and alternative hypotheses are created.

To run the test in Minitab, select Stat > Basic Statistics > 1 Proportion.

In the drop down, select "Summarized data," since you don't have information in columns.

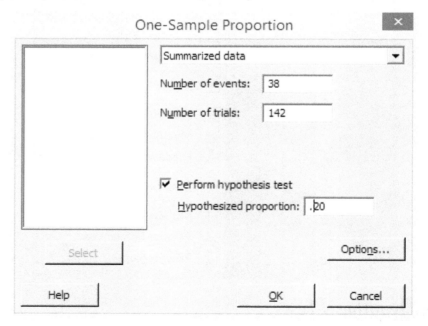

The number of events is the number of outcomes that you are measuring. Here, the administrator was measuring failure rates, and there were 38 failures.

The number of trials is the total number of data points. In this case, the school administrator looked at scores for 142 students.

Check the box to perform a hypothesis test and enter the hypothesized proportion. In this case, you are comparing the actual failure rate of the classroom group to the overall failure rate of 20 percent. The hypothesized portion is written as a decimal between 0 and 1.

Click Options.

Minitab usually defaults the confidence level to 95, which would set alpha at 0.05. Unless you have a specific need for greater confidence, you can leave this as is.

Select the appropriate alternative hypothesis from the drop down menu. In this case, we are testing whether the proportion of our data is greater than the hypothesized proportion.

Click OK. Click OK again.

Minitab displays the results, including a p-value you can use to decide to reject or not reject the null hypothesis.

Test and CI for One Proportion

Test of p = 0.2 vs p > 0.2

Sample	X	N	Sample p	95% Lower Bound	Exact P-Value
1	38	142	0.267606	0.207083	0.031

Example 2: 1 Sample T Test

Problem: An agriculture company growing corn produced an average of 168 bushels of corn per acre each year for five years. The company made a change to its seeding process in an attempt to increase the yield of its fields. The harvest following the seed change resulted in an average of 175 bushels of corn per acre each year over 500 acres of fields. The standard deviation is 2.2 bushels. Did the seeding change result in a statistically different outcome in yield per acre?

Select Stat > Basic Statistics > 1 Sample T.

Choose summarized data.

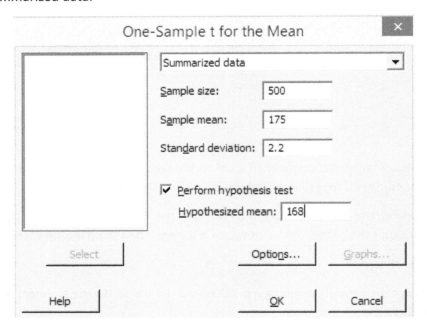

Enter the sample size, sample mean, and sample standard deviation from the problem. Check the box to perform a hypothesis test and enter the hypothesized mean. In this case, you want to know whether the new mean is greater than the old mean, so the old mean is the hypothesized mean.

Click Options.

Choose the appropriate hypothesis test from the drop down menu.

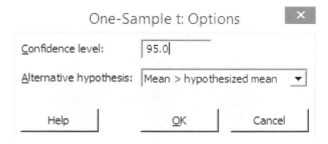

Click OK. Click OK again.

```
One-Sample T

Test of μ = 168 vs > 168


  N     Mean   StDev   SE Mean   95% Lower Bound      T       P
500   175.000  2.200    0.098             174.838   71.15   0.000

|
```

Minitab displays the results, including a p-value you can use to decide to reject or not reject the null hypothesis.

Example 3 – 2 – Sample T Test

Copy the data from the table below into Minitab. If you recall from chapter 21, a law firm believed there was a statistical difference between the time employees on two different teams were spending on tasks.

Minutes Spent on Quarter-Hour Tasks	
Attorney A's Team	Attorney B's Team
10	8
8	7
15	10
16	12
17	18
5	6
8	9
16	12

12	11
11	11
8	9
9	8
15	14
17	15
22	16
25	12
30	19
2	8
9	12
4	6
5	8
7	11
8	12
12	13
13	15
15	17
16	13
18	15
19	15
20	12
22	21
25	32
15	18
14	11

Select Stat > Basic Statistics > 2 – Sample T Test.

From the drop down, select that each sample is in its own column. You can also choose to analyze samples when the data is all in one column or you can enter summarized data about each sample.

Select the appropriate columns into the Samples 1 and 2 boxes. In this case, you are selecting the columns that hold the data for each of the teams.

Click Options.

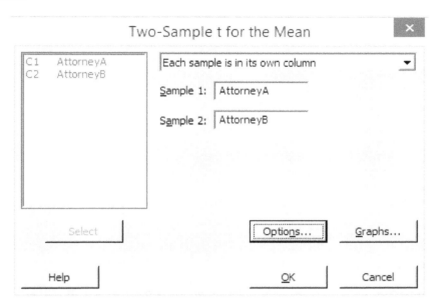

In this case, we only want to know if there is a difference between the two teams, so we'll leave the alternative hypothesis as simply not equal to the hypothesized difference. In this case, we are assuming there is no difference, so we'll leave the hypothesized difference as 0.

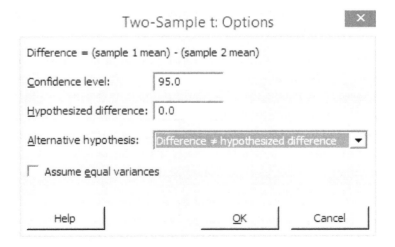

Click OK. Click OK again.

Two-Sample T-Test and CI: AttorneyA, AttorneyB

```
Two-sample T for AttorneyA vs AttorneyB

            N    Mean   StDev   SE Mean
AttorneyA   34   13.76   6.56      1.1
AttorneyB   34   12.82   5.07      0.87


Difference = μ (AttorneyA) - μ (AttorneyB)
Estimate for difference:  0.94
95% CI for difference:  (-1.90, 3.78)
T-Test of difference = 0 (vs ≠): T-Value = 0.66  P-Value = 0.510  DF = 62
```

Minitab displays the results, including a p-value you can use to decide to reject or not reject the null hypothesis.

Hypothesis Test Steps Are Similar for all Types of Tests

All of the hypothesis tests in Minitab are run using basically the same steps as in the examples above. For most test types, you can choose to test the raw data or you can enter summarized data. Remember, each type of hypothesis test requires different summarized data. Proportion testing requires rates, means testing usually requires standard deviations and means of samples, and variance testing requires sample variance. Some of the tests you might use on data that isn't normally distributed require the median instead of the mean.

If you have the right descriptive statistics or have your data in columns in Minitab, it is a matter of a few clicks to set up and run a hypothesis test. The challenge isn't in running, or interpreting, the tests. It is usually in determining which test is the right option for your data. It's worth reviewing the information in chapter 21 again to understand what types of hypothesis tests are used with different data types and scenarios. It's also important to test your data for normality before running hypothesis tests. Remember that you can easily test for normality by running the Graphical Summary under Basic Statistics.

Some other things to keep in mind when dealing with hypothesis tests in Minitab are that you should always click the Options button to verify that your confidence interval is set appropriately and that the appropriate hypothesis test is selected. Minitab defaults to a confidence interval of 95% and an alternative hypothesis of not equal. However, if you are working during the same session – meaning you haven't closed Minitab since the last time you ran that specific hypothesis test, the program will remember what settings you entered and apply them automatically to the new test you are running. This can be a problem if you want to run a test on different data or run a test on the same data with a different confidence interval or alternative hypothesis and you forgot to make the change.

It's also worth noting that a few of the means tests are also located under Stat > Equivalence Test.

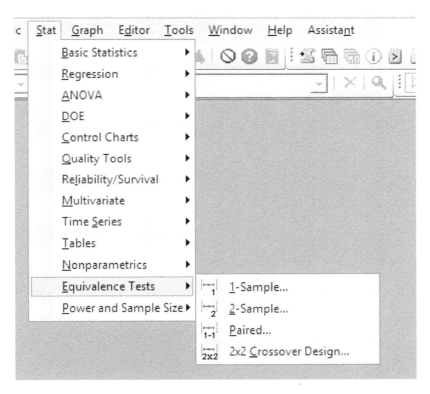

If you are working in Minitab and have questions about these tests, you can access the Help menu for information about choosing, running, and interpreting each test.

Select Help > StatGuide.

The topics are organized just like the Minitab menus. Simply select the test you want help with and Minitab offers a dozen or so pages of help content for each.

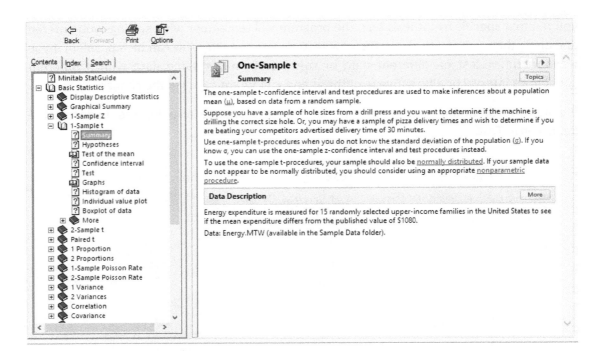

UNIT 7: EXPERIMENTS

CHAPTER 28: ANALYSIS OF VARIANCE (1-WAY ANOVA)

Analysis of variance, often referred to as ANOVA, is a hypothesis test that deals with more than two populations or factors of X. If you recall from chapter 21, we discussed a variety of hypothesis tests for dealing with single factors of x or two factors of x. For example, you learned to conduct a hypothesis test to determine if the mean of a sample was statistically equal to a target mean. You also learned to compare the means of two groups of data with each other for the same reason. ANOVA lets you perform this test with *more* than two groups of data.

Analysis of variance is often used when you have a combination of both discrete and continuous variables – if the independent variance is discrete – a list of employees, for example – and the response variable is continuous – a list of errors or length of time worked – ANOVA can be a valuable tool for analysis.

Before learning more about ANOVA, let's review the other tools for testing means.

- When testing for one mean – usually against a target – you would use the Z test or T test. Remember, the Z test is often used for testing large samples when you don't know what the standard deviation is. The Z test often provides the "lay of the land," letting you gather some information so you can run more accurate analysis with other tests.
- When testing for two means – which involves comparing two samples against each other – you would use the 2 sample T test or the paired T test.

- When testing for three or more means, you can use a specific ANOVA test called the 1-way Anova.

To better understand these designations, consider the real-world applications below.

A Six Sigma team is working to reduce the process time in a manufacturing process. The team was provided with historic baseline metrics for the process. Specifically, in the last quarter, the process averaged 35.8 minutes per output. After working through Define, Measure, and Analyze phases, the team has put an improvement in place they believe will reduce the average time per output. After piloting the change in Improve, the team takes new measurements. *To compare the new sample to the historical baseline, the team would use the 1-sample T test.*

In a different scenario, a Six Sigma team is working to increase the number of calls that can be handled by a call center team in a given day. Call center management has repeatedly asked for additional employees, but executive leadership wants to find out whether efficiency improvements can increase production without adding additional employees. After the first half of the DMAIC process, a Six Sigma team is ready with possible solutions. To verify these solutions, the team decides to implement the changes in half the call center. Over the course of one month, the team measures performance for both halves of the call center. At the end of the month, the team has two sets of data and wants to answer the question: Is the average production for the altered group greater than the average for the unaltered group? *In this case, the team would use the 2-sample T test.*

The two examples above are in line with many of the examples used in the chapter on hypothesis testing. Consider the scenario below, which is slightly different.

A restaurant chain wants to know if its branding and customer-facing activities are working equally across all locations. Specifically, the company decides to look at the customer satisfaction scores for each restaurant location. The chain includes five locations. Satisfaction scores are collected via phone, web, and written surveys at each location. The company averages the scores each week and reports those numbers. After several months, the company has five sets of averages. *If the company wants to know whether the scores for any location differs statistically from the scores from other locations, then the correct test is the 1-way ANOVA.*

Preparing for a 1-Way ANOVA

The way a Six Sigma expert approaches a 1-Way ANOVA is the very similar to the way he or she would approach any other hypothesis test. First, you begin with a real-world problem –

a practical or business problem. In the example above, that problem is whether there is variation in customer satisfaction among the various restaurant locations.

As with any hypothesis test, a null and alternative hypothesis is required. The null hypothesis is that there is no difference in the means of the samples.

$$\mu_1 = \mu_2 = \ldots \mu_x$$

The alternative hypothesis is that at least one of the means is not statistically the same.

After stating the null and alternative hypothesis, a Six Sigma expert should verify that any assumptions within the model are appropriate. This includes assumptions about errors as well as some basic assumptions about the ANOVA model.

First, the samples used for the ANOVA must be randomly selected. Remember, this is always a necessary assumption for inferential statistics.

After ensuring samples are randomly selected, Six Sigma experts must validate six other assumptions about data before running a 1-way ANOVA test.

Between versus Within Sample Variance

ANOVA calculations compare the between sample variance with the within sample variance. **Between** sample variance is the variance that occurs across all of the samples being analyzed. **Within** sample variance is the variance that occurs within a single sample or group.

The reason this distinction is important is that the within sample variance obviously impacts the between sample variance. If you are dealing with five separate samples and each sample has a big variance, then the variance across the samples is likely to be large as well. Part of the ANOVA calculation compares between sample variance to determine if it is large enough relative to within sample variance to denote a statistical difference.

1. The dependent variable, or outcome, must be continuous in nature. This means that it is a ratio or an interval. In previous examples, the dependent variable included the customer satisfaction score (numerical), the number of calls handled per day, and the cycle time for a specific output. All of these are examples of continuous data. Anything that can be

measured in time, temperature, feet and inches (or centimeters and meters), money, or ratios is typically continuous in nature.

2. The independent variable list contains two or more unrelated groups or categories. Teams A, B, and C are three independent variables. If you are measuring performance for five different workers, then you might have five independent variables. In the example about restaurants, the five different restaurants are independent variables. Categorical variables can include people, times, shifts, teams, departments, locations, various demographic groups (age, gender, ethnicity), or professions.

3. Observations are independent. First, you must ensure there are no dependencies within groups. If you are measuring the performance of three different teams in a department but several employees work on multiple teams, then the results are not completely independent. Second, you must ensure that observations within groups are not dependent.

4. Significant outliers don't exist in your data. Outliers throw off the accuracy of the 1-way ANOVA, but you don't have to scrap the entire test because of a single explainable outlier. As a Six Sigma expert, you *do* have to review your data, investigate outliers, and discard them appropriately. For example, if a Six Sigma expert is reviewing the response times for customer emails, he or she might review data samples from nine different employees. The data for one employee includes three outliers where emails were responded to after a much longer amount of time than all other samples seem to indicate. The Six Sigma expert might investigate this and note that the employee in question was on a short medical leave, which skewed results. The Six Sigma expert could remove those three data points from his or her calculations, *but it would be important to note these outliers.* The fact that this particular problem can happen *is still important* to the overall process improvement. The Six Sigma team might recommend instituting a process change that addresses this issue, but they might analyze data minus these outliers to draw other conclusions.

5. The dependent variable (as described in number 1 above) should be normally distributed or approximate the normal curve *within each group.* In the example above, the Six Sigma team gathers data for nine employees. Within each of these nine data sets, the data should be normally distributed.

6. The variance within each set has to be statistically equal to the variances of other sets – also called homogeneity of variances. The test for equal variance can be run in Minitab and will be covered later in this chapter.

After validating assumptions and setting up the hypotheses, a Six Sigma expert can run the 1-way ANOVA manually or using statistical analysis software. In this chapter, we'll use Minitab to run the tests. When using statistical analysis software, you typically spend more time on validating some of the assumptions than you do running the test itself.

Running a 1-Way ANOVA

To understand how to validate all the assumptions, run the 1-Way ANOVA, and interpret the results, consider a real-world example.

A mail-order book company wants to improve customer satisfaction with deliveries. A Six Sigma team working on the process has identified packing materials as a possible factor in negative customer satisfaction scores. The mail-order company currently ships books via cardboard boxes with no other protection, which the team believes is contributing to an increased amount of damage to shipments before they reach the customer or when the customer opens the package.

To test this theory and pilot two proposed solutions, the team implements additional packing options. Some books will be shipped in the regular packaging – the box without any additional materials. Others will be shipped in boxes with packing peanuts and still others in padded envelopes. The team implements the different packing methods at three different shipping stations and records an overall customer satisfaction score for each shipment based on a scale from 1 to 10 with 10 being the most satisfied. That data is presented below.

Original Packaging	Padded Envelope	Packing Peanuts
5	5	6
5	5	8
4	3	8
6	6	6
4	6	5
6	8	5
6	7	8
6	6	7
5	7	8
4	5	6
6	6	6
6	5	10
5	6	7
4	4	9
5	6	6

To follow along with the 1-Way ANOVA for this example, copy the above data into Minitab.

Validate Assumptions:

Is the dependent variable continuous?

Yes, it is measured in interval form.

Is the independent variable made up of two or more unrelated groups?

Yes, the independent variable is how the book is packaged.

Is there independence of observation?

Yes, the three packing methods don't have anything to do with each other and are not combined. The team wouldn't pack one book in a padded envelop and also put it in a box, for example.

It *is* worth noting here that the team has implemented the various packing at three different stations. It would be a good idea for the team to ensure that the packing stations were otherwise treated identically to keep any other factors from influencing the outcome of the pilot.

Are there any significant outliers in the data?

Graphical analysis can be an easy way to check for outliers. The box plot (also called the box and whisper plot) is a good way to check quickly for outliers. Boxplotting in Minitab was covered in Unit 6, but you can run one on the data above now.

1. Click Graph > Boxplot
2. Select multiple Ys
3. Click OK
4. Select all three data columns into the Graph Variables box
5. Click OK.

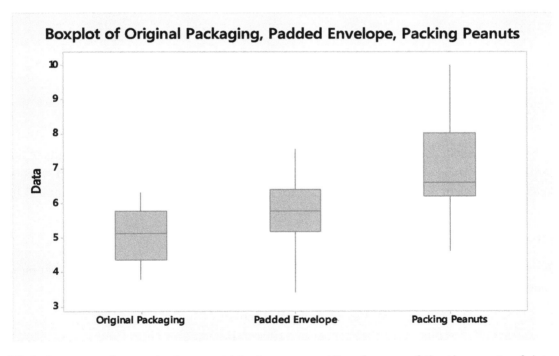

Minitab returns the graph above, which shows no outliers for any of the three sets of data. What if someone recording the customer satisfaction scores made a mistake and entered the number 20 for one shipment? The boxplot analysis changes.

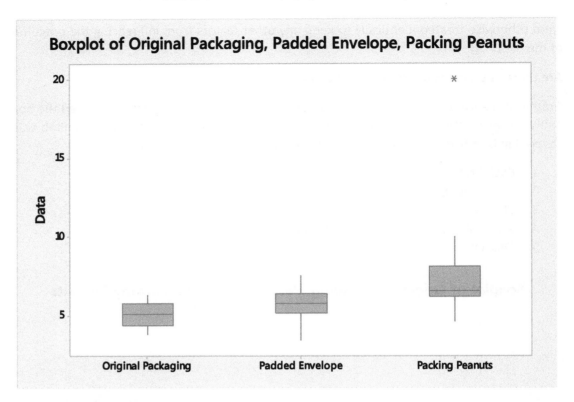

In the graph above, you can see an outlier dot high above the box for packing peanuts. A Six Sigma expert reviewing this graph would see that outlier and realize that it was a measurement error – remember, the scale for customer satisfaction was only supposed to go up to 10. Because there is an explanation for the outlier, it can be removed.

Is the data in each group normal?

The quickest way to test normality for each set of data is probably to run a graphical analysis in Minitab. This was also covered in Unit 6.

1. Select Stat > Basic Statistics > Graphical Summary
2. Select the column for the first set of data into the Variables box.
3. Make sure the confidence level is set to 95.0.
4. Click OK.

Minitab returns the following chart and data.

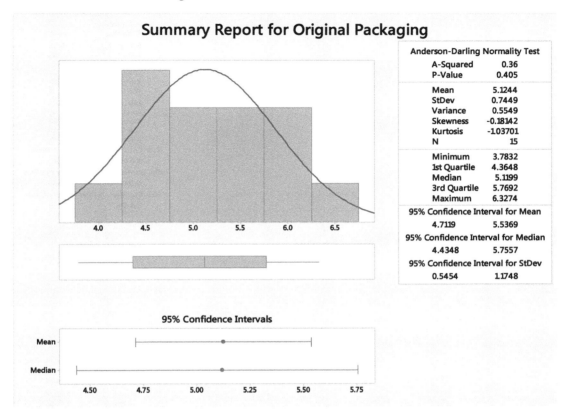

The p-value for the Anderson-Darling normality test is 0.405. Remember, when testing for normalcy, the null hypothesis is that there is no difference between the data and the normal curve. Since the p-value is above our alpha level (0.05), then we fail to reject the null hypothesis and accept that the data is normal.

The graphs generated for the other two sets of data are included below. You can see that the p-values for each also allow us to accept the null hypothesis and validate this assumption. Yes, the data for each group approximates the normal distribution.

Summary Report for Padded Envelope

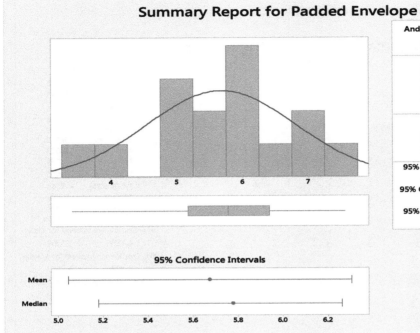

Anderson-Darling Normality Test	
A-Squared	0.27
P-Value	0.625
Mean	5.6755
StDev	1.1386
Variance	1.2965
Skewness	-0.374726
Kurtosis	0.236287
N	15
Minimum	3.4066
1st Quartile	5.1728
Median	5.7797
3rd Quartile	6.4068
Maximum	7.5639
95% Confidence Interval for Mean	
5.0449	6.3061
95% Confidence Interval for Median	
5.1809	6.2630
95% Confidence Interval for StDev	
0.8336	1.7958

Summary Report for Packing Peanuts

Anderson-Darling Normality Test	
A-Squared	0.34
P-Value	0.444
Mean	7.0374
StDev	1.4858
Variance	2.2075
Skewness	0.352309
Kurtosis	-0.011739
N	15
Minimum	4.6152
1st Quartile	6.2027
Median	6.6021
3rd Quartile	8.0132
Maximum	10.0000
95% Confidence Interval for Mean	
6.2146	7.8602
95% Confidence Interval for Median	
6.2459	8.0083
95% Confidence Interval for StDev	
1.0878	2.3432

574

Is there a homogeneity of variances? Are the variances between groups relatively equal?

Minitab includes an option for testing for equal variances that provides two different p-values. One is the p-value for the Multiple Comparisons test and one is for Levene's test. Levene's test is commonly used to test for equal assumptions when data within each group is normal. This test was not previously covered in Unit 6.

1. Select Stat > ANOVA > Test for Equal Variances

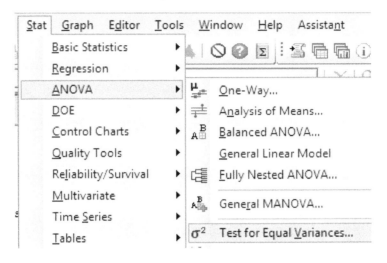

ANALYSIS OF VARIANCE (1-WAY ANOVA)

In the drop down box, select "Response data are in a separate column for each factor level."

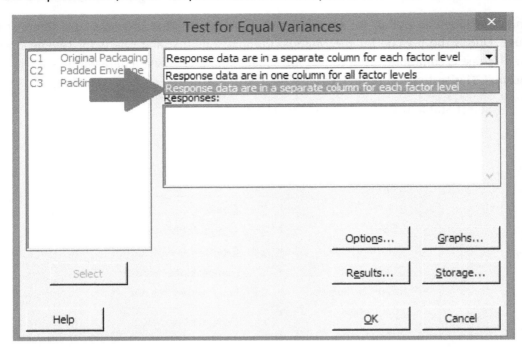

2. Select all the data columns into the Responses box.

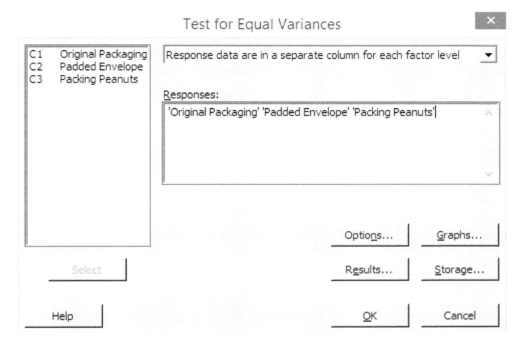

3. Click OK.

Minitab returns an interval graph of all the columns of data along with two statistical values.

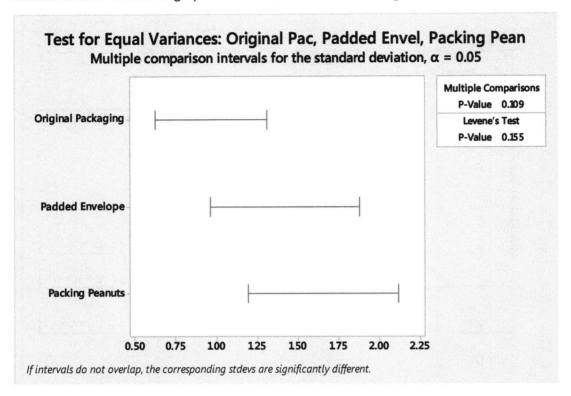

For the test for equal variance, you are usually concerned with the p-value for Levene's Test. In this case, it is above 0.05 (Minitab's default alpha setting), so you can fail to reject the null hypothesis, which is that there is no difference in the variance among the data. In this case, even a look at the interval graph helps you make this determination. The ranges are certainly different, but the intervals are not extremely different in length.

To consider a contrasting example, copy the following data table into Minitab.

A	B
4.01	10.00
4.91	10.06
6.38	10.04
7.98	10.00
6.00	10.06
10.00	9.97
6.50	9.96
4.14	10.01
9.00	10.05
6.45	10.08

Run the test for equal variance under the ANOVA menu using just the two columns of data from the above table.

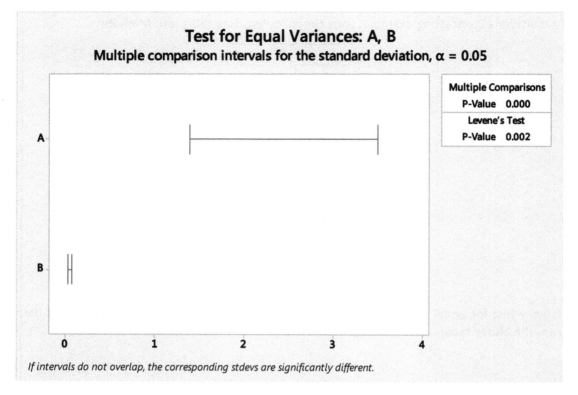

You can quickly see that these two sets of data do not have equal variance. First, the intervals make it fairly obvious. The variance in set B is much smaller. The p-value for Levene's Test is much smaller than the alpha value, which means you reject the null hypothesis and accept the alternative hypothesis that there is a difference in the variance.

You can change the alpha value for the tests by selecting Options on the Test for Equal Variances dialogue box.

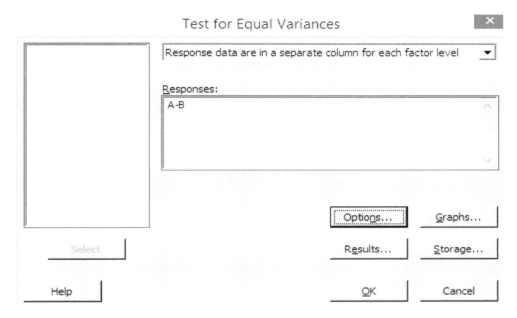

You can change the type of graph displayed by selecting Graphs from the Test for Equal Variances dialogue box.

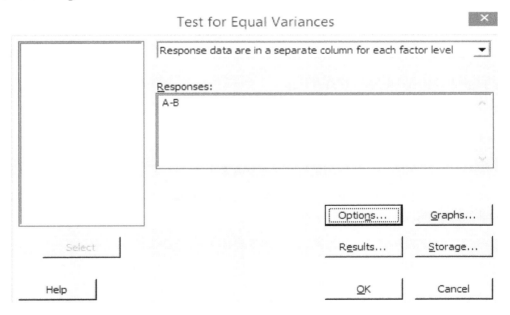

Here are the original three sets of data graphed via box plot.

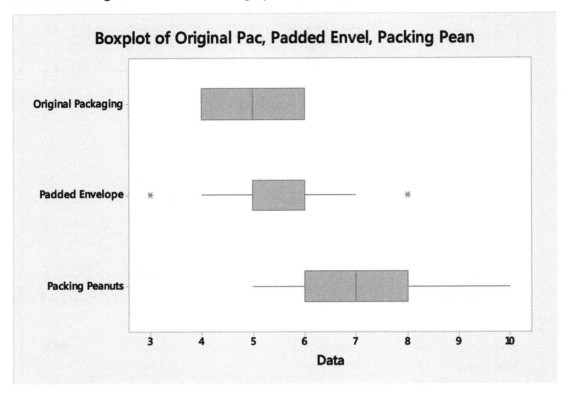

Run the 1-Way ANOVA Test

Now that all the assumptions are verified, you can run the 1-Way ANOVA test.

Select Stat > ANOVA > One-Way.

Select the drop down option that response data are in separate columns.

Select all three of the data columns (the data for the original packing, padded envelopes, and packing peanuts) into the Responses box.

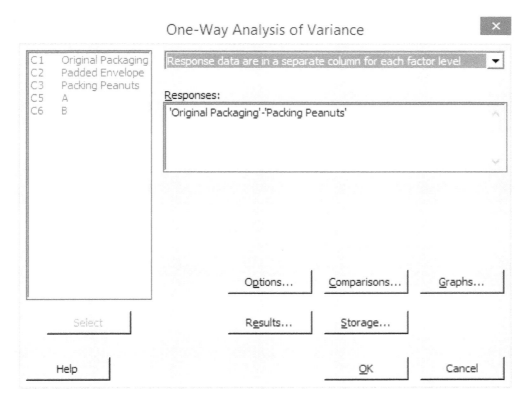

You can click Options to set the confidence interval or ensure it is still set at 95%, if desired. Then click OK.

Click OK on the main dialogue box. Minitab will perform the 1-Way ANOVA calculations. Depending on how much data is in columns when you run this test, it can take a few seconds.

Minitab defaults to returning two things: a graphical analysis of the data and the ANOVA results in the session window.

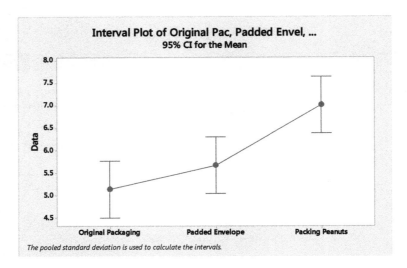

One-way ANOVA: Original Packaging, Padded Envelope, Packing Peanuts

```
Method

Null hypothesis         All means are equal
Alternative hypothesis  At least one mean is different
Significance level      α = 0.05

Equal variances were assumed for the analysis.


Factor Information

Factor  Levels  Values
Factor  3   Original Packaging, Padded Envelope, Packing Peanuts


Analysis of Variance

Source  DF  Adj SS  Adj MS  F-Value  P-Value
Factor   2   27.73  13.867     9.54    0.000
Error   42   61.07   1.454
Total   44   88.80


Model Summary

      S    R-sq  R-sq(adj)  R-sq(pred)
1.20581  31.23%     27.96%      21.06%


Means

Factor               N   Mean   StDev      95% CI
Original Packaging  15  5.133   0.834  (4.505, 5.762)
Padded Envelope     15  5.667   1.234  (5.038, 6.295)
Packing Peanuts     15  7.000   1.464  (6.372, 7.628)

Pooled StDev = 1.20581
```

The data from the session window is included above. Highlighted are the hypothesis and the p-value. The null hypothesis is that all the means are equal. The alternative is that at least one of the means is statistically different.

The p-value is less than the alpha value of 0.05, which means you reject the null hypothesis and accept the alternative hypothesis that at least one of the means is different.

In business terms, the Six Sigma team now knows that "one of these things is not like the other." That might prompt them to work on additional analysis or indicate that there might be an issue with one or more processes. If the team was comparing mean production times between various teams on the same process, they might assume that the teams would complete work in roughly the same time. If the 1-Way ANOVA indicates that isn't true, the Six Sigma team can then ask itself: What is it that makes the outcome statistically different? Is there a team doing it better than everyone else? If so, can the Six Sigma team implement solutions from that group across the other groups? Is there a team performing worse than everyone else? If so, what is going on with that team and how can an improvement be made?

What if Variances Aren't Equal?

If you can't validate the sixth assumption about equal variances between your subgroups, you can still run a 1-Way ANOVA test in Minitab. Minitab uses a different statistical calculation, known as Welch's test, to provide a p-value in such a case.

Use the data we previously found to have unequal variances to run this test in Minitab.

A	B
4.01	10.00
4.91	10.06
6.38	10.04
7.98	10.00
6.00	10.06
10.00	9.97
6.50	9.96
4.14	10.01
9.00	10.05
6.45	10.08

Select Stat > ANOVA > One-Way.

Select the drop down option that response data are in separate columns.

Select the data columns for A and B into the Responses box.

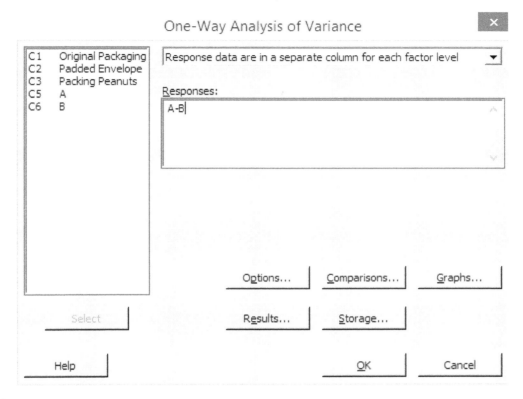

Select Options.

Uncheck the box for assume equal variances.

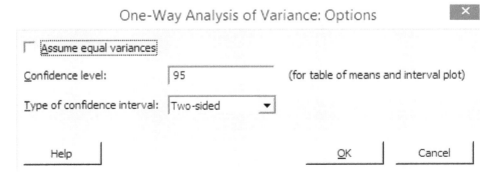

Click OK. Click OK again.

As in the previous example, Minitab generates both a graphical analysis and the test data in the session window.

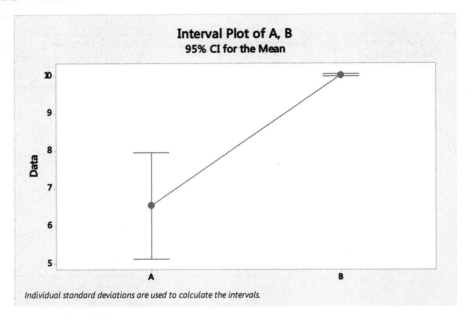

One-way ANOVA: A, B

```
Method

Null hypothesis        All means are equal
Alternative hypothesis  At least one mean is different
Significance level      α = 0.05

Equal variances were not assumed for the analysis.

Factor Information

Factor  Levels  Values
Factor      2   A, B

Welch's Test
         DF
Source  Num   DF Den  F-Value  P-Value
Factor    1  9.00729    30.99    0.000

Model Summary

  R-sq  R-sq(adj)  R-sq(pred)
63.26%     61.22%      54.64%

Means

Factor   N    Mean   StDev       95% CI
A       10   6.539   1.978  ( 5.123,   7.954)
B       10  10.0221  0.0398  (9.9936, 10.0506)
```

You can see from the Minitab results, equal variance was not assumed for this data. You also have a p-value that is effectively 0, which means you reject the null hypothesis and accept the alternative that one of the means is statistically different: something we already did just by looking at the graphical interpretation of this data before. As stated previously, data doesn't always look so different when viewed graphically, which often necessitates statistical analysis.

The Hypothesis Test Assistance in Minitab

At the end of the last unit, we noted that you could use the help menu in Minitab to look up information about all of the functions and read in-depth instructions and summaries on various types of tests. You can also use the Minitab Assistant to help you choose a hypothesis test – including a 1-Way ANOVA – and run that test.

Select Assistant > Hypothesis Tests.

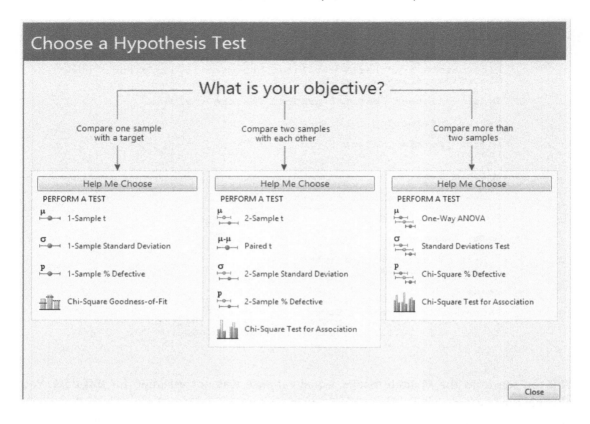

You can have Minitab help you choose a test to compare one sample with a target, two samples with each other, or more than two samples. Minitab will apply the same information included in this chapter and the previous chapter on hypothesis testing to help you make this choice, but this is a good tool to use if you get confused, don't remember which test to choose, or think you might need to use a less common test that wasn't covered in detail in this book.

If you click "Help me choose" under the option for comparing more than two samples, Minitab presents you with a second diagram.

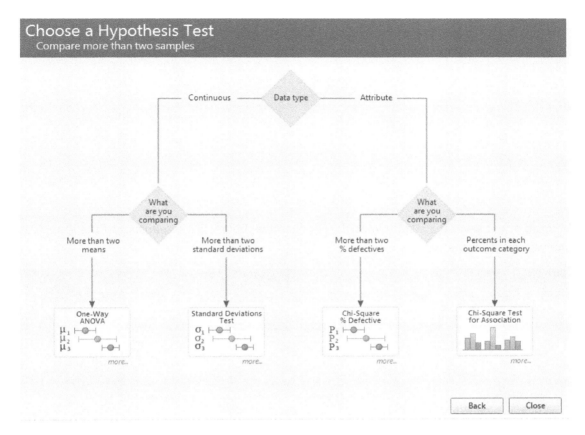

If you are comparing the means for more than two samples of continuous data, you would use the 1-Way ANOVA described in this chapter. If you are comparing standard deviations, however, you use a different test. If you are comparing attributed data, then you would use the chi-square tests. You can hover over any of the tests and click and Minitab will open the dialogue box for performing that test.

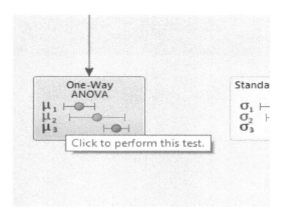

Minitab offers several assistant wizards. For example, below is a screenshot of the graphical analysis assistant menu.

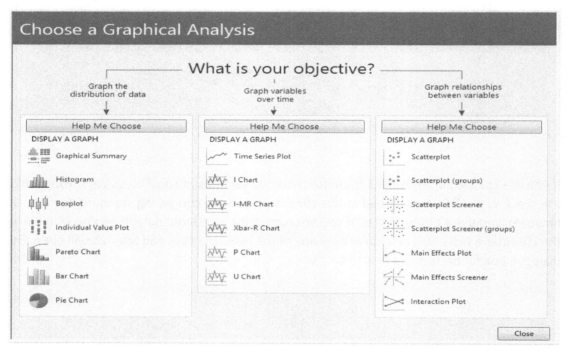

Here, Minitab helps you choose a graph or visual analysis that best matches your data and purposes. You can use the assistant tool for help with regression analysis, measurement system analysis, control charts, and design of experiments, which will be covered in the next chapter.

CHAPTER 29:
DESIGN OF EXPERIMENTS

In the past few chapters, you've learned how to analyze various types of data, conduct hypothesis tests, and draw conclusions from those tests. But simply analyzing data – no matter how accurate you can be – won't help you bring about improvements to the process. It can be easy to get lost in the analysis and forget about the need to make improvements, but continuous improvement is the very heart of the Six Sigma and DMAIC methodology.

Experiments are one way that Six Sigma experts and teams bring analysis and improvements together. Douglas C. Montgomery, author of *Design and Analysis of Experiments* provides a definition for the type of experiment we talk about in relation to a Six Sigma project.

An experiment is a test or series of tests in which purposeful changes are made to input variables of a process or system so that changes in the output responses can be observed and identified.

The fundamental concept of design of experiments, or DOE, is that all processes can be ultimately distilled to the $Y = f(x)$ equation. There are some factors, x, that work together to create some output, Y. The job of the Six Sigma team, as has been stated throughout this book, is to find out what factors (x) actually have an impact on Y and how changes in those factors will change the outcome.

One way teams can achieve this is to run a designed experiment. This involves making purposeful changes in one or more of the input variables – Xs – and then measuring and analyzing what occurs with the output, Y. Designed experiments have to be controlled and well-documented or improper conclusions can be drawn. The process for planning and running such experiments will be covered in this chapter, and you'll probably see similarities between DOE and the scientific method that most learn in primary school.

When Analysis Can Occur on Existing Data

Sometimes, enough data exists or enough change exists within the current process that a Six Sigma team can make decisions about factors without running a designed experiment. In these cases, the data is already available or can be captured in a way to isolate various inputs so that a Six Sigma team can run analysis and hypothesis tests without recreating physical scenarios. For example, in an agricultural setting, a company might already be using various types of planting processes to grow the same crop. Teams could gather data about each type of planting process, ensure no other variables exist between those processes, and then draw valid conclusions about how the planting processes impact the harvest outcomes.

There are benefits and disadvantages to analyzing existing data rather than running a designed experiment. The first benefit is that basing primary analysis and initial solution selection on existing data typically reduces the timeline for the entire DMAIC process. A team might still have to pilot a solution, measuring and analyzing the results to ensure they are in keeping with initial predictions, but they don't have to implement a designed experiment to make those first predictions. Second, basing decisions on existing data or processes can reduce the overall cost of a DMAIC project. This is especially true in processes that involve machines or parts that would have to be retooled to create a change in some inputs. In some cases, it simply isn't possible to make such changes solely so a team can gather information upon which to draw such conclusions, and the Six Sigma expert must use other tools to analyze the process so the team can draw conclusions and suggest improvements for a more formal pilot or test.

The disadvantage of using existing data is that it isn't always clean. You *can* use the existing data in a process when a process includes multiple changes to a factor. You would even run the same analysis that you might run if you made those changes yourself as part of an experiment. The problem is that you don't have control over the other variables in the process. For example, a Six Sigma team might be working on how document printing is managed in a large law firm. The team wants to know if the copy-print station to which documents are sent impacts the speed with which the jobs are processed. The copy and print machines have internal logs that record when a job is received and when it finished printing, so the team *can* compare the speed of the process from all the stations using ANOVA or DOE analysis without actually designing and running an experiment. The team could simply access the historical data for the process from last week – or any time period.

What isn't recorded for the copy-print process are a variety of external factors including how many staff were working at a given time, whether machines experience maintenance needs or paper jams, and whether staff were interrupting printing jobs to handle copying, scanning, or faxing jobs at the same machines. While the historical data might provide some valuable information about the difference in productivity for each machine, the team might not be able to rule out some of these other factors as causation without a designed experiment that captures all the possibly relevant data.

Why Run an Experiment?

A well-designed experiment helps you understand what variables provide the most influence on the process output. This helps a Six Sigma team understand where time, money, and other resources should be spent. In the example above, the experiment might help the team rule out external factors and understand if the type or location of the copy-print station is a major factor in productivity.

Another reason to run an experiment is that it can help you understand how to set inputs to create the best possible outcome. In one of the earliest chapters of this book, we used the example of a manufacturing process that makes chocolate bars. Each of the inputs – the ingredient amounts, the mixing time, and the mixing temperature – has to be set at the right level to create an optimal product. A Six Sigma team working on that process might conduct experiments to test various levels of inputs to find the right combination for the desired output.

Sometimes, Six Sigma teams want to understand how to control or set inputs that are simply influential to a process but don't necessarily directly feed the outcome. In the chocolate bar example, if the team has found optimal settings for the ingredients, time, and mixing temperature, and they still see variation in the outcome of the process, they might then consider influential inputs. Does the temperature in the room influence the process of mixing and setting the chocolate? If the team decides it might, they could conduct an experiment to test various room temperatures to find the right level for the best process outcome.

Finally, every input is not within a Six Sigma team or process owner's control. You can control the temperature in a climate-controlled room, but you can't control the temperature outside, for example. Experiments can help teams understand how to set all the inputs they *can* control to reduce any impact on variation and outcome from the inputs that *cannot* be controlled.

Best-Guess Trial-and-Error versus Factorial Experiments

A designed experiment is just that – it is designed statistically to test a variety of factors. Although a designed experiment does have, at its very basis, the idea of trial-and-error, teams that use design of experiment are not simply taking a best guess approach to the matter. A best-guess trial-and-error approach is actually not efficient in most cases, although some people might think so.

To better understand the different between a designed experiment and a best-guess approach, consider a real-word application. A team is working to improve a process for a regional furniture warehouse that delivers furniture to retail stores based on weekly orders from the stores. The team wants to reduce the average delivery turnaround by 24 hours and does have the baseline measurement – the average turnaround time for orders is currently 72 hours.

Using a best-guess approach, the team would identify what it thinks are the combination of inputs that are most likely to impact delivery times. The team might decide that factors include the delivery driver, the dispatcher who provides instructions and directions, whether the driver has a GPS in the truck, and how many pieces of furniture are being delivered. To find out which factor most contributes to the delivery time or discover which factors can be changed to decrease average times, the team would then have to run a series of trial-and-error tests.

The team sets the factors and runs a scenario. If the delivery time is greater than 48 hours, the result is not as desired. The team changes one of the factors and runs the test again. The team has to repeat the process until it finds a magic combination. Not only is this inefficient, but it uses an approach called the OFAT Approach, or One-Factor-At-a-Time approach. Only one input setting is changed for each trial and a measurement is taken. The measurements are compared to make decisions about each factor. In the furniture example, the team might note that delivery times are faster when a GPS is on board the truck. The might also note that deliver times are faster when a more experienced driver is on board the truck, regardless of the inclusion of a GPS.

One of the major problems with testing one factor at a time—other than inefficiency--is that Six Sigma experts don't gain a true understanding of the interaction between changes. Yes, the presence of a GPS increases efficiency. Yes, the presence of an experienced driver increases efficiency. But what happens when both a GPS and an experienced driver are on board a truck? Does efficiency increase at some exponential level, or does it simply increase to the maximum amount of either the experience-related increase or the GPS-related increase? Likewise, what happens when a negative factor is coupled with a positive factor? If delivery times increase with each item added to the order, what happens to the impact of the experience of the driver on efficiency? One-factor-at-a-time approaches don't usually answer these questions.

Why Do People Think This is a Good Approach?

Based on the scenario above, you can see that the best-guess approach is cumbersome and time consuming. The problem is, many people within an organization often favor this approach because it has worked well before. If you are very familiar with a process, you might be able to get a good result within the first few guesses. In our furniture moving example, you don't even have to be extremely familiar with the process to guess that having a GPS on board each delivery truck is likely to reduce delivery times or that it's going to take longer to deliver more furniture.

Because of a tendency to favor a best-guess approach, Six Sigma experts might have to work to explain the importance of using statistical analysis to help with problem solving. It's important for teams to understand that a best guess approach does usually lead to more trials and tests than are necessary, which creates waste, or *muda*. Yes, teams might get lucky, especially if someone on the team or a subject-matter-expert being utilized by the team is extremely familiar with the process and, thus, understands how the inputs impact the outcomes at a granular level. *However*, that familiarity with the process *can* create the opposite impact. The person might be so close to the process and so ingrained with the traditional way of doing things that he or she cannot make valuable best guesses.

Even if the first guess regarding changes to the inputs yields a result that is within the parameters the team was looking for, *it might not be the best possible guess*. The team in the delivery example wanted to reduce deliver times by an average of 24 hours. Based on historical data, any combination of inputs that averages 48 hours or less would achieve this goal. But what if there is a combination of inputs that averages 24 hours or less? Wouldn't that be something valuable for the team to know? If the combination of inputs is viable to achieve, then the team could not only deliver on the original goal, but deliver *well above* the original goal. It's not something teams should always set out to do, because setting the bar too high can have negative results on a project. But knowing that excellent results are possible is valuable because it lets the team make a more educated decision about the solution.

What is Factorial Experimentation?

The solution to all the problems of inefficiency and lackluster data described above is design of experiment, or factorial experimentation. Design of experiment is also called statistically designed experiments, and it involves running a series of experimental runs that vary all the input factors in an organized way. The information isn't analyzed until you complete all the planned runs, which means you have all the data for all the changes to inputs at that time.

For example, consider the factors from the furniture delivery example again: number of pieces being delivered, experience of the driver, whether a GPS is on board, and the method of providing instruction or direction from the dispatcher. For this example, assume that each of these factors could be set with a low value and a high value as follows.

- Experience of driver: 0 years, 1 year
- GPS: No, Yes
- Dispatcher: No policy, follows a policy
- Number of pieces of furniture: 1, 5

In a grid, you would create a list of all possible runs. Each run creates a unique grouping of the possible factors, which means the number of runs you have is determined by the number of factors and possible settings that you have. The grid for the delivery factors is shown below.

Run Number	Driver Experience	GPS	Dispatcher	Pieces of Furniture
1	0 years	Yes	Follows Procedure	1 piece
2	0 years	Yes	Follows Procedure	5 pieces
3	0 years	Yes	No Procedure	1 piece
4	0 years	Yes	No Procedure	5 pieces
5	0 years	No	Follows Procedure	1 piece
6	0 years	No	Follows Procedure	5 pieces
7	0 years	No	No Procedure	1 piece
8	0 years	No	No Procedure	5 pieces
9	1 year	Yes	Follows Procedure	1 piece
10	1 year	Yes	Follows Procedure	5 pieces
11	1 year	Yes	No Procedure	1 piece
12	1 year	Yes	No Procedure	5 pieces
13	1 year	No	Follows Procedure	1 piece
14	1 year	No	Follows Procedure	5 pieces
15	1 year	No	No Procedure	1 piece

16	1 year	No	No Procedure	5 pieces

This information is then used to generate a worksheet for running the experiment; once data is collected, a Six Sigma expert analyzes the outcome. Minitab actually has tools that help you create the worksheet and analyze the experiment outcome, which we'll cover at the end of this chapter and in the next chapter.

Note that the above experiment is an example of a 2k factorial designed experiment. In 2k factorial design, you limit the factor levels to two: a high and low factor. The driver has less than a year (0 years) experience or 1 or more years of experience. The GPS is there or it isn't.

Experiments that include more than two levels – more than a low and a high – for one or more factors are full factorial experiments. The examples in this chapter all deal with 2k factorials; examples of full factorials can be seen in chapter 30.

Step-by-Step Guide for Creating a Designed Experiment

As with hypothesis testing, most experiments follow a road map of steps required to define the elements, set up data collection, and analyze the data collected. These steps are virtually the same for any type of experiment, though you'll see in chapter 30 that some requirements are slightly different when dealing with full factorials.

Step 1: What, in business or practical terms, is the problem?

As with anything in Six Sigma, you begin with a practical business consideration or issue. This isn't necessarily the big problem statement that the team created in the Define phase for the overall project. It's more likely to be a smaller issue within the larger problem. For example, a healthcare facility might want to address the rate of staph infections for admitted patients. This might be the overall project for the team: reduce the current rate of staph infections, which is 17 percent.

During the project, the team discovers that clinical staff are not always compliant with sanitation protocols when treating patients. For this particular situation, the practical problem might be stated as:

In a 10-point evaluation for sanitation compliance, clinical healthcare workers are averaging a score of 7.1. The hospital requires an average of at least 9.0.

The business problem or concern that the experiment is addressing should be related to the Six Sigma team's overall problem statement. In this case, the lack of sanitation compliance could be linked to the fact that patients are getting staph infections.

Step 2: What is the objective of running a designed experiment?

Unlike some of the other analysis discussed in this book, designed experiments do often take the time and resources of someone besides the Six Sigma expert, which means there is a larger cost associated with DOE than there might be with graphical analysis or even hypothesis testing. Because of this, teams don't want to run experiments without a detailed objective – a detailed understanding of why the experiment is necessary and what the team hopes to achieve via the analysis.

The objective is directly tied to the practical problem. In the healthcare example, the problem was:

In a 10-point evaluation for sanitation compliance, clinical healthcare workers are averaging a score of 7.1. The hospital requires an average of at least 9.0.

An objective might be written as:

Increase sanitation compliance scores from 7.1 to at least 9.0.

That increase would meet the requirements from the leadership team and, since the Six Sigma team believes sanitation is related to staph infections, would hopefully improve the overall problem. Understanding the amount of change the team wants to create in the process will be important in determining the sample size required for the DOE. The objective should be specific enough that the team can use it later to measure success and involve the scale of the change for sample size calculations.

It's important to note that the objective of any given experiment within a Six Sigma project is not going to be the same as the overall project initiative. Instead, each experiment objective should be related to – or supportive of – the project objective. In this case, the team hopes that increasing sanitation compliance will help decrease staph infection rates.

Step 3: What is the appropriate Y for your experiment?

For a designed experiment, you almost always select the output response, or Y, first. The response needs to be related to the goals of the overall project; because there might be multiple output responses related to the project *and* the team's experiment objective, the team should ask some questions about the response and possible associated inputs.

- First, is the measurement system capable enough to support the experiment? You can test the measurement system with a gage analysis. The less capable a measurement system is, the bigger the sample size and more experimental runs you will need. If a measurement system's capability is too poor, then the time or expense for an experiment can be prohibitive.
- Second, what is important for the team to address? Does the team want to address variation within a process or address the center of the process? Is the purpose to bring variation down or to move the mean of the process up or down? In the case of the healthcare scenario provided above, the purpose is to increase the rate of compliance.
- The team must also understand how the response might relate to other responses in the process or whether changes to one response will cause changes to another – particularly if an experiment is being conducted within the live environment of a process. This helps the team manage any downstream changes that could impact other processes or the customer.

The rate of compliance with the sanitation protocol is the Y for the Six Sigma healthcare team's problem.

Step 4: What inputs will be studied?

In the DMAIC chapters, we covered some brainstorming tools for identifying inputs within a process, including the fishbone diagram. More brainstorming tools are covered in chapter 31. Teams can use such tools, along with process maps, to identify the inputs associated with the output decided upon in the previous step. Once you have a list of inputs, you can select the inputs that are going to be studied in the experiment. Note that not all the inputs to a process will be studied, and teams should choose inputs that are:

- Believed to be most influential on the response (consider the Pareto, or 80/20, rule)
- Are quantitative or qualitative in nature (it's harder to work with attribute data due to sample size requirements, and involving too many people in the measurement system can also add variation, so keep these considerations in mind)
- Can be set and controlled appropriately for the experiment

For the healthcare scenario, the team believes that several factors might contribute to a lack of compliance: education of the staff, the length of time a particular staff member has been on shift, and the number of patients on the floor at a given time.

Step 5: What are the factor levels for the experiment?

What levels will the input variables be set at for the purpose of the experiment? If you are running an experiment that involves baking cookies, then oven

> **Response, Factor, and Level**
>
> When talking about design of experiments, Six Sigma experts might use slightly different verbiage to discuss process components. The response is the outcome or output of the process. Factors are the inputs – usually those that have influence on the response and are being studied during the DOE. Levels are the values at which the factors are set for the purpose of experiment.

temperature is an input, or factor. Levels for the factor might be 325 degrees F, 350 degrees F, and 375 degrees F. Remember that in the case of a 2k factorial, each factor only has two levels.

In the healthcare example, the team decides to set each factor at a low and a high:

- Staff education: Received annual compliance update training in the last 6 months versus has not received the training in the last six months
- Time on shift: Less than or equal to 4 hours versus 5 or more hours
- Number of patients on the floor: Below 80 percent of maximum capacity versus above 80 percent of maximum capacity

The levels set for each factor depend on a variety of considerations. If the team is performing a screening experiment – which means they only want to test input impact on outputs or better understand the process – they would set levels at wide intervals. For optimization, the team likely already has an understanding of the input impact on the process; the team might already have conducted analysis or experiments, and that information helps them set the levels appropriately at smaller intervals.

The process itself will dictate how some levels are set. If a Six Sigma team is working with a baking process, for example, it can't set the temperature any lower than 0 degrees and most ovens also have a maximum temperature range. Teams also probably know the temperature around which baked goods will still be raw, so they are unlikely to set temperatures at something like 100 degrees F. Safety should always be a concern when setting levels. An oven might heat to 550 degrees F maximum, but is it safe to attempt to bake cookies at that level?

Finally, the levels should correlate with the type of information the team is looking for and the size of change the team wants to see. If a team is working with a manufacturing process that cuts lumber, it likely wants to see changes at small increments. Setting tool levels several feet apart isn't going to show the change the team wants to see if they are working with the cutting process for 2-by-4 lumber piece that are to be cut into 6-inch pieces.

Step 6: What is the appropriate sample size?

In the case of the design of experiment, a sample size isn't the number of data elements you collect but the number of times you replicate the experiment. The more replications, the greater the accuracy of the statistics, but each run in the DOE takes time and possibly other resources. Six Sigma experts have to balance the use of resources with the need for strong experiment conclusions. When you create a design of experiment in Minitab, the software program generates some predictions about the experiment *even before you run* the experiment, which lets you decide on size and replication before you begin. Specifically, Minitab tells you the size of effect, as measured in standard deviation, that you are 80 percent likely to capture with the experiment as you have designed it.

Step-by-Step Guide to Running a 2k Factorial Experiment in Minitab

To understand more about sample size and replication – and how to run a 2k factorial experiment in Minitab, begin with the Assistant menu. You can also access design of experiments under Stat > DOE, but the assistant wizard is helpful because it reminds you of all the steps previously discussed in this chapter, helps you decide on the proper type of experiment, and helps you create the data collection form and analysis.

For the purpose of setting up this experiment, use the healthcare example discussed above.

Problem: In a 10-point evaluation for sanitation compliance, clinical healthcare workers are averaging a score of 7.1. The hospital requires an average of at least 9.0.

Objective: Increase compliance scores to at least 9.0.

Response: Rate of compliance with sanitation protocols

Factors: Staff education, time on shift, number of patients on floor

Levels:

Factor	Low (-1)	High (1)
Staff education	Didn't receive compliance training in last 6 months	Did receive compliance training in last 6 months
Time on shift	Less than or equal to 4 hours	5 or more hours
Number of patients on floor	Below 80 percent maximum capacity	At or above 80 percent maximum capacity

Select Assistant > DOE > Plan and Create.

Select "Plan optimization experiment" since the team is looking to improve, or optimize, the process.

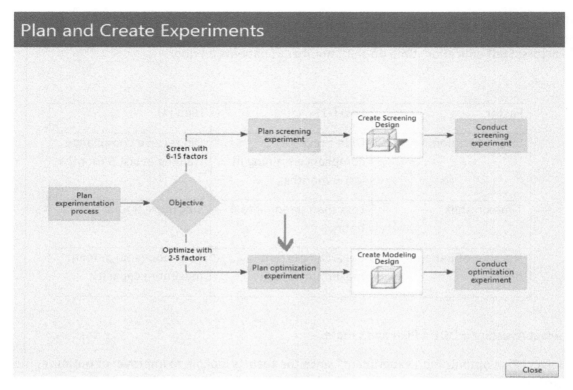

Minitab provides some instructions on identifying factors, setting levels, and choosing sample size. This information is all valuable and worth reviewing, particularly if you are conducting a DOE when it has been a long time since you last did so. It is also all information that has been included in this chapter.

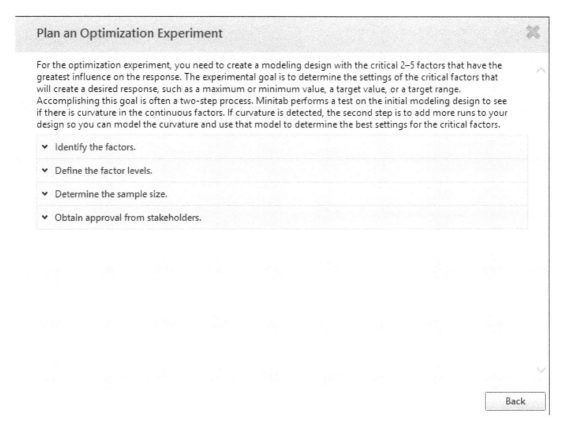

One good note from the above Minitab menu is that it's a good idea to obtain approval from any stakeholders, project owners, or sponsors associated with the project or process. Key stakeholders should understand what will happen during the experiment and why it is necessary to the project. If resources are required, sponsors or other leaders should sign off as required by organization guidelines.

In the particular healthcare scenario being used as the example, running a standalone experiment isn't an option. A Six Sigma team *certainly* isn't going to give patients a staph infection just to find out about inputs. In this particular case, the team would need to use existing data that matched the experiment parameters. This is something that might be an option – or a requirement – for teams in any number of scenarios.

After reviewing any Minitab notes desired, click "Back."

Select "Create Modeling Design".

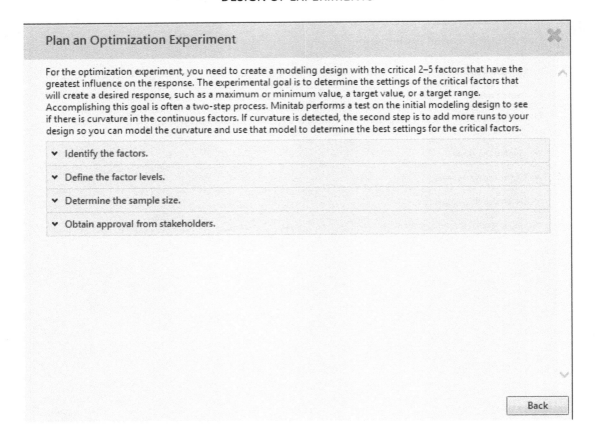

Minitab displays a Modeling Design dialogue box, requesting all the information needed to create an experiment. Enter the information for the healthcare scenario.

1. Name the response variable. The team is measuring compliance with the sanitation protocols, so name it "Compliance." The name isn't important to Minitab, so you can name the variable anything that will make sense to yourself or the Six Sigma team.

2. Choose an option for the response goal. Minitab lets you select minimize the response, maximize the response, or achieve a target. In this case, the team wants to improve compliance to a score of 9, but going above 9 would also be a positive outcome, so select "maximize the response."

3. Enter the number of factors. Remember, factors are inputs, and the healthcare scenario identifies 3 inputs.

4. Enter names and information for the factors. Even though some of the factors are continuous in nature, since this is a 2k factorial experiment, we've divided them into categories.
5. Select a number of times to replicate the experiment (remember, this is relevant to sample size). For this purpose, select 2.
6. Ensure your dialogue box matches the one below and select OK.

Create Modeling Design ✕

Response

Enter the name of your response variable: Compliance

What is your response goal? Maximize the response ▼

Factors

Number of factors: 3 ▼

Enter your factor names and settings:

Name	Type	Low	High
StaffEd	Categorical ▼	No	Yes
TimeShift	Categorical ▼	4 or under	Over 4
NoPts	Categorical ▼	Below 80%	80% or more

Replicates

Adding replicates allows you to detect smaller effect sizes.

Number of replicates: 2 ▼

Number of runs

Total number of center points in your design: 0

Total number of runs in your design: 16

OK   Cancel

Minitab offers you the option to print the data form to make it easier to collect data. For the example, select no.

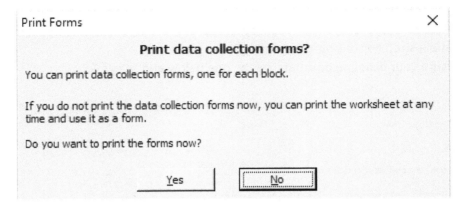

Minitab generates three items. The first is a modeling design report card that provides next steps and tips for completing the experiment.

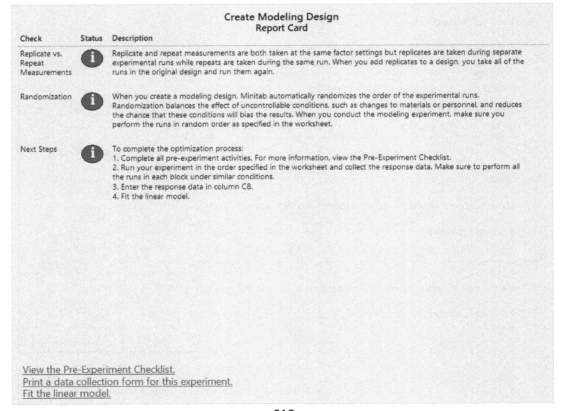

The second item is a summary report. The report summarizes all the information you entered for the experiment and provides an estimated detection ability, which helps you choose a sample size.

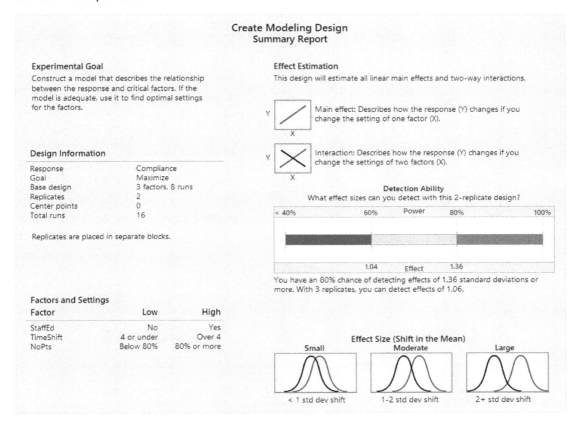

The final item is a worksheet to help you gather results from the experiment. Minitab randomizes the order of the runs, which would be required if you were completing the experiment in real-time.

Worksheet 5.***

↓	C1	C2	C3	C4	C5-T	C6-T	C7-T	C8	C
	StdOrder	RunOrder	CenterPt	Blocks	StaffEd	TimeShift	NoPts	Compliance	
1	8	1	1	1	Yes	Over 4	80% or more		
2	2	2	1	1	Yes	4 or under	Below 80%		
3	7	3	1	1	No	Over 4	80% or more		
4	1	4	1	1	No	4 or under	Below 80%		
5	5	5	1	1	No	4 or under	80% or more		
6	3	6	1	1	No	Over 4	Below 80%		
7	4	7	1	1	Yes	Over 4	Below 80%		
8	6	8	1	1	Yes	4 or under	80% or more		
°	11	°	1	2	No	Over 4	Below 80%		

For the healthcare scenario we entered, the detection ability based on 2 replicas will detect standard deviations of 1.36 or more.

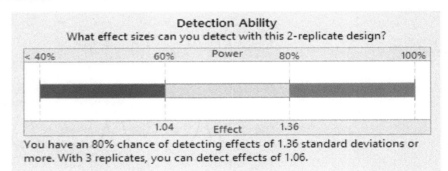

You have an 80% chance of detecting effects of 1.36 standard deviations or more. With 3 replicates, you can detect effects of 1.06.

If the team wanted to detect smaller changes, it would need to add more replicates. Four replications would detect 0.91 standard deviations, and 5 would detect as little as 0.81 standard deviations.

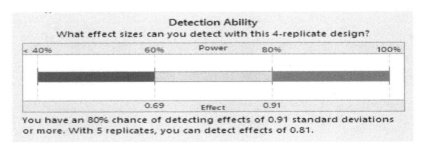

You have an 80% chance of detecting effects of 0.91 standard deviations or more. With 5 replicates, you can detect effects of 0.81.

To make the best possible choice about sample size, it does help to know what the current standard deviation is to understand what measurement is going to be meaningful. Remember, two replicates have an 80 percent chance of detecting 1.36 standard deviations, *not* a 1.36 shift in the actual compliance score.

Before moving forward with the experiment, the team might consider some sample data. Here are the sanitation compliance scores from all of the clinical audits for one week.

7.8
7.5
7.1
7.5
9.1
5.4
7.2
7.2
5.8
8.7
5.8
7.1
6.7
7.8
5.1
7.7
6.5
8.2
7.4
7.1

Copy the data into Excel or Minitab to calculate the standard deviation of that data set.

The standard deviation is 1.028.

According to the first summary, based on the setting for 2 replicates, the detection ability of the experiment is only an 80 percent chance at detecting changes of 1.36 standard deviations. That's too big to make the difference the healthcare team needs to see. At three replicates, the difference is right on the line, and in any other situation, a Six Sigma expert would probably want to go with 4 or more replicates. For the purpose of this exercise, we'll stay with 2 replicates for the rest of the example.

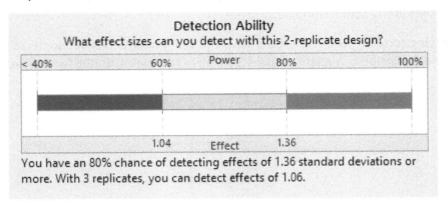

On the Report Card screen, select "View the pre-experiment checklist".

Minitab provides some important tips for completing a designed experiment in the checklist.

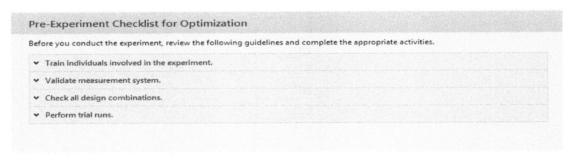

First, anyone involved in the experiment should be properly trained to remove variation from operator error. Individuals involved must know how to measure the output, or response, how to set factor levels if that is required during the experiment, and how to make changes to equipment or processes between runs to affect the experiment. In the healthcare example we are using, the only training that might be required is ensuring the audit – which applies the compliance score – is handled correctly. In another situation, however, a team might be running a production process in a manufacturing plant. The team might want to try different materials, different tools, and different operators as part of the experiment, and they would have to ensure everyone knew how to use the materials and tools.

Measurement systems should be validated for both the response and the levels for every factor. In our healthcare example, the Six Sigma team should have already validated the measurement system used to rate compliance. They might have used a Gage R & R to determine if separate auditors with separate replications would rate the same situation the same way more than once, for example. Teams should also validate the measurements used to set levels. If the speed of a wheel in a manufacturing process is to be set at 1 rpm, 1.2 rpm, and 1.5 rpm as levels of a factor, then calibrations for those settings should be checked.

When running actual experiments, Six Sigma teams should review all possible combinations in the experiment to ensure they are all both safe and possible. Perfectly safe or possible levels for one factor might become unsafe or impossible when combined with another, for example. The team might want to perform a few trial runs to work out troubleshooting issues with the experiment and finalize validations before moving on to the actual experiment.

Finally, the team runs the designed experiment according to the random worksheet created by Minitab. In the healthcare scenario, the team reviewed the data for the last month in random order and recorded the first set of data that fit each experiment scenario. For example, the first run in the list below required that the staff member being audited had received compliance training in the last six months, was over the 4th hour into a shift when the interaction being audited occurred, and was working at a time when the particular floor was at 80 percent or more of capacity. The first score that met those parameters was 7.9. The results of the data gathering are included below, and you can copy this table into Minitab if you want to follow along with the analysis.

StdOrder	RunOrder	CenterPt	Blocks	StaffEd	TimeShift	NoPts	Compliance
8	1	1	1	Yes	Over 4	80% or more	8.2
2	2	1	1	Yes	4 or under	Below 80%	9.5
7	3	1	1	No	Over 4	80% or more	7.2
1	4	1	1	No	4 or under	Below 80%	7.8
5	5	1	1	No	4 or under	80% or more	5.2
3	6	1	1	No	Over 4	Below 80%	5.4
4	7	1	1	Yes	Over 4	Below 80%	8.5
6	8	1	1	Yes	4 or under	80% or more	9.7
11	9	1	2	No	Over 4	Below 80%	7.2
16	10	1	2	Yes	Over 4	80% or more	8.8
10	11	1	2	Yes	4 or under	Below 80%	9.2
9	12	1	2	No	4 or under	Below 80%	6.3
14	13	1	2	Yes	4 or under	80% or more	9.7
13	14	1	2	No	4 or under	80% or more	8.1
15	15	1	2	No	Over 4	80% or more	5.6
12	16	1	2	Yes	Over 4	Below 80%	8.9

To analyze the results in Minitab, select Assistant > DOE > Analyze and Interpret.

Click "Fit Linear Model."

Analyze and Interpret: Optimization Experiment

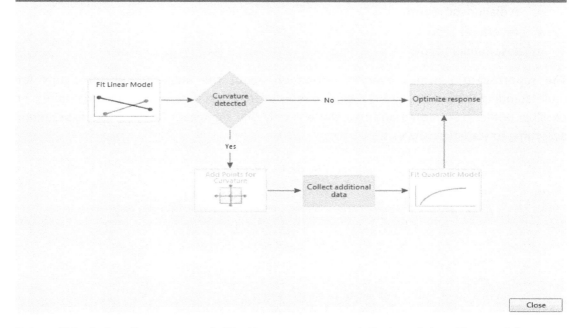

Select "Maximize the response" (Or the response goal that matches the goal for your experiment.)

Click OK.

Minitab generates five items:

- A report card
- A prediction and optimization report
- A diagnostic report
- An effects report
- A summary report

The report card provides overall information about the analysis and some tips for understanding the results. In this case, the report card notes that no unusual data points, or possible outliers, are noted and that there is only one significant factor in the experiment according to statistical analysis.

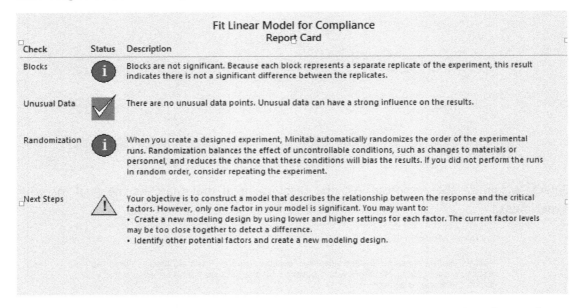

The prediction and optimization report compares the means associated with significant factors and provides an optimized level setting for those factors. In this case, only one factor – whether or not the staff had received compliance training in the past six months – was statistically significant.

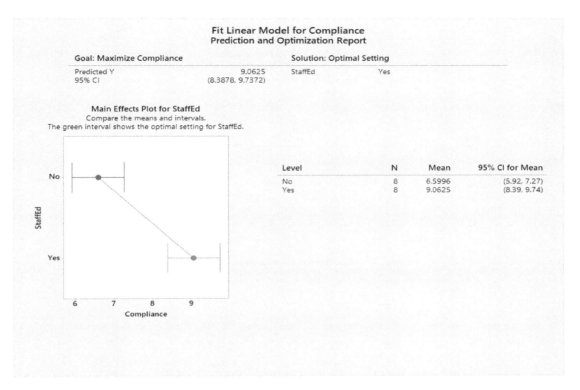

The effects report provides more information about all the factors. In the lower part of the diagram below, you can see the main effects plots for each factor. The main effect is the difference between the mean response at each factor setting. You can see that only a slight difference occurs between the means of the responses for different amounts of time spent on the shift and almost no difference occurs   between the means of the two settings for amount of patients on the floor. The largest difference is seen with regard to the compliance education status. The same is true in the top part of the graph, where different factors are graphed together.

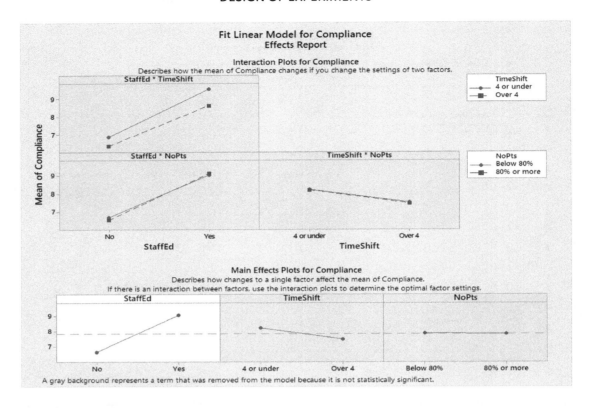

The summary report provides a Pareto breakdown of the influence on the response. In this case, the biggest influence on the compliance number is whether the staff received compliance training in the last six months. The next factor is how long the staff member had been working that shift. The third most influential factor is a combination of A (staff training) and B (time worked on the shift). Number of patients on the floor doesn't make an appearance until the fourth influence.

The summary notes that setting the staff education factor at Yes – the staff member received training within the last 6 months – results in a predicted Y (response) that is above 9. The summary also notes that this model explains 68.64 percent of the variation.

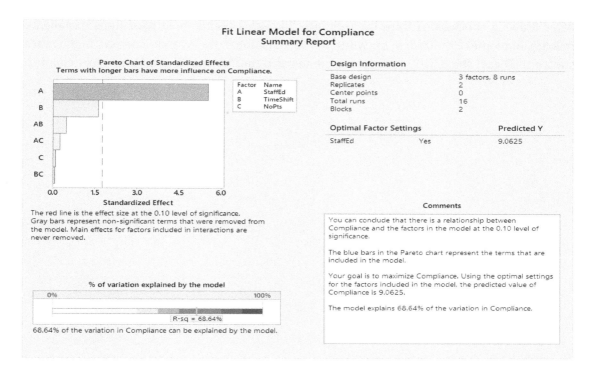

Based on these results, the Six Sigma team might run further tests and analysis, but it would also likely make a recommendation about supplying staff with compliance training. If you remember, the training that was mentioned originally was an annual training. However, this experiment seems to indicate that the training has more impact if staff members have received it within the past 6 months. The team might recommend that staff receive the training biannually going forward.

Next Steps

Remember that an experiment is not usually what solves the large problem that the Six Sigma team is working on. It simply helps approach one part of a solution to that problem. In the case of the healthcare Six Sigma team, recommending the additional training might increase compliance rates with the sanitation protocol, which could in turn decrease the rate of staph infections in the hospital. But that's not likely the only root cause the team has found and not the only solution it will recommend.

After drawing conclusions from experiments, Six Sigma teams must take steps to validate results, implement solutions or work the results into the overall project, and create controls. These steps will be covered in more detail at the end of the next chapter.

CHAPTER 30:
INTERACTIONS, MULTI-LEVEL FACTORIALS, AND CREATING EXPERIMENTS

In the previous two chapters, you saw how designed experiments could lead to the use of an ANOVA or a 2k (two-level) factorial. This chapter will cover more information on the use of factorials, including multi-level factorials, and provide information for setting up designed experiments.

The Importance of Understanding Interactions

Chapter 29 briefly touched on the concept of interactions. Remember, one reason design of experiments is such a powerful tool for Six Sigma teams is that it doesn't only let experts analyze how certain factors and levels impact results. Design of experiments also lets you understand how the combination of certain factors and levels impact results. Because designed experiments run each factor and level against all other factors and levels, they can unearth interactions that other types of analysis, which consider only a single factor at a time, can miss. Understanding interactions helps Six Sigma teams come up with the strongest possible solution while also mitigating potential issues such as waste or error.

In the sample healthcare experiment run in the previous chapter, there wasn't a great deal of interaction between the individual factors, but the interaction plots did show a slight interaction between the education and shift factors. If a staff member had received the compliance education within the last 6 months, they were more likely to be compliant with the sanitation procedures. If the staff member, who had received the training in the past 6 months, was also within the first four hours of the shift, the increase in the likelihood of compliance associated with the training was slightly higher than the same increase in someone who was over four hours into a shift.

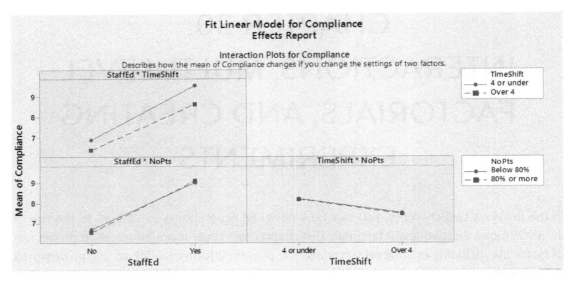

Interactions are indicated in the interaction plots by lines that are not parallel. The less parallel the lines are, the greater the interaction. As you can see, most of these lines are close to parallel, which means that any interaction that *does* exist here is fairly weak. Consider the bottom left graph. The blue line indicates measurements taken when the department was below 80 percent capacity for patients. The red line indicates measurements taken when the department was above 80 percent capacity for patients. Regardless of the capacity status, the behavior of the measurements is roughly the same depending on whether the staff member had received the compliance training within the past six months or not. This means there is not much of an interaction – the setting of one factor does not seem to impact the way the settings for the other factor changes the result.

Understanding the Main Effect

To better understand how interactions are measured, you first have to understand the main effect. Consider a real-world example, again with a 2-level factorial. In this example, a Six Sigma team within a chain of movie theaters is trying to positively impact the performance of concession stands. Specifically, the team has been tasked with increasing profits in the concession stand.

One area the team is concentrating on is the popcorn process, and they have defined waste as a root cause of the problem in this part of the concession stand. The team believes the current popcorn-making process is generating waste because so many of the kernels introduced into the popcorn machine never pop. Those kernels are swept out of the machine regularly and thrown away, and the team believes the amount of kernels thrown away each day amounts to at least 10 large popcorn orders.

While that might seem like a small amount of waste, the team calculates that the concession stand earns a profit of $2.65 for each large popcorn order, which means the stand is losing approximately $9,600 each year in lost popcorn kernels. If the team can use a designed experiment to identify a quick, inexpensive way to reduce kernel waste, it might be worth the effort.

After finding out more about the kernel process, the team decides that the temperature of the machine at the time the popcorn is introduced is a factor. They also decide that the number of kernels placed in the machine and the brand of popcorn are factors as well.

The team designs the following experiment:

Row Number	Brand	Temperature	Kernels
1	A	400 degrees F	1 scoop
2	A	400 degrees F	2 scoops
3	A	600 degrees F	1 scoop
4	A	600 degrees F	2 scoops
5	B	400 degrees F	1 scoop
6	B	400 degrees F	2 scoops
7	B	600 degrees F	1 scoop
8	B	600 degrees F	2 scoops

Following good experiment protocol, the team decides on a sample size. Remember, the sample size for a designed experiment is what tells you how many replications of the overall experiment to run. In this case, the Six Sigma team decides to run 4 replications. Given the above design, that means the team is going to record 32 runs. Also following good experiment protocol, the team randomizes the runs so they aren't recording the information in the same order each time through the experiment.

The Six Sigma expert on the team also knew that simply recording the amount of kernels left after each batch wouldn't provide the ability to draw statistical conclusions about the three factors the team was considering. This is because one of the factors the team was considering was the volume of kernels entering the process. Naturally, if more kernels enter the process, there are likely to be more waste kernels — the team shouldn't need an experiment to test if that is true. The team really wants to find out if a larger ratio of unpopped kernels is left when popping one or two scoops of certain popcorn brands at certain temperatures. The Six Sigma expert ensures the team records both total number of kernels and the percent, or ratio, of those kernels to the number of kernels that entered the process.

The information recorded by the team is shown in the table below. Note that the data has been sorted by brand, then temperature, and then number of scoops for the purpose of analysis. This would not be the order in which the team ran the experiment since it would have been randomized.

Row Number	Brand	Temperature	Kernels	Est. No Kernals	Kernels Left	Percent Left
1	A	400 degrees F	1 scoop	2300	125	5.43%
9	A	400 degrees F	1 scoop	2300	115	5.00%
17	A	400 degrees F	1 scoop	2300	118	5.13%
25	A	400 degrees F	1 scoop	2300	127	5.52%
2	A	400 degrees F	2 scoops	4600	298	6.48%
10	A	400 degrees F	2 scoops	4600	275	5.98%
18	A	400 degrees F	2 scoops	4600	298	6.48%
26	A	400 degrees F	2 scoops	4600	275	5.98%
3	A	600 degrees F	1 scoop	4600	98	2.13%
11	A	600 degrees F	1 scoop	4600	101	2.20%
19	A	600 degrees F	1 scoop	4600	99	2.15%
27	A	600 degrees F	1 scoop	4600	105	2.28%
4	A	600 degrees F	2 scoops	4600	187	4.07%
12	A	600 degrees F	2 scoops	4600	192	4.17%
20	A	600 degrees F	2 scoops	4600	175	3.80%
28	A	600 degrees F	2 scoops	4600	201	4.37%
5	B	400 degrees F	1 scoop	4600	145	3.15%
13	B	400 degrees F	1 scoop	4600	129	2.80%

21	B	400 degrees F	1 scoop	4600	138	3.00%
29	B	400 degrees F	1 scoop	4600	142	3.09%
6	B	400 degrees F	2 scoops	4600	324	7.04%
14	B	400 degrees F	2 scoops	4600	298	6.48%
22	B	400 degrees F	2 scoops	4600	307	6.67%
30	B	400 degrees F	2 scoops	4600	399	8.67%
7	B	600 degrees F	1 scoop	4600	109	2.37%
15	B	600 degrees F	1 scoop	4600	138	3.00%
23	B	600 degrees F	1 scoop	4600	109	2.37%
31	B	600 degrees F	1 scoop	4600	124	2.70%
8	B	600 degrees F	2 scoops	4600	202	4.39%
16	B	600 degrees F	2 scoops	4600	225	4.89%
24	B	600 degrees F	2 scoops	4600	198	4.30%
32	B	600 degrees F	2 scoops	4600	225	4.89%

The *effect* in a designed experiment is the measurement of the change in the result based on changing the levels of factors. The *main effect* describes the measurement of change in the result based on changes in a single factor. The main effect of each individual factor can be roughly calculated by comparing the average of the results at both the low and high end of the factor.

For example, the average percent left for Brand A is 4.45. The average left for Brand B is 4.36. The difference is 0.09. Immediately, it appears that there is not much of an effect for kernel-popping performance between the two brands of popcorn. Remember, though, that a statistical difference doesn't necessarily require a large numerical difference. Whether the difference is worth considering depends on other factors, such as the range of difference the team is hoping to record and the main effect of other factors in the experiment.

The same calculation can be completed for each of the factors in the experiment. The average percent of kernels left for runs with a temperature of 400 degrees F is approximately 5.43; the average percent left for runs with a temperature of 600 degrees F is 3.38. The main effect for this factor is larger than that for brand; the difference between the averages for 400 degrees and 600 degrees is 2.05.

The average percent of kernels left when the team started with one scoop was approximately 3.27. The percent left when starting with two scoops was approximately 5.54; the difference is 2.27.

Here, it's worth noting that the team made an assumption. The team in this example didn't count the number of kernels in each scoop before running the popcorn process. Instead, they made an assumption that a scoop of popcorn kernels held 2,300 kernals. The fact that not every scoop is going to have exactly 2,300 kernels *could* impact the outcome of the experiment. Why would a Six Sigma team make such an assumption if it might impact the experiment?

In chapter 29, the possible expense of designed experiments was mentioned. The time and resources required to run an experiment play a role in whether a team or Six Sigma expert chooses to use this tool for analysis. But time and resources can also play a role in how a team designs an experiment and what assumptions and steps they take in setting factors. In this example, running 64 separate batches of popcorn would be fairly time-consuming, but it would not likely be too time-consuming to be prohibitive. It would also not be too expensive with regard to use of resources, especially if the team handles the runs so that popcorn generated by the runs could be used in concession services.

However, if the team counted every single popcorn kernel that entered the process, two things might happen. First, the team could spend an inordinate amount of time counting what would ultimately be over 220,000 kernels of popcorn. Remember, the savings that might occur from this experiment is only estimated to be approximately $9,600 per year. There's probably not enough return on investment for the team to spend that much time counting kernels. Second, the team could actually impact the quality of the kernels with excessive handling that could occur during counting. That could reduce the efficacy with which the kernels popped, impacting the authenticity of the experiment. Six Sigma teams and experts should always try to avoid impacting the results of an experiment in ways that aren't directly related to setting the levels of various factors.

Sometimes, you might have to make assumptions when conducting experiments. When doing so, you should always try to handle measurements and assumptions in keeping with all of the information provided throughout this book. For example, a Six Sigma expert would never simply decide a scoop equals 2,300 kernels. Some ways you might arrive at this assumption include:

- Counting how many kernels are in several scoops and arriving at an average (remember that sample size and confidence levels would play a role in how confident you might be in this average)
- Weighing 50 separate kernels to get a mean average weight of one kernel of popcorn, and then weighing multiple scoops to see how many kernels, based on weight, might be included (again, sample size and confidence levels would play a role in how you might treat these assumptions.)

Understanding Interaction Plots

When plotted on a line graph the main effects from the above experiment look something like the image below. These images are generated in Excel, but Minitab and other statistical analysis software generate such graphs as part of the overall analysis when running designed experiments.

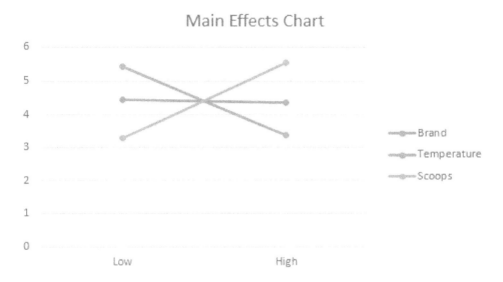

This image makes it easy to see: there isn't much of a main effect for the brand of popcorn, but there are major changes based on temperature and scoop. Since the team wants to reduce the percentage of unpopped kernels, it would seem that they would want to set temperature at a higher level but use only one scoop of popcorn at a time.

But the main effects graph doesn't always take into account any interaction between the factors, which is why it's important to consider interaction plots. You can use Minitab to generate interaction plots, or create your own in Excel. To create interaction plots in Excel, follow the steps below.

1. Import your data, with headers, into Excel. For this example, you can use the data grid provided for the popcorn scenario above.
2. Calculate the average of the result for each combination of two factors. In the popcorn scenario, you would calculate the average of the percent results for three sets of graph data.
   a. Graph 1 (Scoops * Temperature)

          i.   All rows where scoops equals 1 and temperature equals 400

          ii.   All rows where scoops equals 1 and temperature equals 600

          iii. All rows where scoops equals 2 and temperature equals 400

          iv. All rows where scoops equals 2 and temperature equals 600

  b. Graph 2 (Scoops * Brand)

          i.   All rows where scoops equals 1 and brand equals A

          ii.   All rows where scoops equals 1 and brand equals B

          iii. All rows where scoops equals 2 and brand equals A

          iv. All rows where scoops equals 2 and brand equals B

  c. Graph 3 (Brand * Temperature)

          i.   All rows where brand equals A and temperature equals 400

          ii.   All rows where brand equals A and temperature equals 600

          iii. All rows where brand equals B and temperature equals 400

          iv. All rows where brand equals B and temperature equals 600

3. Arrange the results into three small data tables that resemble the data table for the temperature and scoop set below.

Temperature	Scoops	Average
400	1	4.14
600	1	2.4
400	2	6.72
600	2	4.36

4. Use each of the small data tables to create a line graph.

  a. Select Insert > Charts > Line Charts > Multi line graph with markers

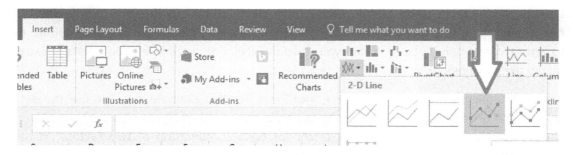

  b. Click on "Select Data."

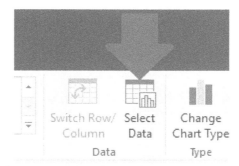

c. Click "Add" under "Legend Entries (Series)"

d. Enter "1 scoop" as the name for the first series. Select the averages for 1 scoop from your small data table into the range for "series values".

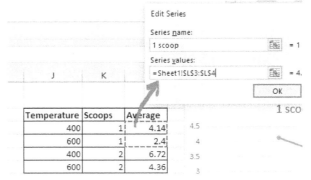

Temperature	Scoops	Average
400	1	4.14
600	1	2.4
400	2	6.72
600	2	4.36

e. Click OK.
f. Click Add again, and repeat step d to create a series for 2 scoops.
g. Click OK.
h. Click Edit under "Horizontal (Category) Axis Labels.

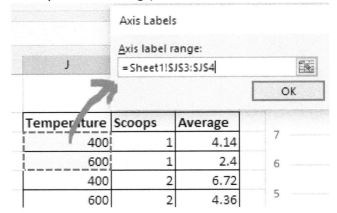

i. Select two cells that hold the names for the other factor settings (in this case, it is the temperature settings) into the Axis labels box.

Temperature	Scoops	Average
400	1	4.14
600	1	2.4
400	2	6.72
600	2	4.36

j. Click OK.

k. Click OK again.

l. Use Excel chart options to add a title and legends as desired so that your chart looks something like the image below.

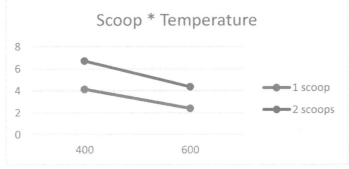

5. Repeat all of the steps in 4 above for each set of paired data elements. The results of all three are show below.

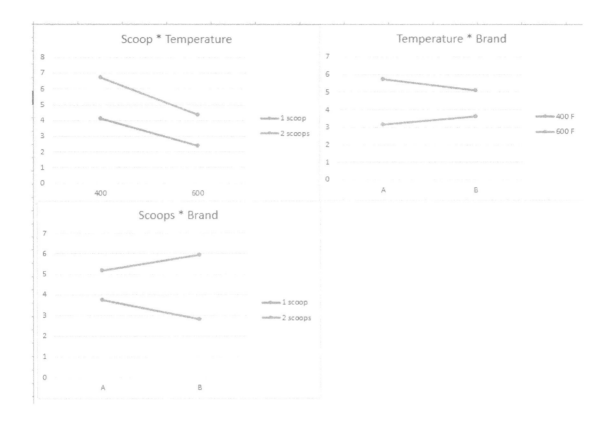

These are the same style of interaction plots that are displayed by Minitab if you run DOE analysis in that program, and they show some interaction that was not apparent when simply considering the raw data or even the main effects plots.

Analysis of the first interaction plot shows what the Six Sigma team might already have gleaned from the main effects. The lowest leftover kernel percentage seems to come when you combine 1 scoop of kernels and the higher temperature setting. This plot doesn't show an interaction – the lines are almost parallel. Regardless of the number of scoops you start with, the highest temperature yields the least waste. Regardless of the temperature setting, the lowest scoop start yields the least waste.

The second graph, to the right of the first, shows the interaction between brand and temperature. Remember, the main effects analysis seemed to indicate that the choice of brand of popcorn was not important. When brand is analyzed with another factor, though, this doesn't seem to hold true. In this graph, you can see that brand *does* make a difference in how the change in temperature setting works. At 600 degrees F, brand A performs better than brand B. At 400 degrees F, brand B performs better. Even though all of this is true, both brands generate less waste at the higher temperature setting when compared to their own performance at the lower temperature setting.

The third graph also shows some interaction between brand and number of scoops. Brand B performs better at the lower scoop setting than brand A, and the reverse is true at the higher scoop setting. Again, both brands generate less waste at the lower scoop setting than when compared to their own performance at the higher scoop setting.

Based on all of the information above, the Six Sigma team is likely to choose to start the popcorn process with 1 scoop and use the 600 degree F temperature setting. Choosing a brand of popcorn, however, is a little tougher. Opting for brand A saves approximately 0.5 percent of waste over brand B when considering the interaction with temperature. However, brand B saves almost 1 percent of waste over brand A when considering the interaction with number of scoops.

Given all of the information and analysis in this experiment, a Six Sigma team might either say brand is not a big enough factor (so the concession stand could choose brand based on other factors, such as cost) or recommend that brand B be purchased when it is equal to or less than brand A in price because brand B is associated with the highest percentage of waste savings. If brand B is more expensive than brand A, the small waste savings associated with brand B would likely be mitigated, though, making brand A the better choice. This is a good illustration of how other data should play a role in decision making – a designed experiment doesn't exist in a vacuum.

This was a basic analysis to help you understand how interactions work. Minitab and other statistical analysis software runs all of this analysis automatically, reducing the workload on the Six Sigma expert. Most such software will also consider all possible interactions and present the factors with the most impact in the analysis. If you have a 2k factorial experiment with three factors, each with two settings, and those factors are A, B, and C, you could have the following possible effects on the result:

- A (the impact of changing only A)
- B (the impact of changing only B)
- C (the impact of changing only C)
- AB (the interaction of A and B)

- AC (the interaction of A and C)
- BC (the interaction of B and C)
- ABC (the interaction of all three factors)

Adding additional factors makes this analysis increasingly complicated; adding additional levels at each factor does the same thing.

2k Factorials Versus Multi-Level Factorials

So far in this unit, all the DOE scenarios used have been two-level (or 2k) factorial experiments. In each experiment, Six Sigma teams chose to set the levels of each factor at no more than two – typically at a high and a low.

Why would a Six Sigma team choose to do this? Wouldn't an experiment with multiple factor levels provide more information for the team? In the popcorn example, why would the team choose the high and low temperature settings? What happens when the temperature is set at 500 degrees F? What about 425, 450, 475, etc.? How does the team know that 400 and 600 are the two most optimal settings?

The truth is that the team *doesn't* know those are the most optimal settings, but adding multiple levels for one or more factors adds to the number of runs that have to be completed. One replication of the popcorn experiment previously described required eight runs. Just adding one more factor for temperature – 500 degrees F – adds four runs to the experiment.

Row Number	Brand	Temperature	Kernels
1	A	400 degrees F	1 scoop
2	A	400 degrees F	2 scoops
3	A	500 degrees F	1 scoop
4	A	500 degrees F	2 scoops
5	A	600 degrees F	1 scoop
6	A	600 degrees F	2 scoops
7	B	400 degrees F	1 scoop
8	B	400 degrees F	2 scoops
9	B	500 degrees F	1 scoop
10	B	500 degrees F	2 scoops
11	B	600 degrees F	1 scoop
12	B	600 degrees F	2 scoops

Now, instead of 32 runs for a designed experiment that includes four replications, the team would have 48 runs. That's 16 additional runs where the time and resources of the team and the company are being used. If the team wanted to also test temperature settings of 425, 450, 475, 525, 550, and 575, that would entail 24 additional runs for every replication, or 96 additional runs for four replications. If the team also decided to add additional levels to other factors, such as a third brand or an attempt at 1.5 scoops of kernels, the team could be looking at an experiment with hundreds of runs required to achieve the appropriate sample size.

For these reasons, 2k factorial experiments are typically the most commonly used among Six Sigma experts. Minitab lets you run these experiments with up to 15 different factors, providing a powerful ability to analyze processes. Minitab *also* lets you run experiments with more than two factors.

Multi-factor experiments are handled in much the same way 2k factorial experiments are handled. Obviously, if you are handling analysis manually, you'll want to limit the levels and factors as much as possible. Minitab removes the need to limit data because of analysis requirements – as long as the team can define a need for including factors and levels in an experiment *and has been given permission and access* to use the resources needed to run an appropriate number of replications for accurate statistical conclusions, then Six Sigma teams can certainly run multi-level factor experiments.

Tips for Creating Successful Designed Experiments

As with almost any other tool in the Six Sigma arena, ANOVA and design of experiment are only as strong as the foundation you create each time you run an experiment and associated analysis. In addition to the instructions and information in this unit, this section provides some tips for successful experiments and analysis

Take Time to Think About the Y, or Response, of Your Experiment

In chapter 29, defining the Y, or response, of the experiment is one of the first steps in the procedure for conducting a DOE. Remember, a good response is related to the overall DMAIC process or the overall need associated with the experiment. The team must know what it wants to address and whether the response it is considering is a good measurement.

Often, training materials or tips for DOE in Six Sigma provide two pieces of common advice:

- Ensure that the Y is continuous for the purpose of later analysis
- Take the Y from brainstorming or other work done in previous phases – specifically from Define or Analyze tools such as fishbone diagrams.

While those are both pieces of good advice, Six Sigma teams shouldn't be afraid to think outside of the box when it comes to the response for an experiment. Ultimately, the response should be something that will help you truly understand what you set out to understand at the beginning of the experiment. In the popcorn experiment used as an example in this chapter, the team could have chosen any number of responses. Possible responses from the popcorn popping process might include how long the overall process took, how many kernels were popped, how many orders were generated by each process, or customer satisfaction with the taste of the popcorn that was popped. But the team wasn't seeking answers to questions related to production efficiency or product performance with this particular experiment. The team was asking questions about waste of raw materials, and the amount of unpopped kernels let the team know exactly how much waste was created in the process.

When considering an appropriate Y for your experiment, don't get too caught up in the current metrics a process or department uses to measure success. The concession stand probably never considered unpopped popcorn before this experiment – it likely used number of sales or sales dollars as a metric for success. If you're having trouble identifying a Y that you think will help answer the questions the team is asking, consider conducting a brand new brainstorming exercise focused solely on coming up with an appropriate result type.

Plan Ahead, and Keep Excellent Documents

You've seen throughout this unit that experiments and ANOVA analysis can become complex quickly. First, you have to validate all assumptions, select the right method, and choose an appropriate sample size. Then, you have to run the experiments and record all the data. Finally, you have to conduct the analysis. At any point in the process, you might introduce an error or create confusion. Planning and documentation are critical to keeping this from happening, and they can be equally important when you present the conclusions of your experiment to others. Some specific areas where documentation is especially important are highlighted below.

- Take notes when working through either the ANOVA steps in chapter 28 or the DOE steps from chapter 29. You *will* forget or confuse some number or element of the analysis at some point and need to refer back to the notes. Consider recording:
  - Your reasons for choosing a specific method or test.
  - Lists of responses, inputs, factors, and levels with a reason for choosing each. You might need this information to justify the number of runs in your experiment.
  - The process for choosing sample size and any data or assumptions used in that process.
- Record any outside assumptions made regarding the experiment, the components of the experiment, or the result. You might need to review these assumptions or data linked to the assumptions to rule out outliers or understand what might seem like otherwise unexplainable experiment behavior.
- Document any instructions or information provided to any operator within the experiment. Your sponsor or other decision-makers will likely want to understand

exactly how the experiment was performed before they make decisions based off of the results.

- The outcome of any measurement system analysis, particularly as it relates to the confidence in experiment outcomes.

Account for Confidence Levels

In any type of statistical analysis, testing, or DOE, the Six Sigma expert is always mindful of confidence levels. *There is always some chance of an incorrect conclusion* – the alpha and beta errors covered in the chapters on hypothesis testing tell us this. More accurate data, larger sample sizes, and choosing the right test or experiment help reduce the chance of these errors, but decision-makers *do need to know* how big of a possibility such an error might be.

When reporting the outcome of a designed experiment, make sure you take all confidence levels into account. The confidence interval for the actual experiment is not always the only relevant consideration. Did you make assumptions based on previous analysis to help you set up the experiment? What were the confidence intervals associated with those analyses? Consider the popcorn example again: how sure is the team that each scoop holds an average of 2,300 kernels? What is the variation of that measurement? The answers to both of these questions contribute to the accuracy of the experiment analysis.

If enterprise leadership or a Six Sigma team will be basing resource-heavy or resource-contingent decisions on DOE analysis, then those decision-makers must know how confident the Six Sigma expert is in what he or she is presenting. You should always do everything you can statistically to increase confidence – such as validating data and assumptions and choosing proper sample sizes – but you should never falsely inflate confidence in a conclusion to encourage leadership to support a certain decision.

Use Multiple Analysis and Experiments Together

You should not – and often cannot – do everything you want to do in a single experiment. If there are 25 possible factors, do you really want them all in a single, unwieldy experiment that could become costly to run and impossible to control? Often, when you are considering running an experiment with so many factors, you are actually trying to integrate multiple experiments into one. Stop and consider the possibility that you are comparing apples and oranges in an experiment when you really should run separate experiments for various product types or processes.

If you are actually working on a single product type or process, consider that you might need to run experiments serially. You might need to find out a certain piece of information or narrow down interactions and factors to better set up other experiments with new factors and level settings. For example, the Six Sigma team in the popcorn example isn't done with their project just because they've found out how to best pop the popcorn to reduce waste. There are other ways to increase profits. Since brand wasn't a major factor in the waste-related experiment, the team might conduct a second experiment to find out which brand customers like more and whether increased customer satisfaction drives increased sales.

Designed experiments are one of the more challenging aspects of Six Sigma to learn because exact rules don't always exist. Six Sigma teams can set up experiments in a variety of ways, which increases the flexibility of the tool but can also make it difficult to know exactly how to proceed. This is an area where experience pays off, so the more experiments and analysis you handle, the better you are at setting up DOE. This is also a reason it's a good idea to work with a more experienced Six Sigma expert or a Master Black Belt, who can act as a sounding board for your ideas and guide you in creating the best possible experiment.

UNIT 8: MINITAB

CHAPTER 31:
BRAINSTORMING AND PROCESS
IMPROVEMENT TOOLS

Throughout this book, you've learned to deploy a number of Six Sigma tools, including brainstorming tools. Some tools you've already learned to use include the SIPOC diagram, the in-and-out-of-the-box method, and the 5 Whys brainstorming model. This chapter provides an appendix of additional tools and methods that can be integrated into meetings for DMAIC projects or simply to help a team or department gain insight into a problem or process.

As a Six Sigma expert or process leader, having access to multiple process improvement and brainstorming tools is helpful. While all of the tools previously covered in this book are extremely powerful when used correctly, if you use the same approach all the time, you risk coming up with the same solutions and hitting the same obstacles. Sometimes, switching the brainstorming method or tool can help break a team out of a rut, encouraging a different perspective or sparking different discussions or debates.

Activity Network Diagram

An activity network diagram helps a Six Sigma team chart either the activity involved in a project or the activity involved in a process. The point of the diagram is to understand sequential and time relationships within a project or process. Which items come first? Which activities happen at the same time?

When applied to an overall project, the activity network diagram helps teams and project leaders understand what resources will be required at each point during the project. It can also provide project managers with the ability to better estimate project timelines.

When applied to a process, the diagram helps teams identify all the activities in a process. It also helps teams understand which activities are up- and downstream and what activities happen together. Once teams know these things, they can begin to discuss whether the current sequence is the most effective sequence and understand how changes to one activity might impact the outcome of another.

An activity network diagram is created by following these steps:

1. List all of the activities involved in the process. Teams can draw from their own knowledge or from previous tools used by the group such as SIPOC or process maps.
2. Write each activity on a separate card or sticky note.
3. Place activities in order from left to right. Activities that are simultaneous are placed in a vertical line in one horizontal space on the diagram.
4. Write an estimated time for each activity.
5. Draw a critical path line through each step. Where vertical (simultaneous steps) are noted, the line goes through the step that takes the longest.
6. Add up the times listed along the critical path to get an idea of the overall estimate of time for the process. In the example below, the total time for the critical path in minutes is: 5 + 2 + 12 + 9 + 10 + 5, or 43.

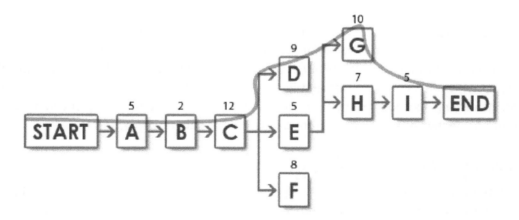

Affinity Diagram

An affinity diagram is a tool that lets the team list and group a large number of ideas quickly and systematically. Affinity diagrams work well when you are first approaching a process or idea because they help you sort through all of the associated ideas to identify some of the main points the team will need to consider throughout the DMAIC project. Affinity diagrams are also a good tool to use if you have a larger-than-normal brainstorming group, which means they can be used in department meetings or in DMAIC meetings that include subject matter experts that aren't part of the core team. The goal of an affinity diagram is to help the group understand the relationships between inputs, outputs, products, services, workers, customers, processes, and ideas – or any subgroup of those things.

To conduct an affinity diagram, you'll need a large workspace, such as a flat table, wall, or floor. You can also use a white board, and if you are working with a group across multiple locations, you *can* conduct the exercise via web conferencing software, though, as with most brainstorming tools, this would not be optimal.

An affinity diagram session is conducted by following the steps outlined below.

1. Provide everyone in the session with small notecards, sticky notes, or pieces of paper.
2. Begin brainstorming ideas about the process or problem. Ideas at this stage are very loose – encourage the team to write down anything that comes to mind. The ideas should be short – one or two words or very simple sentences, otherwise the team might be recording two ideas on one note card. Encourage participants to record inputs, outputs, challenges, obstacles, customers, people, processes, actions, etc. If you are attempting to address a specific question, that question should drive the type of things recorded on the notes.
3. Brainstorming can occur individually for a few minutes or as a group. Individual brainstorming is likely to present a number of ideas that aren't influenced by others' input, which can be valuable.
4. After brainstorming, have everyone spread the cards on a floor or table, or stick the notes to a wall or white board.
5. Work as a team to identify ideas that are related. Place those ideas next to each other. Consider working as a team without talking during this step to shift ideas around the diagram for a few minutes until most ideas are lumped into larger groups.
6. If one idea could belong to more than one group, make multiple cards with that idea on it so it can be put with multiple groups.
7. It's okay to have groups of one when an idea doesn't seem to fit with anything else.
8. Once all the notes are grouped, hold a discussion time with the team to answer questions:
   a. Are there patterns in the ideas?

    b. Does the diagram spark any new ideas or clarify ideas or relationships?

    c. Do ideas fall into natural sequences for processes or timelines?

    d. Do ideas fall into natural groups of causes?

9. The questions asked and answered will depend on what process or overall question the team is addressing with the affinity diagram.

10. Title each group of ideas by pulling out what seems to be the *main* idea of that grouping.

11. Record the diagram for use later. You can have someone copy it onto a piece of paper, convert it to a computer diagram, or simply snap a digital picture for storing with other team documents.

Interrelationship Diagram

An interrelationship diagram is similar to a fishbone diagram in purpose. The goal of an interrelationship brainstorm is to understand what causes and effects are primary with regard to a problem or process. The outcome of the brainstorming session is a visual depiction that makes it easy to see which items are likely causing most of the effects and which effects are tied to which causes within a process.

As a Six Sigma expert you can deploy this exercise when teams don't fully understand the relationships between causes and effects within a process, can't agree on which causal factors might be primary within the process, or are just beginning to understand the process and need more overall knowledge before moving into a fishbone diagram process or measuring processes.

Conduct an interrelationship diagram session by following these steps:

1. Define the problem on a white board, piece of paper, or sticky note.

2. On other sticky notes, write brainstormed ideas about the problem. Specifically, what might have caused the problem? What might be causing things that cause the problems? What other issues might the problem cause?

3. Place the notes all around the problem on the white board.

4. As a team, consider each idea on each note. Decide whether that idea is somehow related to any other idea on the board.

5. If the idea is related in such a way to a second idea that it could cause, or be an input or factor, for another idea, draw an arrow going from the first idea to the one it might be an input, factor, or cause for.

6. If the idea is related in such a way to a second idea that it might be an effect or output from the second idea, draw an arrow going from the second idea to the first idea.

7. If necessary, draw multiple arrows to and from each idea.

8. At the end of the exercise, count the number of arrows coming in to the idea. Write those numbers in one color on each sticky note.

9. Count the number of arrows going out from each idea. Write those numbers in another color on each sticky note.

10. The notes with the highest total count – when you add those two numbers – are likely the key factors in the process or problem. You might also be able to identify key inputs (causes) and outputs (effects) based on the number of arrows coming in or out of various notes.

Force Field Analysis

A lot of Six Sigma education has to do with statistical analysis, but the methodology doesn't work if Six Sigma leaders are too caught up in the numbers and data to realize that people play an important role in every process, every project, and every improvement initiative. One way Six Sigma teams can understand how people and other factors might support or challenge a process, project, or change is to conduct a force field analysis.

A force field analysis lets teams understand how factors surrounding a process might support (or drive) change or challenge (or restrain) change. In addition to people, factors might include culture, materials and resources requirements, customers, needs, machines, rules, and regulations. Sometimes, Six Sigma teams can work to change some of these factors to create additional support for an improvement. In other cases, the team cannot change restraining factors, but must be aware of those factors as they move forward with improvement initiatives.

Create a force field analysis by following these steps:

1. Start with the definition of the problem. This can be either the overall problem statement or a more detailed and smaller problem within the scope of the entire project.

2. Write the problem on the top of a white board or large piece of paper.

3. Draw a bold line down the center of the page. This line represents the status quo – the current state of the process.

4. Define the solution or desired state. If the team is just starting out, the desired state might be the overall project objective statement. If the team is working to solve a specific problem within the project scope, it might have a solution in mind.
5. Write the solution or objective statement at the bottom of the white board or page.
6. Brainstorm driving factors – factors that would move the status quo "forward".
7. Write driving factors on the left side of the status quo line.
8. Brainstorm restraining factors – factors that would keep the status quo as is.
9. Write restraining factors on the right side of the status quo line.
10. Draw an arrow under each driving factor toward the status quo line; the length of each arrow represents the perceived strength of the driving factor. For example, the sponsor who holds financial decisions is on board with the solution. This would be a strong driving factor and might get a long arrow.
11. Draw an arrow under each restraining factor back toward the status quo line. The length of each arrow represents the perceived strength of the challenge. If the sponsor *wasn't* on board with the solution yet, this would be a fairly strong restraining factor.

Once the diagram is completed, the team can see quickly:

- Whether there are more driving factors or restraining factors
- Whether driving factors or restraining factors have more "weight" (based on the number of longer arrows on either side)
- Which factors are strongest

The team can then discuss whether any of the restraining factors can be weakened or converted to driving factors, which can be helpful in paving the way for smoother solution implementation.

Responsibility Chart

A responsibility chart helps Six Sigma teams identify which people, teams, or departments have various types of connections or responsibilities to a process. The reason for understanding such relationships is for Six Sigma teams to understand who actually acts on or within the process, who needs to be informed about the process, who is ultimately accountable for the process, and who might offer valuable information about the process. Often, these various people can be identified with a charting process known as RACI, which stands for:

- **R**esponsible – the person or team who actually does the work (an employee who is responsible for collecting money at the cash register)
- **A**ccountable – the person in charge of the work (the supervisor of that shift)
- **C**onsult – any person involved in steps prior to the activity that should be kept in the loop (the sales person on the floor, the bookkeeper who creates starting drawers each morning)
- **I**nform – any person involved in steps after the activity that should be kept in the loop (the bookkeeper, who also balances the drawers at the end of shifts)

Create a RACI matrix for your project or process by following these steps:

1. Create a list of all activities and decisions that are part of the process. Teams can get this information from previous brainstorming sessions or tools such as process maps.
2. List those items down the right side of a page or white board.
3. Create a list of all functional roles associated with a process. List those as the row headers across the top of the page or white board.
   a. Activities and decisions might include items such as:
      i. Measure lumber.
      ii. Cut lumber
      iii. Review lumber.
      iv. Decide if lumber is the right length.
   b. Functional roles might include:
      i. Lumber measurer
      ii. Lumber cutter
      iii. Auditor
      iv. Lumber packer
4. For each functional role and activity, decide if the role is responsible or accountable for each activity listed or if the role should be consulted or informed. In the example below, you can see that the cutter is responsible for measuring and cutting, the auditor is responsible for reviewing and deciding whether the lumber is correct, and the supervisor is accountable for all of it. The packer needs to be informed about whether the lumber is correct so he or she knows whether to pack it.

	Cutter	Auditor	Packer	Supervisor
Measure lumber	R			A
Cut lumber	R			A
Review lumber		R		A
Decide if lumber is correct		R	I	A

Nominal Group Technique

A Six Sigma leader has to develop a good understanding of group dynamics. Not every project team will work the same, and sometimes Six Sigma leaders face interpersonal challenges within the group environment. Some of these challenges can derail brainstorming efforts because of personality clashes. If you have one or more quiet or shy individuals, for example, you might not be getting all of their perspective. Even if everyone on the team is fairly vocal, if there is a natural leader, bully, or more outspoken member, they might be getting more ideas in than others. On way you can reduce the impact of personality on brainstorming sessions is to use the nominal group technique to encourage input from everyone.

1. Provide everyone with pen and paper.
2. Being with a question, topic, or concern that is relevant to the project or the phase you are in.
3. Take 5 to 10 minutes and invite everyone to brainstorm their own ideas. Make sure you note that at this stage, there are no bad or wrong ideas.
4. Once everyone is finished writing, go around the table, having each person state an idea from their list. Each person should only state one idea at a time before letting others have a turn.
5. Write the ideas down on a white board or flipchart, but don't discuss the ideas at this time.
6. As ideas are shared, individuals can pass if every idea on their list has been shared by themselves or someone else.
7. Once all ideas are listed, lead a discussion based on the ideas or use the ideas to fuel a secondary activity, such as an affinity diagram or fishbone diagram.

Nominal group technique is also a good tool to use if the team is stuck or is dealing with a particularly difficult concept. The technique helps break thoughts out of ruts in two ways. First, it removes some of the fear individuals can have at sharing half-formed verbal ideas. Team members who are writing ideas down can think through those ideas a bit more and might feel more comfortable listing them later. Second, the act of writing itself is proven to break down creative and thought barriers, and can help the team members brainstorm more ideas.

Check Sheets

Check sheets as a tool have been touched on multiple times in this book, but it's worth mentioning them again in a more formal way. Check sheets are simple tools that can be extremely powerful for managing teams, people, processes, and data. The reason check sheets are so powerful is that they require an action, and when you require a physical and recordable action, personal responsibility for the action involved is usually higher.

A check sheet is any templated form used to record information. The information you record can be a specific piece of data, but it might also be a notation that a routine check, analysis, or certain other task was performed. The purpose of a check sheet, beyond formalizing and mandating an action, is to streamline the process of reporting the action.

Consider the check sheets often seen in public restroom facilities in restaurants or stores. These check sheets are usually on the door or wall near the door. Each hour, a staff member initials and dates the check sheet to indicate that the restroom was checked. By requiring the staff member to initial and date the check sheet, companies make it more likely staff will check the restroom at appropriate times. The initial and date indicates that staff ensured the facilities were stocked, clean, and in working order.

This premise can be used in a variety of processes to ensure data collection or certain tasks are performed at the right time by the right person. Check sheets can also be used to manage tasks within a project environment – a Six Sigma leader might provide check sheets to each subject matter expert during a project meeting so that each person knows what needs to be done before the next meeting and has a physical requirement for recording process.

As a Six Sigma expert, it's important to understand when the simplest solution fits your need, and the checklist is often that solution.

SWOT Analysis

SWOT analysis is a common business brainstorming technique that helps teams understand high-level strengths, weaknesses, opportunities, and threats (challenges) for a project, improvement, or process. SWOT analyses can be conducted anytime during the DMAIC phases, but are especially helpful during define phases or anytime storming has occurred and the team needs something fast and easy to help them get back on track.

Some people break up SWOT analysis into a visual depiction, drawing a large grid of four squares, one each to represent Strengths, Weaknesses, Opportunities, and Threats. This can be helpful if you have a project group that is especially visual, but is not necessary. The point of a SWOT analysis is really to answer some fundamental questions through brainstorming.

1. Strengths: What about the process works? What is done better, faster, cheaper, more unique?
2. Weaknesses: What doesn't work? What are the disadvantages, problems, losses, errors, or customer dissatisfaction points?
3. Opportunities: What can be fixed? What are some easy-to-fix issues? Where are improvements needed?
4. Threats: What obstacles exist to improvement? What risks will the project team face? What resource challenges might there be?

Starburst Brainstorming

Starburst brainstorming is a method for generating a series of questions about a problem, process, or idea. Those questions can later be used in defining processes, problems, products, or other ideas. On the surface, the starburst tool is similar to the 5 Whys, but instead of answering each question and then asking another question, the team simply comes up with as many various questions as possible.

Conduct a starburst brainstorming session by following these steps:

1. Draw a six-pointed star on a white board or large piece of paper.
2. On each of the points, write one of the following: Who, What, Where, When, Why, How.
3. At the center of the star, write one or a few words describing the central idea.
4. For each point of the star, brainstorm questions about the center that start with the word at that point. For example, a team might be working to create more customer

satisfaction regarding a food-service product. For the purpose of this example, imagine a team working to solve a problem of customer satisfaction with an individually-wrapped snack cake that is typically sold in convenience stores and newsstands.

    a. The center of the star might simply state "ABC Snack Cake."

    b. Questions at the "Who?" tip of the star might include:

        i. Who is the primary customer for the snack cake?

        ii. Who is most likely to eat the snack cake?

        iii. Who will buy the snack cake? (not always the same person who eats it)

        iv. Who will sell the snack cake?

        v. Who will market the snack cake?

        vi. Who will make the snack cake?

    c. "What?" questions might include:

        i. What flavor or flavors should the snack cake be?

        ii. What packaging is best for the snack cake?

        iii. What ingredients are important to the snack cake?

    d. Go through all the points of the star, asking questions that match the word at that point. Generate as many questions as you can within a set period of time. It's a good idea to set a time limit for question generation for each point of the star – up to five minutes is usually good – to keep questions from become too detailed or out of scope for the problem, process, or idea you are dealing with.

The purpose of the starburst session is not to answer the questions you come up with, and that can be a challenge for Six Sigma leaders. Team members will naturally want to move immediately from one question to an answer, which can derail the process and result in a discussion that is not productive or ranges out of scope. Direct team members back to asking questions for the duration of the brainstorming session. Those questions can later be compiled and used when conducting other exercises, such as SIPOCs or process maps. The questions help ensure details aren't left out and that all possible queries are considered.

Role-Play or Figuring Brainstorming

One of the biggest challenges with brainstorming as a Six Sigma team is that, after a few meetings or as the team gets deeper into the DMAIC process, the team can become stuck on certain beliefs and ideas. Once certain ideas are proposed, it can be hard to "get away" from them. Teams might find themselves circling back around to the same ideas repeatedly. Sometimes, this means the team is on the right track and the iteration of the same concepts throughout the DMAIC process and brainstorming is confirmation that those are the right things to be thinking about. Other times, however, it can be a sign that the team is stuck.

It can be difficult at times to tell the difference, and Six Sigma experts do have to rely on analysis and data to help make a decision about whether the team is going in the right direction or not. If a Six Sigma expert believes that the team is *not* going in the right direction, he or she can try figuring brainstorming to try to get team members to think more creatively or from a different perspective about the issue.

Figuring brainstorming, or role-play, can be combined with many of the other tools in this chapter to generate new thoughts. Choose one of the simpler brainstorming exercises or simply ask a question and brainstorm responses. However, ask participants to brainstorm as someone other than themselves. They might brainstorm as the CEO of the company. They might brainstorm as a person working on the product line. The might brainstorm as Johnny Depp, the President of the United States, or Cookie Monster.

Here is where Six Sigma leadership is important. Is the group likely to respond better to a silly situation that cracks some of the boundaries they've built, or are they more likely to respond to a serious role-playing situation? This helps you decide whether to go with Cookie Monster or CEO.

One challenge with this type of team activity is balancing the stress release and creativity of the silly activity with a true need to be productive. If things are devolving into pure fun without productivity, then the Six Sigma team leader should wrap up the activity and move on with another. The time is usually not wasted, though – breaking away from the seriousness of the project for a few minutes is often itself enough to help teams think more creatively.

Brainwriting

Brainwriting is somewhat like the nominal group technique. In fact, nominal group technique is actually a form of brainwriting. Reasons you might incorporate this type of brainstorming in your meetings include increasing input from quieter or more reserved team members, reducing how only one or two vocal members impact the outcome of a meeting, and generating ideas that other brainstorming methods are not generating. Remember, the physical act of writing itself contributes to thought processes and can help the brain make connections between ideas that it is less likely to make during verbal brainstorming.

There are numerous types of brainwriting exercises that you can use in a team environment. Nominal group technique is one, and this section provides some other options.

The Pool Brainwriting Method

The pool method can help generate different ideas because participants build off of each other's ideas without the pressure of a fast verbal brainstorming sessions. Each participant gets a piece of paper and a pen. You can print the pages with a question or idea at the top or state the prompt for the session once everyone is ready. Each person writes two to three ideas on their paper and then places the paper back in the center of the table. Each person takes another paper from the pool (one that already has ideas written on it from someone else) and adds two to three more ideas. Papers are written on, replaced, and repulled repeatedly. There aren't timed rounds – each participant moves at his or her own pace and pulls from the center pool as pages become available.

At the end of the exercise, which lasts a predetermined time, the team records all ideas on a single page or white board and categorizes and sorts them appropriately. The length of time the session might last depends on the number of people involved and how complex the problem is. A good time limit for this exercise is typically between 10 and 30 minutes, and the exercise works best with four to eight participants.

The Card Brainwriting Method

Often, the goal of brainwriting is to build upon each other's ideas, which is accomplished by returning and pulling pages from the pool in the above method. The card method uses a similar approach but records each idea on a separate card for more flexibility during the analysis or categorization portion of the exercise.

The card method works well with groups of four to eight people. Begin by providing each participant with a stack of index cards and a pen. Pose a question or problem – it sometimes helps to write this question or problem on a whiteboard or large piece of paper so participants can reference it throughout the exercise.

Participants start by brainstorming their own ideas by writing each idea on one of the cards. After an idea is written down, the card containing that idea is passed to the left. When a participant has written as many ideas as he or she can think of quickly on cards, they begin picking up and reading the cards passed from the person on their right.

If a participant can add anything to the idea on any card they read, they write the new or extended idea on a new card and attach it to the existing card. Those cards are then passed to the left. If the participant can't add anything new, then the cards are simply passed to the left.

When a participant receives his or her own cards back, then they keep them. The brainwriting session ends when all participants have received all of their original cards back, hopefully now with attachments of other ideas. The moderator then picks up the cards and the cards can be used in further brainstorming and idea organization. You could use the cards to create an affinity diagram, for example.

The card brainwriting method is also a good way to start a group effort to create a process map. Instead of writing ideas for solutions to a problem, the team writes down individual parts of a process — including activities, inputs, and outputs. Those pieces can then form the bare bones of a process map, which can be added on to by the team.

Brainstorming Alone

This chapter, and most of the information throughout this book, concentrates on activities and methods to be used in a group environment. This is because facing and solving problems as a team is a fundamental part of the Six Sigma methodology. Brainstorming as a team is critical because it presents multiple perspectives and lets individual team members build thoughts on top of ideas generated by others. However, it's not always possible or even a good idea to brainstorm about every single issue as a group.

Sometimes, the Six Sigma leader must consider an issue or idea before presenting it to the group. Other times, the issue about which you want to brainstorm isn't something that is appropriate to share with the entire team. Remember, if you are in a Black Belt or project leadership role, you might have access to information that is sensitive or confidential. While Six Sigma projects and process improvement work best in transparent environments, it's simply not always possible for every member of a Six Sigma team to know all of the information about a process. As a Six Sigma leader, you should work to create a team that you feel is capable of dealing appropriately with sensitive information, but you should also be prepared to facilitate a team in unique situations when some information sharing is limited. This can be especially true in industries such as healthcare or finance, where the data itself is sensitive.

Other reasons exist for brainstorming on your own as a project leader or Six Sigma expert. Your team might be floundering due to storming or scope creep, two challenges covered in earlier units. You might want to come into a team meeting prepared with some ideas or understanding of the problem -- although you should always be careful not to lead others too closely with your own ideas because you might reduce the efficacy of the team. As a Six Sigma expert, you might also face your own problems or information needs outside of a team environment.

Whatever the reason, you can use abbreviated forms of many of the brainstorming tools in this chapter to brainstorm alone. Tools such as starburst brainstorming, SWOT analysis, and force field analysis can be conducted as an individual. For example, if your team seems to be stuck in a certain DMAIC phase, you can use the force field analysis to help you identify what problems or people are holding you in place. As a Six Sigma leader, you can then use that information to address the issues so the team can move forward with a project.

Brainstorming is a powerful tool whether you use it as a team or as an individual. It takes practice to be able to best implement brainstorming methods within various group dynamics, but when you follow the basic guidelines in this chapter, you almost always have at least some positive result from a brainstorming session.

CHAPTER 32:
PROCESS MAPS

Process maps are a vital part of many Six Sigma projects. Process maps are valuable tools in all stages of a DMAIC project. While good process maps can take a long time to create, they can be reused throughout the project and after the project for a variety of purposes.

Why Create Process Maps

Process maps are not just simple flow charts, although teams might choose to create a flow chart as the process map for a specific project or phase. Process maps are visual depictions of a process and usually include all of the activities and decisions within the process. They can show various levels of process, and we'll look at the difference between high-level organizational process maps and detailed process maps in this chapter.

Teams create process maps for a variety of reasons. First, a process map is a good place to start when teams are trying to understand the overall process. If a visual depiction of the process doesn't already exist, the team can work with subject matter experts to create such a depiction. The act of creating the map is actually valuable in itself because it lets the team ask many questions about the process and explore the process deeply in order to convert knowledge gained into a working diagram.

During the Measure phase, process maps can help teams understand what inputs or outputs should be measured, and when and where during a process data can or should be acquired. Process maps are also helpful during the Analyze phase, because visual depictions of the flow of a process often make it easier to see where rework is occurring or where bottlenecks are possible.

Process maps also let the team visualize a future state for a process. A Six Sigma team might begin with a current-state process map during the Define phase of a project and create a desired-state map in the Analyze or Improve phase. Side-by-side comparisons of the current- and future-state maps let teams see exactly what changes need to be made, ensure that all current-state functionality is addressed in the updated process, and double check that all challenges are solved by the new process. Process maps can also help teams see whether they might be creating new challenges, such as rework loops or bottlenecks within an updated process.

Finally, process maps in their various forms are valuable documentation for a Six Sigma team and for an organization as a whole. Six Sigma teams can use all or part of process maps they create in tollgate and other presentations to ensure decision makers, sponsors, and auxiliary staff understand the process before moving forward with any aspect of the project or with making decisions about the project or process. Organizations can use process maps in training documents or as a guide for non-Six Sigma staff who need to understand new processes or changes to existing processes.

Two Types of Process Maps

This chapter will cover two basic types of process maps. The first is the flow chart, which presents a view of the process that typically flows down the page. Flow charts usually give the overview of a process or detail a specific part of the process. When multiple flow charts are used for detailed pieces of a process, they can reference each other to provide an entire description of a process.

The second type of process map covered in this chapter is the swimlane process map, which usually provides a left-to-right and top-to-bottom visual of the process. A swimlane process map breaks up the process into different sectors, often by who is responsible for the work, when work occurs, or what type of work is being performed. At a glance, teams can not only see the flow of the work through the process, but can see who or what is responsible for each step.

Process Map Symbols

Many people attempt to create process maps using various shapes, connecting them with arrows to show the flow of work. That *is* the basic idea of a flow chart or process map, but each type of shape actually says something specific about the information presented inside or near it. Anyone who is familiar with process map symbology should be able to look at a process map and discern numerous details just from the shapes and the way they are presented. In this section, we'll cover most of the common flow chart/process map shapes and what they are used for.

Process Shape

The process shape is the most common shape in most process maps or flow charts. It is a rectangle. Depending on how you plan to use the process map and what your company's design specifications are, you can use default colors of your Word, Excel, or Visio program, update shape colors to match branding or publication requirements for your enterprise, or create a simple black-and-white rectangle. This is true for all of the shapes in this chapter.

A process shape is used to denote an action step within the process. Something is happening, and usually it is a person or people doing the action. The description of the action is usually typed as text within the shape, which is also true for most of the shapes presented in this section.

Alternate Process Shape

The alternate process shape is used to indicate that an action is an alternate to something that is normal within the process. It is a rectangle with curved corners.

Predefined Process Shape

A predefined process shape is used when there is a process *within a process* and that subprocess is already defined in another document. The shape lets readers know that more than one step is occurring at this point in the overall process, and that those steps are formerly documented somewhere else in the organization. The documentation might be via standard operating procedures, but could also be in the format of another process map.

If a subprocess is known and a Six Sigma team decides not to fully document those steps – *but the process isn't formerly documented elsewhere or the team doesn't know if it is* – then this shape should not be used.

Terminator Shape

When viewing a map for a complex process, it can be difficult to tell where the process begins and ends. This is especially true when a printed process map spans multiple pages and might have more than one possible end point. The terminator shape is used to show the beginning and endings of a process. At the beginning, the terminator shape usually includes an action that triggers the rest of the process.

Preparation Shape

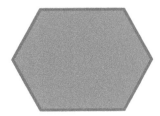

The preparation shape, which is a hexagon, indicates that a step in the process is in preparation for something else. An example might be cleaning a piece of equipment before using it or setting the oven temperature before preparing a recipe.

Manual Operation Shape

The manual operation shape indicates a part of the process that is performed by a person and is not automated. In processes that are mostly human-driven, you don't necessarily have to differentiate between manual operation steps and regular process steps. The manual operation step shape is actually more important to use when depicting mostly automated or computerized processes because you would want the sudden need for human interaction within the process to stand out.

Delay Shape

The delay shape lets you indicate that a waiting time occurs in the process. Delay shapes can be valuable to Six Sigma teams because they often indicate a possible point where *muda* is occurring. When teams see delay shapes on process maps, they should ask questions about why the delay is occurring – is it, for example, because one step in the process is batching outputs, so the next step is awaiting a batch? Is it because a bottleneck is occurring upstream in the process? These are valuable insights for a Six Sigma team.

Decision Shape

The decision shape indicates that a decision is being made in the process. Typically, the decision indicated by the diamond shape is a yes/no or go/no go variety. One example of this type of decision branch in a process is seen when further approval is needed for certain types of actions. For example, a team that processes customer refunds might have some leeway to process lower dollar refunds without approvals. If the refund is under $50, the staff request is processed without further action; if the refund is over $50, a supervisor might need to be involved.

Connector Shape

A connector shape usually indicates a jump from one part of a process to another. Sometimes, this shape is used to indicate that an audit or inspection occurs at a certain part of the process.

Document Shape

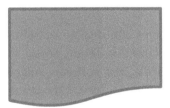

The document shape indicates that a step in a process creates a document. Using the refund example above, at some point in that process, a check is printed. A check is a document, and that step in the process could use this shape.

Multi-Document Shape

The multi-document shape indicates a step in the process that creates multiple documents. Using the same refund example, it's possible that the accounting department batches the checks, printing all refunds at one time each day or week. That step in the process could use this shape.

Display Shape

The display shape is used to show that a step in a process involves the display of some information to a person. For example, a person using a company communication portal to send email might have to log into the portal first. During that process, the software might display a user agreement; if the process for using the software were mapped, this shape could be used to indicate that step.

Data Shape

The data shape is used to show that inputs are going into a process or that outputs are coming from a process. It is also called and In/Out (or I/O) shape.

Manual Input Shape

The manual input shape is used to show a step that involves manual entry of information by a person, usually using a computer.

Off-Page Connector Shape

The off-page connector shape is used to show that part of the process is depicted on another page. You can also use off-page connectors to link multiple processes that are documented on various pages.

Or Shape

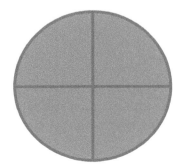

The or shape is different from the basic diamond decision shape depicted earlier in this list. The or shape also indicates a branch of the process, usually in more than two possible directions. Typically, the process map provides some data for how to decide which branch the flow should take at the or shape. For example, consider the refund example used above.

In the previous scenario, there were two options for each refund request: either the request was under $50 and could be processed or over $50 and had to be worked by a supervisor. In a new version of the process, the work can take one of three paths. First, if the refund request is $20 or under, it is approved automatically when entered by a staff member and is routed to check generation. If the refund request is $20 to $50, it must be reviewed by a second staff member, who must agree with the refund decision before it is routed to the check process. If the refund is above $50, it must be approved by a supervisor before a check is cut.

On a process map, the three-prong decision would come out of the or shape. The instructions for which path to choose could be as simple as "Refund </= $20," "Refund $20 to $50," and "Refund > $50."

Merge Shape

If processes can branch off based on decision shapes and or shapes, they might also come back together. When multiple branches of work flow within a process come back together, you can indicate this with a merge shape.

Extract Shape

If processes split into two or more parallel flows without a decision or criteria, then you can use an extract shape to indicate this fact. This isn't one of the more common symbols seen on process maps, and sometimes the triangle indicates something else. When the triangle is presented with an M inside of it, it can show that a measurement must occur at a certain point in the workflow.

Collate Data Shape

The collate data shape is used when data or material in a process has to be organized using a standard format. Cutting fabric into certain lengths before sewing or ordering the admissions forms before considering them are both examples of when this symbol might be used.

Sort Data Shape

The sort data shape indicates that information or materials must be arranged in a certain order. Sorting materials by color before moving to the next step in a manufacturing process might warrant this symbol, for example.

All of the shapes within your flow chart or process map are connected with lines and arrows. The arrows are important, because they guide the reader through the map in the proper sequence.

Where Do These Shapes Come From?

All of the shapes listed in this chapter are available in Microsoft programs, including Word, Excel, and Visio. For those without specific process-mapping software, Excel is probably one of the easiest programs to use for creating process maps and flow charts. Simply turn off the view gridlines function to give yourself a clean slate with which to work.

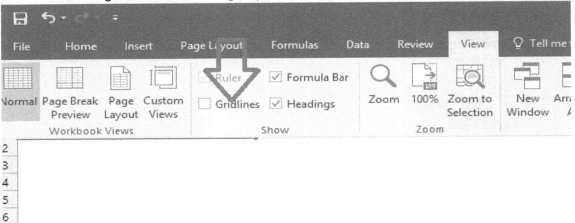

You can insert all of the flow chart shape into Excel using the Insert > Shapes option.

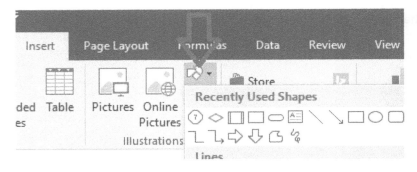

Include a Key with Your Process Map

While someone familiar with process mapping tools will recognize most of the above symbols quickly, not everyone in a business environment will. Most people in business environments *are* familiar with the basic process shape, decision and connector shapes, and terminator shape. Because of this, you can create the bulk of most process maps using these shapes. If you think another shape is warranted, then it's a good idea to add a process map key to your diagram to ensure anyone who looks at it can follow it.

It's also a good idea to add a process map key because not everyone uses all of the above symbols for exactly the same reasons. The connector shape can mean several different things, as can several of the other shapes.

You probably noted as you were reading through the list of common shapes that some activities might be appropriate for two or even three process shapes. Outside of some basic rules, there isn't a right and wrong way to add details on a process map. Ultimately, the goal for creating a process map should be clarity. If adding a different type of shape is going to make the process easier to understand on your visual, then do it. If you can simply use the basic process shape along with text to spell out the process, then remember that in Six Sigma, *less really is more.*

Basic Flow Charts

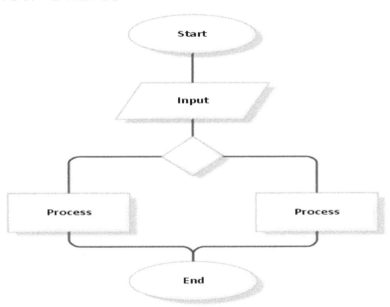

A basic flow chart begins with a trigger activity, includes inputs and processes, decisions, and a final action. Flow charts usually begin at the top of the page and flow down the page. Secondarily, you would read a flow chart from left to right as you move down the page, if a secondary direction is required. In the above flow chart, you can see that a trigger activity occurs, which involves some type of data input. Using that input, a person makes a decision. That decision directs the flow of work either to the process on the right or the process on the left. After that action is done, the overall process, as recorded on this flow chart, ends.

It's important to note that the terminator that ends the process being mapped on the flow chart or process map *rarely ends the work itself.* The only time the final terminator signals the complete end of the work is when you are mapping the very last process before the end customer or you are mapping the entire enterprise process at a very high level. In most cases, however, the final terminator on your process map is likely to indicate the end of this particular process and the beginning of the next. For example, in a beverage bottling plant, a team might be mapping the process that prepares bottles to receive ingredients. The process map begins when a fresh, new bottle is introduced to the process and it ends when the bottle is cleaned, has a label, and is put on the line to receive the liquid it will house. After the process that was mapped, the bottle goes through other process to fill it, cap it, inspect it, and pack it.

Creating a Swimlane Diagram

One of the most widely used process map formats in the Six Sigma world is the swimlane diagram. The swimlane diagram *is* a flowchart, but it is one that is constrained somewhat by rows and columns, known as swimlanes. You can design your swimlane as you want to best depict the process you are working with. Two common options are:

1. Using columns to depict time or activity phases in the process and using rows to depict the person, department, or group responsible.
2. Using columns to depict the person, department, or group responsible and using rows to depict the time or activity phases in the process.

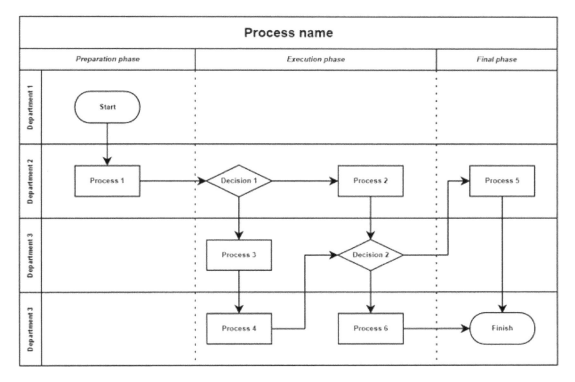

No matter which method you choose, someone should be able to read your swimlane diagram by starting at the top left and reading to the right and down.

Begin by Identifying the Swimlanes

Start your process map session by identifying the swimlanes associated with the process you plan to map. If you've already done a SIPOC as part of the Define phase of a project, then you can use the information from that activity to create your swimlanes. If not, you can use some of the brainstorming activities from the previous chapter to help generate ideas for your process map. Responsibility diagrams, for example, can help you understand how the activities within the process might be broken into organic categories.

If you don't yet have a basic idea about possible swimlanes, first ask yourself or your team: what are all the steps in the process? Don't worry yet about putting the steps in order or even getting all the detailed steps brainstormed. You can add to your map as you create it. Because you don't want the team to start worrying too much about the order of steps or about how they are connected, use notecards to write steps on for this stage. Once the team thinks all major steps are written down, you can sort the steps into groups to get a better idea of possible swimlanes.

To understand how swimlanes might look for a real-world process, consider the process a brand uses to generate ideas for blog posts, write blog posts, and post blogs to a website. You can see, just from the previous sentence, the process is already somewhat broken down into major categories:

- Ideas are created
- Blog posts are written
- Blog posts are posted

Those three sections might become the row designations for the swimlane process map.

Now, consider that different people or groups handle each of the subcategories within the process. The marketing team generates the ideas for content, a team of contracted writers writes the blog posts, and an internal quality team reviews and then posts the blogs.

The foundation of the swimlane diagram might look something like the figure below.

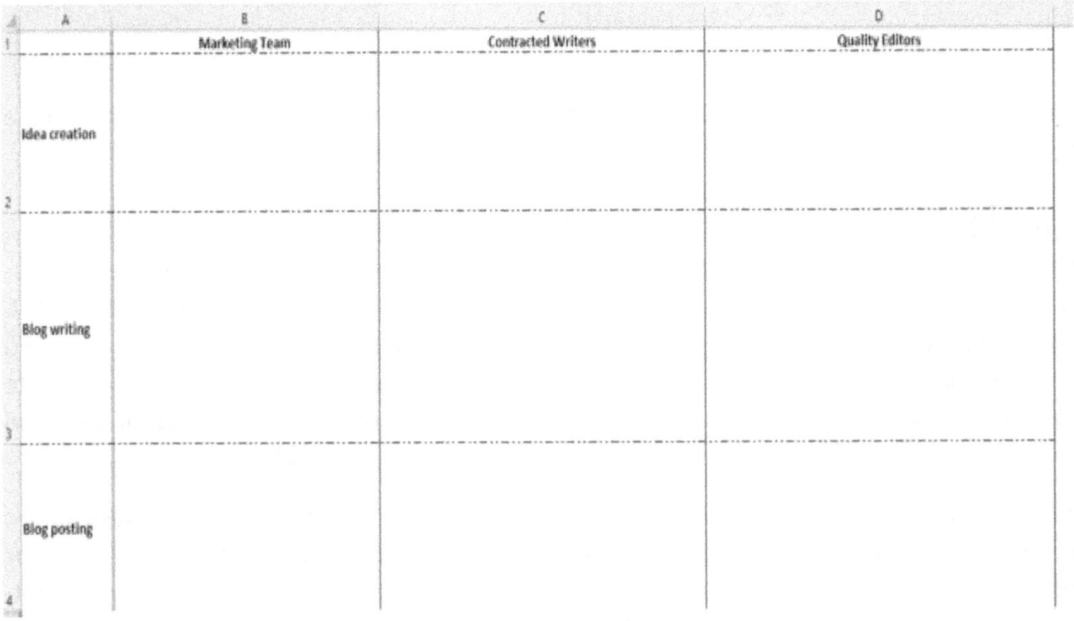

	A	B	C	D
		Marketing Team	Contracted Writers	Quality Editors
	Idea creation			
	Blog writing			
	Blog posting			

Create Step-by-Step List for Process Activities

Next, create a simple step-by-step list for all the activities within the process. If you are familiar with a process and are making a process map on your own, you can start putting the steps into shapes on the grid – you can always move them around as needed later. If you are not familiar with the process or are working with a group to create the process map, it helps to gather data first.

For the purpose of the blog generation example, here are some steps that are included in the process.

1. At the beginning of each month, the marketing team generates ideas for the next month's content.
2. The marketing team generates 15 to 25 ideas, but chooses only 8 to 10 ideas to be written.
3. Once the 8 to 10 items are chosen, the marketing team chooses a title and keywords for each blog post.
4. The topic, along with any necessary special instructions, the titles, and the keywords are provided to the contract writing team.
5. Writers draft blog posts.
6. Writers check that blog posts fit guidelines.
7. Writers submit blogs posts.
8. Quality editors review blog posts.
9. Quality editors check that blog posts fit guidelines and request revisions if they do not.
10. Quality editors line edit blog posts.
11. Quality editors format blog posts.
12. Quality editors enter posts into blogging platform.
13. Quality editors schedule blog posts for publication in the next month.

You can break the above steps into various swimlanes and rows. Steps 1 through 4 belong under the marketing team and mostly in the row for idea creation. The very last step begins to cross the lines into the next phase of the process.

Steps 5 through 7 belong under the writing team and typically fall into the writing phase of the process. The last steps belong under the quality editor section, but they do involve a decision step that could send work back to the writers.

Consider how steps 1 through 4 might be placed on the swimlane diagram.

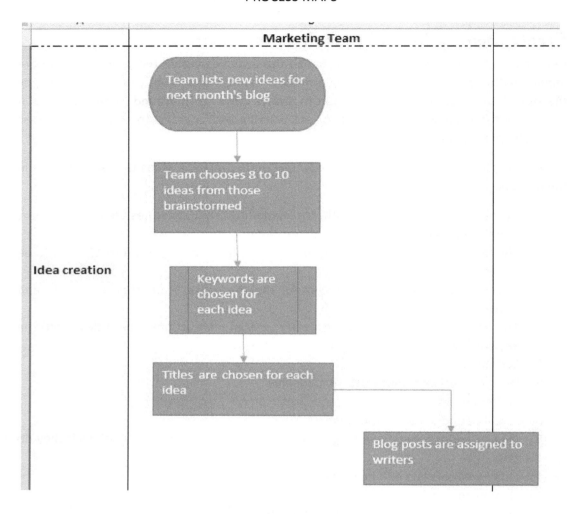

The terminal shape – the activity that starts the entire process – is that it is time to brainstorm the blog ideas for next month. The team brainstorms ideas and then chooses 8 to 10. For the next step, the activity is a predefined process. This means that somewhere, the company has a published SOP or guidelines for researching and applying keywords to blog post ideas. Once that is done, someone chooses a title for each idea and the blogs are assigned to the writers. Note that the final activity – assigning the blogs to the writers – is in a rectangle that somewhat straddles the swimlane line. This is a helpful visual cue that the responsibility for work at this point in the process shifts from the marketing team to the writers.

Next, consider how steps 5 and 7 might look on the process map.

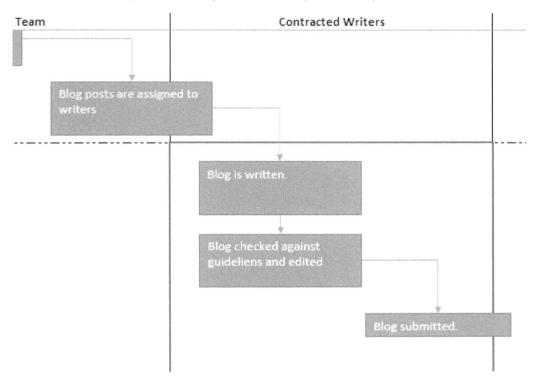

The three steps are presented under the contracted writers swimlane and in the row associated with writing blogs. The final step crosses the line slightly, indicating responsibility is being passed to the quality editors. Consider the remainder of the process map, which falls under the quality editor swimlane.

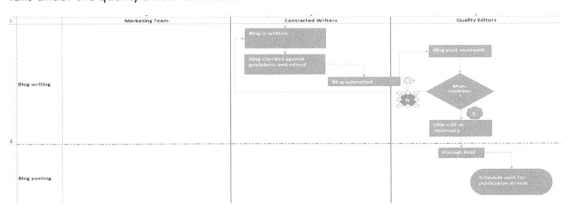

You can see that the quality editor responsibilities actually span writing and posting phases. More importantly, you can see that if the blog doesn't meet guidelines, the editor sends it back to the writer. The team can see here that there is a possibility for rework in this process, and it can see exactly how that rework is handled. The entire process map is shown in the image below.

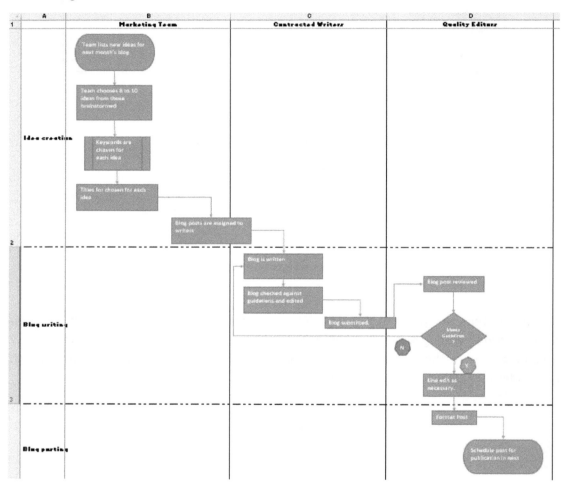

While this is a fairly basic example as process maps go, it includes all of the basic premises of creating a swimlane process map. You can apply these basics to create simple to very complex process maps of any process in Excel or with Word or other any programs that include process map shapes as an option.

Tips for Creating Concise, Attractive Process Maps

Admittedly, the process maps shown in the above images are a bit rough. That was done on purpose to show you how the creation of a process map occurs as you are working through brainstorming and thinking about the process. If the sole purpose of the process map is to provide a Six Sigma team with visual guidance as it works through the DMAIC process, you can leave the process map in a rough-draft state.

If you plan to use the process map in presentations or training documents, however, consider cleaning it up a bit. First, make sure all the color combinations that you used will translate well to whatever medium you plan to use the map in. The above map features the white-on-blue text in each shape, which might not translate well to black-and-white hardcopy documents.

Next, take time to make sure shapes and arrows line up in an aesthetically pleasing and logical fashion. Review your map to ensure arrows are pointing in the right direction, try to keep arrows from crossing over each other too much, and ensure the start and end of each arrow is touching a process shape. This helps reduce confusion when you aren't there it.

Finally, use concise and active language when possible to keep text in each shape short and understandable. Here are some edits that could be made to the example above to make language more active and concise.

- "Team lists new ideas for next month's blog" becomes "Generate blog ideas"
- "Team chooses 8 to 10 ideas from those brainstormed" becomes "Choose 8 to 10 ideas"
- "Blogs are assigned to writers" becomes "Assign posts to writers"
- "Blog is written" becomes "Write blog"

You can see that the shorter versions almost always start with an action verb, which is ideal in process mapping and flow charting.

CHAPTER 33:
VALUE STREAM MAPPING

Value stream mapping is similar, but in some ways different, to process mapping. Value stream mapping is a tool perfected by lean manufacturing and works best in processes that are manufacturing, delivery, shipping, or factory oriented. However, value stream mapping can be useful in a variety of other industries if the Six Sigma expert understands the purpose of the exercise and how to translate the method into his or her process.

What is Value Stream Mapping?

Value stream mapping is a pictorial representation, including the addition of numerical data, of the value stream of product or ideas. When used properly, value stream mapping provides Six Sigma teams with the big picture of a process, lets teams understand what the process looks like today, helps teams create a vision for improving a process, and links the flow of materials, people, and information in one image. A value stream map also helps break down communication barriers because the symbology used tends to be similar or at least intuitive; as such, it makes it easier for teams and support staff to understand where waste – or muda – is occurring in a process.

Evaluating the Seven Flows

A value stream map is one of the few tools that truly captures all of the flow that occurs in a process. It's possible to capture some information about all of the major seven flows on a value stream map, though most value stream maps concentrate most on raw material, parts, and products than on the other four types of flow. The seven types of flow are:

- People
- Raw material
- Parts
- Products
- Equipment
- Information
- Engineering

Value Stream Map Symbology

Value stream maps use different symbols than most process maps do, and the symbols tend to be more specific. For example, if the value stream involves the delivery of goods via truck, the map includes an actual picture of a truck – usually with a text indication of how many times the shipments occur in a given period.

The image above indicates one truck shipment per week. A number of other common value stream map symbols are included below. You can download common symbols for Excel from www.lean.org/ common/display/?o=866 to create value stream maps in Excel. You can also use a value stream map software to create a map.

Note that value stream mapping *doesn't require the use of these exact symbols*, especially if you are using the concept of value stream mapping in an industry where such symbols are less useful. You could use the value stream concept to map the workflow in an emergency room department, for example, where different symbols would make more sense. Consider these symbols as a starting point.

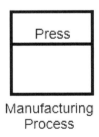

The manufacturing process box indicates a specific action in the production process. The name of the action goes in the top part of the box – in this case, "press." In the bottom, you can put text notes or illustrations as desired. One common use of the bottom section of the process box is indicating how much time occurs during that particular step.

Outside Sources

Outside sources are either suppliers or customers. Use this shape to indicate when inputs come from outside the organization or process or when outputs go to the end customer of the process.

| C/T= 25 |
| C/O= 40 |
| 2 Shifts |
| Takt= 1s |

Data Box

Data boxes are important because they house the analytical meat of the value stream map. Common information recorded in data boxes include:

- Cycle Time, or C/T. Cycle time is the time it takes for the process as a whole – or a step within the process – to complete one iteration.
- Changeover Time, C/T. Changeover time is the time it takes for a change in shift, tools, or other resources in the process or a single step within the process.
- Number of operators
- Number of shifts
- Time worked in a shift
- First-pass yield quality
- Batch sizes
- Takt time, which is the rate at which products must be finished to meet the demand of the customer. Takt time for an individual step in the process might be seen as the time in which the step needs to be finished to keep from slowing down the process.

Inventory Box

The inventory box indicates that inventory usually stacks up at a certain point in the process. It is usually coupled with text that says how much inventory is available in amount, time, or both. You might note that there are 100 pieces of inventory regularly at that point in the process. You might note that there are two-day's worth of inventory at that point in the process; you could note both.

PUSH Arrow

A push arrow indicates that something – either product or information – is pushed from one part of the process to another part of the process. The push arrow means the product or information is generated by that part of the process *regardless of the need* for it in the downstream parts of the process.

The opposite of a push arrow would be a pull indicator, which means that downstream processes pull inventory, parts, or information as needed from upstream locations.

Finished Goods
to Customer

The finished goods arrow indicates that the output of the process is being pushed or delivered to the customer – whether that customer is internal, external, or another process.

First-In-First-Out
Sequence Flow

The FIFO arrow indicates that this part of the process features a first-in, first-out sequence, which is important in some processes. Consider processes that deal with food ingredients; if a recipe in a manufacturing plant calls for milk, then the operators should pull the oldest (still good) milk from storage first to keep from wasting product that goes bad while in inventory.

Supermarket

The supermarket is an area in the process where small amounts of inventory are stored. Downstream processes can stock as needed from the supermarket instead of stocking from the larger inventory supply, which might be more difficult to access. An upstream process feeds the supermarket, ensuring enough inventory is stocked. An example of a supermarket might be seen in a large office. One team might have a drawer where supplies, such as paper, pens, paperclips, and staples, are kept. The team can pull from that drawer instead of requisitioning from the larger stock room or from the actual office supply store every time supplies are needed.

Physical Pull

The physical pull symbol indicates that product or materials have to be physically pulled from the previous step, station, or supermarket to the next step.

Move by
Forklift

The move-by-forklift symbol is self-explanatory, though not always necessary in every process. You might, however, have a symbol for other types of movement, such as move by hand cart or conveyor belt. The only time you need to include specifications about how items are moved is when those details might become important to the process analysis.

Boat Shipment

This is also a self-explanatory symbol and also not necessary in every process. You might, instead, have train, plane, or even bike shipments listed on your value stream map.

Manual Info Flow

The type of information indicated by the straight manual flow arrow is typically communicated via memos, face-to-face speaking, phone calls, and reports. The manual information arrow might be accompanied by notes regarding the type of information and the frequency with which it is delivered.

Electronic Info Flow

The crooked electronic info flow arrow indicates information that is electronic in nature, such as information communication via Internet, portals, EDI, and automated reporting systems. The type of data and the frequency with which it is delivered can also be included with this symbol.

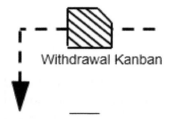

Withdrawal Kanban

The withdrawal Kanban shape indicates that there is a Kanban card or signal at that process step. The Kanban card instructs the operator at that particular step to withdraw inventory from a supermarket or other stock location.

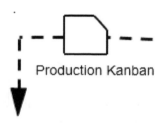

Production Kanban

The production Kanban shape indicates that a production Kanban card or signal is located at that part of the process. This card tells the operator to produce a certain number of parts to feed a process that is downstream.

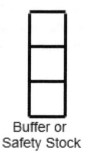

Buffer or
Safety Stock

The safety stock icon indicates that a "just-in-case" storage of inventory exists at this point in the process. Safety stock is not like a supermarket – it is not intended to be a permanent storage of inventory. Instead, it is a temporary storage of inventory that reduces the chance that downtime or other issues upstream will keep all the downstream processes from occurring. For example, in a fast food restaurant, someone stocks the cup and drink dispenser each morning. These stocks are not meant to be the permanent storage for those items, but a smaller number of items are kept at hand so employees can quickly supply drinks to consumers.

Operator

The operator shape indicates a human operator or employee within the process. You don't have to include the operator shape in every diagram where people are – in some cases, the nature of the value stream map allows readers to assume people are part of the process. However, if automated processes are included amid people-powered processes, this symbol can be used for clarity where needed.

Weekly Schedule

Schedule

The schedule box is simply a text box that lets you note how work, orders, or other parts of the process are scheduled. You can couple the box along with arrows to show that orders are sent weekly, for example, or that a production schedule for staff is created each month.

Value Stream Mapping Tips

Creating a value stream map is very different from creating a process map. One point of value stream mapping is that it forces you to really experience the process, which means that committee-creation of value stream maps isn't going to provide the best outcome. The entire team *can* get involved in value stream mapping, if you as the Six Sigma expert think that is valuable, but the best results often come when everyone starts with their own individual value stream map. This is also a good process for the Six Sigma experts in a team, because it forces each one to view the process individually.

While you can use the icons above and numerous software programs to create a final copy of your value stream map, use paper and pencil for your first drafts. This lets you record information as you walk through the process, changing it quickly as you go.

When creating process maps, you often concentrate on the process, the employees, and the requirements. When creating value stream maps, you should always concentrate most on the customer and the product.

Physically walk the process whenever possible instead of sitting at a computer or working with a brainstorming session. Some experts recommend walking the process backwards; others say start at the beginning – find a method that works best for you. Don't try to map every single part of the process, especially if you are mapping a large-scale production process. Instead, follow the major raw materials through to the outputs. If you put all the processes on a single map, it becomes too hard to read and you lose the value of the tool.

While you might eventually create a value stream map of a desired future state, *start by mapping the way things are*. Even if you see they aren't working, record the actual process. Use real-time data for the value stream map whenever possible. For example, don't use historical production and changeover times; when you walk the process, use a stopwatch to record your own observations.

Value Stream Mapping Steps

Begin value stream mapping by selecting the product family or process you are concerned with. In a manufacturing environment, you might select product type C and only concern yourself with that product. For example, a toy factory might make dolls, doll houses, and toy cars, but the Six Sigma team might only be concerned with doll houses. In fact, the Six Sigma team might only be concerned with the doors that are made for the doll houses – you decide what scope of value stream map makes sense for your project.

Next, collect as much relevant data on the *current* state of the process as possible. Do this by walking the process and taking notes, reviewing actual data, and speaking with subject matter experts.

Create a Value Stream Map Drawing

To create an example of a value stream map while going through the following steps, we'll consider a simple real-world example. In our example, a factory makes crayons. The Six Sigma team is concerned with the process that makes the 8-pack of primary colored crayons.

The value stream map will need to include information such as:

- The suppliers of raw goods (wax, dye, and paper)
- Wax melting
- Dye addition
- Pouring into molds to create crayon shapes
- Inspection points
- Wrapping crayons with appropriate paper
- Packing crayons into boxes of eight
- Shipping to final customer -- in this case, retail stores

1. Begin with the major process steps in the value stream. These are indicated by process boxes and are joined in a left-to-right line by the appropriate arrows – often by push arrows. For our example process, let's assume a few basic process steps:
   a. The wax is melted and dye is added
   b. Wax is poured into molds
   c. Molds are emptied
   d. Inspection occurs
   e. Shaped crayons are wrapped with matching colored paper
   f. Crayons are packed in boxes
   g. Shipping

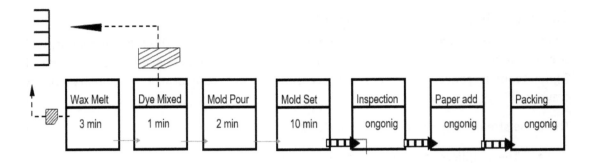

Above, you can see a rough sketch of the process part of the value stream map. Kanban cards or signals tell employees when to pull wax and dye from the supermarket inventory. (The signal might be a light that the previous batch has been processed and the machines have returned to process start parameters). The employees add the ingredients and start the first piece of the process, which is automated after the initial ingredient measurements. The wax is melted, the dye is mixed in, the colored wax is poured into molds, and the mold sets for 10 minutes before crayons are emptied to the inspection station.

You'll note that the arrows connecting the first processes are different, because we want to show that they are automated and the process simply runs together unless someone intervenes in that batch. The rest of the processes have push arrows, because inspection, paper addition, and packing don't operate on a batch process and work as long as inventory is flowing through.

2. Add the important aspects from outside of the process, including process controls, supplies, customers, and shipments.

3. Add data boxes for each part of the process.

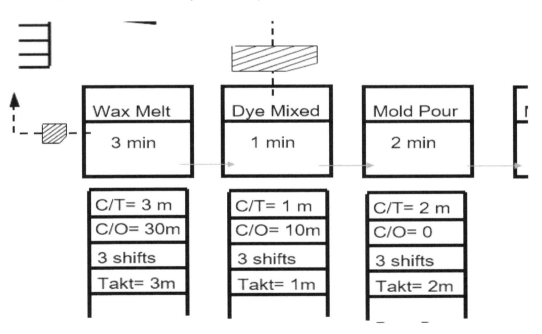

4. Add inventory signals and any other information you think would be pertinent for the value stream map. For example, in reviewing the crayon process used in the

example, the Six Sigma expert might note that inventory builds up before the packing process because it is slower than the inspection and paper-wrapping process. That could be indicated with an inventory signal and text.

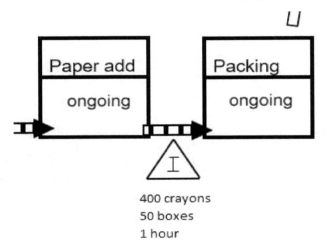

400 crayons
50 boxes
1 hour

You can also add controls for the process. In this case, the retailer places orders one month ahead for how many boxes it will need each week in the next month. The crayon-making company creates a monthly forecast, but orders once a week from suppliers. Suppliers deliver in multiple batches a week. Production control manages every part of the process with scheduling to keep up with the demands of the retailers.

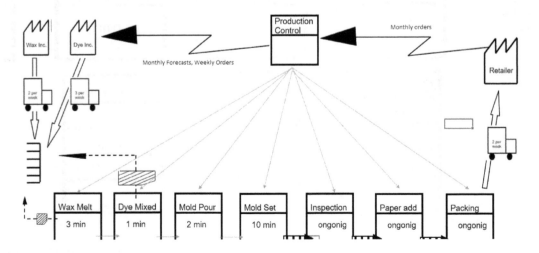

Finally, add a timeline at the bottom that notes the time it takes for a single item to process through the enter process, breaking the time into value added and non-value added.

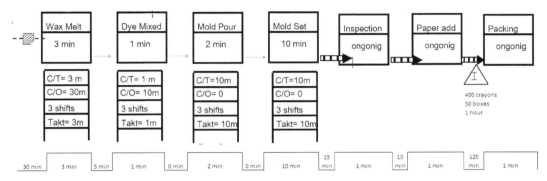

In the above example, the yellow portions are value added. They represent time that the product is actually being made or changed. The white portions are the setup, lead times, and inventory wait times – and this particular process is for a single color of crayons and doesn't take into account any time spent preparing machines for changing colors.

You can add up the times to see that the total process time is 194 minutes or 3.23 hours.

The value added time is 19 minutes, so the team can assume there is definitely waste that can be removed from this process.

Remember, value stream maps aren't supposed to be formal documents – they are working pictures of the process to help you and the rest of a Six Sigma team better understand the process and related challenges. So, you can add as much or as little information as you think is necessary. You can also come back and add information later if needed. The first draft of a value stream map, whether using pen and paper or a computer program, is probably going to be messy, and that's okay. In fact, that's a sign that you are doing it right. You can always make a clean, final copy for inclusion in presentations and training documents if desired.

What Do You Do with Value Stream Maps?

Value stream mapping is a helpful tool for all of the DMAIC phases. During Define, value stream mapping as an activity forces you to become involved with the process at a physical and daily level, which can boost your understanding of the process you are working to improve. It also provides the entire team with another visual that helps when discussing the process and the problem. A good value stream map lets the team visualize exactly where the process and problem might occur with respect to overall production.

Creating a value stream map means you've already conducted some measurement, creating a foundation for the Measure phase. The value stream map also points to measurement and data collection points that can be further used in Measure, though teams should never limit themselves to just the first types of information gathered in value stream mapping.

During Analyze, value stream maps are a tool that helps teams brainstorm and identify root causes or problem points in a process, and you can use the initial value stream map to identify activity or resources that don't provide value – those that create *muda* in the process. Finally, during Improve, teams can begin creating a future state value stream map, building off the old map and using the information and solutions they have come up with through the DMAIC process. By putting those solutions on paper in the form of a value stream map, teams can better understand where issues might arise and alter solutions appropriately to reduce the number of issues experienced during implementation and beyond.

Tips for Creating a Future-State Value Stream Map

1. Use the current-state value stream map and all other information gathered and analyzed to identify as many sources of waste in the process as possible.
2. Categorize waste into two types: those that are the result of remote locations, machinery, and product designs which are all necessary elements to the end product and those that are *not* the result of these things.
3. Concentration on the second type of waste and create a future state value stream map that removes them all.
4. Review the future state map to ensure processes can flow appropriately. Ask yourself questions such as:
   a. What is the Takt time required at each station to meet overall demands, and is each step in the process capable of meeting that Takt time? If not, the team might need to address steps that are not capable.
   b. How will production be scheduled? Usually, there is a specific part of the process that controls the production schedule. Ultimately, the best and most optimal control is by the customer (The customer needs 100 per day,

so the process should make 100 per day). However, there are times when a specific part of the process is only capable of X units per time period, and the team is unable to change that capability because of resource or other restraints. If the process is not controlled by this "pacemaker step," then inventory is going to build up before it.

c. Is batch processing needed, or can it be removed?

d. What process changes and improvements are required to implement the future state value stream? Sometimes, machinery changes, staffing changes, or capital investments are required, and these aren't always possible. Before moving forward with future-state plans, Six Sigma teams have to make sure resources will be approved and available.

As with anything in Lean and Six Sigma processes, the value stream map isn't a *requirement*. In fact, one of the cardinal rules of value stream mapping is *not to map just to map*. Yes, a finished and polished map looks nice – and can be especially impressive in presentations or documents when other people in the organization are not fully familiar with the tool. However, if creating a value stream map isn't going to help a Six Sigma team through any of the DMAIC phases or if the process involved simply doesn't lend itself to mapping in this fashion, then skip this tool. A Six Sigma expert should always be aware that *muda* can creep into any process – and that includes the process of evaluating and improving something. If you're creating a value stream map without reason, then you are creating   muda   of   overproduction.

UNIT 9:
SIX SIGMA IN PROFESSIONAL FIELDS

CHAPTER 34:
SIX SIGMA IN HEALTHCARE

For the purposes of this chapter, healthcare is considered to be inclusive of the entire industry. In addition to providers – both small practices and large organizations such as hospitals and hospital campuses – healthcare can include support services, equipment manufacturers and distributors and insurance companies. Six Sigma experts who work in or with any organization that is concerned with patient care, federal and state healthcare compliance, and auxiliary services such as claims billing, should understand how the methodology integrates into the field.

Some overlap does exist between the industries covered in these last few units. A company that manufactures medical devices is likely to operate in several spheres, including both manufacturing and healthcare. Within that company, departments such as human resources and IT are concerned with both the manufacturing and healthcare needs *as well as* the functions and needs specific to their own department. Because of this type of overlap, the Six Sigma expert should understand how the methodology can be implemented across multiple functions and industries. Throughout these next few units, you'll discover how Six Sigma can benefit specific industries and departments and how the environment within certain industries can be challenging to Six Sigma implementation. You'll also read about Six Sigma cases and success stories in a variety of industries.

Benefits of Six Sigma in a Healthcare Environment

According to the American Hospital Association's Trendwatch, hospitals in America averaged operating margins between 2 and 7 percent between 1993 and 2015. Total margins for the same time period were between 4 and 8 percent.[8] With fairly small profit margins, hospitals and healthcare organizations have to keep tight reins on processes and costs. But costs can't be cut at the expense of patient care or compliance, which means strategic improvements are a must within healthcare environments.

Becker's Hospital Review notes that hospitals compete heavily in multiple areas, including quality of care and the cost of service[9] – and they aren't just competing for end-users such as patients. Hospitals, and all healthcare providers, compete for referrals, industry partnerships, accreditations and contracts with insurance companies and payers. Because processes in healthcare organizations have so many customers, it can be difficult to make improvements that enhance services for one customer without negatively impacting outcomes for another. A change that makes a service faster for a patient might make it more expensive; a change that reduces costs could be noncompliant with one or more regulations. The DMAIC methodology helps teams consider all customers and outcomes to avoid such issues.

At the heart of most healthcare organizations – even those that serve in auxiliary capacities – is service to the patient. This is particularly true in clinical circles, where errors can lead to negative patient outcomes, including longer treatments, healthcare-related illness and injuries, and even death. Not only do these outcomes create a negative impact to the organization's brand *and* open possibilities for expensive malpractice suits, but they are also undesirable because healthcare employees are in the business of saving lives and improving living, not in making things worse. Six Sigma can be used in clinical settings to improve processes and make positive outcomes more likely.

Finally, Six Sigma can be used to reduce errors throughout the healthcare service chain. Errors in administrative tasks, such as patient enrollment or claims billing, lead to delayed care or payment. Errors in inventory ordering lead to shortages that impact the ability to serve patients' immediate needs. Six Sigma has been used in healthcare to reduce physician

---

[8] http://www.aha.org/research/reports/tw/chartbook/2015/chart4-2.pdf
[9] http://www.beckershospitalreview.com/lists/200-hospital-benchmarks-2015.html

error, reduce patient wait times, decrease supply chain steps and costs, create stronger reimbursement flows, and decrease the time it takes labs to return results. Those are just a few uses of Six Sigma in healthcare.

Challenges of Implementing Six Sigma in a Healthcare Environment

While Six Sigma can be extremely valuable in a healthcare setting, the methodology does face some challenges specific to the industry. One of the first, and arguably one of the largest, unique challenges Six Sigma experts face in a healthcare setting is compliance. Yes, almost every industry these days has a compliance or regulatory requirement somewhere – and you'll see that throughout these last units. However, the compliance element for healthcare can be constraining in ways that require creative and strategic thinking on the part of Six Sigma experts.

Six Sigma experts *should never try to work around or over compliance requirements*. First, the regulations of the industry are automatically part of the critical-to-quality characteristics a Six Sigma team should consider. If something is truly a regulatory requirement, then Six Sigma teams must honor it and treat it as a quality requirement. Working over that requirement means you are producing a process or product that is *not within quality standards*. That being said, this can be frustrating for Six Sigma experts, particularly if they are used to working in other industries. Healthcare quality requirements, which include clinical requirements, HIPAA (Health Insurance Portability and Accountability Act) requirements, and dozens of other requirements from insurances companies and state and federal agencies, can force muda into a process. Regulations often require duplication, intense quality reviews, or overproduction. In such cases, Six Sigma teams must "make the best" of these situations by finding other areas to work with.

It's important to note, however, that some muda that healthcare organizations associate with compliance *is unnecessary*. One job of the Six Sigma team is to identify unnecessary compliance work and replace it with processes that ensure quality without waste. Here, you find a second big challenge Six Sigma experts are likely to find in healthcare settings – a challenge that is found in most industries and which was covered in the beginning of this book. When people are used to doing something a certain way, they come to believe *they have to* do it that way. In healthcare, this often takes the form of the statement, "We have to do it that way because of the regulation/law/government/accrediting organization." Six

Sigma teams must work hand-in-hand with compliance to understand when this is true and when a more efficient quality process can be put in place.

While healthcare environments present numerous challenges for Six Sigma teams, the last challenge we'll highlight here has to do with statistical analysis. Six Sigma experts must know what outcomes will be affected by decision-making within the DMAIC process and must set confidence levels and sample sizes appropriately when conducting analysis. When dealing with processes that involve administrative functions such as claims billing, teams might default to the 95 percent confidence level (alpha = .05). When dealing with processes that directly impact patient welfare, such as surgical procedures, teams might consider setting confidence levels at 99 percent (alpha = .01). Remember, higher confidence levels require bigger sample sizes or more runs in a designed experiment. In some cases, they are more expensive overall, so teams need to truly understand the impact of confidence levels on both the cost of statistical analysis and the accuracy of conclusions before moving forward in healthcare arenas.

Six Sigma Healthcare Case Study: Virtua Health's Cardiac Program

Located in New Jersey, Virtua Health spanned four hospital systems at the time it launched a Six Sigma project to create solutions to challenges in cardiac medication processes. The healthcare organization started to look at quality improvements in this area in 2001; one of the goals at the time was to align the processes of the organization with the goals required by the Centers for Medicare and Medicaid Services (CMS). The organization collected and reviewed data, noting that the process for providing cardiac patients with medication and documenting that provision needed work to come up to standards.

The organization launched a traditional quality program in 2002. It called the program POE, or Cardiac Program of Excellence. Through the program, Virtua Health attempted to adopt best practices and advanced technologies and increase connections between providers, but the results were lackluster. Data from the first quarter following the implementation of the program showed no measurable improvement. At that time, the organization launched a Six Sigma project. The team included subject matter experts from multiple disciplines and they approached the issue via a DMIAC methodology.

- **Define**. The team created a definition of the project: "Increase quality of patient care by use/non-use and appropriate documentation of aspirin, beta-blockers, and

ACE (angiotensin-converting enzyme) inhibitors in CHF or AMI patients to achieve or exceed Virtua benchmark goals."[10]

  o Scope: all four hospital campuses
  o Goal: Meet Joint Commission Accreditation standards and improve patient outcomes

- **Measure**. During measure, the team conducted a Gage R&R analysis on the quality review process and DPMO was calculated regarding the administration of medication process.

  o The team defined a defect as any failure to properly administer medicine, which meant errors in dosage amounts or the time medication was provided would count as defects. Defect rates for administering medication to CHF patients was 10.2 percent; defect rates for administering medication to AMI patients was 4 percent. (CHF and AMI are two types of cardiac patients.)

  o The team also noted that there was an issue in the quality review process. The reviewers were not consistently reporting quality in a way that matched their own review results. To address this problem, the Six Sigma team, along with subject matter experts from the quality review teams, created a detailed process map. They also came up with a standard for reviewing and a plan to communicate that new standard to all quality reviewers.

- **Analyze**. During the analyze phase, the Virtua Health Six Sigma team met biweekly and focused on approximately half a dozen issues identified during Define, Measure, and Analyze. The team noted that concurrent reviews of CHF and AMI patients required better coordination of staff. They also noted that nursing and clinical staff needed better access to information about core indicators, especially when that information evolved or changed. The Six Sigma team identified common areas for these staff, including lounges, nurses' stations, and cardiac units, and planned to post storyboard templates featuring core indicator data at each location. Other information and activities that developed in the Analyze phase included:

  o A need for better communication between clinical staff and physicians
  o Discovery of overproduction in reviewing charts – multiple staff were all reviewing the same charts on a regular basis without a real clinical need to do so

---

[10] https://www.isixsigma.com/new-to-six-sigma/dmaic/achieving-and-sustaining-improvement-cardiac-medication/

- o Real-time communication and service administration was not always available
- o All of the activities needed to work together, requiring a point person assigned to supervise and coordinate
- **Improve**. During Analyze, the team noted that the majority of medication errors involving physicians were related to defects in documentation. Specific factors included missing documentation, inconsistent patient census, missing diagnostics , compliance issues with regard to completing discharge instructions, and inconsistent patient care across multiple disciplines within the hospital setting. Remember, some cardiac patients might have other diagnoses and be treated in other areas or by other staff. The team considered each of these factors, developed root cause analysis, and proposed solutions.
- **Control**. The team created a flow chart for the distribution of key information and trained appropriate staff members on that process. Standards were put in place for physician-to-physician communications and a monthly dashboard was built so the staff and organization could track ongoing process. A standard data collection form became part of the process to reduce inconsistencies, some forms were shortened to make consistency more likely, and certain medications were stocked on each floor to reduce administration times.

At the end of the project, the Virtua Health organization did see statistically significant results. Some Y benefits from the process improvements included:

- An increase in the compliance requirement for administering aspirin to cardiac patients
- Increased compliance in documentation
- Increased quality of care for patients
- Increased timeliness of patient care
- New processes that brought the organization in line with CMS requirements for cardiac medication provision.

Six Sigma Healthcare Case Study: Medical Transcription

A medical transcription company in India servicing physicians and other providers in the United States was having difficulty returning transcriptions within a desired time period while maintaining appropriate quality.[11] The company worked with a Six Sigma consulting firm to make improvements to the process. After some initial training regarding Six Sigma and Lean methodologies was provided to key employees at the transcription company, the consultants and transcription company staff began a journey through an improvement project.

The first challenge was identifying what the customer wanted. Staff members knew customers wanted dispatches by 5:30 p.m. each day, but what information did that include? After using some Define tools, the team noted that all files received between 7:30 a.m. on day 1 and 7:30 a.m. on day 2 must be transcribed and returned by 5:30 p.m. on day 2. Once this was defined, the team began to gather data about the process, noting that there was a wide variation in performance that was causing the target to be missed. The team also noted that work arrived steadily from the United States but peaked between midnight and 2 a.m., making it difficult to catch up if processing of work batches began at 8:00 a.m. each day.

Ultimately, the team arrived at the conclusion that at least one night team was required. The team decided to use two night teams and one day team; work processing would start at 8:00 p.m. instead of 8:00 a.m.

At first, some team members vocalized worries that staff working the night shift would be less productive. The general feeling of team members was that people would be more tired at night or that night work would not be managed as well. The Six Sigma team ran a pilot to test this theory and found that there was no statistical different between efficiency for night teams and day teams.

The pilot was successful – leading to on-time or early delivery of all piloted work. The transcription business quickly adopted the changes across the organization, resulting in an average delivery of work that was 134 *minutes early* rather than 89 minutes late. The system was also able to handle 22 percent more work on a regular basis.

---

[11] https://www.isixsigma.com/new-to-six-sigma/dmaic/medical-transcription-six-sigma-case-study/

Tips for Using Six Sigma in Healthcare

To be successful with Six Sigma in healthcare, teams and Six Sigma experts must:

- Understand all of the customers of the process
- Take time to develop a deep understanding of compliance requirements related to the process at hand
- Work hand-in-hand with clinical, administrative, and auxiliary staff to make appropriate improvements
- Work with the appropriate confidence intervals depending on the type of process involved

CHAPTER 35:
SIX SIGMA IN FINANCE

Every organization – in any industry – has a finance component. Money is made and collected, invoices are generated, and bills and employees are paid. This is true even for nonprofits. And while the information in this chapter might be somewhat relevant to the accounting, purchasing, receiving, or finance departments in any organization, this chapter is going to concentrate on organizations in the finance industry. Note, however, that finance-related departments should often be included in Six Sigma projects in every organization, if only from the perspective of as-needed subject matter experts that can provide details or assistance regarding budget, costs, and revenue data.

For the purposes of this chapter, finance organizations are considered to be those that deal with money, investments, collections, mortgages, debt, and related services and products. Banks and credit unions, insurance companies, loan companies, and collection agencies all fit this description. Other types of entities that might fall into this arena include CPA firms, financial software vendors, money transfer services such as Western Union, and online and app-based money services such as PayPal.

Benefits of Six Sigma in a Finance Environment

All of the typical benefits of Six Sigma can be experienced when applying the methodology to finance processes, including increased efficiencies, reduced defects, and an increase in profits. As with healthcare, the finance industry as a whole is managed under some very specific regulatory laws and requirements. Requirements address how investments must be handled, how data – particularly personally identifying data – must be secured, accessed, and transferred, and who can do what with financial information and when they are allowed to do it. For example, if you work for a company and have insider information about that company's product, you can't use that information to facilitate personal gains in investments before the knowledge might be considered public; doing so is called insider trading and is a felony. Failure to comply with regulations can mean enormous financial and brand implications for an organization – and on an individual level, can even translate to criminal charges for those involved.

The ability to maintain compliance in a complex industry with so many moving parts is a big benefit of Six Sigma. The critical-to-quality approach of Six Sigma helps ensure that processes are designed and improved with compliance factors in mind, which can help organizations avoid damaging expenses and negative brand publicity from regulatory issues.

Challenges of Implementing Six Sigma in a Finance Environment

The challenges of implementing Six Sigma in an organization in the financial industry are often similar to those experienced by Six Sigma experts in healthcare. First, you face the compliance and regulatory factor: you can't do anything that is outside of regulations, and you often have to fight a false perception of what those regulations might be.

Second, while the finance industry has embraced technology innovations such as app-based money management, it is still steeped in tradition and outdated policies to some degree. One reason so many financial industry employees and leaders are reluctant to embrace change is because of the high stakes that are inherent when you deal with money – especially when you deal with someone else's money. Six Sigma experts will have to work hard to create an atmosphere where financial leaders are comfortable relying on the methodology and the statistical analysis process for decision making.

Third, like healthcare organizations, financial organizations often deal simultaneously with multiple customers – and often, the goals and desires of those customers are somewhat at odds with each other. For example, a publicly-traded financial institution has both shareholders and end-user customers. The end-user wants the best possible product at the lowest possible cost and highest possible return. The shareholder wants maximized profits for the biggest return on investment. While these things are not always mutually exclusive, they are also not always aligned, which can be a challenge for Six Sigma teams looking to improve outcomes for one customer – teams have to consider the outcomes for all other customers too.

Fourth, unlike healthcare industries, which tend to remain fairly siloed within national borders unless you are working with agencies such as Doctors Without Borders or the World Health Organization, companies in the financial sector often work across borders. Depending on the location and scope of a Six Sigma project, teams might deal with global processes or interactions. Challenges in a project that spans cultural and government borders are many: language barriers might exist, and even when everyone speaks the same language, they typically don't use the same words or phrases. Government regulations are different, and teams must understand how varying government entities play a role in a process and project. Finally, cultures and dynamics are different, so Six Sigma leaders must be sensitive to different ways people deal with communication, assignments, and each other.

Finally, like some of the other industries on this list, the financial sector often deals with services and ideas that are not immediately – or never will be – tangible. This is even more true in the digital age. *Yes,* some services and products have very definitive values. An insurance policy is worth a certain amount; an investment portfolio has a specific current value. But these aren't products that the end-user can hold and touch. These aren't items made from raw goods through a manufacturing process. Because of this, many people who only have a basic understanding of Six Sigma falsely believe that it is not the right methodology for improving processes in their organization or department. Because there isn't a tangible product being manufactured, some people believe the tenets of Six Sigma and Lean are not applicable. It's up to Six Sigma leaders and experts within an organization to develop training, explanations, and successful initiatives that continue to create a culture of Six Sigma-driven process improvement.

Six Sigma Finance Case Study: Citibank's Approach

The case study presented for the finance industry illustrates how Six Sigma can become a long-term culture in an organization, creating constant improvement not just through months or years, but through decades. In an effort to become a premier financial institution across the globe, Citibank turned to Six Sigma as early as 1997.[12] At that time, the bank partnered with Motorola, which had developed its University Consulting and Training Services in the last part of the 20th century. As part of its commitment to quality and process improvement, Citibank wanted to reduce cycle times, increase customer satisfaction and loyalty, empower team members to make decisions and help customers, and improve cash management processes.

In 1997, the Motorola University Consulting and Training Services team started teaching key Citibank employees about Six Sigma methods – how to reduce defects and why that was important and how to use Lean concepts to positively impact cycle time. Here, in the late

---

[12] http://www.qualitydigest.com/dec99/html/citibank.html

1990s, a financial organization asked itself: could what has worked so well in manufacturing circles be applied to financial services? It turned out that CTR (cycle time reduction) *did* provide benefits outside of a manufacturing or factory environment. Citibank used CTR strategies to create faster, less costly, and higher quality consumer banking processes; it also used CTR to maneuver in emerging markets in a manner that kept up with the quickly evolving economies.

In addition to identifying defects using traditional Six Sigma tools discussed throughout this book, Motorola worked with Citibank to apply a method developed by Motorola called cross-functional process mapping, or CFPM. The purpose of CFPM is to reduce cycle times via a series of steps.

- Plan for the project for two to four weeks. Planning includes choosing a process for improvement, identifying a champion and team members for the project as well as a steering committee to guide the project, and choosing a Six Sigma team leader.
- Over the course of two to five days once a team is created, they map the current process, asking questions about where waste is, what might create dissatisfaction for the customer, and what are the value added activities of the process.
- Over three to five weeks, teams work to validate their map and assumptions with other departments, using the time to create a culture that is accepting of the need for change.
- During a second two to five-day session, teams create a process map or flow chart of what they want the process to look like.
- Over five to tenth months, teams work with the organization to design and implement the process.

You can see, Motorola's CFPM is simply another take on the DMAIC process—Citibank used both Six Sigma statistical approaches and Motorola's CFPM in the beginning of its process improvement journey to reduce waste and defects in its processes.

While Citibank began the Six Sigma journey in the late 1990s, it has continued to develop a culture of process improvement throughout the decades. Leaders with Citibank have deployed Six Sigma thinking to create ongoing improvement and to solve real-time issues. One managing director identified a problem when a function in his purview was relocated to an office in a different state. Because not all employees wanted to relocate, the function ended up in the hands of staff who were not experienced with the work. This resulted in a process that now took much longer than it traditionally had because employees and their supervisors didn't always know how to troubleshoot issues within the process. Issues were being increasingly routed to higher levels, adding to the overall cycle time.

The manager implemented a cross-functional performance challenge, modeled in part on the CFPM method. Through that process, the team learned to handle issues and they *were also given the authority to do so*. Empowering employees at appropriate levels to make decisions is an innate part of Lean and Six Sigma methodologies because it can reduce waste. In the Citibank case, process times were reduced to 30 minutes from an average of two hours.

Six Sigma Finance Case Study: Dot-com Deposits

In 2000, dot-com fever in the United States and across the globe was still at a high pitch, and financial institutions were funding all types of online projects. The industry began to see a growing emergence of online banking, and some banks were opening via Internet only. The thought process behind online banks was, and still is, that cutting out physical banking locations results in substantial savings and those savings can be passed on to end users.

Online banks without branch locations faced a number of challenges in the early part of the 21st century. One of those challenges was how to accept customer deposits; before the advent and wide adoption of mobile deposits, banks had to rely on mailed deposits. One bank in particular made some decisions based on basic customer input and founder intuition regarding deposits.

First, the bank decided that customers would be more comfortable mailing their deposits to a local or regional address. Second, the bank decided that if a deposit was mailed to a local address, it would take less time to process than if it were mailed to a central location. Based on these assumptions, the bank created a process whereby customers mailed individual deposits to a local or regional address. Every day, the local depositories would overnight all deposits received to a central location.

The bank was surprised when customers complained that deposits were taking too long to process, and a Six Sigma Black Belt was brought in. The Black Belt worked through the DMAIC process to identify root causes for the problem, come up with a solution, and implement it. Because the Black Belt relied on data and statistical analysis rather than some basic feedback and intuition, he was able to determine that the local deposit structure *was not* faster than a central deposit structure. Some problems he found with the local deposit structure are included below.

- Mailing, even locally, took up to three days on average, not including weekends.
- Local deposit locations didn't receive deposits every day, which meant there was not a daily process that could be engrained in staff. Because of this, when deposits *were* received, they weren't always overnighted the same day.
- The local deposit process did not operate at a high sigma level.

The Six Sigma team performed data analysis and hypothesis testing. They also compared the process for the bank to benchmark processes, finding that competitors were using the central mailing process. Hypothesis testing showed that central mailing processes were statistically faster than local mailing processes when the measurement was time to deposit funds once they were mailed by a customer. The team also conducted customer surveys and found that customers were not, in fact, overly worried about what address payments would be mailed to.

The result of the DMAIC process was the implementation of a central mailing location and the savings of $4 million annually for the bank.[13]

Tips for Using Six Sigma in Finance

To be successful with Six Sigma in finance, teams and Six Sigma experts must:

- Understand all of the customers of the process so that positive changes for one customer do not result in unacceptable changes for another customer
- Take time to develop a deep understanding of regulatory requirements, particularly when working for publicly traded entities or dealing with processes that handle personally identifying information
- Work to create a culture of process improvement and an understanding of Six Sigma methods throughout an organization.

---

[13] https://www.isixsigma.com/new-to-six-sigma/dmaic/bank-deposits-black-belt-case-study/

CHAPTER 36:
SIX SIGMA IN HOSPITALITY

Hospitality is a broad industry that is sometimes considered to include any entity that deals with lodging, food, beverage, and entertainment. Food and beverage is considered as its own industry in a later unit. For the purposes of this chapter, the hospitality industry is considered to cover the services and products that deal with tourism and certain services related to travel and events. Examples of hospitality companies might be those that deal with hotels or accommodations, travel arrangements, theme parks and attractions, cruises, transportation for travel or leisure purposes, tourism, wedding planning, general event planning, and festivals. Companies that support all of these services and products might also fall within the hospitality industry but likely have a foot in another industry too. For example, caterers definitely have hospitality-related concerns, but they also have to follow guidelines and requirements for the food service industry.

Benefits of Six Sigma in a Hospitality Environment

Hospitality organizations typically walk a very fine line between productivity and customer satisfaction, and where that line is depends on the type and level of service being performed. Hotels that cater to business travelers, for example, must provide efficient, no-hassle services with enough amenities to make the business traveler comfortable. Too many amenities might price the service out of range for most business travelers; not enough comfort, and the business traveler goes elsewhere. Luxury resorts walk a different line, as do discount services that entice family vacationers with integrated pricing deals.

To appropriately walk the most profitable line, hospitality organizations must be plugged into what their target customer needs and wants. Six Sigma helps organizations do that through tools such as Voice of the Customer and statistical analysis. One reason customer satisfaction is critical for hospitality organizations is that so many companies in this sector rely on customer loyalty to bolster revenues. From hotels to theme parks, hospitality organizations offer loyalty programs and rewards for a reason: they want repeat customers. Hospitality organizations also rely heavily on social media and online reviews to ensure new customers are more likely to choose their service or location. Employing Six Sigma – and statistical process control – lets hospitality organizations create consistent quality service so customer satisfaction wins can be repeated.

Like manufacturing organizations, hospitality companies have to keep a close eye on inventory. Too much inventory increases costs and contributes to waste, neither of which are good for profits. Too little inventory leaves the customer without, though, which can result in poor customer satisfaction, loss of repeat business, and poor word of mouth marketing. Recall the principle of Just in Time manufacturing, or JIT, from the chapter on Lean in Unit 1: that principle is very important to hospitality. A hotel customer doesn't want overstocked towels taking up all the space in his or her bathroom, but the customer *does* want clean towels when they are needed. Using Six Sigma and Lean methods lets hospital organizations meet customer needs in a timely, cost-effective manner.

Challenges of Implementing Six Sigma in a Hospitality Environment

Possibly the biggest challenge facing Six Sigma experts in the hospitality industry is the large role people outside of the organization play and how much control those people seem to be able to exert. Hospitality is a people-facing service, and you don't have success in the industry without a lot of people coming through your door or making use of your service. Six Sigma experts can't always expect customers to conform to guidelines, rules, or controls, which means there is always an inherent unknown in a hospitality process.

This is true in almost any industry to a certain degree. Certainly in a healthcare environment, the patient is at least partially responsible for outcomes in some processes. If the patient doesn't follow through with discharge instructions, then the outcome of treatment might be different. If the patient doesn't get information to the facility in time, billing can be impacted. In many other industries, including healthcare, the staff within the industry command a greater authority by weight of the situation, their credentials, or the response ingrained in culture. In general, people are more likely to listen and respond to instructions provided by a doctor than they are by a theme-park ticket taker, for example. When designing or improving processes, Six Sigma experts must keep the fact that people are so involved in the process in mind.

Another challenge that Six Sigma experts might face in the hospitality industry is that so many processes are seasonal. While successful Six Sigma projects can actually reduce the woes associated with stocking, staffing, and running a seasonal venture, the fact that teams must think seasonally in scope can be difficult if Six Sigma experts are used to applying the methodology in more long-running processes.

Turnover rates in hospitality organizations, and the level at which many of these organizations hire, can present another challenge for Six Sigma experts. First, with high turnover rates at all levels of the industry, it can be difficult to get enough buy-in to support Six Sigma initiatives. Once buy-in at leadership levels does occur, a changing of the executive or middle-management guards can impact that buy-in, leaving Six Sigma experts within the organization constantly working to educate leaders about the importance and efficacy of the methodology. Second, constant change in the lower ranks of employees can mean an ongoing need to retrain. This is actually something Six Sigma and Lean methodology can address, making it easier to control processes despite the people involved, but attrition is something Six Sigma experts and teams should always be aware of.

Six Sigma Hospitality Case Study: The Starwood Hotels & Resorts Example

The Starwood Hotels and Resorts chain was reportedly one of the first hotel organizations to embrace the change-management and continuous process improvement methodology of Six Sigma, and it was certainly one of the first to do so at enterprise and global levels. Among other brands, Starwood owned both the Westin and Sheraton hotel names, and the organization wanted to distinguish those chains from others on the market. Beginning in the early part of this century, Starwood harnessed Six Sigma tools to drive efficiencies and improvements – all without impacting the signature creativity that backs the brand's design and hospitality elements.[14]

The need to protect brand creativity was an important factor in how the hotel company chose to implement Six Sigma – and a reason many people in the industry were surprised that Starwood chose Six Sigma over what were considered more traditional approaches in hospitality. In the last part of the 20th century, Six Sigma garnered a reputation for being somewhat "stodgy," though this reputation was unfair and was perpetuated by individuals who didn't fully understand how the methodology works. Professionals in industries outside of manufacturing believed that Six Sigma and Lean methods were about making everything the same to increase productivity, which they believed would naturally decrease creativity.

---

[14] http://www.bloomberg.com/news/articles/2007-08-30/six-sigma-kick-starts-starwoodbusinessweek-business-news-stock-market-and-financial-advice

Hopefully while studying the various components and tools of Six Sigma, you've come to see that this is far from the truth. Six Sigma, when properly implemented, actually greases the wheels for creativity by involving everyone in improvements and fostering out-of-the-box thinking. The goal isn't to stop people from thinking creatively, but to combine creative approaches with data to ensure that final decisions are more likely to work out as desired.

One of the reasons Starwood integrated Six Sigma into its processes was to increase its ability to drive creativity across the organization and to repeat the results of successful programs. One example of the Six Sigma approach used by Starwood can be seen when reviewing a 2006 initiative called Unwind.

Unwind was an initiative Starwood launched to engage travelers within its upscale hotels. While the project itself was definitely creative in nature, the Starwood team chose it after reviewing industry trends, customer needs, and other data. Specifically, an industry study indicated that travelers often feel lonely because they are away from friends and family at home. Approximately a third of travelers expressed this feeling, and Starwood saw a good opportunity to align its own desires with a real customer need.

As previously stated, customer loyalty and engagement is critical in the hospitality industry, and Starwood believed that it could grow customer loyalty for its brand by providing solutions to these feelings of loneliness. The organization used Six Sigma to come up with and deploy solutions – and those solutions aren't always the same for each local hotel. Teams properly using Six Sigma recognized that every hotel – all in disparate locations across the country – serve customers with very different desires and needs. What works for vacationers in a tropical resort won't also work for business travelers in Chicago, and Starwood leaders know that. It wasn't about making everything the same – it was about making everything better.

As part of its Six Sigma approach, Starwood trained hundreds of black and green belts. These Six Sigma experts led teams across the globe, constantly coming up with ideas for improvements and new programs. The teams had to pitch ideas to company leadership, and only those ideas that met certain criteria were green lighted, because resources – even for a large, upscale hotel chain – are never unlimited.

One of the outcomes of Starwood's Unwind initiative was a complimentary massage offering for travelers. The suggestion came after a black belt, some green belts, and subject matter experts in a Chicago hotel met to brainstorm. The fitness director suggested massages, and everyone liked the idea. The Six Sigma team launched a project to pilot a complimentary massage offering. The pilot was so successful, teams had to figure out a way to solve a new problem: How could the hotels tactfully communicate that complimentary massage time was limited? Customers wanted more time in the massage chairs!

Working through Six Sigma processes, the team addressed those issues and later launched the program across many hotel locations. The project was a large success – not only was customer satisfaction and loyalty increased, but massage-based revenues went up 30 percent in locations where the hotels offered paid spa services. Apparently, customers agreed with Starwood: a massage was just the thing a traveler needed.

Massages weren't the only feature generated by the Unwind initiative. Across hundreds of hotel locations, the Starwood team designed, piloted, and launched 120 features to engage customers and increase loyalty. Features ranged from added amenities, such as massages, to entertainment such as Chinese water painting classes and fire dancing. Amenities and entertainments were matched to the look, theme, feel, and purpose of various hotels so that they best met the needs of the clients staying in those facilities.

Starwood's approach of creative innovation through Six Sigma paid off big, according to reports. In one year alone, the company says it saw an additional $100 million in profits thanks to new programs designed and implemented using Six Sigma.

Tips for Using Six Sigma in Hospitality

To be successful with Six Sigma in the hospitality industry, teams and Six Sigma experts must:

- Be able to account for the uncertainty that people bring to every process and know how to mitigate that uncertainty with Six Sigma and Lean tools
- Understand the seasonal nature of the industry and take trends into account when developing processes and projects
- Be able to expertly convey Six Sigma principles in a manner that is relevant to hospitality industry professionals.

CHAPTER 37:
SIX SIGMA IN HUMAN RESOURCES

As with accounting and finance, human resource departments – or, at least, human resource functions – are present in any company that has more than one employee. Six Sigma is a valuable tool for improving human resource departments and functions *as well as* improving human resource companies. For the purpose of this chapter, we'll actually consider Six Sigma in human resources from two perspectives. First, we'll consider how Six Sigma plays a role in organizations that provide human resource services as a product. Those companies include recruiters, human resource consultants, HR software vendors and developers, and payroll companies. You can already see that some of those companies span multiple industries – a software developer might have to concern itself with human resource issues, but it also falls in the information technology field.

Second, we'll look at how human resource departments within any industry interact with Six Sigma initiatives both within the department and within the enterprise as a whole. Like finance departments, human resource departments are important partners for any Six Sigma initiative. HR staff are typically the ones fulfilling open requests for new hires or working with knowledge management on training programs, which makes them essential for projects that involve adding staff or changing workflows and functions. It's important to note that the team members on the Six Sigma project can't always handle every piece of a project themselves. If a project involves creating new training material, the core Six Sigma team doesn't always have the time or skill set to do so. In some cases, the core team doesn't have the enterprise's permission to complete a function – as might be the case with recruiting and hiring – which is why involving auxiliary departments such as human resources is necessary.

Benefits of Six Sigma in a Human Resource Environment

Within a human resource company or department, the common benefits of Six Sigma are similar to those felt in any industry. Six Sigma can reduce costs and defects and increase productivity and quality for the human resource organization. Within an enterprise, improvements in human resource functions typically cause improvements across the organization – think of human resources as the root of the plant that is the whole company. If the roots of a plant aren't spreading to nutrient-rich soil, then the plant itself isn't growing well or producing quality fruits. If the human resource functions are flawed or full of defects, it can't supply the organization with quality staff or excellent support, which often results in the wrong team members on the job, poor onboarding and training, and poor staff morale. Six Sigma methods can help human resource departments improve functions to better serve the entire enterprise.

Modern human resource departments are also facing new challenges in recruiting and staff management. The amount of data available to human resources departments today is astounding, but without the ability to assimilate the data into something meaningful for recruiters and hiring managers, HR employees are tied to traditional hiring methods. Six Sigma can help HR organizations create data-rich processes that integrate information into real-world workflows that are built for recruiters who don't always have data analysis skill sets. The results can be faster times to hire and better accuracy in filling open positions with qualified applicants.

In a human resource company – one that provides auxiliary services and products to other organizations – the Six Sigma DMADV process can be used to design and improve products and services for end customers and remove waste and defects to make those services more profitable. Dr. Mikel Harry of iSixSigma provides a number of other ways Six Sigma can benefit an organization, including reduction in employee turnover, increasing employee satisfaction, improving the management of benefits and payroll, managing healthcare costs, gaining useful information from employee exit interviews, increasing compliance with safety requirements, and deploying policies and training in a more comprehensive and timely manner.[15] In this chapter, you'll see some case studies that illustrate how Six Sigma can help with some of these areas.

Challenges of Implementing Six Sigma in a Human Resource Environment

Six Sigma faces the same challenges in human resources that it does elsewhere, including a need to convince key stakeholders and sponsors of the need to make improvements and the efficacy of the methodology. One challenge Six Sigma leaders face when working with

---

[15] https://www.isixsigma.com/ask-dr-mikel-harry/ask-six-sigma-methodology/ask-dr-mikel-harry-how-can-six-sigma-be-applied-human-resources/

human resource functions that isn't always a consideration with other areas and industries has to do with the nature of the data and processes being addressed. Almost no human resource function is without some access to confidential or sensitive information. When dealing with Six Sigma projects in this environment, it's likely that team members will come into contact with such information or that Six Sigma leaders will have to work around restrictions on what information can be made available.

Often, organizations work around confidentiality issues by choosing team members who *can* work with the data by virtue of their level or position in the company. While this approach can work well if the team is led by a Six Sigma black belt, some precautions are still necessary. First, Six Sigma teams must make sure everyone on the team understands the importance of confidentiality. In some cases, organizations might even require team members to sign confidentiality agreements – especially if the Six Sigma initiative involves consultants or vendors. Data must be safeguarded both during the project and after – team members can never use the information they see during a project for purposes outside of the project. This is especially true of team members who might be in supervisor roles.

Data used during a Six Sigma project should never be used in a retaliatory manner, and enterprises should be very careful when using such data as a disciplinary reason for an employee. If a process has never indicated an issue with an employee's performance and a Six Sigma human resource project discovers there *is* an issue, the Six Sigma team and supervisors should consider: is it the employee's fault that the process is not working? The employee might be under the impression that everything is going well, and disciplining someone out of the blue because of a Six Sigma project can create a negative culture regarding Six Sigma in the future. Instead, Six Sigma teams and relevant supervisors should work on retraining or correcting the process – and this is true even when the project is not in the HR realm.

A final human-resource specific challenge faced by Six Sigma teams is the fact that cutting costs often means eliminating jobs. This can be true of any Six Sigma initiative and is one reason why human resources should be involved in projects. Across industries, there is a mistaken belief that "efficiencies" and "cost-cutting" automatically means removing jobs, but that is actually far from the truth. Companies spend a great deal of time and resources recruiting good employees, and letting good employees go *can* actually be a form of muda. It's important for Six Sigma experts in the human resource niche to understand that removing a position *is not the same thing* as removing a job. Often, Six Sigma improvements make better use of the skills of existing staff, and that can mean a change in function or position once improvements are made to a process. Human resource personnel and the Six

Sigma experts working with them face the challenge of communicating and implementing such changes in the most positive way possible.

In cases where process improvements *do* mean cutting jobs, then human resource experts are challenged with helping teams conduct such activities in the most positive manner possible. Some ways to mitigate the negative aspects of such an activity could include helping employees find positions elsewhere in the company and ensuring employees are provided with excellent references where applicable.

Six Sigma Human Resources Case Study: Océ Business Service's Payroll

Payroll processing can often be improved in organizations of any type, and general estimates are that organizations lose around 5 percent of revenues to payroll mistakes and inefficient payroll processes. One company that provides document management services to clients across the globe turned to Six Sigma to save money and time on payroll processing.

The company, Océ Business Services, operates multiple locations that support thousands of clients, and at the time of the Six Sigma project, the company paid approximately 5,000 employees based on hourly wages. The Six Sigma team, led by a Master Black Belt, included subject matter experts from human resources, operations, IT, and payroll, as well as a Green Belt. The goal for the team was to decrease costs and risks associated with payroll errors or fraud. The team approached the goal via the DMAIC method.[16]

Define and Measure

The team spent the Define phase understanding the current payroll process and identifying a scope for the project. "Improve the payroll process" is simply too big of a scope when you are dealing with 5,000 hourly employees, and the team needed a more tangible and measureable goal. Through the define process, the team learned that a single payroll process didn't exist across all teams. Instead, managers were using disparate methods – often manual in nature – to calculate the number of hours worked by employees during each payroll period. Managers were then transferring those numbers into the company's payroll application, which was proprietary and called I-Times.

---

[16] https://www.isixsigma.com/implementation/case-studies/case-study-making-accurate-payments/

Applying what you've learned about processes throughout this book, you can likely already see many places where the business's payroll process could go wrong. Manual calculations are notoriously fraught with errors when compared to automated calculations – no matter how careful the managers are. Consistency was a problem too – one manager might be rounding up and one down while another entered time exactly to the minute or second. And what about time off? How did each manager handle such situations? The opportunities for error were many, and the managers were spending time on an inefficient manual process. The Six Sigma team estimated a loss of approximately $1 million every year because of the payroll process.

Moving into the measure phase of the project, the Six Sigma team was able to validate many of their assumptions. The team surveyed 325 of the managers – a plentiful sample size to ensure statistically valid conclusions – and found that only 15 percent of the sites were using the propriety company payroll system for tracking, and less than a third of sites even featured time clocks for tracking employee hours. Approximately a fourth of sites used hand-written time sheets, and disparities didn't end at how time was tracked. Managers at each location were, indeed, treating time off, tardies, and other attendance issues differently. Managers were giving grace periods for tardiness that ranged from 0 to over 30 minutes, and some weren't deducting time at all for tardies. Not only did this mean the company was paying for time not being worked, but it also meant that employees were being treated differently in various locations and departments. Disparate treatment of employees can lead to a range of human resource issues, including claims of discrimination or favoritism.

Analyze and Improve

Using the data collected during the measure phase, the Six Sigma team identified two main root causes for payroll errors. First, manual calculations led to errors in the number of hours reported. Second, disparate methods for calculating and managing time sheets led to inconsistencies in the process.

The team wanted to show that improvements to the process for capturing and managing time worked would result in savings, so it started with a pilot program. Using the pilot as a sample, the team estimated potential savings that would occur if the improvements went live successfully across the organization. The data captured during the pilot indicated that manual time management processes featured a defect rate of 0.5 percent. By reducing those errors, the team felt it could save up to $1.2 million each year for the company.

As part of the project, the Six Sigma team and relevant company subject matter experts evaluated numerous options for capturing employee time worked. The team created a checklist of capabilities it wanted in such a solution, and it settled on an ATAS, or automated time and attendance system. The team implemented the ATAS, which included features such as web and phone-based logins and rulesets to ensure employees were compliant with schedules.

After implementing the solution, the team presented new data compared to the baseline data. Prior to the change, the company paid an average of a bit over 80 hours per employee per pay period. Simply switching to the more accurate system dropped that to approximately 78.6 hours per pay period. In other words, the old time management practice was off by a couple of hours each week on average for each employee – the new system also drastically reduced variation in reporting.

Control

Océ Business Services transitioned completely to the new system over a two-month period. Throughout the transition, they saw increasing savings as the system was integrated across more locations. The company put a control chart in place to monitor improvements, and after about four months, the process was still working and estimated annual savings were as much as $1.9 million.

Tips for Using Six Sigma in Human Resources

To be successful with Six Sigma in human resources, teams and Six Sigma experts must:

- Understand the confidentiality needs that might be involved with human resource projects and related data
- Be able to tactfully approach improvements that have a real impact on the jobs and positions of other staff members
- Understand overall company needs and how human resources support those needs
- Be able to leave certain knowledge learned within the project environment and not use it for specific supervisory or retaliation purposes

CHAPTER 38:
SIX SIGMA IN INFORMATION TECHNOLOGY

As with human resources, the information technology industry can be considered from two perspectives. First, there are those companies that provide IT products and services. This includes app development companies, tech startups, web development firms, and companies that consult in IT fields or deliver software-as-a-service models. Second, the information technology field also encompasses departments in many other industries that handle database administration, networking, hardware and software support, and the design and build of proprietary systems. IT employees are often involved in Six Sigma initiatives, even if they aren't the Six Sigma experts themselves, because in today's computer-driven world projects are rarely completed without some need for specialized data retrieval or changes to existing software or hardware.

Benefits of Six Sigma in an Information Technology Environment

While information technology does present some challenges to the Six Sigma expert, it is also one of the fields where benefits are easiest to apply because information technology often deals with either automated or people-powered workflow processes or the design and implementation of a product. In the first case, Lean Six Sigma principles are easy to apply; in the second case, DMADV approaches are helpful. In addition to cost savings, defect reduction, and efficiency wins, Six Sigma helps IT organizations implement strong change management programs and interface better with the business.

One of the biggest challenges that IT organizations of all types face is communication and integration with the operations side of the business. The purpose of IT is to support the needs of the business, but it can often feel like business employees and technical employees are speaking two different languages. A common fail point for many products or improvements is that the business explains a need, IT works to support what they understand about that need, but a communication problem causes the mark to be missed, even if only slightly. Six Sigma is actually a solution to this problem. By enveloping changes and product design in a Six Sigma methodology, organizations create an even playing field. The DMAIC and DMADV approaches *force* teams to find common communication ground, and when you are dealing with data and process maps, it can be easier to visualize what the other side is talking about. Once organizations start using Six Sigma to approach specific problems or needs, they often find that staff grow increasingly accustomed to communicating in such a manner, and general communication between IT and the business can be improved too.

Another challenge common to IT environments is the possibility of getting "lost" in the technical requirements and abilities. When creating a new product or computer process, IT employees can be tempted to add features as they work because they sound like a good idea. If those features don't serve a business purpose, though, the work put into them is muda. It's also possible that what sounds like a good idea in an IT arena might actually cause a problem in the business arena. Because Six Sigma always starts with business needs, it can help IT organizations reduce both muda and defects in its design and build processes.

Resources are often a challenge for IT departments and companies. Surveys of employers consistently show a lack of skilled technical workers in many industries, which means IT organizations often overwork the resources they do have. That can lead to burn out, high attrition rates, or losses in productivity. Implementing a culture of Six Sigma helps teams quickly implement solutions in a way that meets constantly changing business needs without damaging IT resources for the future.

Challenges of Implementing Six Sigma in an IT Environment

When Six Sigma experts or leaders begin working with an IT organization that hasn't implemented Six Sigma before, they are likely to run into employees and departmental leaders who don't believe the methodology is relevant to the industry. Measurement and data is the foundation of Six Sigma, and there are still some IT professionals who don't think IT and software is measurable. In reality, though, IT functions are some of the most measureable processes in the business world. It's up to the Six Sigma expert to find the ways that specific IT functions are measureable *and why those measurements matter*.

Six Sigma experts have to understand and communicate why IT measurements are important both to the business and to the IT organization. For example, if a large automated report process takes three hours to run and causes slowdown of a particular operating system while running, this is a problem for both the business and the IT organization.

Measurements – how much does the report really slow the system down? – are critical and of interest to everyone. Some questions Six Sigma answers that can benefit both the IT organization and the business include:

- Is the report really necessary to a business process, or can IT discontinue it and use those resources elsewhere?
- Is the slowdown to the system negligible or is it impacting productivity?
- Can the report be run at another time, such as at night when no one is working?
- If the report is run at night when no one is working, does that decrease the time it takes for the report to run? This can be important if the IT organization wants to run more automated reports but doesn't have the time or bandwidth to do so each day.
- Why does the report take so long to run? Is the report pulling fields that are unnecessary for the business use? Can the report be streamlined to create a faster process?

This is just one example where measurements of all types can help the IT organization.

Another challenge Six Sigma experts might face when working with IT organizations is a perception that there are never enough resources and a new project or initiative is simply not possible. This challenge is especially hard to deal with at times *because the perception is not wrong*. As previously stated, many IT organizations *do* struggle with resources, and it is probably true that there are too many things to get done and never enough time. IT employees might already put in numerous hours of overtime every week without clearing the workflow backlog, so when you present them with what sounds like another opportunity for work, it's not surprising that they balk at it. Six Sigma experts working with others in such an environment – IT or otherwise – must be adept at explaining Six Sigma principles so that they don't sound like additional work but do sound like a smarter way to approach work, processes, and problems.

A final obstacle for Six Sigma in some IT organizations is the fact that Six Sigma often comes after numerous other attempts at quality improvement programs and tools. In seeking a fast, reliable way to implement IT solutions, some organizations have wound their way through half a dozen or more methodologies, and by the time Six Sigma is broached as a tool, the IT staff are tired of learning and integrating different programs. They might see Six Sigma simply as the next flavor of the month, which means they won't take it seriously – and that leads to failures that *will* make Six Sigma simply another thing organizational leadership tried. Six Sigma experts dealing with such situations have to work hard to approach technical staff in a way that is unique and highlights the benefits of the methodology. Starting with how Six Sigma is an ongoing methodology and not a quick-fix tool is a good idea – IT employees often know that *there is no quick fix*, and they are usually happy to work within a methodology that takes that to heart.

Six Sigma IT Case Study: Cellphone Provider Web Service

A cellphone provider featured a top-up service through its online web portal. The service let customers log on and add minutes to prepaid cellphone plans. The purpose of the service was to offer a fast, easy way prepaid cellphone holders could manage their minutes and plans. In reality, however, the service had about a 40 percent failure rate for top-ups and about a 20 percent failure rate for registration. That means that a large percent of individuals had to call customer service to seek help with either adding minutes or registering for the online service.

The defects from the online top-up system created extra work for both the customer and the customer service call center. That meant increased costs for the organization on top of potential loss of revenue associated with customers that would simply not top up because the system wasn't working and they didn't have time to call the customer service center. Some customers might even seek another provider, especially if they dealt with the issue more than once.

The cell phone provider created a team to address the problem. Following a DMAIC methodology, the team stated a problem, defined processes, and began brainstorming inputs and root causes for the problems. During the early parts of the DMAIC project, the team listed nine core inputs it felt were related to the process and the issues. During the Analyze phase, the team employed hypothesis and regression testing to determine which inputs were actually driving fail rates for registration and top up.

The team originally thought that certain elements would have a strong correlation to top up success. For example, the team believed that the customer's history of successful top ups would correlate to future success with top ups. At a common-sense level, this seems plausible: if the customer was able to top up last time he or she used the system, then the next top up should be successful too. A statistical analysis of the data showed this wasn't the case – history of successful top ups had no statistical correlation to the problem at hand.

The team did note that some inputs it believed would not be related at all presented a high statistical correlation to the failure rate of top ups. One of those was the value of the top up – varying dollar or minute values seemed to correlate to varying failure rates. Since the system for topping up was the same for all values, it didn't make sense that various values would perform differently. This, along with several other correlations in the data, led the team to look at the algorithms and internal rules of the system itself. The team came to believe that the internally programmed process that rejected or accepted each transaction was flawed.

During the Improve phase, the team created a new ruleset for the internal system. One specific area they improved was how the system detected a fraudulent transaction. Prior to the change, the system was rejecting legitimate transactions because they met encoded criteria for possibly fraudulent transactions.

After addressing the fraudulent transaction process and other issues with the top-up system's automation, including how IP addresses were blacklisted, the team launched an updated process. The new process had a registration success rate of 91 percent compared with the previous success rate of 80 percent. It also had a top-up success rate of 90 percent compared to only 60 percent previously. Increased annual revenues from the new process were estimated to be $300,000.

Six Sigma IT Case Study: IT Components of Control

Even when a Six Sigma project isn't directly linked to a technical, software, or web product, IT is likely to be involved in some part of the process. Most organizations involve IT representatives in almost every Six Sigma project because all processes are somehow linked to computers. One area where technical resources are likely to be required is in automated control phases. While teams can conduct control methods – including control charting – manually, you've learned throughout this book that manual processes often come with additional failure points. If someone has to manually measure, enter, and chart data, more opportunities for error exist. IT departments often work with Six Sigma experts and process owners to automate control process to mitigate risks of errors.

ResMed, a medical device company, uses such automation in its control process. One example is how ResMed uses Minitab macros and other automation to manage control charting of the process that manufacturers machines and masks. After using some Minitab solutions during improvement processes, the team decided to continue using Minitab for control. The team also attended a workshop on leveraging Minitab for addition functions that helped them come up with an automated process.

The production line is continually tested and that data is stored in a database. Every 30 minutes, Minitab automatically queries the database file and creates a control chart. The control charts are automatically saved following a filename convention that lets the company's SharePoint system retrieve and display the updated control charts on a dashboard for review by leadership and process employees. The SharePoint system itself updated every 10 minutes, so the team always has access to control data that is no more than 40 minutes old.

The automation lets the team identify and address problems quickly. If a process is out of statistical control, the team knows within the same day, if not within a few hours, reducing losses associated with defects or process problems. If the team relied on a business analyst to pull and compile data to be presented in a control chart, it is likely that the team would not gain such insight within the hour or, possibly, even within the day.

Tips for Using Six Sigma in IT

To be successful with Six Sigma in the information technology industry, teams and Six Sigma experts must:

- Be able to convey and illustrate the benefits of the program to engage IT resources effectively.
- Be well-versed in or able to quickly become fluent in technical functions and ideas
- Work well with both technical and business resources and be able to bring together teams that are comprised of both

CHAPTER 39:
SIX SIGMA IN ENGINEERING

Unlike the previous fields covered in this unit, engineering has a more formal definition. For this chapter, engineering covers any organization or department that is engaged in engineering work – whether that work is civil, industrial, mechanical, or chemical in nature. While engineering is sometimes part of an organization or project with bigger scope – a metal building manufacturer has an engineering department, for example – engineering isn't typically an auxiliary service such as IT or HR. Six Sigma project teams are most likely to work within the engineering space because the project at hand is engineering in nature and not because they are meeting a compliance need or seeking assistance with a workflow. That being said, when an engineering question comes up in a project that is not, at its heart, an engineering project, Six Sigma teams are probably wise to consult an expert in the field.

Benefits of Six Sigma in an Engineering Environment

Successful Six Sigma engineering projects reap all of the benefits that have been highlighted throughout this book, including reduction in defects and costs. When property deployed, Six Sigma can also improve the ability of engineers and teams to meet timelines and budgets on projects, particularly in a civil engineering field.

Engineering projects usually involve many, many moving parts. Civil projects require both design and build phases. During both phases, teams have to manage costs and resources, meet compliance requirements from a variety of government and private agencies, meet the demands of the client, and ensure safety – and those are just *some* of the things that have to be considered. The DMADV and DMAIC processes force teams to consider all requirements, understand the project details and timelines, and identify challenges to be worked through. On the surface, it might seem like DMADV or DMAIC would slow down the overall engineering process. In reality, applying the same methodology to every project actually speeds up processes without impacting quality.

Six Sigma also provides benefits with regard to safety. Engineering processes in all industry subsets come with safety risks. Mistakes in civil engineering can cause safety risks to people working to build or remodel a structure; even if the structure is already built, if engineering integrity is faulty, then dangers continue to exist for those using the structure in the future. Industrial and chemical engineering come with other safety risks, especially to engineers and employees working closely with machinery or chemical processes. Some fields closely related to engineering, such as the oil field, feature some of the highest numbers of workplace accidents in the United States, and statistics for other countries tend to be similar. Implementing Lean Six Sigma tools helps create consistent quality throughout engineering processes, and that quality improves safety at the process point and further down the line.

Another benefit of Six Sigma in the engineering industry is that the methodology fits very well with the mindset of most engineering teams. Engineers are trained to think by the numbers, so they are less likely to balk at a data-driven approach than individuals in other industries are. Engineers also usually appreciate a step-by-step approach that is used across all projects because they understand the value of consistency. The appreciation for this type of approach makes it somewhat easier for Six Sigma experts to work with engineering personnel – as a Six Sigma expert, you might have to fight fewer battles in support of your methodology.

Challenges of Implementing Six Sigma in an Engineering Environment

Even though Lean Six Sigma methodologies align well with engineering mindsets, Six Sigma experts are not without challenges in implementing the method in this field. The challenges you might face in working with engineering projects depend heavily on the culture of the organization in which you are working and the mindset of the subject matter experts.

When working with any group that is highly educated, you might run into the problem of expertise. This is true of almost any specialist industry where individuals have achieved years of school and special certifications. You might find this problem in healthcare with physicians, in legal fields with lawyers, or in financial fields with CPAs, for example. The problem of expertise occurs because someone feels they *know* something because they have the education or experience to know it. They don't need a methodology such as Six Sigma; they don't need to brainstorm with others or review statistical analysis. You might hear someone say "I have two degrees and 16 years of experience, I've dealt with this type of problem before, and this is the way you fix it."

In such cases, the Six Sigma expert must do two things. First, the Six Sigma expert must see that someone with that much experience and education has a lot of knowledge and insight to offer. Simply because you are trained in Six Sigma doesn't mean that the methodology is appropriate in *all* situations. If you remember from Unit 1, Six Sigma is not the right approach when the solution is already known. However, as a Six Sigma expert, you need to be able to tell when a solution actually is known and when someone only believes they know the best solution.

Second, the Six Sigma expert must work tactfully to convince everyone involved that there is value in the process. The typical fix to a problem might work and work well, but with the collective experience of the group and an outside-the-box mentality, the team might discover a way that is even better.

In addition to challenges that come from those within an organization, Six Sigma experts who *are not also* engineering experts might face internal challenges when working in this industry. Any process in an engineering field is going to deal heavily in technical ideas including mathematics and science. Six Sigma experts don't have to be experts in the fields they deal with – you don't have to be a doctor to work as a Black Belt in the healthcare field, for example. However, you do have to be able to understand processes and how they flow, and in the engineering field that could require the ability to quickly learn at least some basics about the science or math behind the process.

Six Sigma experts working in engineering fields must also understand that all engineering is not about building structures such as bridges or buildings. Those types of projects are specifically in the realm of civil engineering. Industrial engineering, as you'll see in the case studies in this unit, is often much more tied to manufacturing processes, and chemical engineering is yet another very different field.

Six Sigma Engineering Case Study: IE in the Automotive Industry

Often, Six Sigma projects are conducted by subject matter experts within an organization and Six Sigma experts from a consulting company. In one such case, a consulting firm called Product Modeling Corporation, or PMC, worked with an OEM automotive parts manufacturer. The OEM hired the consulting company to assist with improving and controlling a process in a plant that stamped and assembled some parts. PMC used Six Sigma and industrial engineering knowledge during the improvement process.

SIX SIGMA IN ENGINEERING

As with all Six Sigma projects, the team first worked to understand the existing process within the large manufacturing plant. The plant included 2.5 million square feet of space and 23 press lines. Stamping lines ran linear, usually beginning on one side of the plant floor and ending on the other – a traditional setup for assembly or plant line production. Raw goods were stored in racks or containers and dollys, forklifts, and people were used to transport materials throughout the lines.

During the Define, Measure, and Analyze phases, the PMC team noted several opportunities for improvement in the plant's processes. Barcoding systems and storage areas were inadequate, as was the reporting system for how equipment was used and maintained. Too many forklift operators on some shifts also represented muda.

PMC worked with plant subject matter experts to develop both static and dynamic simulation models that helped predict the needs of the plant and the flow of material through the plant. Engineering analysis helped make these simulations as accurate as possible so that business decisions could be made based on the simulators. The plant wanted to be able to use such solutions to make ongoing decisions and changes to resource allocations.

PMC also worked with the plant to improve bar coding processes. Bar codes were essential for management of both resources and automated industrial processes. Bar codes let machines identify parts and work appropriately; they also let the plant better manage inventory.

The simulations and bar code improvements were tested before being rolled out to the entire plant. The result was a total of $5.6 million in savings annually.

Six Sigma Engineering Case Study: Consistent CAD and PLM Solutions

The same consulting firm, PMC, worked with a company that manufactured curtain walls, doors, and skylights. At the time PMC was brought in to facilitate improvements, the client company was working with three different processes for each product. While the engineering processes were somewhat similar, the client was using different software to design and manage the manufacture of each product. Disparate systems not only opened the door for more possible defects, but they also increased resource use and expense. PMC was tasked with reducing muda and improvement the processes in part by assisting with the implementation of singular CAD and PLM systems for all the engineering and manufacturing processes. (CAD and PLM are both engineering software tools.)

PMC first conducted audits of all the sites involved in the three processes. In conjunction with client subject matter experts, PMC identified the requirements of all the processes – a single engineering solution would have to meet all the requirements of *all* the processes. Standards for drawing were developed and the team converted AutoCAD libraries so that all the data and functionality matched. Some of the processes were using 2D libraries. Those were converted to 3D libraries so that the necessary functionality of all processes could be handled with a single format.

In addition to the implementation of consistent software tools for all processes, PMC made recommendations that would help to control quality and consistency going forward. The team recommended implementing change management controls so that future changes in one process would be rolled out appropriately across all processes and locations. To support these changes, the facility followed a six-step assessment and upgrade method that included upgrading software and engineering workstations and adding version control components to both drawing and engineering processes.

Ultimately, a single CAD software solution was implemented across all the processes and locations. The CAD solution draws from the same pool of rulesets and engineering knowledge regardless of location, which reduces consistency issues and eliminates muda associated with extra knowledge resources. The CAD solution feeds directly to the PLM software, mitigating risks of data disparity or mistakes and reducing manual work between the two processes.

The benefits to the organization included the elimination of rework at design; that helped to increase bidding efficiency so the organization could make more accurate and timely bids. Use of the same resources across all processes reduced overall costs, increasing profits, and version control helped eliminate mistakes and misunderstandings stemming from processes using outdate versions of drawings or rulesets.

Tips for Using Six Sigma in Engineering

To be successful with Six Sigma in the engineering industry, teams and Six Sigma experts must:

- Develop a deep understanding of the compliance and safety requirements associated with any project

- Be able to encourage and work with highly educated and experienced subject matter experts who might not immediately buy into the methodology
- Be able to work with multiple complex and technical ideas and integrate new knowledge quickly
- Understand how engineering plays a role in various types of projects, particularly with regard to different engineering fields, and not take a one-sized-fits-all approach to various initiatives outside of the consistency of Six Sigma

UNIT 10:
SIX SIGMA IN CUSTOMER-FACING FIELDS

CHAPTER 40:
SIX SIGMA IN FIELD SERVICE

Field services are those that rely on a person or team going into the field to perform the job. In some ways, delivery companies such as UPS or FedEx might be categorized as field service companies, but for the purposes of this chapter we'll concentrate more on companies that perform services such as HVAC repair, plumbing, electrical maintenance, or cable or phone hookup. Business-to-business services are also included in this sector, such as businesses that supply and maintain copy machines. For all of these businesses, simply getting to the right place at the right time is a big priority, so they will share some Six Sigma benefits and challenges with the shipping industry. However, field service employees also perform processes once they arrive on site.

Most field service organizations include a few common processes or departments. First, someone has to take customer calls and dispatch field service technicians appropriately. This might involve managing work orders, scheduling field calls, and routing drivers. Most field service organizations also have to manage inventory and parts, ensuring that the right tools and parts for the job make it to each location. Drivers or teams must then find the service location, assess the problem or need, and offer recommendations or a quote for service. Finally, if a quote is accepted, the field service representatives provide the service. Once service is provided, the organization must capture the data and use it to manage any invoicing processes.

Benefits of Six Sigma in a Field Service Environment

Given the above definition of a field service organization and what you now know about Six Sigma, it shouldn't be difficult to imagine benefits the methodology would bring to such companies. Six Sigma can help field service teams boost relative revenue – the amount of money that is made for the time a team or field service representative spends in the field. Remember the lessons on Lean process management – in every process, there is value added and non-value added time. In some field service organizations, value added time might be considered time you can bill for. Non-value added time would be time you can't bill for.

Consider a plumbing company that charges a set amount for some basic service calls but charges hourly for major plumbing jobs such as installations or lengthy repairs. The clock for the billing starts when the plumber starts work and ends when the work is completed, but it wouldn't be fair to charge the client for time the plumber spent taking business calls that were not related to the job. If the field service rep has to leave the job and return because he or she forgot a tool or supply – through no fault of the client – then the company probably won't include that travel in the billable time. Applying Six Sigma to these processes can help the plumbing company eliminate the non-value added time so that more of the field service representative's time in a day is billable.

The same benefit is even more applicable when a company charges a flat rate. A company that charges a flat rate for an HVAC spring maintenance job doesn't want the field service staff spending any more time on the job than is necessary for excellent customer service.

Organization is a key factor for success in field service companies, which often deal with numerous moving parts at the same time. People, supplies, and tools all have to be routed appropriately. Not all jobs are the same, so the company needs a process by which it can efficiently and accurately assess job needs for planning and dispatching purposes. If a single rep is dispatched to handle three jobs in one day, but the first job ends up taking 7 hours, then the last customer might not be served that day. Likewise, if a level one rep is dispatched to handle a level three job, there might be a problem because skills and experience won't align with the work required. Six Sigma can help field service organizations create processes that minimize such mistakes.

Another area where Six Sigma can benefit field service companies is in the quoting and assessment processes. Poor quoting processes lead to miscommunications, errors in cost information provided to the customer, loss for the company, or a dissatisfied client. Without processes in place that remove error and create consistency, representatives might quote varying prices to clients, leading to poor word of mouth or the belief that some customers are being unfairly treated. Someone might under quote a specific job because they forget to include necessary supplies or labor in the calculation. This is especially true when field representatives provide same-day quotes while on the job site, because they are often performing these tasks in a short amount of time and with the potential customer looking on and interrupting with questions. While field service companies usually make it clear that a quote is not a binding agreement regarding cost, consistently being too far off the quoted amount isn't good customer service. Six Sigma tools, including templates and poka yokes, can help reduce the chance of these issues arising.

Challenges of Implementing Six Sigma in Field Service Environments

Field service companies can benefit greatly from Six Sigma, particularly when it comes to customer service, increasing revenue, and decreasing costs. However, implementing Six Sigma in such an environment is not without challenges. One of the first challenges depends on the type of field service company involved. Field service companies are often somewhat unique because they hire skilled experts in specific niches. Just as individuals with high education credentials can prove difficult to convince of Six Sigma's value, experienced technical or vocational staff can balk at the concept that a method involving statistics and brainstorming will help them repair a plumbing problem or fix a business copy machine quicker and better.

A particular challenge of the Six Sigma expert or leader in this field is to meet the communication needs of all the people involved. Administrative and corporate managers in field services might respond to business-speak, but technicians and many field service representatives will not. They might have been told too many times how they should do their jobs by people who do not have the skills they do. In a large HVAC service company, managers might constantly tell service technicians to complete work faster or provide tips from industry literature on how to handle certain tasks. These tips don't always line up with what the service representative faces on the job – ultimately, a good field service technician knows his or her job and wants the ability to use experience on the site to provide a better fix or better customer service.

In such situations, Six Sigma experts must do a good job at communicating the ultimate freedoms that the methodology affords service representatives. Remember, a Six Sigma process reduces defects in part by making it possible for individuals to address specific problems during production. That concept is usually explained with regard to a manufacturing line – the defect is addressed before it reaches the end of the line and a quality assurance check point. But the same concept is relevant in field services – the field representative shouldn't have to call the home office for every single decision, and he or she shouldn't have to go through the motions of a previously decided process if they get to the site and see that the original process isn't going to work or fix the problem. At the same time, field service representatives can't go about applying solutions without a framework that makes decision-making similar across the company. Six Sigma helps teams build that framework, empowering field service technicians to make decisions on site without impeding overall company performance or consistency.

Another challenge you might face when implementing Six Sigma in field service companies – especially if you work as a consultant with numerous field service organizations – is that each company has its own unique requirements, processes, and goals. Yes, all field service organizations ultimately want to provide quality customer service while making a profit. But what works for an insurance adjustor team is not going to work for a team that paints houses or fixes roofs. As a Six Sigma expert in this environment, it isn't enough to know the DMAIC methodology or to understand how to apply statistical analysis. You have to be able to quickly understand the basic tenets of the companies you are working with so you can provide active advice and Six Sigma leadership that is relevant to the niche. That doesn't mean you have to become an expert in plumbing or foundation repair, but you do have to know what makes plumbing different from foundation repair or any other field service niche if you are working with a plumbing process.

Six Sigma Field Service Case Study: Automated Routes

Route management is a common trouble spot for many field service companies. Companies need processes that quickly route drivers and teams to job sites without muda – which means teams shouldn't be criss-crossing each other's paths, driving far out of their way, or arriving at job sites without the information that lets them be prepared to perform appropriate work. Many times, the introduction of automated route-generation software helps makes dispatching easier, but automation isn't always perfect and, as you've learned throughout this book, there is always room for more improvement.

One company learned this lesson and applied a DMAIC project to increase improvements that were originally experienced from an automated routing solution. The company in question provides business-to-business services that involve collecting and processing both non-hazardous and hazardous materials from automotive and industrial clients. The corporation handles approximately 45,000 service calls every week throughout the United States, and the work is managed by regional or local service branches. Each service branch has a manager who dispatches work crews each morning.

The company wanted to improve both user satisfaction and the stability of its work system, so it implemented a third-party transportation management system (TMS). The TMS was loaded with data about routes, work requirements, and customers. Each day, work order information is entered into the TMS and the system generates a dispatch list for each team. The goal of the process is to create a list that can be handled by each team in a single day while maximizing value-added time and minimizing drive time. To do this, the TMS considers best routes to and from customer locations, the amount of work the customer is requesting, and the capacity of the trucks driven by each team.

While the TMS works to create many efficiencies, the automated system alone cannot account for certain factors. For example, if a customer requires work on three machines, then the TMS allocates the time it takes for all three jobs to be completed on site. It doesn't, however, account for factors such as a customer's worksite spanning blocks and three machines being located far apart from each other. When something like that occurs, the team takes longer than expected at the job site, making every other service call that day late. In some cases, there might not be enough time to handle all of the scheduled service calls.

As a result, the automatic routes were being reviewed by management to determine if they were actually feasible. They were then being provided to service workers. During the define and measure phases, the Six Sigma team noted a bottleneck in the process. The service workers were making suggestions to alter the routes for better performance, but that required the manager to go back and make changes. This slowed the entire process down, created additional work for everyone, and created more opportunities for defects.

The Six Sigma team also noted some inconsistencies with TMS estimates of travel time and distance. Investigation during the measure phase showed that the TMS could not always parse an address fully, and it applied a certain type of geocode in these situations. The Six Sigma team noted that the geocode could be used as a measurement to determine whether the TMS was likely to be accurate about time and distance details.

Ultimately, numerous changes were made to the routing process. First, the geocode scoring was made visible in the TMS application and reporting, which let branch managers see immediately where human analysis might be necessary in improving a route. The process was also altered to offer a chance for service representatives to provide feedback on routes. Service representatives are the direct link to the client, and they are the people who have most recently been on a client site. They know how big the sites are, where equipment is likely to be located, and whether any abnormal challenges might be experienced on site. By providing feedback about route feasibility early in the process, service representatives avoid rework or scheduling problems later in the day.

The outcome of the Six Sigma project was an increase in both user satisfaction and return on investment above the increases already experienced by implementing the TMS to begin with.

Tips for Using Six Sigma in Field Service Environments

To be successful with Six Sigma in field service environments, teams and Six Sigma experts must:

- Be able to communicate and educate about Six Sigma in ways that resonate with both business and administrative staff and technical and vocational staff.
- Take time to understand the unique challenges experienced by the specific business.
- Understand the tools and requirements of the specific business.

CHAPTER 41:
SIX SIGMA IN MARKETING AND SALES

Like many of the niches covered in these last few units, sales and marketing are both their own niche and a very necessary part of almost every organization. Without sales and marketing, almost no brand or business can succeed, though the way in which organizations go about these critical functions differs broadly. While sales and marketing are often integrated, they are two different slices of the same pie.

Sales functions are often associated with the act of selling. This is the direct act of selling goods or services to a customer or client, and it usually involves time spent engaging with the customer face-to-face, via telephone, or online. The goal of sales functions is typically to close the deal – to convince the customer to buy the product or the service.

Marketing functions, on the other hand, are often more general in nature and are about generating prospects, or leads, for sales teams. Marketing includes functions and campaigns to reach potential customers and convince them that the product or service is of interest. At a car dealership, for example, the marketing work might be what brings a new customer onto the lot to look at a potential vehicle. The sales person then takes over to work directly with the new customer to ensure a deal is struck.

It's not uncommon for companies to use marketing and sales terms interchangeably, but technically the niches work closely together while following some basic boundaries as stated above. What is usually called the sales cycle, however, involves both marketing and sales functions. As you'll see in this chapter, technology, automation, and Internet resources have also combined to create more integrated sales and marketing approaches in some organizations.

Benefits of Six Sigma in Marketing and Sales

The general benefits of Six Sigma in marketing and sales organizations are similar to those experienced in any organizations that deploys the methodology. Increased production – and revenue – and decreased defects – and cost – are all benefits that are applicable to sales and marketing departments and processes. The customer-centric nature of Six Sigma actually makes it a great methodology for supporting improvements in these two areas. The Voice of the Customer tools – and the fact that any good Six Sigma project uses those tools for a foundation -- help provide critical success to functions that rely on customer response as a success measure.

Remember, the Voice of the Customer tools help Six Sigma teams understand what the customer needs and wants. Advanced analysis of VoC information can also help teams understand where customer needs are different than customer wants – a very important concept for both sales and marketing. If customer needs aren't the same as wants, then the marketing message has to be tailored appropriately. Organizations can't speak to wants and then deliver needs, but speaking only to needs without understanding wants might not result in a good conversion rate on marketing campaigns. By implementing VoC and critical-to-quality measurements, Six Sigma teams can help marketing organizations better understand all aspects of the target audience.

On the sales side of an organization, Six Sigma can help teams convert more prospects into customers, retain more customers, and even win back customers who were previously disgruntled. If you haven't worked in or adjacent to a sales organization in the past, then you might see sales as a one-and-done proposition. The sales person engages the customer for a short time, closes the deal, and moves on to the next opportunity. Outside of some non-specialty retail establishments, modern sales functions don't actually work like this. Sales has become a more complex process that often involves forming lasting client relationships, providing essential client education, and understanding client values and needs to better make product and service recommendations. For many sales teams, long-lasting client relationships are actually more important than today's sales numbers.

Because of the long-term nature of the modern sales relationship, sales organizations must present a consistent, quality approach. Clients who are offered varying information from the same sales organization or who deal with inefficient communication and processes aren't likely to make purchases or become repeat customers. The consistency of Six Sigma and the ability to continuously improve processes help sales organizations avoid these troubles.

Another reason Six Sigma has become a go-to methodology for sales and marketing organizations is that it offers proven results without impacting flexibility and creativity. Sales and marketing organizations have to be able to move quickly to deploy new strategies, particularly in an environment imbued with connectivity and technology. The Internet offers many options for connecting and engaging with potential clients, but online marketing trends evolve at a breakneck pace. Six Sigma lets companies develop processes that can keep up with trend evolution, and DMAIC projects ensure organizations validate all assumptions before making major changes.

Challenges of Implementing Six Sigma in Marketing and Sales

While Six Sigma is being embraced by an increasing number of executives in the sales and marketing fields, Six Sigma experts do still face some challenges when implementing projects in these areas. One of the most common obstacles to Six Sigma success in sales and marketing organizations is related to a misconception about how processes within such departments can be measured. Obviously, sales can be measured in the number of transactions that occur, but the impact of a marketing campaign is harder to understand. Six Sigma experts must work with sales and marketing employees to understand *how* success can be measured and assure those involved that measurement is possible.

In some cases, the Six Sigma expert doesn't have to convince anyone that success can be appropriately measured, but they might have to convince someone that the current measurement isn't working. While successful sales organizations are known for their ability to evolve to customer demands, they are also often known for a strict adherence to metrics that don't always make sense.

Consider an American electronics and appliance retail chain that measures sales success based on a variety of factors, including conversion rates. The retailer arrives at an estimated conversion rate by creating a ratio between the number of people who enter the store's door and the number of transactions that occur during the day. Sales staff were held accountable for this ratio – and sales manager bonuses were somewhat impacted by this measurement. Without any other information about the scenario, you can likely apply the knowledge gained from this book to see some obvious flaws with the door count metric. What if someone went in and out of the store multiple times? They would be counted more than once at the door, but would likely only make one sales transaction if they chose to buy. What if children stood near the automatic door, causing it to open or close multiple times? What if a group of people came in at one time, but they weren't shopping together? These are just some of the scenarios that might throw off the door count metric. Six Sigma experts working with sales organizations might have to work diligently to illustrate why some metrics aren't working as well as leadership and others believe.

Another challenge Six Sigma experts face in sales and marketing is the perception that processes aren't a foundational element for such organizations. Sales and marketing staff might argue that their work is about building relationships, and putting specific processes in place would limit their ability to do so. Sales staff, in particular, sometimes hold tightly to the perception that structure inhibits their ability to sell. In reality, though, some of the most successful sales people are planners – they arrive early to structure their day, follow plans they set for each interaction, and always return calls and messages immediately. Successful sales people are usually already following a process – Six Sigma just helps engage the entire organization in processes that work.

As a Six Sigma expert, you'll be challenged with presenting the benefits of process – and illustrating how much process already exists in sales and marketing organizations. Writing and posting blog posts is a process; maintaining social media presence is a process made up of many smaller processes. Calling a customer is a process. Receiving a lead from marketing is a process. Signing a contract or closing the deal is a process. Putting in the right information to invoice the customer is a process. Once sales and marketing professionals understand that process already exists in their organization – and Six Sigma isn't designed to flood their day with additional processes that make it more difficult to engage with customers – they are more likely to be open to continuous process improvement.

Six Sigma Marketing and Sales Case Studies

Six Sigma experts applied the DMADV approach to marketing and advertising campaigns associated with the Corporation of the City of Kawartha Lakes, which is a location in Ontario, Canada. Remember that DMADV is a phased-approach to Six Sigma projects similar to DMAIC. DMAIC is used to address existing processes that are in need of improvement and include five phases: Define, Measure, Analyze, Improve, and Control. DMADV is usually employed when a new process needs to be created or a process is being overhauled completely. The five phases of DMADV are: Define, Measure, Analyze, Design, and Verify.

During the define and measure phases of the project, the Six Sigma team worked to understand what issues faced the city's advertising processes and what might be improved upon. The team came to understand the following information about the location and its advertising requirements.

- The city and surrounding area includes 250 lakes, which leads to numerous recreational and tourist activities.
- The area includes around 73,000 residents who live mostly in rural environments and around 31,000 additional temporary residents or tourists in summer months.

- Tourism and activities play a large role in the area economy.
- Advertising events and branding the area is critical to the success of those events and to the overall economy.
- The full-time residents also rely on advertising in the form of brochures, web copy, newspaper adds, and mailers to understand options for entertainment and events in the area.

The Six Sigma team discovered two major issues during the first phases of its DMADV project. First, it discovered that no one had ever taken time to understand how the residents of the area preferred to receive advertising information about the area and its events. Second, each city and activity organization handled its own advertising processes, creating confusion, disparity, and additional costs for the city.

To better understand how each department or facility managed advertisements, the Six Sigma team worked with each area to track that information. Specifically, the team wanted to understand what staff were involved in the process and how much time was spent on these tasks. The team used the information gained to create a process map of the current process commonly used by the organizations, and it found that the process was imbued with both financial and time muda. As many as 56 percent of the process steps required to play an advertisement about events or programs required the action of senior management. That meant that someone at the city level, or a director or manager at the department or organization level, had to approve or take action, in almost every campaign and for many of the steps within that campaign. According to statistical analysis from the Six Sigma team, the city was spending up to $1,198 per hour worked on a campaign that could be cut with more efficient processes.

During the analyze portion of the DMADV project, the Six Sigma team illustrated an important point covered several times in this book: assumptions are not always correct. The population of the city in question featured 39 percent over the age of 55, and this led the city departments to believe that print advertisements would be preferred. Analysis of data gathered via focus groups, surveys, and one-on-one interviews indicated otherwise. In fact, the analysis showed that 75 percent of individuals wanted to receive information via email, 59 percent wanted to see information on the city's website, and 47 percent often used internet searches to find information. Only 41 percent wanted the information in print format.

Because the information generated by the analysis was so different from the long-term assumptions, it was questioned. There were feelings that the data was not representative of the city – a good illustration of the challenges mentioned above relating to the acceptance of new data when sales and marketing staff have always relied on certain assumptions or metrics. The Six Sigma team alleviated these worries by performing a Chi-square goodness-of-fit test, which showed that the sample was a statistical representation of the population concerned.

The team also used the focus-group and other VoC data to understand what was important to residents who received event and location advertising. Specifically, customers wanted to receive information in a timely and immediate manner, wanted information to be accurate, wanted access to both specific and general information, and wanted to be presented with information in an accessible and aesthetically pleasing manner. Using all of this information, the team entered the design phase.

Leveraging all of the VoC data compiled, the team created a requirements document for the new advertising process. Following that document, the team drafted a process map for a more efficient process that better met customer needs and allowed supervisors to make some advertising decisions, reducing the costs associated with constantly involving senior management. The define phase involved implementation of standard operating procedures, templates, creative briefs, and branding guidelines, all of which increased efficiency and removed disparity between advertisements.

Verification of the changes illustrated they were successful. The immediate savings were approximately 15 percent, or $90,000 annualized, saved on supplies and other costs. The city also saw an increase of approximately 20 percent in production and efficiency, leading to an additional cost savings estimated at $53,000 per year.

Tips for Using Six Sigma in Marketing and Sales

To be successful with Six Sigma in marketing and sales environments, teams and Six Sigma experts must:

- Be able to expertly apply Six Sigma tools such as the Voice of the Customer and CTQ trees.
- Be able to educate sales and marketing staff about the fundamentals of process and apply those lessons to the individual organizations and teams.
- Understand sales and marketing metrics.
- Be able to apply statistical analysis to validate metrics, create new metrics, and measure success with a high confidence level.

Links:

https://www.isixsigma.com/operations/marketing-and-sales/guidelines-making-lean-six-sigma-work-sales/

https://www.isixsigma.com/operations/marketing-and-sales/10-challenges-overcome-when-deploying-lean-six-sigma-pharmaceutical-sales-and-marketing/

https://www.isixsigma.com/operations/marketing-and-sales/

https://www.isixsigma.com/methodology/design-for-six-sigma-dfss-methodology/case-study-a-dmadv-approach-to-marketing-and-advertising/

https://www.isixsigma.com/operations/marketing-and-sales/customer-winback-concept-begs-use-six-sigma/

http://www.sellingpower.com/content/article/?a=1751/how-to-apply-six-sigma-to-sales

CHAPTER 42:
SIX SIGMA IN CUSTOMER SERVICE

In most organizations, customer service departments are adjacent to sales and marketing, and overlaps often occur. Some companies combine sales and customer service within the same teams – sometimes even within the same functions. Investopedia defines customer service as any process that works to ensure customer satisfaction with a service or product. Commonly, these processes involve interaction with the customer – either face-to-face, over the phone, via mail or email correspondence, or via the Internet. In fact, the Internet has drastically changed how organizations provide customer service today, allowing for the evolution from mostly in-person and phone support to a mix of digital support options.

Every organization that provides a service or product to any other person or organization must consider at least some elements of customer service. Customer service even occurs within organizations, as departments serve employees in other areas.

While important in every industry, customer satisfaction as a driver does rank differently in each niche. In most retail environments, for example, customers have many options for seeking service and products. Someone shopping for groceries can usually travel just a little further down the street for goods if they believe a store doesn't offer good customer service. Even individuals shopping for specialty items can turn to online stores for products if a local store isn't meeting their service needs. For these types of companies, customer service isn't just important. It can be the major distinguishing factor for the brand – especially when all other things, such as product quality and price, are equal.

For other organizations, customer choice is not as prevalent. If you are taking advantage of government services, for example, there is very rarely a competitor to which you can turn if you are unhappy with those services. While government organizations don't discount customer service completely, it isn't always their highest priority. In some niches, this is also true in part because of the type of service being performed. Consider a hospital: many patients do have *some* choice about where they receive their medical treatment, even if those choices are limited by geography and payer plans. That makes customer service a high priority for medical facilities – but good customer service will never supersede priorities such as patient safety or outcome. Emergency department staff, for example, are more likely to act quickly and present terse explanations to patients or family because, in a trauma situation, time may be of huge importance.

It's important not to confuse *the function* of customer service with the Six Sigma idea of the customer. You've learned throughout this book that customers are critical components of any process and that Six Sigma teams should always be aware of both critical to customer and critical to quality characteristics within a process. However, meeting critical to quality requirements doesn't always mean customer service in the traditional sense. In the emergency room, the CTQ is keeping a patient alive; secondary metrics might include patient satisfaction and comfort. But a good medical team will generally sacrifice patient comfort if it is required for a viable treatment. Remember, an important factor in applying Six Sigma and its customer quality methods to any process is first understanding both who the customer actually is and how quality is and should be defined for the process.

In this chapter, we'll look specifically at how Six Sigma works with customer service organizations and processes. For the purpose of limiting scale and providing appropriate examples, this chapter will concentrate on organizations and processes that would naturally put a high priority on customer service, including service, retail, and call center companies.

Benefits of Six Sigma in Customer Service

One of the biggest benefits that Six Sigma can bring to any customer service organization is that it opens the doors for teams to concentrate clearly on customer outcomes. Yes, any organization that identifies itself as a customer service department should already be concentrating on the customer, but companies often fail to do so with the right mindset, perspective, and data.

In the last chapter, you saw how a well-meaning marketing organization sought to provide the market with a certain product based on what it assumed was a customer preference for hard copy information. The Canadian city, however, later found out that its assumptions were incorrect, and thus it was potentially wasting time and money on customer service endeavors that did not best serve the customer. Six Sigma helps organizations pinpoint true customer demands and desires and then provide the products or services that best meet that criteria. The results of such changes usually include additional sales and the ability to demand more money because the product is more valuable to the end customer.

Six Sigma also helps customer service organizations dig deeper into metrics for better data-backed decision-making. As with marketing and sales organizations, customer service organizations often already have metrics in place. Common metrics might include the average time it takes someone to answer or handle a telephone call, the number of customers served in a given period, or a customer satisfaction score calculated from surveys and feedback forms. While these are all fine metrics for a customer service organization to be concerned with, you know by now that they might not be the right metrics by which specific process success should be measured.

For customer service organizations, continuous improvement related to Six Sigma can result in increased customer loyalty. Statistically, many customers leave an organization because they are not satisfied with the experience they had at that business, but it's easy to blame what seem like more obvious factors. This is why so many organizations rush to reduce prices or compete with others on what type of price or services are offered. But they might be doing so at great expense to the organization without favorably impacting customer loyalty. Yes, prices and products are important. If your prices are simply outrageously high, most people cannot make a case for remaining loyal. Prices and products also help you get customers in the door. But service levels are what keep customers coming back, and Six Sigma helps you reduce defects and non-value added processes to increase customer satisfaction.

Finally, Six Sigma provides a framework that makes it possible for all customer service employees to reach achievement milestones and serve customers well. This increases employee morale, thus increasing the chance that employees will be confident and happy when serving customers. This circular improvement impacts the customers, who are happier, which in turn might also improve employee morale. Serving happy customers is much easier than serving upset customers.

Challenges of Implementing Six Sigma in Customer Service

The challenges of implementing Six Sigma in customer service are similar to those of implementing it in sales and marketing organizations. First, individuals might argue that people-centric processes can't be analyzed and improved in the same way that manufacturing processes can, but you've already seen that isn't true. Second, customer service leaders or employees might argue that a strict framework for processes will remove the representative's ability to creatively and helpfully deal with customer issues. Throughout this book, you've seen that Six Sigma doesn't have to quash creativity, but that it can build a stable foundation where creativity flourishes alongside consistency. In fact, in a customer service organization, Six Sigma can help ensure everyone is heard so customer service representatives who have excellent ideas for assisting customers can help the company turn those ideas into overall processes.

Another challenge in implementing Six Sigma in a customer service environment can actually come from both sides. Six Sigma experts who are not experienced in customer service can be somewhat gung-ho in how they approach improvement, and that *can* result in processes that seem to smother the life of the customer service organization. At the same time, individuals on the business side might balk at any measurement or quality program that threatens to change the status-quo, especially when those measures are being put forth by what the customer service organization sees as "analysts" or "consultants" without applicable experience. In such a situation, the Six Sigma expert must take time to understand the needs of the customer service organization and present Six Sigma as a solution in the context of those needs.

Six Sigma Customer Service Case Study: Financial Services Help Desk

The case study for this chapter comes from a company in India. The company provides financial services to a range of customers, and one of those services is a telephone and email helpdesk that is supposed to respond to customer queries for information or assistance. The organization began a project during which team members would be trained on both Six Sigma and Lean approaches while applying those methodologies to achieve increased positive results for the help desk.

At the start of the project, the help desk was already being measured. The response time of the help desk on each call was a time measurement that began when the call was registered with the system and ended when the call was "closed." During the define phase of the project, leadership teams brainstormed possible issues and a Voice of the Customer tool was used. The leadership team decided that customer service was critical to help desk success, so the project would concentrate on applicable improvements in customer satisfaction.

Through the define and into the measure phase, the team discovered that the current measurement -- help desk response time – wasn't consistent and might not be doing a good job of showing whether the processes were successful or not. Specifically, the time stopped when a ticket was considered "closed," but various processes considered an item closed at different times. Sometimes, tickets were closed when a response was issued to the customer; other times, the ticket was held open until a resolution was finalized. Other consistency issues arose because different calls required different standards of service and the help desk often had to rely on work from outside departments, which it had no control over.

Because it was learning about the Six Sigma methodology, the team knew that it couldn't address *all* issues in one project. The leadership team had identified 25 different problems, but you know at this point that attempting to improve all problems in one DMAIC project is setting a Six Sigma team up for failure. To bring the project into a workable scope, the team considered two major factors.

First, it looked at the fact that two major measurements existed. Calls could be measured via response time – the time it took to provide the customer with a first-level response to a call or email. They could also be measured in resolution time – the time it took to fully resolve an issue for a customer. But the help desk team wasn't always in charge of resolving an issue. Many times, the issue had to be escalated to another department; at that point, the help desk no longer had any control. As you've already learned, Six Sigma teams can't successfully implement an improvement project over processes that are out of their control. In this case, the team made a choice to concentrate on response times, because response times were always within the purview of the help desk staff.

The team also looked at disparate types of tasks, which came with various service level requirements. Different calls had to be responded to within two days, five days, or seven days. The team created a Pareto chart illustrating these calls and found that almost all calls – 98 percent – were of the type that should be responded to within two days. Following the 80-20 rule, which had an obvious choice in this case, the team decided to concentrate on these types of calls.

The team took a baseline measurement and noted that the calls were being handled in an average of 12.7 days. The goal was to bring that into compliance with the two-day call time limit, which meant reducing call responses by 10.7 days.

At this point in the project, the team was beginning the analyze phase. Instead of relying solely on brainstorming and analytical tools, the team again turned to the customer to find out more about root causes and customer needs. Going back to the customer is rarely a bad idea, especially when additional customer feedback can help solidify assumptions for root cause analysis. When you are dealing with a customer service oriented process, you might have to return to customer data frequently during a Six Sigma project.

The team in question found that customers who called or emailed the help desk very often wanted to know when something would occur. Even when the customer wanted to know what the problem was, he or she also wanted to know when the resolution would happen or when an answer could be given. The Six Sigma team decided that answering the "when" questions would result in closure of help desk calls more often than answering "what" questions.

If "when" answers were the customer driver, then how long should each call or email take to close? The team looked at various factors and brainstormed answers to this question, and decided that when information was available within the help desk's direct environment, then a call could be closed in approximately 20 minutes. Clearly, if the current average close rate was over 12 days, there were some major problems with the processes.

Obviously, the gut reaction of help desk staff was that information was not available to them in most cases. Because they depended on other departments for the information, they had no real control over how long it took to respond to a customer. You can probably guess: while it seemed like a valid assumption at the time, it wasn't completely true.

As data was gathered about the calls and emails, it seemed that about 2/3 of the time, the help desk did have the information – or *could* have the information – to respond. Even if the other third of the calls took a few days to handle, if 2/3 of calls were answered within 20 minutes, the average would be much lower than 12.7 days.

To apply Lean process management principles that would let the help desk department schedule staff according to call volumes and handle resources appropriately, the team first created a process map of the current process. You probably won't be surprised to learn that the process map was confusing and fraught with muda. Processes often involved half a dozen people and included back and forth movement of the work without any real value added. The team noted that the manager actually resolved about 15 percent of calls himself during the measured time period. Ideally, most calls should be answered with only the involvement of the customer, the help desk staff member, and one other person who might be involved in doing the work the customer was inquiring about.

The team used what it had learned to create a new process map. The goal was to reduce wasted effort, which meant providing help desk staff with the resources and training required to close more calls themselves. The Six Sigma team also put solutions in place that would keep difficult calls from getting caught in the back log. Specifically, the help desk team would handle calls in a first-in-first-out (FIFO) method whenever possible. Difficult calls – ones that might require more work or communication than normal – would be swept twice each day at preset times, and calls that must go up to another level would follow a specific path that ensured they reached individuals who were most likely to be able to resolve the calls.

The results of the improvements – which basically included applying Lean methods to the call processes – were enormous. Within four weeks, the help desk had reduced response times by 66 percent. The goal was achieved within six weeks, and staff were surprised at how easy it was to maintain those results using Lean process management.

Tips for Using Six Sigma in Customer Service

To be successful with Six Sigma in customer service, teams and Six Sigma experts must:

- Be able to communicate the benefits of Six Sigma to people-centric processes
- Take time to understand the needs of customer service organizations and how to present Six Sigma tools and analysis in light of those needs
- Understand the difference between customer service as a function and the idea of customer satisfaction within the Six Sigma methodology

Links

http://www.processexcellencenetwork.com/lean-six-sigma-business-transformation/articles/6-ways-six-sigma-can-benefit-your-company
http://www.unitiv.com/intelligent-help-desk-blog/bid/98278/How-Six-Sigma-Improves-Customer-Service
http://www.qualitydigest.com/may03/articles/01_article.shtml
https://www.isixsigma.com/implementation/basics/measuring-and-improving-service-processes-six-sigma/
http://www.investopedia.com/terms/c/customer-service.asp
https://www.isixsigma.com/new-to-six-sigma/dmaic/helping-help-desk-satisfy-customers-case-study/

CHAPTER 43:
SIX SIGMA IN CALL CENTERS

A call center is an organization or department that is set up to handle high-volume calls from customers, prospective clients, or other interested parties. Typically, a call center involves a large office space inhabited by numerous individuals who work in shift environments to ensure calls are answered within appropriate times. In some cases, call center employees are tasked with making outbound calls in addition to or instead of taking inbound calls. Inbound calls occur when a customer or someone else calls into the call center; outbound calls occur when an employee calls someone outside of the call center.

Usually, call centers handle telephone work associated with assisting customers to place an order, troubleshooting customer service issues such as missing orders or returns requests, providing account assistance such as bill payments or service upgrades, offering technical support on products, or helping customers with any other issues. Call centers can process hundreds or even thousands of calls in a day or week because of call routing. If there are one hundred individuals in the call center ready to take calls, then the call center can handle up to 100 customer calls at any given time. Calls are routed to individual work stations, usually based on algorithms programmed into the phone system, to help reduce the time it takes to reach an operator. If an operator can't pick up for any reason, however, the call isn't usually dropped into a voicemail system. Instead, it routes to the next employee who can answer the phone.

While traditional call centers usually have hundreds of employees working in the same building – often in large open spaces that are divided by cubicles – modern connectivity has made the digital call center possible. Digital call centers don't house employees in a single building – often, workers answer calls from their own homes using VPN or web portals to perform work. Calls are routed to off-site employees the same way they would be routed to individuals in an office environment. One example of this type of setup can be seen in the way Apple handles technical service calls from customers. Many Apple technical representatives work from home, taking calls from those locations. This lets Apple maintain long call center hours and employ thousands of representatives without overhead expenses associated with maintaining numerous office locations.

One final type of "call center" is the chat call center. These aren't really call centers, but the premises by which they are managed are very similar. Chat representatives can work in an office or in their own homes and they answer customer service needs via Internet chat rather than phone calls. Many eCommerce and web service companies employ chat reps that are available at certain times of the day to immediately assist with customer needs. Verizon Wireless, for example, offers a chat contact option online. Verizon customers can chat with someone online about bills, service questions, or troubleshooting needs.

When discussing Six Sigma in the context of call centers in this chapter, we will mainly focus on traditional call center environments. However, Six Sigma can also be applied to virtual call center and chat call center processes.

Benefits of Six Sigma in Call Centers

Call centers benefit from Six Sigma in many of the same ways customer service organizations do. More organized, streamlined approaches lead to better service and let call center employees handle calls more efficiently. Because Six Sigma puts control for many decisions at the production level – in this case, in the hands of the person first answering the call – employees are empowered to take action. But Six Sigma isn't a free pass to take just any action – by coupling the principles of Lean process management and Six Sigma, call centers can create consistent action, even across hundreds of representatives. The results are increased performance, lower costs, and happy customers.

While such benefits are critical to the success of any organization, being able to measure performance and meet specific metrics can mean the difference between keeping or losing a contract for some call centers. Call centers often operate at the behest of partner organizations. Third-party call centers might provide service for consumers who deal with cell phone providers, computer companies, health insurance companies, or even online retailers. When the call center signs a contract with the company for which it will provide service, it typically agrees to meet certain requirements. Often, these are known as SLAs, or service level agreements. Failure to deliver on SLAs could mean loss of revenue or bonus payments, payment of a fine, or loss of the entire contract.

Six Sigma can be extremely beneficial to organizations that are SLA heavy. First, implementing Six Sigma approaches helps the call center improve processes so that it can make SLAs. Second, Six Sigma actually improves the way organizations measure and control processes, which makes it easier to document compliance with an SLA. In cases where measurement systems don't hold up, organizations might be meeting SLAs but not be able to prove it or even know it.

Challenges of Implementing Six Sigma in Call Centers

One of the biggest challenges of implementing Six Sigma in call centers is a misconception regarding the methodology's primary goal. You know from the lessons throughout this book that the primary goal of Six Sigma is continuous improvement that both increases customer satisfaction and business performance, where overall business performance is often measured as a revenue or bottom-line goal with other, more specific goals, used to measure the performance of processes.

While Sigma levels, as discussed in the first chapter of this book, are a relevant measurement for many processes, reaching a level of 6 sigma is not always easy or even possible for every process. Often, reaching a defect level of 3.4 defects per million opportunities isn't possible consistently in a call center environment because no call center can control every input and the definitions of what is considered a defect are too unrealistic. The processes are too reliant on people – and some of the people-based inputs are customers or those calling in. Reaching a level of 6 sigma within the first year of implementation – or even several years – can require grueling or impossible process changes that set the entire call center up for failure if Six Sigma experts try to push for too much improvement – or too much change – too quickly. Call center jobs are already considered stressful because they involve stringent response and resolution performance, so you can quickly alarm employees if you come in heavy with discussions on improving metrics that you might not fully understand or which aren't actually realistic for the process.

One of the lessons about Six Sigma presented throughout this book is that a successful approach to process improvement involves defining challenging, yet realistic, goals. If the goals you set as a Six Sigma team are too easy, there's really no need to go through the entire DMAIC process. You can probably achieve those goals with some minor changes based on define and measure. If the goals are too hard, they can't be realized without extreme measures that might negatively impact customer service, morale, or the bottom line in the end. In a call center environment, Six Sigma teams have to be able to understand the current processes and capabilities as well as the available and likely resources so they can set appropriate goals.

Not only do Six Sigma experts have to be able to set appropriate goals and motivate call center leaders and employees to continue making improvements via new projects as they succeed in implementing and controlling changes, they must also be able to communicate about Six Sigma in a proactive manner. Six Sigma leaders working in call center environments have to be prepared for these types of objectives and they should be able to present illustrations and explanations that use call centers as examples. Presenting manufacturing examples to illustrate the benefits of Six Sigma could help cement the idea that the process won't work in a call center.

Six Sigma Call Center Case Study: The SLA-Troubled Call Center

The case study for this chapter is a call center that was facing the potential loss of a contract because it was failing to meet the service level agreement it had with the client. The third-party call center was answering customer calls for the client, providing information and resolution to customer questions. The call center had a contract with the client that agreed to a 75 percent first-call resolution and a 90 percent five-day resolution. That meant that 75 percent of the calls that came into the center should be resolved within that first call – the representative should not have to call the customer back or the customer should not have to make more than one phone call. Additionally, 90 percent or more of the calls had to be resolved within a five-day period following the initial call. Statistically, that means that 15 percent of the calls not resolved within the first call had to be resolved within five days.

It was known that the client was considering termination of the contract with the call center, but no one knew what the real problem was. In fact, a first look at the call center from a Six Sigma perspective revealed an enormous issue of measurement. The call center was not collecting data relevant to the SLAs – it could not provide information about the first-call resolution or five-day resolution success. It was, however, tracking data such as hold times and availability of representatives to answer calls. Additionally, someone with the client's office was keeping track of the number of customer calls she received because customers weren't receiving answers through the call center. Not only was this person receiving an average of 15 calls every week, she was also a key decision maker for the client.

The Six Sigma team first worked to gather baseline data about the company's SLA goals, since none existed. It found that the company had a 50 percent first-call resolution and a 62 percent five-day resolution – both metrics were far below the SLA goal.

Analysis also uncovered a number of issues associated with both metrics and process capability. Data collected during measure and analyze made the team aware of a Catch-22 type problem in the call center. Performance of representatives in the call center was measured primarily by a single statistic: how often the person was available when a call came through. If the representatives were not available – even if they weren't available because they were currently helping another customer – it reflected badly on them. The speed with which they handled the call – not the customer problem – was seemingly more important.

The Six Sigma team discovered that many times, the reason a customer issue could not be closed on the first call was because it required a level of research that would keep the representative on the phone and unable to take calls. The representative, feeling limited in how much time he or she could spend with a single caller, would not take the extra time to close the issue. The call center also didn't have a good system for follow-up on issues that were not resolved during a call. This resulted in these customers having to call back a few days later – often customers made several calls to get an issue handled. The result wasn't just that customers were not satisfied and the SLA was not met. All those extra, and unnecessary, calls created muda in the call center and negatively impacted productivity.

The Six Sigma team continued to gather data by monitoring random call center work, speaking to subject matter experts, and measuring performance. The team also used tools such as fish bone diagrams to identify root causes and begin brainstorming possible solutions. Throughout the DMAIC phases, a new process was born and new metrics created. The call center team was divided into two – half the employees took calls and the other half performed research. Call center representatives took turns handling each task, and metrics to measure performance accurately were designed for both groups.

The IT department was also included in work to improve the process. They modified the system to include fields in the call logs where research and requested information could be entered and tracked. If issues weren't resolved within four days, they were forwarded to management. Within a few weeks, the call center saw incredible results. Not only were first-call and five-day resolution times well within SLA requirements, but the decision maker at the client was receiving less than one customer call each month as compared to dozens.

Tips for Using Six Sigma in Call Centers

To be successful with Six Sigma in call centers, teams and Six Sigma experts must:

- Understand the people-inherent nature of the call center environment
- Realize that automated solutions and templates are valuable in call centers but that they can't solve every problem

- Understand the level of stress many employees in a call center might feel to meet performance requirements and position Six Sigma as a tool to help them meet the *right* requirements rather than a demand for additional requirements
- Be able to communicate regarding Six Sigma in a way that invokes examples and illustrations that are relevant to the call center and not to manufacturing or similar industries.

Links:

https://www.isixsigma.com/implementation/case-studies/using-lean-six-sigma-improve-call-center-operations/

http://www.sixsigmaonline.org/six-sigma-training-certification-information/can-a-call-center-benefit-from-six-sigma-certification/

http://www.callcenter-iq.com/operations/columns/six-sigma-may-be-dangerous-to-your-call-center

CHAPTER 44:
SIX SIGMA IN THE RETAIL INDUSTRY

Most people take retail for granted, happy that they can simply pick up the items they need from a local store. However, a great deal of logistics and effort lie underneath the surface to make this happen.

Retail operations mainly take place in a storefront, where cashiers and front end personnel are aided by store management, receiving personnel to handle the receipt of new products, and back end employees to stock shelves. If a retail chain has multiple stores, it increases the work force and presents challenges in rolling out changes to all locations. Additionally, each retailer must work with a long list of vendors to order new products, coordinate deliveries, and return spoiled merchandise.

While the physical brick-and-mortar location is the foundation of retail, the industry is becoming increasingly reliant on online sales. Online retailers enjoy the benefit of being able to sell products that are not sold in stores, increasing the options of their customers without wasting valuable shelf space. The online model has its fair share of potential issues, particularly shipping times, shipping costs, and the availability of products listed on the company's website.

Another growing concern for retailers is the merging of the physical location and the online shop. The most popular use of this synergy is items purchased online for in-store pickup. This requires the store and the website to be in sync in real time so that inventory figures are accurate and customer wait time is minimized.

The retail industry comprises 42 million jobs and contributes more than $2.5 trillion to the GDP of the United States. (https://nrf.com/advocacy/retails-impact) It's in the interest of every retailer to operate as efficiently as possible and to maximize their profit margins. Six Sigma can help virtually any retailer to eliminate inefficiencies, improve customer service and encourage customer loyalty.

Benefits of Six Sigma in the Retail Industry

Inventory Management

Marketing and generating interest in products is only one small part of increasing revenues. Companies must actually have the products desired by consumers in stock. Although the inventory process has become increasingly automated, Six Sigma can still play a role in effectively managing inventory resources.

The typical inventory process has multiple potential bottlenecks. From the physical process of ordering to delivery time to loading the products off the truck, there are many ways in which the normal flow of products can be disrupted. Identifying these problem areas can help any company to zero in on the true reasons for delays or delivery of the wrong products.

Companies that deal with products that have longer lead times stand to benefit the most from a thorough analysis and process improvement initiative relating to inventory. However, companies of all sizes can streamline their approach to inventory, creating an iron-clad process that can be followed in locations across the country.

Scheduling

The bigger a company gets, the more difficult the small tasks become. Scheduling is a major issue for retail companies, particularly in those operations with multiple locations and longer hours.

Automated scheduling solutions can help in a variety of ways. With the use of forecasting based on historical data, modern technology enables the schedule to meet the anticipated inflow of customers. Like many Six Sigma tools, this allows store managers to see the ideal solution, rather than simply what they believe the answer to be. Managers can also maximize in-store personnel while minimizing salary, a major benefit since most retail employees are hourly employees. Utilizing part-time on the lower spectrum of the salary scale can help retailers to achieve significant cost savings. Six Sigma can help retail stores to find the right mix of reliable full-timers and part-time help.

Employee Productivity

The insistence on keeping customers happy and moving through the store means it's often difficult to focus on the productivity level of employees. Six Sigma can help managers to identify the metrics most closely aligned with productivity, then track these areas over time. For customer-facing employees, these metrics can include items scanned per minute, credit card applications or extended warranties sold per day, customer survey ratings, and add-on items sold.

Six Sigma can also help to track the productivity levels of back end employees as well. More importantly, the potential exists for process improvements that can overhaul internal operations, increasing efficiency and employee morale. Implementing processes that are easy to follow and track is vital due to the high turnover rates associated with retail.

Challenges of Using Six Sigma in the Retail Industry

Tracking Difficulties

Although a great deal of potential exists for the future of Six Sigma in retail, there are significant hurdles that stand in the way of progress. Initiatives to track inventory and productivity go only as far as the individuals using those systems. Inadequate training and lack of attention to detail can make it very difficult for an organization to fully understand the issues at hand.

For example, many stores use electronic reordering systems that receive its figures from the number of items scanned at the point of purchase. As long as the correct number of items is scanned, the store can successfully reorder the correct number of items. However, if the items aren't scanned as directed - for instance, if a cashier scans one can of cat food 24 times instead of accounting for all of the different varieties - the store doesn't get the true picture of what's being sold. Therefore, the reordering process hits a snag; along the same lines, productivity analysis of the cashiers who fail to follow the typical process is similarly derailed.

Lack of Interest

Retail operations rely heavily on part-time talent for their scheduling flexibility and for their lack of financial burden. Not only do part-timers make less money than full-time employees, but they don't require the company to invest as much money for their benefits packages. However, these advantages come at a cost.

Part-time employees may not have a good enough incentive to buy into a company's Six Sigma initiatives. These employees likely won't be there to see the changes come to fruition, but more immediately, they often can't be bothered to deal with the scrutiny and inevitable change that comes with Six Sigma. A high school student who works in a retail store on the weekends has no real motivation to comply with the employee dedication that's necessary to make a Six Sigma project work. It takes the right set of employees to implement Six Sigma, and many retail stores struggle to come up with the winning mix of resources.

Difficulty Implementing in Multiple Locations

Embarking on a Six Sigma initiative is an arduous task for any company. The prospects become that much more difficult when multiple locations are involved.

On one hand, having many retail locations within one organization can be helpful in terms of obtaining the most data points and coming up with new ideas. But the reality is that getting people to buy in and take ownership of the Six Sigma project is hard enough in one location. Expanding the scope to more than one location comes with serious challenges. Even if the actual project is limited to one store and subsequently rolled out to the other locations, convincing entire stores to change so much can be very difficult.

Additionally, each retail store within a larger company may have its own culture and ways of doing things. What boosts morale at one location may derail another store entirely. Implementing a consistent set of policies and metrics across all physical locations may be the biggest challenge faced by the company.

Six Sigma Retail Case Study: Amazon.com

Amazon's rise from online bookstore in the late 1990s to the eighth-largest retailer in the world in 2016 was the result of careful planning and consistent dedication to performance improvement.(http://www.forbes.com/sites/laurengensler/2016/05/27/global-2000-worlds-largest-retailers/#7b21c79b29a9) While the company has not published information about any Six Sigma projects to date, a review of Amazon's internal proceedings shows that the principles of define, measure, analyze, improve and control have been in place from Day One. (https://www.isixsigma.com/community/blogs/six-sigma-amazoncom/)

The internal assignment of the titles of green belt and black belt to the company's best problem solvers is a testament to the influence Six Sigma has had on Amazon. The fact that Amazon has received such a benefit from adhering to the principles of Six Sigma is no surprise. Managing warehouses all over the United States means keeping track of the inventory levels of these warehouses and knowing which warehouses have to ship to a given area. This is especially critical given the costs of shipping merchandise and the responsibility that comes with guaranteed delivery dates.

In the company's early days, Jeff Wilke - a former engineer who is now one of Amazon's CEOs - explained that the philosophy of Amazon held the Six Sigma principles dear. Amazon adopted technological solutions to decrease the variability of the warehouse workflow, increasing the reliability of the company's operations. This was vital in light of notable failures by large companies to handle online ordering, such as Toys R Us during the 1998 and 1999 holiday seasons (http://articles.sun-sentinel.com/1999-12-24/business/9912231103_1_toysrus-com-order-status-shoppers) Internally, Wilke and his colleagues retrained Amazon's staff and presented their improvements in a way that everyone could understand and that everyone could get behind. This type of buy-in is the goal of all Six Sigma operations, and it's helped Amazon as the company has increased its number of products and services over the years.

Whereas many businesses compete on one core competency, Amazon aims to achieve every strength conceivable - the biggest selection, for the lowest price, with the best customer experience possible. Amazon has famously sacrificed profits in the name of re-investing into the company, aiming to become even more efficient and prolific. The results have paid off in a big way. Amazon's 2015 net profit was $596 million, while the company posted a $513 million profit in the first quarter of 2016. (http://www.cnet.com/news/amazon-says-first-quarter-sales-and-profit-blew-out-expectations/)

Amazon's focus on efficiency has spilled into each new initiative undertaken by the company. Newer services, such as Amazon Fresh (online grocery shopping) and Amazon Web Services receive the benefit of years of the practice of Six Sigma methodology in other areas. Because Amazon has gotten the process of order fulfillment and timely delivery down to a science, Amazon can use this knowledge to increase the company's offerings while maintaining a vigilant eye on the internal metrics that translate into success.

Six Sigma Retail Case Study: Home Shopping Clothing Retailer

As stated earlier, a major challenge for retailers is reconciling their in-store retail operations with online sales. In the midst of navigating these waters, the company is still responsible for maintaining its usual workflows and sales targets. Given the uncertain timeframes that come with technical solutions, this is a difficult problem for many companies to solve.

A popular home shopping retailer noticed inefficiencies within both their in-store and online sales processes. The most notable issue was their cycle time when it came to issuing new products. The length of time between the conception of a new product and its subsequent launch became prohibitively long, which is a dangerous situation for a clothing company to be in. It is vital for apparel retailers to be the first to the market and to always be on the cutting edge in terms of fashion. Featuring outdated fashions in a catalog or on a website can spell disaster for even the most prominent retailers.

The company decided to work with a consulting agency, which recommended a Six Sigma project to solve the company's problems. (http://www.palomaconsulting.com/case-studies/retail/case-study-2-improving-process-efficiencies-within-the-creative-process-of-leading-home-shopping-retailer/) While the company wanted to improve its online process, it was decided that focusing on this area would have to wait. Due to the company's massive growth, it was already undergoing a series of IT initiatives, meaning that solutions of a technical nature would have to wait until those projects had completed. Besides, the real problem was the cycle time between a product's creation and its' on-sale date. The consulting group and the company agreed that this cycle time should be the main focus of the Six Sigma project. Additionally, while the company owned 30 different clothing brands, it kept the focus to only one brand in order to narrow the scope of the analysis.

Before beginning, company leadership and the consulting agency met with the stakeholders for the processes at hand. Both groups knew that the only way the project would succeed was if every member of the organization bought in. To that end, employees were allowed to ask questions and make suggestions based on their everyday work experiences. In the end, a series of smaller projects was devised based on the feedback from the staff of the company.

The Six Sigma initiative focused on two main areas - reducing variability and minimizing waste. Improving performance in these areas meant that the process to move a creative vision into the company's catalog would be streamlined and predictable. The consulting group and the company worked together to improve the use of internal resources; they also simplified the creative briefing process, which meant the catalog writers and online store personnel could more easily describe and promote new products.

In the end, the company achieved its goal of reducing its cycle time. Furthermore, the time necessary to produce creative briefs was reduced, as were the number of errors related to artwork. Most importantly, the improvements made in this Six Sigma process proved to be repeatable. When the company implemented these changes in their other clothing brands, they saw similar positive results. The benefits this company received from their Six Sigma initiative was well worth their investment, and the resulting improvements have stood the test of time.

Tips for Using Six Sigma in the Retail Industry

Six Sigma methodology has the potential to transform an entire retail operation, turning it from an unstable environment into the model of efficiency and customer satisfaction.

Developing a plan to convince employees to buy in may be the most critical step in the Six Sigma journey. It may be difficult to sell a teenage cashier on the merits of a Six Sigma project, but it's a necessary step for any process improvement initiative. Additionally, buy-in may be hard to achieve when there are multiple locations involved. Coming up with a strategy to convince employees to go along with the plan is essential.

A clearly defined project scope is vital for success. If a retail operation has many stores, it should focus only on one location as it begins to implement and analyze changes. Once the modifications prove to be successful, then - and only then - should the new process be rolled out in other locations.

Retail is a highly competitive industry that must always be able to change with the times. However, Six Sigma requires a strict inward focus. The more a company worries about what everyone else is doing, the more ill-equipped the company will be to accurately assess its own flaws and defects. Any strategy can be tweaked to fit into the context of a competitive landscape after the fact. To really make positive internal changes, the company must keep its eye on the ball.

Source

http://www.forbes.com/sites/laurengensler/2016/05/27/global-2000-worlds-largest-retailers/#7b21c79b29a9
https://www.isixsigma.com/community/blogs/six-sigma-amazoncom/, http://articles.sun-sentinel.com/1999-12-24/business/9912231103_1_toysrus-com-order-status-shoppers,
http://www.cnet.com/news/amazon-says-first-quarter-sales-and-profit-blew-out-expectations/
http://www.palomaconsulting.com/case-studies/retail/case-study-2-improving-process-efficiencies-within-the-creative-process-of-leading-home-shopping-retailer/

CHAPTER 45:
SIX SIGMA IN ECOMMERCE

The eCommerce industry has exploded over the past two decades. Today's marketplace has seen large online retailers like Amazon expand to areas far beyond their original niche, providing a fantastic, low-cost customer experience that everyone can enjoy. As a result, many retailers have chosen to move to an online-only model, while others have simply chosen to close their businesses altogether.

The eCommerce industry is one that's sure to continue to grow in the future. While people do prefer the instant gratification they derive from making an in-store purchase in some cases, they're likely to conduct their repeat business online, where prices may be cheaper and the immediate need for an item is diminished . (http://www.chicagotribune.com/lifestyles/sc-cons-0904-savvy-shopper-20140904-story.html) To that end, more than 75 percent of consumers aged 15 and over made an online purchase in the first three months of 2014. (http://www.business.com/ecommerce/retail-or-e-tail-buying-online-vs-buying-in-person/)

eCommerce isn't just a winning proposal for shoppers seeking a good deal. eCommerce also provides many benefits to retailers. Because they have limitless space to advertise their products, companies can sell more products online than they can in stores. Additionally, because they don't have to worry about the costs of owning and running a physical showroom, their overhead expenses are far less than those of brick-and-mortar retailers.

While eCommerce is a term that generally describes any online purchase, there are several different platforms in which eCommerce takes place. The traditional model is where one company hosts its own website and inventory storage systems. This company handles all aspects of the order, from its inception to its ship date. The eCommerce retailer is also charged with handling after-sale support functions such as refunds, shipping issues and general product support. Another way companies can embrace eCommerce is through the use of online storefronts, in which a company takes orders, but the actual items are processed and shipped by a third party. This practice is also referred to as drop shipping.

User-based online stores give individuals the ability to sell their products online through a larger site. Companies like eBay and Etsy take a cut of each sale, but this fee entitles the seller to the protection and security that comes with partnering with a well-known name brand. These affiliate-based models are highly beneficial for the producers of the materials sold because it gives them a much more visible platform. The retailer benefits because they always have a steady stream of products and interested customers that are ready to buy.

Benefits of Six Sigma in the eCommerce Industry

Shipping and Shipping-Related Logistics
Shipping is the lifeblood of any eCommerce company. Without a system in place to process and fulfill orders, the company has no chance of succeeding.

But it's not just about how the company handles shipping. It's about how much of the shipping burden is placed on the customer. The customer needs their item within a reasonable amount of time, and the customer needs to not pay an exorbitant amount of money to have the item shipped. Excessive shipping costs are the top reason why consumers abandon items in their online shopping carts. (https://www.shopify.com/blog/8343330-how-to-choose-a-shipping-strategy-for-your-online-store) The price can't be prohibitive for the customer, but at the same time, the company can't lose money on every sale due to shipping issues.

Six Sigma can help online retailers to notice inefficiencies in their shipping processes - assuming those processes even exist in the first place. Variability in the process can make it difficult for companies to guarantee a delivery date for consumers, which then disappoints potential customers to the point that they look elsewhere. Additionally, poor deployment of internal resources can help to increase shipping costs and delays. This is especially true for companies that have multiple warehouses or fulfillment centers. Six Sigma can help companies to straighten out the logistics behind the process, clarifying the responsibilities of each fulfillment center so that each unit can produce at optimal levels.

Scope of Products Offered
Many eCommerce retailers take advantage of their ability to offer an increased amount of products to their customers. A product list that would otherwise be limited by shelf space can now be displayed in full, giving customers a potentially endless list of products from which they can choose.

However, this isn't always the best approach to take. An excessive amount of items can make it difficult for consumers to find what they want; they may also find it hard to choose between potential options. As a result, those prospects may end up buying nothing, victims of the "paralysis by analysis" that plagues businesses worldwide. Worse, those same consumers may end up seeking out other retailers with simpler layouts and product pages that are easier to locate.

The temptation for all eCommerce retailers is to offer more products as opposed to fewer items, but they don't realize that there may be diminishing returns in such an approach. This is one area where Six Sigma can be highly beneficial. In addition to using purchase and website activity data to identify the best performing items on the website, a Six Sigma project can also dig deep into the unspoken desires of consumers. Companies may not realize that an expanded slate of products can result in their audience feeling alienated, believing that the company has abandoned its niche and its core customer base. A Six Sigma initiative will show a company where its focus should lie, both in terms of product categories and the varieties of those products that should be carried.

Enhanced Ability to Track How Purchases Originate
The digital marketing landscape provides organizations with a variety of ways to spread the word about their products. This is vital because the Internet is the best way for a marketer to attract traffic. It's easier for someone to click a link than it is for them to take out their phone or computer, then search for the company's site.

Because of the many marketing options available - social media, pay-per-click and organic search engine optimization, just to name a few - it can become very challenging for companies to understand what works and what doesn't. While traffic is always a good thing, it can be fleeting if the company doesn't truly know what caused people to come to their site. How can they repeat what worked if they aren't even sure what got people curious?

Implementing Six Sigma can help any company that wants to get a better handle on their marketing. Such an initiative can help the company to curtail unnecessary spending, identify areas where the company is successfully reaching customers and eliminate any marketing channels that simply don't work. This allows the organization to fully understand which avenues it should pursue from a marketing perspective, and it also enables the company to calculate its marketing return on investment. Knowing this number will help the business to anticipate demand in future marketing campaigns so that the proper infrastructure - order fulfillment, online servers, customer support - can be put into place ahead of time.

Challenges of Using Six Sigma in the eCommerce Industry

The Role of Outside Parties in Shipping
One of the best aspects about Six Sigma is that it encourages total control over the internal process. This is a major problem in eCommerce because so much of the order fulfillment

process relies on the outside world. If the post office doesn't do its part, the customer doesn't get their product, which may potentially motivate that individual to post negative reviews and complain on social media. Even though it's not the company's fault, the fallout from the postal snafu can have dire consequences for the business.

Products that arrive on time, but were damaged during shipping, can be just as problematic. In this instance, the company may be forced to incur the cost of return shipping as well as the costs to ship a non-defective item. Furthermore, the company now has one less item to sell. Once again, a problem not caused by the company can significantly impact normal operations.

While these defects in the process are not part of the normal process, they're still defects all the same, and the organization is forced to deal with them. As these instances pile up, they can make tracking normal process flow difficult. It may also potentially sour business owners on implementing Six Sigma initiatives. After all, if they follow the process to the letter, and the product becomes defective through no fault of their own, why even bother doing the project in the first place?

Working with Outside Vendors
Shipping is just one way in which outside factors can interfere with a company's normal work flow. The other external players in a process can be just as damaging.

Any force outside of the direct control of an individual can cause a disruption. For example, an independent retailer who sells their goods on eBay may have seen a dip in business because of their data breach in 2014. (http://www.forbes.com/sites/gordonkelly/2014/05/21/ebay-suffers-massive-security-breach-all-users-must-their-change-passwords/#65fcb3173c15) Just the same, a large retailer like Sears that employs drop shipping may experience a downturn in users selling on their site because a competitor, such as Amazon, begins offering better margins to sellers.

Outside vendors that experience difficulty in fulfilling orders not only contribute to inefficiency, but can also create public relations nightmares for the company. Many printing-based storefronts actually have their prints fulfilled by larger companies. This helps them to save on resources while offering their end users a variety of printing options. However, if there's a problem at the printer, customers will be quick to blame the storefront, while the printer gets off scot-free. These problems would also lead to the company's inability to accurately measure lead times and the quality of the prints, inhibiting their ability to gather the data necessary to begin a Six Sigma project.

Changes in Customer Preferences

Perhaps the biggest deterrent to eCommerce success has nothing to do with outside vendors or product defects. The main threat, it could be argued, is the fickle nature of online customers. Slow-loading sites, layout changes and a general shifting of tastes can dramatically alter traffic and revenue figures.

We've already seen this shift take place in eCommerce. More people access the Internet via mobile devices than go online via laptops or their home computers. (http://www.smartinsights.com/mobile-marketing/mobile-marketing-analytics/mobile-marketing-statistics/) As a result, online retailers have had to adjust the layout of their sites to appeal to online customers. In fact, companies that didn't have a mobile-friendly site were heavily penalized by Google in the form of unfavorable search engine rankings. (http://searchengineland.com/mobilegeddon-beginning-not-ending-220512) In light of this rapid growth of mobile-based eCommerce, each retailer had to adjust. Those that failed to do so lost out on significant revenues. Worse yet, they probably didn't even realize why their numbers took such a hit.

This ever-changing nature of eCommerce is a major deterrent that might not even show up in a Six Sigma project because it goes deeper than just numbers. Public tastes can't always be quantified. And even if a company suspects that their site might not be cut out for modern times, the leadership team might not be prepared to admit that change is necessary. Staying on the cutting edge and keeping an eye on eCommerce trends isn't just a Six Sigma thing. It's an everyday thing.

Six Sigma eCommerce Case Study – eBay

eBay is one of the world's most popular eCommerce sites. Its mixture of conventional online retail business (known on eBay as "Buy it Now") and auction-based bidding ensures that the site has something for everyone.

At its core, eBay is essentially a middleman that links sellers of goods with people who want to buy those products. The site allows users to list products and facilitates buyer bidding; eBay also provides pre- and post-sale support and integrates with PayPal to handle user-to-user payments without disclosing any of the financial information of either party.

The governing body of eBay's transactions is a feedback system that allows both buyers and sellers to see how many transactions each individual has been part of, as well as any complaints that have arisen from previous customers. Leaving negative feedback on a purchase is a major negative mark that can have long-lasting ramifications, creating skepticism among the customer base and affecting future business. Before a buyer or seller leaves negative feedback, he or she is encouraged to exhaust all possibilities for resolving the issue before taking that last step. To accomplish this, eBay customer service must sometimes get involved.

A Six Sigma project was undertaken by Pete Abilla, former employee of eBay, to eliminate inefficiencies and defects that existed in the customer service department. While eBay's customer service team always utilized the principles of DMAIC, additional study was needed to identify some of the causes for customer dissatisfaction.

One of the more notable areas for concern was the online chat department, which handled customer concerns and provided service in real time. (http://www.shmula.com/lean-six-sigma-ecommerce-presentation-case-study/12002/) This eliminated the need for a lengthy email chain that could take days, if not longer, to resolve. Online chat would resolve issues virtually immediately, unless there was a bigger issue that required intervention from a manager. However, the online chat model had some major flaws that interfered with the customer's ability to receive support.

After opening the chat window, the user was asked a few questions to verify their identity before the chat could begin. The user had to provide their User ID and email address so that the customer service representative could locate the user's account and provide the necessary support. However, as soon as the customer service representative joined the chat, he or she began by asking the user for additional information - the user's name, address and telephone number, along with the same User ID and email address that the user had just provided.

Not only was this a significant redundancy, its fallout affected everyone. First, it frustrated the customer, who had already provided this information and didn't see why it was needed a second time. Furthermore, it added to the time of the chat. This kept the user in the chat for longer than necessary, and it also reduced the overall number of users that the customer chat team could help. Additionally, some users may have developed concerns that they were being phished for their personal information. Although the initial message from the eBay chat team clearly stated that they would never ask for information such as credit card numbers and passwords, users had reason to be skeptical, given that they were just asked for information they already provided.

By using Six Sigma methodology, eBay realized that they were asking for basic information too often. They also realized that the pre-chat survey didn't do an adequate job of acquiring the necessary information needed by the chat team. As a result, the pre-chat survey was expanded to ask for all necessary information to initiate the support chat. This also helped the support team to have this information laid out in a predictable and organized way, increasing their ability to help eBay's users.

In the end, eBay was able to reduce the verification time from 3:42 to 2:57. This difference of 45 seconds shaved 20 percent off the average verification time, enabling eBay to serve more customers and giving customers a little more time to do what they most like to do on eBay - buy and sell items.

Tips for Using Six Sigma in the eCommerce Industry

Six Sigma can be a valuable tool for identifying the strengths of an eCommerce operation. Six Sigma can also help a company resist the urge to become something it's not or to stretch itself too thin in the search for revenues.

Keeping a narrow focus on what brings customers to an eCommerce store helps to keep that store well-positioned within its chosen niche. Understanding the customers that frequent the store is crucial when it comes to changing with the times and adapting to the needs of the customer base.

Knowing the company's limits is essential. Six Sigma only works if the scope of the project is manageable. Adding to the product mix may result in sunk costs and excessive inventory, not to mention a bloated data set that's incompatible with Six Sigma.

Understanding that the Internet is a constantly changing medium is a necessary component of any eCommerce business. Incorporating Six Sigma while knowing the entire industry could change at any minute is a bit tricky. However, sticking to the pre-established company principles will keep the company on track and enable the organization to focus on getting the desired results out of their Six Sigma project.

Source

http://www.chicagotribune.com/lifestyles/sc-cons-0904-savvy-shopper-20140904-story.html
http://www.business.com/ecommerce/retail-or-e-tail-buying-online-vs-buying-in-person/
https://www.shopify.com/blog/8343330-how-to-choose-a-shipping-strategy-for-your-online-store

http://www.forbes.com/sites/gordonkelly/2014/05/21/ebay-suffers-massive-security-breach-all-users-must-their-change-passwords/#65fcb3173c15

http://www.smartinsights.com/mobile-marketing/mobile-marketing-analytics/mobile-marketing-statistics/

http://searchengineland.com/mobilegeddon-beginning-not-ending-220512

http://www.shmula.com/lean-six-sigma-ecommerce-presentation-case-study/12002/

UNIT 11:
SIX SIGMA IN NON CUSTOMER-FACING FIELDS

CHAPTER 46:
SIX SIGMA IN WAREHOUSE

In a sense, the warehouse is the unsung hero of the retail industry. When things are going well, nobody notices the work the warehouse puts in to keep operations running smoothly. However, when something goes wrong, people are quick to blame the warehouse for its inability to handle seemingly simple tasks.

The truth is, there's nothing simple about the work done by the warehouse. Warehouses rely on intricate processes to fulfill and ship orders in a timely fashion. Even the smallest failure can result in serious problems that can derail an entire retail operation. In other words, without an efficient warehouse, it becomes impossible for the retailer to locate and sell its products.

If the showroom of a business is the front end, the warehouse is the back end. The typical image of a warehouse is a back room where employees are tasked with locating and transporting the items requested by a customer. This can take the form of simply bringing up an item from the basement and handing it to a salesperson on the sales floor, or it can be an online transaction in which the order is shipped. Customers do not interact with the warehousing process; it is their assumption that everything will operate smoothly. And since this is what the customer expects, it must become the reality of the customer experience.

The responsibilities of the warehouse become more complex when looking at larger corporations with multiple warehouses. A company like Amazon, which hosts 90 warehouses around the world, has serious choices to make about each item it stocks.

(http://www.wired.com/2014/06/inside-amazon-warehouse/) The company has to decide which warehouses it will be stored in, how many units to distribute to each warehouse and how many different locations that item should be placed in each warehouse. The actual fulfillment isn't as important as the logistics behind the process. And that's where Six Sigma comes in.

Benefits of Six Sigma in the Warehouse Industry

Process Overhaul
Warehouses are constantly in action. Employees of warehouses are so consumed with fulfilling orders and doing what has to be done that they rarely get the chance to think about how operations could run more efficiently. Even if a warehouse worker were to come up with a good suggestion for what could be changed, it would most likely be impossible to implement without incurring downtime. That's a luxury most warehouses are unable to afford.

A Six Sigma project is the perfect opportunity to create these necessary changes that will improve the warehouse's workflow. There are two main reasons for this. First, the Six Sigma project will illuminate the ideal solution, not just what an uninformed observer thinks should be done. The solution brought about as a result of the Six Sigma initiative will have input from everyone involved in the process, making it easier for staff-level employees and management to embrace the new process. Second, and perhaps more importantly, carrying out the Six Sigma project means that the data to support these findings will be present, removing any doubt about the proposed solution. This also means that if the company is forced to take a segment of the warehouse out of commission for a period of time, the data will show exactly why this is necessary and what the eventual benefits will be. As a result, management can make the choice that will help the warehouse to become more efficient in both the short term and the long term.

Many warehouses carry out obsolete and outdated process on a daily basis, partly because that's how they've always done it, partly because there's simply no time to consider the alternatives. Six Sigma can help to foster meaningful changes that will benefit the entire company, with minimal upheaval to the current level of operations.

Enhanced Communications
Although the warehouse process is focused on the efficient processing of customer and retailer orders, that process cannot start without receiving the order. If there are any communication issues that prevent the warehouse from receiving the order in a timely

manner, or if the instructions on the order are often unclear, the warehouse cannot do its job effectively. As a result, the warehouse that gets the blame, even though the information provided was incomplete, if it arrived at all.

Six Sigma methodology is designed to identify these breakdowns of communication. More specifically, Six Sigma can help tailor the process so that the warehouse picking team gets orders in the exact specifications they prefer. When communication is streamlined, the team can get right to work fulfilling the order, which makes the retailer and the customer happy.

This practice can also help to improve communications between the warehouse and the company's customer service team. Last-minute order changes and cancellations are inevitable, but if handled incorrectly, they can cost the warehouse time and money, damaging the warehouse's overall productivity while creating additional work. Enhanced methods of communication can let the warehouse know when an order is changed via a flag in the warehouse's computer system.

Additionally, Six Sigma can help the warehouse to identify the ideal time to start filling an order. Because the customer may have a grace period in which changes can be made, jumping on a customer order right away might not always be the best idea. Using Six Sigma to analyze the order fulfillment process can help the warehouse to zero in on the best way to handle new orders.

Inventory Management
The proper and cost-effective management of inventory is a vexing issue for warehouses worldwide. Carrying too much inventory minimizes the possibility of stock-outs, but it can become costly in short order. On the other hand, maintaining a low level of inventory on hand reduces costs, but presents a risk in terms of keeping up with demand.

Using Six Sigma can help warehouses to determine their magic number for how much inventory to keep of each item. It won't solve every problem faced by the warehouse in this area - for example, sale items must always have higher quantities of inventory because they're more desired by the average customer - but Six Sigma can give a general guideline and philosophy that the warehouse can utilize in its daily processes.

Every business is different, and what works in one industry might not work in another. That's why Six Sigma is so vital in determining the right amount of inventory to carry. Frequent orders may incur additional shipping costs, but can provide equal or greater savings in terms of inventory-based expenses. It's impossible to tell what a company should do without looking at its numbers and seeing how the figures align with the actual processes carried out by the company. The use of Six Sigma in this area is essential.

Challenges of Using Six Sigma in the Warehouse Industry

Outside Factors

Six Sigma is an ideal discipline for situations in which the organization has full control of its operations. On one level, warehouses fall into this category. But in many ways, outside forces can completely unravel anything a Six Sigma program sets out to accomplish.

For instance, a manager may initially decide that a Six Sigma project is worth undertaking, only to change their mind when they see how much time and manpower the project is truly costing the company. A rush to return to the old system may be in order, even if the eventual benefits of the project are undeniable. The unfortunate reality is that the show must go on, and the company still has orders to fill. If those orders can't be adequately filled during the project, company leadership may impose its will, even if it hurts the company over the long haul.

Another challenge comes in the form of communicating with the customer service team. Representatives who are not properly trained in the proper methods of order transport not only slow down production, but they may even create more work for warehouse staff. Additionally, changes to orders can be problematic for the warehouse, even with a comprehensive process in place.

Labor Issues

A Six Sigma initiative can only be successful with the consistent effort of the stakeholders. This becomes an issue in the warehouse industry in two ways. First, the staff-level employees of the warehouse might be resistant to the changes that arise as a result of the project. The employees may fear that the company is being downsized, which would eliminate their jobs, or they may simply be disinterested in a large project at a place in which they don't tend to stay long-term.

The issue of turnover is one that plagues warehouses around the world. Due to the relatively low wages, the mundane nature of the work and the physical exertion required each day, warehouse staffers have a high turnover rate. (https://www.kaneisable.com/blog/warehouse-labor-the-real-cost-of-associate-turnover) The bigger the warehouse, the more turnover there is.

(http://www.emeraldinsight.com/doi/abs/10.1108/09600030710758437) While there is undoubtedly value in an experienced warehouse employee, management is likely to see this as an area where costs can be cut, figuring that it's easy to find low-cost, unskilled labor anywhere.

The impact of this philosophy regarding overall warehouse performance is debatable. However, the fact remains that if employees aren't able to be in place for the duration of a Six Sigma project, that initiative has some serious challenges to consider. The only way to get to the heart of a problem is to talk to experienced staffers and identify the issues they face in their daily responsibilities. Similarly, the only way to truly know if a solution is viable is to present it to those same employees and verify that it meets their needs. A high-turnover situation makes this sort of fact-finding and analysis extremely difficult. A Six Sigma project needs to rely heavily on the veteran employees who are unlikely to leave and make those workers the basis of the investigation.

Practical Limitations
The ultimate goal of any Six Sigma project is to generate the solution that will allow the company to operate at the maximum level of efficiency. And while it may be possible to obtain this solution, it still might not be good enough to satisfy the desires of management.

This isn't the fault of the employees of the warehouse, nor is management to blame. Instead, there are simply some constraints that cannot be avoided. In particular, space and capacity can limit the company from achieving its goals, even if the Six Sigma project is a success.

Creating the perfect process that helps the warehouse to become streamlined, fast and defect-free is a great end product of a Six Sigma initiative. But that solution only goes so far when the holiday season begins and the company is inundated with orders. Though the warehouse may be able to process and fulfill orders faster than ever, the warehouse staff might not be able to keep up with demand.

This is a good problem for the company to have, to be sure. If the process put in place is well-documented and easy to follow, temporary workers can be hired to continue the work that was started during the project. However, this also opens the door for inadequately trained employees to introduce defects and inefficiency into the system. It's up to leadership to ensure that anyone who joins a smoothly operating process knows exactly what their roles and responsibilities are. More importantly, those new pieces to the puzzle need to know what not to do.

The physical size of the warehouse can also become problematic. Once again, a warehouse that's so effective that it can properly manage a large and diverse inventory of products means the company is doing something right. But if the company expands, there are some tough decisions to be made. The company can continue to work beyond its capacity, putting additional strain on the employees and the system that was created during the Six Sigma project. On the other hand, the company may decide that additional warehouse space is needed, potentially creating logistic problems that can cause the defects and interruptions that the Six Sigma initiative was designed to avoid.

Six Sigma Warehouse Case Study - IBM Warehouse Inventory

Although IBM has largely abandoned the hardware computing industry in favor of software and consulting solutions, the company is still synonymous with the high-powered business computers and servers that made IBM a household name. IBM and Lenovo (the company that purchased IBM's computer business) have been the preferred hardware suppliers for the business industry for the better part of two decades, and will continue to be for the foreseeable future. Part of the reason for the continued success of IBM is the company's dedication to responsible inventory management.
(https://www.isixsigma.com/implementation/case-studies/case-study-using-measurement-drive-behavior-change/)

Inventory is a major issue for technology-based companies. Hardware is expensive, and having an excessive amount of inventory on hand means a great deal of cash is tied up in goods that are manufactured, but not yet sold. More troubling is the fact that this excess inventory might never be sold at all. Because technology moves so fast, there's a good chance that surplus inventory becomes waste. With new products and features becoming available all the time, what's created today could be obsolete in mere weeks.

IBM's sales process stated that after a salesperson made a sale, an order was placed by the fulfillment team, and the physical order would sit in a warehouse in the recipient's country until the order was shipped to the customer. This shipment to the customer did not necessarily happen right away. As a result, inventory numbers remained high, even though the company's sales team made sales on a regular basis. Keeping such a large number of computers in inventory, even if sold, hurt IBM's internal processes. Not only were inventory numbers inaccurate, but outdated machines were kept in circulation, which cost the company money. IBM decided to embark on a Six Sigma project to determine why inventory numbers were so high in spite of consistent sales.

The company discovered that the problem had nothing to do with the warehouse staff, or the internal processes carried out in the warehouse. Instead, it was the sales team that had the most culpability. It was the sales team that directed the ordering process, and if a sale fell through, an item that was ordered remained in the warehouse. Instead of shipping it back to IBM for refreshing, the sales team would frequently keep the item in the warehouse in the hopes of selling that item to another customer. Other issues included changes made by customers after the sale, as well as salespersons ordering items early in anticipation of potential future sales that may or may not come to fruition.

Adding to the problem was that the sales team didn't see the value in reducing inventory. In the minds of the sales team, having inventory on hand meant it was easier for them to do their jobs. The more computers they had in a warehouse, the quicker the sales team could move those items.

The first solution brought about by the Six Sigma project was ensuring an across-the-board understanding of the importance of inventory. Though the sales team benefited from the extra items in the warehouse, they did not realize the financial burden that came with these additional machines. Once the sales team understood why inventory mattered so much, they were able to buy in to the additional solutions generated by the initiative.

The most critical change was the implementation of detailed record keeping of sales and the inventory tied to those transactions. The company mandated that if an order wasn't shipped to the customer within 30 days, that order would have to be sent back to IBM's headquarters so that the hardware could be retooled. Doing this meant that inventory would no longer become obsolete. It also ensured that the sales staff would be accountable for the end results of their orders.

Before the project, IBM experienced a failure rate – that is, the number of items commissioned for shipping that never got to the customer – of 50 percent in its largest country of business. In another large country, IBM had an 80 percent failure rate. Thanks to the changes brought about by the Six Sigma project, IBM reached a failure rate of less than 20 percent in both of these areas. Additionally, warehouse inventory levels across the entire company were cut in half.

It's easy to assume that a warehouse inventory issue is due to inefficiency within the warehouse. However, as discussed earlier, outside factors play a major role in the productivity of a warehouse. All parties involved must understand the role inventory and a coherent process plays in the warehouse. When the warehouse can function at optimal levels, every aspect of the company benefits.

Tips for Using Six Sigma in the Warehouse Industry
A warehouse that undergoes a Six Sigma project will see tremendous benefits. Obsolete processes can finally be discarded, and warehouse employees will have their say in making sure that the new process is effective and practical. In the end, everyone wins, from the warehouse staff, to management, to the customers who receive products quicker and with fewer defects.

When beginning a Six Sigma initiative, it's important to communicate the goals of the project with everyone who may be affected. It should be clearly stated that any changes made will benefit the warehouse. It's not an attempt to single out underperforming employees. Instead, it's a way to make everyone's life easier, which will ease the burden typically felt by the warehouse and it staff.

It's also essential to get buy-in from all stakeholders, particularly the staff-level employees. These are the people who will be carrying out the changes that are made as a result of the project. The warehouse staff has the power to make or break any change that is implemented. By getting on the good side of these individuals early and giving them a chance to have a say in the new process, the company sets itself up for prolonged future success.

The warehouse has many masters to serve. However, it cannot serve any of those masters if its own house is not in order. The project should focus only on improving the efficiency of the warehouse. Outside factors, such as corporate directives and the whims of other departments, should not be considered. If the warehouse is able to focus on its own issues and come up with its own solutions, improved efficiency and reduced defects are virtually guaranteed.

Source

https://www.isixsigma.com/implementation/case-studies/case-study-using-measurement-drive-behavior-change/
http://www.emeraldinsight.com/doi/abs/10.1108/09600030710758437
https://www.kaneisable.com/blog/warehouse-labor-the-real-cost-of-associate-turnover
http://www.wired.com/2014/06/inside-amazon-warehouse/

CHAPTER 47:
SIX SIGMA IN DISTRIBUTION

If an item can't be purchased, it stands no chance of making money. The power of distribution is what enables businesses to recoup their investments and profit from their creations. Without a carefully planned strategy for distribution, it's impossible for a business to increase its exposure, nor can that business plan for the future.

There's more to distribution than simply getting a product into the biggest stores or the most visible online retailers. In the case of brick-and-mortar retailers, the store needs assurance that the item is worth the financial investment and shelf space that comes with stocking that item. Just the same, online distribution might not be the utopia it seems, particularly with so many third-party sellers cluttering up the marketplace on sites like Amazon and Etsy. It takes the right mix of product availability, choice of retailer and the product itself to draw up a winning formula.

These days, thanks to the advent of online sales, anybody can be a distributor. But if the business succeeds, consumer demand will increase to a point where it's not feasible for the owner to singlehandedly ship every item to its destination. That's where knowing the ins and outs of the distribution industry comes in handy.

Distribution can come in a variety of forms. A local band selling its demo tape on consignment at a mom-and-pop record store is one form of distribution. A clothing retailer that signs an exclusive agreement to sell its clothes at Target stores around the United States is another. At the end of the day, distribution is what allows a company to tell its audience where those customers can find the company's products.

The level of reach and the number of distribution outlets is ultimately up to the company selling the product. A home-based drop shipping operation might not want to attract too many customers since there's little chance the company will be able to keep up with demand. On the other hand, a larger manufacturer might only partner with a retailer that has a specific number of locations across multiple states. The ultimate distribution equation is one that satisfies both sides in the short term, while allowing for flexibility and room for growth over the long term.

Benefits of Six Sigma in the Distribution Industry

Developing a Universal Process

Six Sigma is an effective methodology to employ because it highlights issues that even the stakeholders of the process are unaware of. Just because the company doesn't know about a problem doesn't mean that an issue doesn't exist.

Consider the case of a company that has multiple distribution channels. It sends out orders to brick-and-mortar retailers; at the same time, it has to fulfill online orders, and it also distributes items to sites that will be hosting trade shows in the near future. It's easy to see where employees can get confused by the many destinations of these orders, as well as the various order sizes and specifications that are unique to each distribution outlet. In this situation, the potential for things getting lost in the shuffle is extremely high.

Using Six Sigma, the company can develop one universal process that works in all of these different situations. This enables the company's staff to approach all orders in the same way. Even if certain retailers call for certain specifications, the vast majority of the order preparation can be accomplished in line with all other orders, and any unique tailoring that must be done can be incorporated into the process. Having this process set in stone also helps companies to work with retailers and manage the expectations of those retailers

Setting up a universal process accomplishes far more than simply making the lives of the company's staff easier. It also provides insight into the true bandwidth of the company, potentially opening the door for new distribution opportunities.

Identify the Best Retail Outlets

Distribution is all too often viewed from a "bigger is better" perspective. In other words, the more stores that carry an item, the better that item is performing. In reality, though, it's not quite this simple. It's very possible that a given item is underperforming at several stores, turning a seemingly great distribution arrangement into a net loss for the company. Unfortunately, figuring this out in the midst of filling orders and developing relationships with partner retailers is very difficult. As a result, companies often stick with what they've always done, not wanting to decrease the number of products available on shelves.

A Six Sigma project gives a company the opportunity to take a step back and evaluate the best practices for that organization as it relates to distribution. It's possible that a given retailer sells a great deal of products, but doesn't return as much money back to the company. On the other hand, another retailer might yield more revenue for the company, but ample supply cannot be provided due to commitments to other retailers.

Six Sigma not only shows the best channels for a company to use in its distribution, but it also provides the hard data necessary to encourage management to change its philosophies. Without the presence of evidence, it would be difficult to get leadership to consider alternative methods for distribution. However, when the potential benefits - as well as the lost revenues associated with maintaining the status quo - are displayed, it's easy to demonstrate why change is necessary.

Another hidden benefit of employing Six Sigma in this way is that it can help the company to zero in on its niche. It's quite possible that the company is marketing and distributing its products in the incorrect manner. Six Sigma can help the company to clearly see how distribution should be handled, both in terms of revenue and in satisfying demand.

Determine ROI for Distribution Outlets
When product is scarce, it's up to the company to determine which distribution outlets should receive these precious few items. While reach is a consideration in this situation, the company is best served using the stream that will provide the biggest bang for its buck. Without the opportunity for in-depth analysis, obtaining these figures is virtually impossible.

Using Six Sigma gives a company the ability to calculate its return on investment for each distribution channel it uses. This is a great way for a company to see if it's really getting what it wants out of its relationships with retailers and vendors. Going through this analysis will illuminate the best distribution channels when it comes to exposure and generating the most revenue per dollar spent.

Once the company knows how much its products are worth to a retailer, it can renegotiate its terms with its distribution partners. This negotiation is a lot easier to stomach if the company knows exactly what it should be getting, along with the potential benefits and drawbacks of partnering with different retailers. This is an example of one Six Sigma project opening doors in many other areas of the company's operations.

Challenges of Using Six Sigma in the Distribution Industry

Multiple Distribution Streams in One Project
In order for a Six Sigma project to be successful, it must have accurate measurements taken across a manageable project scope. In other words, a large company cannot consider the entire breadth of its distribution process, as this would prove to be unmanageable in terms of data collection and process improvement.

This is problematic for companies that have multiple outlets for distribution. For example, the parameters of online distribution are completely different from those of brick-and-mortar storefronts. A company that wants to improve its efficiency and return on investment across the board may find it difficult to narrow its focus on just one small area of distribution. They would find it even harder to extrapolate any new implementations to their other means of distribution, since there is no guarantee that the new model could work on multiple platforms.

Part of the preparation for a Six Sigma project is to use root cause analysis to identify the heart of the problems that plague a company from a distribution standpoint. The company can then isolate the area with the biggest problem and the most lucrative potential benefit. Once the project is complete, the company can evaluate whether the solution would work with other distribution streams, but they should understand that each outlet is different. What works in one area is not guaranteed to work in another.

Dollars Versus Brand Image
Using Six Sigma to identify the most beneficial revenue streams, as well as the ROI incurred when accessing those channels, is an endeavor any company would be wise to employ. However, there may be a disconnect between the findings of the Six Sigma project and the brand image that the company wants to portray.

A company that produces merchandise aimed at high-end customers might not see great returns in working with specific retailers that fit their key demographics. However, in order to reach this desired audience, the company must continue making its products available at these retailers. Just the same, the company might not want to sell its merchandise at more common retail outlets, even if their return on investment is higher. The prestige factor is one that cannot be quantified easily, but it's a major factor for many companies that want to control the image of their products and their brand as a whole.

Six Sigma can help companies to find a happy medium that enables their products to maintain a certain status without putting the business in a financial hole. The problem arises when management doesn't accept these findings, instead believing that their products must be showcased in a specific way. This is just one example of why poor distribution agreements continue to exist in spite of data that shows better options for the company.

Limited Control in Third-Party Arrangements
Today's online marketplace makes it easy for both large and small companies to gain exposure. Sites like Etsy, Amazon and Sears allow companies to sell on larger platforms, which in most cases is a mutually beneficial relationship. The retailer is able to offer a larger

selection of products, while the company benefits from a far greater distribution platform than they'd otherwise be able to access.

However, this relationship can quickly turn sour if the retailer makes any changes that might negatively impact the wholesaler. Changes in service fees or reduced royalties can significantly impact the bottom line for companies that distribute through these third-party sites. Even small changes, such as a site layout change or a modified ordering process, can become catastrophic if customers react so negatively that they stop making purchases.

The impact of these changes sheds light on the amount of control that is ceded to retailers when companies distribute in this way. Retailers will always aim to maximize their profits while minimizing costs, and their every action reflects this mindset. Modifying a relationship with a manufacturer might only mean a small increase in revenues for a company like Amazon, but for a small wholesaler, such a change might put that business in financial peril. Worse, since the cost of losing a distribution outlet like Amazon is far greater than that of a diminished revenue stream, the small business has no choice but to comply with these changes.

Six Sigma can't help a business to work around these issues. Even the best laid plans can be completely derailed by the whims of a third-party retailer. The Six Sigma project can and should include the development of contingency plans that can help a company to anticipate and react to changes made by third-party sites. Unfortunately, even creating these plans is no substitute for a controlled distribution environment that allows the company to plan for the future with confidence.

Six Sigma Distribution Case Study – Therma Tru Doors

Based in Butler, Indiana, Therma Tru Doors has been a leading force in the door industry for more than 50 years. (http://www.thermatru.com/company/overview/) In 1982, Therma Tru Doors unveiled the first-ever fiberglass door to the public. Over the years, Therma Tru Doors has continued to innovate and expand its audience, enabling the company to reach its current status as one of the world's leading manufacturers of doors of all types.

In 2001, Therma Tru Doors began experiencing difficulty in shipping products from the company's Matamoras, Mexico warehouse to the Therma Tru Doors manufacturing plant in Indiana.
(http://www.lasaterinstitute.com/casestudy/Logistics%20&%20Distribution/Six%20Sigma%

20in%20Logistics%20&%20Distribution.pdf) After an initial review, it was decided that the utilization of trailer space in the Mexico warehouse was the main culprit. A Six Sigma project was initiated in order to identify ways in which the trailer space issue could be resolved.

Christopher B. Anderson and his project team set out to obtain baseline numbers and try to improve those figures. At first, the utilization in the average trailer was 57 percent. In other words, more than 40 percent of the space in a given trailer was unused. While the obvious goal would be 100 percent utilization, Anderson and his team decided that a reasonable goal for the project would be 90 percent utilization. This represented an attainable goal that would still leave room for further improvement.

To assess the situation, Anderson sought out input from the very people who are tasked with loading the trailers on a daily basis. These employees had great ideas for how the process could be more efficient, but they simply never had the opportunity to make their voices heard. Additionally, Anderson noticed that the large racks used to transport glass from Mexico to Indiana were too unwieldy to properly utilize the trailer's space. He also took note of the fact that some items were shaped in a manner that made it hard for them to reliably be stacked or organized within the trailer.

Improving the process required some outside intervention. Anderson recruited a warehouse supervisor from Oklahoma, who had already undergone his own trailer space utilization project, to come to Mexico and make some suggestions. One of his key contributions was the suggestion that the company purchase additional pallets that could better fit the various shapes and sizes that previously made the trailer hard to organize. This approach allowed for more pallets to fit on a trailer, enabling the company to transport more materials while using less space.

Solving the issue of the glass racks posed a bigger challenge. Not only did these items take up more space than anything else, but they were also extremely fragile. However, the solution for this problem came in-house. Anderson asked the staff-level employees if they had any ideas for how glass could better be organized and transported. The employees stated that the racks could be reconfigured so that they could be double stacked, effectively doubling the amount of space available on each trailer.

The numbers showed a slight decline in trailer space utilization during the first three months of implementation. However, this dip in productivity soon gave way to a massive increase in utilization. Within six months of identifying the solutions to these issues, the Mexico trailers experienced a 99 percent utilization rate. This was far beyond the goals of the project. A process for monitoring productivity and maintaining control was established so that the utilization would never go below the stated goal of 90 percent capacity.

The distribution implications of this project were twofold. First, Therma Tru Doors was able to increase the productivity of the average trip from Mexico to Indiana. This meant that more goods could go onto shelves more quickly, resulting in additional revenue while keeping costs at a minimum. Furthermore, employees at the Indiana plant had a better idea of what they could expect when opening a trailer from Mexico. This allowed them to take a more organized approach to their jobs, which also translated into increased efficiency. Although distribution was the main focus of this Six Sigma initiative, the impact of the project touched many departments in a positive way.

Tips for Using Six Sigma in the Distribution Industry

Although there are some inherent challenges in using Six Sigma to improve a company's distribution, it is still a valuable tool that can help any company to become more efficient and knowledgeable about the true performance of their distribution channels. A company that carries out a Six Sigma initiative will develop an iron-clad process that will not only help internal work flow, but it will also help companies to understand the nuances of their operations when negotiating with retailers.

The best way to incorporate Six Sigma is to do so with a clearly defined project scope. It can't possibly cover every distribution outlet, and trying to do so would mean a failed project. Careful analysis should be done to uncover areas of subpar performance, and those areas should receive the focus of the Six Sigma project.

Understanding the company's vision for the future is another vital element of any Six Sigma initiative. As stated earlier, sometimes distribution means entering areas that aren't as financially rewarding. A company that has a clear understanding of where it wants to go is well-equipped to weigh the positives and negatives of each distribution partnership. This enables the company to carry out its vision while attempting to create workable relationships with its desired retailers.

Communication is key in all aspects of business, and this is certainly true in distribution. Those involved in the Six Sigma project must inform other departments about the project and clearly state how they may be affected by the initiative. These stakeholders should also come to understand that the project will ultimately help everyone, and each group should be informed about how the unique benefits they will receive as a result of their cooperation.

Source

http://www.thermatru.com/company/overview/
http://www.lasaterinstitute.com/casestudy/Logistics%20&%20Distribution/Six%20Sigma%20in%20Logistics%20&%20Distribution.pdf

CHAPTER 48:
SIX SIGMA IN MANUFACTURING

There is perhaps no more important discipline in the entire retail industry than manufacturing. Simply put, a poor manufacturing process means that products take longer to make, and the quality of those products is questionable at best. As a result, fewer finished products reach the marketplace, reducing the revenue brought in the by company, which in turn causes the company to make cuts in other areas. The trickle-down effect of a manufacturing process rife with defects, or even occasional inefficiency, can turn a successful business into a struggling one without warning.

On the other hand, an effective manufacturing system opens a variety of doors for the company. If the manufacturing team operates at maximum efficiency, the company will experience savings in terms of both labor and resources. It also enables the organization to take note of any defects that may enter the usual process.

The typical manufacturing process involves taking raw materials and turning them into finished products. While this task is usually aided by machinery, manual intervention is necessary for the machines to operate successfully. For instance, machines may need to be cleaned, while others have to be reconfigured to execute another step of the manufacturing process. When the process is complete, products assembled during a given time period will be placed into a specific batch so that the company knows what products were made during at various points in time. A sample from each batch is tested so that the company can identify any issues before those products are shipped to retailers. If there is a problem with one of the samples, the entire batch will be inspected, and other batches from similar time periods may also be reviewed to ensure that the defects did not spread into other batches.

In order for manufacturing to go smoothly, every aspect of the process must be carefully planned and documented in detail. This is the only way to keep tabs on underperforming areas of the process. Many manufacturing processes experience bottlenecks - steps where production significantly slows down, creating a backlog that adds to the company's lead time. The ultimate goal of Six Sigma is to spot these bottlenecks and find solutions that allow the entire process to function smoothly.

Benefits of Using Six Sigma in the Manufacturing Industry

Examine Existing Processes

The initial phases of any Six Sigma project require the project team and its shareholders to define the scope of the project and review the existing processes that have been in place. Since it's the failure of these processes that have necessitated the Six Sigma project, it's imperative to review every facet of each action taken by the company.

Manufacturing is more than simply flipping the switch on a machine. It's all of the little things that makes the process happen, and often, it's the smallest things that make the biggest difference. Something as small as the need to clean a machine on a regular basis may cause serious delays, particularly if it's discovered that the machine is being cleaned too often, or that it's not being cleaned at a satisfactory level. The Six Sigma project may uncover that a more thorough cleaning done less frequently can increase production significantly.

These discovery steps highlight the need to break down every aspect of the manufacturing process. Six Sigma can help companies eliminate inefficiencies and redundancies, but it can only do so if these smaller parts of steps are documented and examined. Some employees might not feel it's worth bringing up these minor parts of their job; they may also be reluctant to talk about aspects of their job that they don't handle particularly well. However, by discussing these issues, they can take a hands-on approach in developing a better process that not only increases productivity, but makes the jobs of staff-level workers easier.

Revamp Processes to Increase Productivity

One of the most difficult parts of monitoring the quality of a manufacturing operation is that even if the company notices a part of the process that isn't working, it's very difficult to fix that job. Because the company requires that products continue to be produced, shutting down operations to make an efficiency-based fix is virtually impossible. This is why so many companies continue to operate in the way they've always done things, even if it comes at the cost of increased productivity.

Six Sigma gives companies the impetus to make large changes to processes where necessary. When a proposed change is presented to the stakeholders of a Six Sigma project, there is supporting data that suggests how much the company might benefit. This can help decision makers to consider the true impact of the change. Even if a short-term decrease in productivity occurs due to the reworking of the process, the overall benefit will compensate for the diminished efficiency many times over.

Of course, there is more at stake than simply overseeing a more efficient process. A process with a shorter lead time will naturally yield the creation of more products than the previous method of operation. Over time, this increased haul can lead to a much greater amount of products created, giving the company the ability to either sell the excess amount or save on labor costs by reducing the number of hours the manufacturing plant operates each day.

Identify Cost Savings Opportunities
The big benefit of creating extra products is the financial impact of additional inventory on hand at virtually no cost. Since these additional items will be made using the same labor and mechanical resources as the typical load in the previous system, the only added cost comes in the form of raw materials. This increased productivity can have massive implications for the company.

As is the case with any business, internal improvements that save money should end up in a less expensive product for the consumer. If a company finds a way to make a cheaper product, the company's margins on those products increase. Passing along those savings to the customer is a great way to gain market share and provide the company with additional revenue - income above and beyond what the company would generate with the old process.

The average staff-level employee might not be too concerned with the price the customer pays for a product he or she produces. But seeing the big picture is an important part of any Six Sigma initiative. If the company is able to show manufacturing employees how their money-saving efforts can benefit the business - and ultimately, themselves - they'll be that much more likely to support the project.

Challenges of Using Six Sigma in the Manufacturing Industry

Diverse Array of Processes
To an outsider, manufacturing is often thought of as a singular function. However, as anyone who has ever seen a manufacturing process up close knows, the steps required to create each unique product is different. Even multiple product lines of the same item that have differing features can have unique processes.

This presents a problem as it relates to Six Sigma. Since the typical project scope of a Six Sigma initiative is limited to one process, a company with multiple products - and multiple inefficient manufacturing processes - may have difficulty drawing conclusions on a large scale. In other words, the solutions they find as a result of the project may not be able to be extrapolated to other manufacturing processes.

In most cases, since at least one flawed process can be overhauled, the project is still worth undertaking. While the entire solution cannot be replicated in every other process performed by the manufacturing team, the lessons learned along the way may be applicable to other activities that need improvement.

Outdated Machinery
Six Sigma can accomplish many things, but the analysis by itself is unable to transform an organization. It takes strict adherence to the recommendations of the project to see results, and sometimes the implementation of a revamped process requires an investment of financial capital. And even if a business is able to hire a project team to run a Six Sigma initiative, there might not be enough money to do what's necessary to see the project through to its ideal conclusion.

In manufacturing, it's not uncommon to see outdated and obsolete equipment in use. Due to the prohibitive cost of upgrading machinery, many companies try to get by with the equipment they've used for years. It's not difficult to see that a Six Sigma project might identify this old machinery as the bottleneck for a broken process.

Therein lies the dilemma. The project makes it abundantly clear that the company will benefit tremendously from upgrading its machinery. The employees, tired of using old equipment to carry out modern tasks, are excited to see this new technology that will make their jobs easier. And yet, it can never come to fruition because the company simply can't afford to buy new machines.

In this case, the impact is a two-pronged effect. Because the old equipment has been isolated as the bottleneck, the company sees that its efficiency won't improve unless the upgrade is made. At the same time, employee morale is likely to take a dip as staffers realize that their jobs won't get easier anytime soon. The company is then presented with a serious dilemma - either go on with the process as is and continue to experience difficulties, or go into significant debt to buy a machine that may not pay for itself for many years.

Although the project has achieved its preliminary goal of identifying the weak link in a process, it ultimately fails because the solution is impossible to achieve. It's a risk that manufacturing companies take every time they embark upon a Six Sigma project.

Encouraging Buy-In
From an executive level, implementing Six Sigma in a manufacturing facility always seems like a good idea. At that level, the only thing that's apparent is the benefit that will be realized from executing a project and improving an inefficient process. However, at lower levels, employees might not be so enthusiastic about the idea of a Six Sigma project.

One of the main aspects of any Six Sigma initiative is that it must receive complete buy-in if the project is to be a successful one. Just as a process is only as good as its weakest link, a Six Sigma project is only as effective as its least interested participant. And in an industry like manufacturing, it's easy to see that the staff-level employees manning the machines are the people with the real power in any project.

The Six Sigma initiative can only work if the lowest-level workers want it to succeed. While it might not be obvious to the executives, these staffers may have some good reasons why they don't want a more efficient process. In a world where outsourcing and downsizing are feared in every organization, manufacturing employees may be afraid that a more efficient process could mean that their services would no longer be needed. That may be all the motivation these individuals need to rebel against this initiative that seems far more like a threat than an asset.

It's up to the project team to explain to these employees that any changes that occur as a result of a Six Sigma project will ultimately be to their benefit. Additionally, these workers need to understand that not only are they needed after the solution has been implemented, but they will also be an important part of creating the solution. At the end of the day, the ultimate goal of a Six Sigma project based around a manufacturing process is to make the jobs and lives of those staff-level employees executing the process easier. The earlier they understand that, the more receptive they'll be to change - and the more likely they'll be to make positive contributions to the project.

Six Sigma Case Study - Machines vs. Human Capital

A manufacturing company based in the Midwestern United States was plagued with an inefficient manufacturing process. (https://www.isixsigma.com/implementation/case-studies/case-study-increasing-machinery-throughput-without-more-machines/).The company's manufacturing plant used a 24-hour around-the-clock operation that burned out employees, many of whom had to work 12-hour shifts on the weekends.

The main role of the manufacturing employees at the plant was to clean machines that malfunctioned. Given the sticky nature of the company's products, this happened as many as ten times per hour. Although the employees were skilled at identifying issues and cleaning them, the company felt it could benefit from a more efficient approach, and it was decided that a Six Sigma project would be the best way to identify ways the company could improve its manufacturing process.

Under the existing setup, the company operated at an efficiency rate of 65 percent. The company's ultimate goal was to get to 70 percent. If the company was able to get to this number, it could reduce the plant's operating time to 16 hours a day, creating two eight-hour shifts that would enable employees to approach their jobs with a more positive attitude. This model would also help the company to save money; for every one percent increase in efficiency that was achieved, the business would save $250,000.

To start the project, the company collected data over several data points - the machine in use, the type of product, the name of the individual operating the machine and the time of day. After six months, the organization was able to begin to review its figures.

One of the things that was obvious right away was that there were significant differences between the parties involved in the operation. Some types of products performed far better than others, and the same was true for the machine operators. The company's next step was to figure out how these data sets worked together.

The company ran a series of regression analyses to determine the relationships between these factors. The first analysis showed that there was a strong correlation between efficiency and the number of machines worked by each operator. In order to reach the goal of 70 percent efficiency, each operator could only work on one machine at a time.

Another regression analysis was run, this time incorporating all of the data points collected during the Measure phase of the project. While several combinations of variables proved to be statistically significant, the two biggest factors were the time of day and the machine operator. Further investigation showed that the main reason for time being a contributing factor was the drastic drop in productivity that occurred during shift changes twice each day. Additionally, the project showed that each operator tended to work best on their preferred machine; however, since operators generally worked on whatever machine was available, they often weren't on their favorite machines.

Given the data, the solution was a rather simple one. Operators would be assigned to the machine on which they were most efficient. This one change not only brought efficiency to the desired goal of 70 percent, but the company's efficiency improved to more than 73 percent after a six-week implementation period. Because of the change, the company was able to save $1.7 million, and the employees had the opportunity to enjoy the more relaxed schedule that they had earned.

This case study is a classic example of a situation in which many companies would have been tempted to invest money in new machinery. However, investing in human capital can often be just as effective, if not more so, than simply buying new machines. Companies should consider all options when making improvements, especially those that allow their employees to shine.

Tips for Using Six Sigma in the Manufacturing Industry

Manufacturing is a vitally important aspect of the operations of any retail-based business. It's not an area for inefficiency and skimping on costs. A happy and well-run manufacturing team can make the entire company more successful through cost-saving measures, increased quality and a larger inventory of products that the company can sell.

When implementing Six Sigma, choosing a manageable and purposeful scope for the project is essential. Although the solution can't be ported everywhere, a project that comes to a successful conclusion will yield positive insights that can impact other divisions of the manufacturing operation. These findings will make subsequent Six Sigma projects within that company easier to manage.

Getting staff-level manufacturing employees involved early and often will help them to take ownership of the initiative. The success or failure of the project lies in their hands, and they'll make the leadership team look very smart - if they're properly motivated to do so.

Tracking all data is a major component of any Six Sigma project. That's especially true in the manufacturing industry, where something minor can end up being the bottleneck that derails an entire process. No piece of data is too insignificant to track, and as the case study showed, no potential solution is too simple too consider.

Source

https://www.isixsigma.com/implementation/case-studies/case-study-increasing-machinery-throughput-without-more-machines/

CHAPTER 49:
SIX SIGMA IN FOOD SERVICE

Food Service

Nobody wants to cook every meal. To those people who want a night out, or to those who simply don't have access to home-cooked meals, the food service industry is a godsend.

The United States Department of Agriculture defines food service as any meal or snack that is prepared for immediate consumption. (http://www.ers.usda.gov/topics/food-markets-prices/food-service-industry.aspx) While items can be brought home, the majority of the meals consumed as a result of the food service take place at commercial venues like restaurants and fast-food outlets.

There are many different types of products offered by the food service industry. Cafeterias and college food courts don't necessarily offer the best-tasting options, but they do provide affordable meals for people without disposable income. Basic fast-food restaurants take pride in delivering a meal that's uniform, consistent and quick, all at a lower cost than other types of restaurants. Sit-down restaurants vary from family-friendly and basic to elaborate and very expensive. The mix of price point, quality and customer experience varies depending on what type of message the restaurant wants to send to its patrons.

The type of restaurant has a significant impact on the way the business is run. While fast-food restaurants take for granted that people will come and go quickly, sit-down restaurants must manage additional factors related to customer flow. Table turnover, wait times and the potential for additional courses being ordered by a given party all interfere with the normal flow of operations. When a restaurant of this type experiences a dip in attendance or revenue, it can be difficult for them to understand exactly why their numbers are changing. Careful analysis is required to determine if the change is related to the food, the customer experience, wait times or some other factor.

The food service industry has had to change with the times, navigating the always fickle waters of customer tastes and preferences. The modern climate poses perhaps the biggest challenge that the food service industry has seen. Today's customer is more educated than ever in terms of the health impact of food, as well as matters relating to the quality of food. People are increasingly demanding fresher ingredients and higher quality meals. While some are willing to pay a premium for better ingredients, many want better quality at the same cost. Additionally, specialized diets have become commonplace in modern culture. Food outlets that don't offer gluten-free, vegan or organic options may alienate segments of the marketplace.

With so many ways in which a food service operation can disappoint customers, it's difficult for companies to know where they should focus in order to improve. Six Sigma can be tremendously helpful in helping a business understand what they do best and how they can improve their products, as well as their internal processes.

Benefits of Six Sigma in the Food Service Industry

Ideal Serving Size

Serving size is just one of many things that the average customer doesn't think much about, but poses a major problem for food service operations of all sizes. In fact, even some restaurants don't think about serving size, which makes it very difficult for them to track the true cost of their average portion.

Serving size can be a competitive advantage for some food service companies. Restaurants that serve a large portion are usually commended for giving people their money's worth. This can also be a form of advertising for them. Knowing that people often bring leftovers to work the next day, someone that brings a restaurant's food to work and talks about their experience can serve as promotion for that restaurant. However, the restaurant might not know for sure that this is the right way to go. They may be shocked to find that this approach could actually lose money. On the other hand, a food service location that offers a smaller portion will likely never know that its inadequate serving size is alienating its customers. Instead, those people will simply never return.

The only way to know for sure is to analyze the serving size in relation to its cost to produce, the price the customer pays and the potential benefits of a smaller or larger portion size. Six Sigma can be very useful in this area. Instead of putting off this analysis, as many companies do, or simply letting assumptions dictate the company's philosophy, Six Sigma provides concrete data that shows exactly how each unique restaurant should handle the serving size dilemma. In addition to simply running numbers, Six Sigma gives the company the chance to talk directly to its customers to see what they really think. Between the internal number-crunching and customer feedback, restaurants have a great chance to settle on an ideal portion size that satisfies customers while maximizing revenues.

Minimize Food Waste

A 2005 study conducted at the University of Arizona stated that nearly 10 percent of all food in fast food restaurants was wasted, while more than 3 percent of food in sit-down restaurants ended up in the garbage .
(http://www.endfoodwastenow.org/index.php/issues/issues-restaurants) Not only is food waste a big problems in terms of corporate responsibility and environmental concerns, but it can also seriously cut into the margins of the food service industry.

An estimated 4 to 10 percent of food becomes wasted before it ever reaches the customer's plate. This can be due to innocent reasons such as over-preparing foods on a slow night, but it can also point to bigger issues. Spoiled food and food that's improperly prepared are also reasons for food waste, but the difference is that these two categories are preventable.

Like all businesses, the food service industry is plagued with issues that it would like to solve, but can't because managers can never find the time due to the busy workflow that plagues most restaurants. Problems like spoiled food may be easily solved by ordering in smaller quantities more frequently, but the average restaurant is too consumed with filling current orders, leaving it unable to consider other possibilities.

Implementing Six Sigma gives these companies the impetus to begin considering the reasons for their food waste, as well as potential solutions to these problems. One of the best parts about Six Sigma is that it doesn't rely on what managers and owners think the problem might be. Instead, Six Sigma incorporates the input of the people closest to the process - the people who work with the very food that ends up spoiled - and allows those people to help find a solution. Six Sigma can't solve every problem faced by restaurants, but it can help a company significantly cut into its food waste dilemma.

Freshness Initiatives

Today, everyone wants fresh ingredients and high-quality food items. The problem is that as the level of quality goes up, so does the cost. If all of these costs were passed on to the customer, even the most loyal patron would be taken aback and begin to look elsewhere. It's up to the restaurant to find its own internal way to get the best ingredients in a cost-effective manner that doesn't drive the price too high.

This is an area in which many restaurants have been hesitant to change. After all, their business works right now using their current level of quality. Why scrap something that works in favor of something that's just going to cost more? The problem with this mindset is that if customers do end up leaving because of poor food quality, it's very difficult for restaurants and food service outlets to understand that the lack of quality is the reason. All they know is that they have fewer customers than they once did. Worse, even if the restaurant does improve its food quality, it'll still have the stigma of selling low-quality food.

The best way to get around this issue is to find a compromise before the company's revenue is affected. Six Sigma can help restaurants find ways to bring their food quality to a reasonable level without drastically increasing costs. Better yet, Six Sigma may be able to help zero in on exactly what aspects of a food service operation need a quality makeover, eliminating the need to improve everything all at once. This makes the change more manageable and more affordable, meaning that customer prices will remain affordable.

Challenges of Using Six Sigma in the Food Service Industry
Changing Menus and Public Tastes
The emerging trend of customers preferring fresh ingredients and healthy options is a microcosm of what food service establishments have had to deal with for the past century. Restaurants, fast-food chains and even school food courts have had to recognize trends and adapt to the times. Navigating these waters of change hasn't always been easy, and in some cases, it's come with a significant hit to the bottom line.

While Six Sigma can do a lot of things, it can't necessarily predict the tastes of the consumer, especially considering how frequently those tastes change. Six Sigma is highly effective in terms of shoring up internal processes and making sure that all processes are as efficient as they can be. Unfortunately, it's not as helpful to a company like McDonald's, who suddenly finds itself rushing to add healthy options to a menu full of cheap fast-food items.

Food service restaurants must always stay close to the tastes of their customers so that they can be ready to modify their food offerings as tastes change. Of course, it's easier to do this if their current processes are efficient and have room to grow. And while Six Sigma can't magically predict customer preferences, it can certainly help a restaurant become efficient to the point that it's ready to change along with its customers.

Unskilled Labor and High Turnover
While there are some servers and managers who have aspired to be full-time employees, much of the food service workforce is young and unskilled. Those who are older, yet still remain working non-management roles in fast-food restaurants, largely do so because of a lack of other options. The average age of fast-food workers is 29, and of the adults in that group, many receive public aid.
(http://www.politifact.com/punditfact/statements/2013/nov/04/bill-maher/bill-maher-average-fast-food-worker-29-most-are-pu/)

That's because the average wage in the fast-food industry is barely above minimum wage. Servers at sit-down restaurants have the potential to make more money, but the vast majority of their income is derived from tips from customers. One or two slow days in a month may mean that a server is unable to pay their bills at home. It's not hard to see why many are so quick to abandon this industry; anyone who sees an opportunity to make more money and learn something new is usually very willing to take that chance.

Because of this high rate of turnover, and the unskilled labor that typically fills lower-paying positions in the food service industry, Six Sigma is hard to implement. Six Sigma relies heavily on employee input, and it's impossible to get good insights from employees if they haven't been there long enough to understand what's really wrong with a particular establishment. Adding to the problem is that new employees, particularly those who might not be staying very long, might not be inclined to buy into the proposed changes. A 16-year-old fast food cashier doesn't care about increasing revenues. He or she just cares about making enough money to support their hobbies.

The increasing number of full-time adults who work in fast food provides a glimmer of hope that Six Sigma can help food service restaurants of all types. However, until turnover becomes more stabilized, it's hard to implement a solution with any sort of staying power.

Public Relations Crises
The findings of a Six Sigma project aren't always pretty. Many executives of companies that have undergone Six Sigma projects find themselves disgusted to find out about the true conditions of their workplaces and processes. However, most of these businesses have the ability to keep these findings under wraps so that the public never knows just how dire things really are. The worst case scenario is a product recall, in which anyone who has purchased a faulty product receives a new one free of charge.

This cannot be said of the food service industry. If the public becomes aware of any issues regarding the quality or freshness of a restaurant's food or the lack of hygiene of restaurant employees, the perception of that restaurant is irrevocably damaged. A rat spotted in a fast food establishment is enough to turn people off of that restaurant forever. Worse, if one branch of a chain restaurant is found to have an issue, all of the other branches feel the impact.

Adding to the problem is the fact that restaurants undergo safety inspections on a regular basis. If inspectors find something that's not up to code, the public will find out and business will suffer drastically - even if the Six Sigma project was working on fixing that very flaw.

Six Sigma is a great tool for fixing a company's internal processes, but it cannot control public perception. Once the general public turns on a brand, it's very hard to regain that trust. Ideally, Six Sigma should be implemented before a preventable occurrence does irreparable damage to the restaurant, as well as the other locations related to that establishment.

Six Sigma Case Study – Reducing Quality Cost

A Taiwanese food company specialized in producing pork buns for mass consumption. (http://www.academicjournals.org/article/article1380706320_Hung%20and%20Sung.pdf) The preparation required for the buns to be steamed, then frozen. The frozen buns were then sold, after which the buns had to be re-steamed in order to be served. However, after re-steaming, people found that the buns were often defective. Common defects included shrinking, cracks in the buns and additional objects being found in the bun. The company decided to use Six Sigma to find ways to reduce the defect rate.

The company began its analysis by trying to identify which of the buns was the most problematic. While all of the buns the company produced suffered from defects, the small custard bun (32g) was by far the biggest culprit, accounting for 44 percent of the company's defects. Additionally, while there were various types of defects, the one that was most common was shrinkage. Therefore, the company decided to focus its energies on fixing the small custard bun so that it would not shrink nearly as often.

Early analysis showed that the baseline defect rate for the operation was 0.405%. The goal of the Six Sigma project was to reduce this number by 70 percent to 0.141%. Once all stakeholders came to an agreement regarding what constituted a defective bun, the company could begin measuring and analyzing data.

The company chose nine main data points to track. The main analytical tools used were ANOVA analysis and main effects plots. Of the nine factors tracked, five proved to be statistically significant - temperature, color of dough, shift, amount of ice water and steaming time. Subsequently, factorial analysis was used to determine the main culprits in causing shrinkage. The analysis showed that the volume of ice water was the biggest reason for the shrinkage, at a rate more than double that of the next closest factor.

Using the data collected, an optimization tool was used to calculate the best possible recipe that would incorporate just the right amount of ice water. It didn't take long for the recipe to click. In the six months that followed the implementation of the revamped recipe, the company only exceeded its goal of a 0.141% defect rate once. In fact, the other five months were well below the goal rate. Encouraged by the results, the company carried out further Six Sigma projects to further improve its performance in the food service industry.

Tips for Using Six Sigma in the Food Service Industry

The food service industry can be a difficult place for revamping processes and planning ahead. However, Six Sigma can be highly beneficial for those who use it wisely.

Because inefficiencies can have a wide variety of causes in food service, considering all possibilities when implementing Six Sigma is advised. Brainstorming is a great idea for generating ideas as to why a restaurant is underperforming. As the case study shows, sometimes it's the simplest factors that make the biggest difference.

Getting the real scoop about a process is imperative for success in Six Sigma. Usually, the higher-ups don't know what really goes on inside of their kitchens or on their restaurant floors. Speaking with the lower-level employees that deal with food and customers on a daily basis will yield the best insights about what's wrong and how it can be fixed.

Defining a manageable scope for a Six Sigma project can help an establishment to fix one very important problem instead of getting bogged down by every problem that the restaurant faces. Fixing one major flaw can have a trickle-down effect that impacts other processes in a positive way. Identifying the aspect of the business that can benefit the most from one change is key for success in Six Sigma.

CHAPTER 50:
SIX SIGMA IN CONSTRUCTION

Construction is one of the most valuable and lucrative trades that exists. There are very few people equipped to perform the tasks required of construction workers, which makes working with the construction industry a necessity for many people around the world. Even laypeople with technical know-how are often more comfortable hiring someone to do the job right the first time, not wanting to risk making a costly mistake.

Construction comes in a variety of forms. Most people immediately think of workers on the side of the road when the term "construction worker" comes to mind, but there's a lot more to construction than road work. Construction also covers the building and restructuring of homes and businesses. Adding onto existing buildings, fixing internal structural errors and refinishing outdated elements of those buildings are just a few of the tasks that fall under the jurisdiction of construction.

Many construction employees work for contractors, which are project leaders that are well-versed in communication, workflow and time management. Contractors must also purchase and transport the raw materials that are necessary to get the job done. Additionally, they must deal with customers and adhere to rigid time deadlines that may change during the duration of the project. Ultimately, if something goes wrong with the project, even months after its completion, the contractor is the one blamed for the error.

The construction workers who handle the nuts and bolts of a project are skilled in manual labor. However, they also perform high-risk labor for a wage that's not necessarily commensurate with their work. According to U.S. News & World Report, the median construction worker salary in the United States is less than $32,000. (http://money.usnews.com/careers/best-jobs/construction-worker/salary) Construction workers usually become members of unions, through which they receive their benefits. Given the health risks and potential long-term health ramifications associated with construction, good health benefits are essential for any construction worker.

The scope of construction jobs vary from site to site and from region to region. The bigger job, the more money paid to the contractor. Construction jobs can be as small as knocking down a wall in a basement, or they can be as big as building a billion-dollar sports stadium. No matter the size of the job, any construction business could benefit from being more efficient. Six Sigma is able to help the companies in the construction industry in their quest to reduce defects and increase productivity.

Benefits of Using Six Sigma in the Construction Industry

Reduced Labor Costs

Aside from doing a good job, the ultimate goal of any construction job is to get done on time. Running past schedule has many ramifications, such as added costs and a damaged reputation for the contractor. An organized workflow is necessary to ensure that the job is completed on schedule, if not ahead of time.

Incorporating Six Sigma can help contractors and construction companies to streamline the planning process. Collecting data from previous construction jobs is a vital element in creating plans for future projects. When each member of the team is in a role he or she enjoys and excels in, the entire operation benefits. The work is done more safely, more efficiently and with more care.

Of course, it's up to the project leadership team to come up with the ideal solution that will put these pieces in place. Six Sigma will not only help with data collection, but it may also recommend new planning ideas that will enable contractors to schedule jobs more efficiently. This added efficiency will increase productivity, not to mention the quality of the work.

Furthermore, seeing the proper alignment of a labor force may highlight areas where labor is no longer needed. Perhaps there are some redundant processes, or maybe the work simply gets done faster because it's better organized. Either way, those savings can help the business to purchase new machinery or provide more flexible schedules to employees. The surplus money can also encourage the contractor to offer lower prices for better quality work.

Reduce Injuries

Safety is paramount in the construction industry. And while nobody wants to get hurt, it's an unfortunate reality that comes with the territory. All of the safeguards in the world can't prevent every injury, but it's the duty of the construction company to try to minimize risk wherever possible.

Injuries impact a construction crew in many ways. First and foremost, suffering an injury is devastating for the employee, who now has to miss work and may be facing a lengthy recuperation time. That employee must also fight for worker's compensation benefits, which is not always an easy task. The injury also has a residual effect on the other members of the team, who might find themselves a little less enthusiastic about engaging in the risky parts of their job. It also affects the contractor, who not only has to soothe the concerns of the injured employee, but must also find an equally effective replacement capable of working with the existing team. After all, the job has to get done by the guaranteed end date, regardless of who's injured.

The use of Six Sigma can help construction companies to go further than simply installing safeguards. Now, the company and the Six Sigma team can work together to rework processes as much as possible in order to mitigate the amount of risk undertaken by construction workers. As is the case with all Six Sigma projects, data analysis will be accompanied by insightful feedback provided by the very workers who perform dangerous tasks on a daily basis.

Due to the nature of the industry, not all risky activities can be removed. However, the company can incorporate Six Sigma in order to make the job as safe as possible for its employees.

Create Defined Processes
One of the more frustrating aspects of managing construction is that most of the people on a given construction crew have different work backgrounds. This means that each of them learned how to do their jobs differently. While this might not seem like a big deal on an individual basis, having an entire team of people that work differently from each other can create massive headaches when laying out processes.

This disconnect can also result in jobs being inadequately completed, with the mistakes only becoming apparent when it's too late to fix them. All construction workers have their own ways of doing their work, but they don't always communicate those methods to their co-workers. Additionally, there are sometimes language barriers, particularly between an English-speaking contractor and a Spanish-speaking crew. When such miscommunications are downplayed, the true message doesn't come across, creating the possibility of defects or diminished productivity from employees.

These conflicts highlight the need for defined processes that are largely set in stone. When employees know exactly what's expected of them and they know exactly how to execute each task, it's much easier for them to complete the task in a way that satisfies management. Additionally, laying out processes in this way makes it easier for contractors to bring in new labor after someone leaves a project.

Building a new process isn't always easy to do, especially when there are deadlines that must be adhered to. Fortunately, Six Sigma allows for the necessary analysis and reworking to take place. Temporary dips in productivity are offset by periods of sustained efficiency. Solutions that may take time to implement are accompanied by supporting data showing why change is necessary. Most importantly, a new process from which everyone involved will benefit is created, creating a workflow that eliminates many of the barriers that prevented maximum efficiency.

Challenges of Using Six Sigma in the Construction Industry

Cost of Machinery

Six Sigma's ability to identify the heart of a broken process and suggest workable solutions is second to none. The only problem is if the bottleneck is proven to be a piece of outdated machinery. This puts the entire project, as well as the company who commissioned the project, in a tough position.

For the company, it's a tough pill to swallow. Management expected to receive an actionable plan that would help the company to better structure its construction jobs and lower costs. Instead, the leadership team receives a bill for a new machine that could cost tens of thousands of dollars. And although the new equipment would help a great deal, it's simply not an option for a cash-strapped construction company.

This puts the business in a no-win situation. Either they spend money they can't afford on a new piece of machinery, or they go without the new equipment and continue to operate at a suboptimal level. Furthermore, the company has to deal with disillusioned employees who thought they were getting a great solution, only to find out that the status quo will continue to remain intact. This can have a subsequent impact on morale, potentially making productivity even lower than it was before the project began.

Six Sigma projects always aim to provide the best possible solution at the lowest cost. Unfortunately, sometimes the ultimate solution is one that's cost-prohibitive for the business.

Difficulty Testing New Processes

Even the best Six Sigma processes go through a great deal of testing, as well as a period of expected inefficiency while the solution is being implemented. Though this may work in most industries, it's impossible to carry out in construction.

Construction jobs come with high costs and big expectations. For the price paid, the person hiring the construction team wants the job done their way, as quickly as possible. That person would not be very happy if he or she was told that the construction team was testing out a new process as a result of their recent Six Sigma initiative. In fact, they'd most likely be very quick to hire a new team altogether.

In such a high-stakes business, nobody wants to be the guinea pig, and understandably so. That puts extra pressure on the Six Sigma project team, as well as the contractor and his or her employees. No matter what solution is presented as a result of the project, it has to work, and it has to work the first time. If the solution fails, the project has failed. Worse yet, a failed solution can't simply be backed out. It might require additional work, which comes with significant costs, not to mention the aggravation that comes from dealing with an angry customer.

Whenever possible, a contractor should arrange to have a revamped process tested on a small scale before making it part of the regular routine. This in itself might cost money, but it will provide the team with some sense of assurance before it's fully implemented.

Increased Rates

Sometimes, Six Sigma can unwittingly have an adverse effect on a company. A business uses Six Sigma to improve its processes; as a result, additional quality measures are implemented to ensure that the job is done quickly and effectively the first time. These added parts of the process, while helpful in ensuring quality and efficiency, force the company to increase the cost of the product or service.

In many cases, the recipient of this product or service is happy to pay the additional money, knowing they'll receive the best value for their dollar. However, it's not always this simple in construction. People want a good job done, but they also want to pay as little as possible. In the end, money is usually the factor that wins out.

A construction company that incorporates Six Sigma and irons out its broken processes should expect to find itself in a great position. And yet, it may find itself unable to attract new business because of the new price tag associated with its services. Even though the company does better work than ever and its employees are happy and safe, nobody wants to hire this construction team simply because someone else will do the job for less money.

It's an unfair reality of the business. However, becoming a more efficient and safe construction company is its own reward. Over time, enough work will come in to compensate for being passed over by cost-conscious customers. That said, the initial rejection is bitterly disappointing for companies that have strived to improve their processes.

Six Sigma Case Study - Concrete Panel Production

A construction company was hired to build 405 villas in Saudi Arabia. (http://www.iglc20.sdsu.edu/papers/wp-content/uploads/2012/07/102%20P%20033.pdf) Since the project required the company to build so many of the same structure in a short period of time, it was decided that pre-constructed walls and floor panels would be used to build the villas. A year into the project, the company realized that it was 25 percent behind schedule. A Six Sigma project was undertaken in order to examine why the project had fallen so far behind its expected level of productivity.

The Define process of the project showed that the focus of the project should be the number of panels sent to the construction site each day. The initial measurement indicated that 18 panels were being delivered, while the goal of the project was to increase that number to 75 panels daily.

The company had many potential factors for change; these factors covered the scope of the entire project. Instead of one massive change dictating the future of the project, the company and the Six Sigma team made several smaller changes aimed at increasing the production and delivery of the concrete panels.

The management of the project changed, with four foremen hired to oversee six areas of production each. Additionally, a full-time project quality engineer was brought on to ensure that the quality of the panels was consistent. Defects in the panels themselves would only serve to add further delays and costs to the project.

To construct the panels more quickly, the company incorporated the use of a ready-mix concrete truck that was ready to pour at a moment's notice. Cranes and a concrete bucket were also purchased in order to facilitate the more expedient production of the panels.

Most importantly, a night shift was added in order to help the company to get back on schedule.

In addition, the inventory system was overhauled. The stockyard was reorganized in order to make it easier for employees to find the parts they needed. At the same time, the inventory level was reduced to a maximum of 250 units per item. Electronic inventory management was also implemented so that the company could easily re-order materials as needed.

Lastly, the company took the time to clearly define the process, the stakeholders in each part of the process and who was responsible for each aspect of the production. The company also began measuring cycle times in order to implement benchmarking and measure productivity.

Many changes were needed to make this process a viable one, both in terms of making it efficient and getting back on the established schedule. Fortunately, the changes proved to be highly effective. By the project's end, the company had achieved its goal of delivering 75 panels per day to the construction site. Furthermore, internal control charts proved that the process was indeed in control, proving that the solution would be sustainable for the foreseeable future.

Tips for Using Six Sigma in the Construction Industry

Given the diverse nature of projects undertaken, construction might not seem like the most obvious industry that would benefit from Six Sigma. However, its need for constant precision and productivity makes the construction industry a candidate for the process improvements that Six Sigma is known for delivering.

Although the company in the case study used their Six Sigma project to make widespread changes to their process, this is often the wrong approach to take. Looking for specific improvements that will make massive change with minimal effort is the best way to incorporate Six Sigma, particularly in a high-pressure, results-oriented industry like construction.

In some cases, a Six Sigma project will indicate that investment into machinery is necessary to improve efficiency and reduce defects. However, there are often other solutions that can improve workflow without requiring such a large investment of capital. These alternate fixes might not present the improvements that the new machinery would have, but they may come at a much more reasonable cost.

Each construction process is different, and even the best Six Sigma process improvement might not be able to be replicated across other functions. However, there are always tips and positive developments to be derived from a process improvement initiative. Finding ways to incorporate the improvements made via Six Sigma into other processes can help the company to become more well-rounded and productive, which results in a better experience for everyone.

Source

http://www.academicjournals.org/article/article1380706320_Hung%20and%20Sung.pdf, http://www.politifact.com/punditfact/statements/2013/nov/04/bill-maher/bill-maher-average-fast-food-worker-29-most-are-pu/,
http://www.endfoodwastenow.org/index.php/issues/issues-restaurants
http://www.ers.usda.gov/topics/food-markets-prices/food-service-industry.aspx
http://www.iglc20.sdsu.edu/papers/wp-content/uploads/2012/07/102%20P%20033.pdf
http://money.usnews.com/careers/best-jobs/construction-worker/salary

CHAPTER 51:
SIX SIGMA IN MILITARY/DEFENSE

Six Sigma is primarily associated with the business world, but it has applications that reach far beyond producing consumer goods. Six Sigma can help improve any process, no matter how large. Even an organization as secretive and as tradition-based as the military, stands to benefit from a Six Sigma project.

The military may be best known for physical combat, but the actual responsibilities of the military go far beyond fighting wars. Above all else, the military is charged with protecting its country by any means necessary. This means more than simply fighting when force is required. It means being privy to enemy attacks and knowing what's going to happen before it happens so that the best plans for defense can be devised. For this reason, intelligence measures are just as important as physical combat, if not more so. It's up to these groups to keep the military safe from sneak attacks, ambushes and unannounced strikes. Their role in aiding the military is paramount.

In addition to the more exciting aspects of the industry, the military must also deal with the same issues as any other job category. Recruitment and turnover are just two of the more difficult internal tasks the military must handle. Furthermore, the military must also process a great deal of information, including the current load of individuals serving, new initiatives, updated equipment and revised processes. Since the military is a subsidiary of the government, any change is usually accompanied by a fair amount of red tape. Military agencies must find ways to incorporate this lead time into their actions, which can sometimes work to the detriment of the operations they are in charge of carrying out.

The military and defense units of any country are synonymous with obtaining key pieces of intelligence, operating efficiently and identifying problems before they arise. Six Sigma can help in all three of these areas, as well as countless others. In fact, Six Sigma is becoming commonplace in military operations around the globe, becoming an important tool in keeping the world safe. (http://www.villanovau.com/resources/military/six-sigma-for-defense/)

Benefits of Using Six Sigma in the Military/Defense Industry

Decreased Processing Time

Most civilians see the military largely as a combat-based group. They typically don't get an inside look at what happens behind the scenes. People outside the military might be surprised to find that there's just as much bureaucracy and red tape in the military as there is in any other industry.

While difficulty in getting things done is found in industries of all types, it's different when it comes to the military. In the business world, not being able to bring in a new hire for two weeks might put a drain on productivity, but it's not a major concern in most cases. However, in the military, a lengthy delay can literally be a matter of life or death. Since disaster can strike at any time, the necessity for deployment may be just moments away. Any delay in bringing in new team members may result in unprepared soldiers that haven't been properly trained in military procedure. This doesn't just result in one individual not being ready. Instead, it puts the entire military operation - and the country defended by that nation - at risk.

Six Sigma has been proven to assist with the processing of paperwork and speeding up of internal affairs. This increase in efficiency isn't just significant in terms of the flow of operations. It's a critical improvement that could be life-saving.

Improved Repair Time

As is the case in the civilian world, equipment in the military industry is in constant need of maintenance and repair. From combat weapons to behind-the-scenes computers, there's always something that needs fixing.

This poses two potential problems. First, and most obviously, the repair of broken combat weapons or intelligence systems is imperative. The absence of up-to-date equipment in these areas could be catastrophic. The second issue is not as obvious, but might be even more important. There needs to be an internal system to categorize and prioritize the repair jobs faced by a given branch of the military. It's not simple enough to repair items as they come in. A high-level intelligence system used by the CIA is far more important than the radar detector on a tank.

Additionally, the military needs to have a strong sense of assurance built into its repair work. These repairs must work the first time, every time. Therefore, a fool-proof testing system must be put into place so that military personnel can test repaired equipment before it's used in battle. This also gives soldiers the assurance that comes with knowing that their equipment is in good hands.

Using Six Sigma gives the military the tools necessary to organize its repair effort, as well as reduce defects inherent in the existing process. A well-executed system for repairs saves a great deal of time and money while simultaneously providing quality assurance for the rest of the military operation. Implementing this approach is just as important as battle tactics, intelligence briefing or any other function carried out by the military.

Identify Security Breaches
Defense intelligence operations are designed to identify potential security issues and to thwart those threats before they become bigger problems. While every potential security concern must be taken seriously, it's imperative that the defense unit has a way of prioritizing more serious threats, making sure that those crucial matters get the full attention of the team.

This issue of security breaches highlights the importance of having a defined process set in stone. It gives defense employees the best chance at success because it shows these individuals exactly what they should look for each day. When everything is lined up in a specific way at all times, and then something deviates from that usual pattern, employees will know for sure that something is amiss. As a result, they will be able to take the correct defensive action.

Incorporating Six Sigma can be very advantageous for the defense industry. Not only can it help the unit to identify, track and stop threats, but it can help to pinpoint where suspect activity comes from. This knowledge will help the defense to move beyond merely responding to threats, allowing the department to develop policies and processes that will prevent those threats from occurring.

Challenges of Using Six Sigma in the Military/Defense Industry

Emergency Situations
Process improvement initiatives do a lot to benefit any company in any industry. However, even the most helpful improvements take time to establish and implement. While it might seem like this time is available at the start of a project, plans can change at any minute, especially in a high-stakes industry like the military.

The military is trained to respond to emergencies, and any moment can bring about an all-hands-on-deck emergency that requires immediate action. In the event of such a situation, there's no time for measuring data or implementing new processes. The unit must simply get to work doing what they're relied on to do.

Although the military has become increasingly friendly towards Six Sigma, the reality remains that the time for implementation isn't always available. While the analysis and data collection that occurs in Six Sigma projects is always helpful, the ideal solution that is realized at the end of a project isn't so easy to implement. Military units must understand that this is a risk that comes with the territory, and that they should weigh the positives and negatives before beginning a project.

Ordered Initiatives from Superiors
In the business world, Six Sigma is utilized by a company that wants to become more efficient, and that company is generally able to carry out a Six Sigma project at their leisure. This is not always the case in the military, and the reason isn't always because of an emergency that necessitates action.

Because the military is subject to the whims of government, the military doesn't always have the final say in how things are run. For example, a newly elected president that strives to focus on a specific area of military operation may supersede the desires of military leadership. Even if a Six Sigma project yields data that clearly shows that a new process will improve the workflow of the military, such a change can quickly be overruled by someone with the power to get their way.

In this way, the military is just like a regular business when it comes to Six Sigma. The numbers can tell many things, but without complete buy-in from all stakeholders, the project cannot succeed.

Lack of Funding
Like all other branches of the government, the military must operate on a pre-set budget. Once again, like many businesses, the military must find ways to achieve the most good while using minimal resources. This is one area where Six Sigma can be particularly helpful.

Unfortunately, sometimes a Six Sigma initiative is impossible to implement because there simply isn't enough room in the budget. Although Six Sigma almost always saves money in the long run, it does cost money to undertake the project. The additional resources incurred and the lost productivity put a drain on the military's financial reserves. Additionally, receiving additional funding isn't as easy as simply asking for more money. The budget decisions come from many levels above military leadership, and those numbers are derived so that other branches of the government can have budgets of their own.

Adding to the problem is the potential for elected officials to slash the military budget. These promises may be made before candidates are close enough to the situation to truly understand why the military needs its funding. However, because a promise was made, the elected official must find a way to stay true to his or her word, regardless of whether or not it's the right choice - and regardless of whether Six Sigma initiatives have to be put on hold.

Despite the potential for budget cuts at any point, the military should always strive to maximize productivity and reduce the occurrence of defects. Six Sigma projects should be conceived and executed without worrying about the possibility of funding decreases. As is the case with all military operations, anything can change at any time.

Six Sigma Case Study - Military Process Improvements

Due to the confidential nature of military operations, there are very few Six Sigma case studies available that include information regarding improved processes or internal metrics. However, Six Sigma does have an important role in military operations. The United States military has greatly benefited from Six Sigma, and it has disclosed information about several of its successful initiatives. These improvement projects include the following:

- The United States Army began its use of Six Sigma in 2005. Within three years, the Army had completed more than 1,000 Six Sigma projects, with another 1,600 projects in progress. The Army had trained 2,000 workers in Six Sigma methodology, with the total savings incurred due to Six Sigma reaching nearly $2 billion. (https://www.minitab.com/en-us/Press-Releases/Department-of-Defense-Saves-Billions-with-Lean-Six-Sigma-and-Minitab/)

- The U.S. Navy started using Six Sigma in 2006. Between 2006 and 2008, the Navy certified more than 5,000 officers as Six Sigma green belts or black belts. The total savings brought about by Six Sigma projects conducted in 2006 and 2007 was $450 million, which represented a 400 percent return on investment.

- The U.S. Air Force has also begun utilizing Six Sigma, boasting a Six Sigma staff of more than 500 black belts. To date, the Air Force has completed several Six Sigma projects, and the results have been so positive that the Air Force decided to reduce its staff of officers by 40,000 employees, which was expected to be completed without any sacrifice to the Air Force's current level of operations.

- The Red River Army Depot Repair Facility in Texarkana, Texas has undergone a series of fruitful Six Sigma projects. The facility has used Six Sigma to increase its ability to produce High Mobility Multipurpose Wheeled Vehicles (Humvees) by more than 7000 percent, going from three units a week to 32 in a day. Furthermore, the cost of each vehicle has been cut in half, with an $89,000 cost of production turning into $48,000 per vehicle as a result of Six Sigma. The main tools used to bring about these changes were the implementation of an assembly line process, improved time and personnel management and enhanced methods for keeping parts in stock. Front-line staffers were particularly helpful in suggesting and implementing these changes. In addition to the workflow modifications, the Red River Depot began placing stickers on the job site reminding workers that their work ultimately affects the lives of soldiers who fight to defend their country   .
(http://www.dtic.mil/dtic/tr/fulltext/u2/a493547.pdf)

- The Pine Bluff Arsenal, located in Arkansas, used Six Sigma to find a better way to produce and repair gas masks. Thanks to their improvements, the rate of gas mask production has increased by 50 percent, while repair time has decreased by 90 percent.

- The Corpus Christi Army Depot saw Six Sigma drastically overhaul their previous process for helicopter repair. Their Six Sigma project showed that the group was overhauling engines far too regularly. As a result, the depot began overhauling engines after 900 hours of work, as opposed to the previous baseline of 309. In the end, the overhaul time was reduced by nearly 65 percent, while the reliability of the overhaul rose to more than 90 percent

Tips for Using Six Sigma in the Military/Defense Industry

The trend of Six Sigma usage in the military is a positive development. Although several projects have returned outstanding results, the industry is still merely scratching the surface of what Six Sigma can do to help. Future projects are sure to have major positive ramifications that will benefit all aspects of the military.

Because Six Sigma has become so popular in the military, units are encouraged to use any and all resources at their disposal when working on a project. Although budgets are often subject to the whims of politicians, there are plenty of ways military personnel can improve their own processes, as well as the functions of others.

While the military strives to operate at maximum efficiency, it's simply not possible to overhaul everything at once. Choosing the proper project scope will help military units to get the most out of their projects. Projects should be big enough to make a huge difference, but not so big that management gets bogged down by the over-analysis of data and processes.

It's important for military personnel to consider all possibilities when coming up with solutions. Any process improvement, no matter how small, can provide tremendous benefit to the unit and, by extension, to the entire country. Encouraging lower-level soldiers to speak up and identify their pain points will help the project team to come up with solutions that help everyone.

CHAPTER 52:
SIX SIGMA IN GOVERNMENT

At first glance, the government might not seem like the poster child for Six Sigma implementation. The government doesn't produce goods, and in many cases, it doesn't truly have to answer to its superiors or its constituents. And yet, in many ways, the government is actually the perfect forum for Six Sigma process improvements.

The term "government" typically calls to mind elected officials that are responsible for helping the people in a given geographical area. These individuals are tasked with many duties that are unseen by the average person. Organizing local activities and appearing at community events barely scratch the surface of the responsibilities of an elected official. Politicians must work with groups such as law enforcement and special interest organizations in order to facilitate changes that are demanded by the citizens of their local area. Additionally, any progress made by the politician is subject to further review by other politicians, which results in many proposed changes never seeing the light of day.

The workflow of politicians would be less difficult if not for the non-stop stream of outside considerations that interfere with their duties. Lobbyists and fellow politicians want support for their own causes, which prompts them to make pitches to other elected officials to garner support. As a result, politicians are forced to devote time, energy and money to causes that they might not be passionate about, but that they must support because it's the right thing to do from a political perspective.

Elected officials must also work diligently to raise money, both for their own re-election campaigns and for the parties to which they belong. Cold-calling in order to request donations is a harsh reality for many lower-level politicians, and fundraising dinners are the norm for higher-level officials. These politicians are also required to acquire endorsements from important people in the community, including newspapers and unions. With so much in the way of making actual progress, it's easy to see why politicians are often forced to rely on promises for the future in order to gain support, as opposed to showcasing their track records from previous jobs.

While elected officials may be synonymous with the popular definition of government, there are plenty of other people that keep the industry running. Everyday people that take jobs working in the government also have a say in how well the industry serves its people. Civilians working in the government have a wide variety of responsibilities, including serving as court officials, DMV clerks, IRS auditors and countless other positions. The politicians in the higher ranks may set policies in place, but it's up to these staffers to carry out those initiatives.

The need for government employees to work with elected officials, and the potential for disagreements along the way, highlights the need for Six Sigma in government. Additionally, Six Sigma may be able to help politicians to manage the many demands on their time.

Benefits of Using Six Sigma in the Government Industry

Eliminate Red Tape

While the government is commonly associated with being the ultimate ruling body, it's not frequently cited for implementing change in a swift manner. That's because virtually every decision made by government members involves outside parties. Citizens may be asked to vote on certain changes, while others simply require approval by higher authorities. These added steps add significant lead time to the execution of approved items, often resulting in added costs and unhappy citizens. (https://www.isixsigma.com/industries/government-non-profit/six-sigma-government-focusing-customer/)

Incorporating Six Sigma can help any government office to increase its efficiency. One of the main ways in which Six Sigma can make a notable difference is by identifying common areas where progress initiatives stall out. It may turn out that a certain office is a culprit in delaying new actions, including improved processes that will help everyone. Officials can then work with these offices to develop new ways of gaining approval that will speed up the implementation of new programs and processes.

Six Sigma can also highlight the true costs that come as a result of these delays. For instance, a delay in the execution of an increase for automobile registration fees can ultimately cost a town or county millions of dollars. Not only do these delays present the image of a disorganized government, but they also hurt the citizens of that community. Even if people feel as though they dodged a bullet by not having to pay the increased registration fee this year, they will ultimately have to pay additional money in other areas, such as taxes or park fees, to make up for the government's lost revenue.

The elimination of red tape allows the government to run more efficiently and transparently. This makes it easier for the community to have more faith in its government, which ultimately will benefit all elected officials at re-election time.

Improved Usage of Funding

One of the most difficult aspects of government is getting things done with a limited budget. Contrary to what some might believe, most branches of the government can't simply print money at will. Financial prudence is important in government, just as it is in any business or industry.

A branch of government that incorporates Six Sigma will have a better idea of where their money is going, but the applications of Six Sigma go much deeper. Thanks to the quality measures taken and the data collected over the course of the project, the government will have a better idea of how much of a return each investment provides. A government group that spent $500,000 to renovate an ice skating rink may be pleased to find that residents have attended skating sessions at that rink twice as often over the past three years. Discovering the financial potential of improving recreational facilities may inspire those officials to further enhance other government-owned properties, such as golf courses and batting cages.

This ability to track spending and return on investment may have tremendous benefits for politicians. Instead of merely thanking donors for their contributions, elected officials can now state exactly where each individual's donations went, as well as how the community was positively impacted as a result of their generosity. Such personalized shows of appreciation and consideration would be impossible without the data-driven philosophy of Six Sigma.

Time Allocation

Government officials have a lot to do. In addition to dealing with the red tape that swallows many of their desired implementations, officials have to take time to meet with their constituents, maintain a presence in the community and attend important local events, such as graduations. This is above and beyond the responsibilities typically associated with government, including passing laws, identifying avenues for process improvements and lobbying for the necessary support to get their initiatives pushed through the system.

These many activities take a great deal of time. With so much that needs to get done, taking a step back to evaluate the typical workflow seems impossible. Once again, Six Sigma comes to the rescue, prompting a re-evaluation of existing process and identifying ways to free up time without sacrificing productivity.

Just as with financial distribution, politicians will have the chance to see exactly how many hours each week they devote to the various aspects of their jobs. Furthermore, as they did with funding, they will be able to see just how productive each of those hours turned out to be. For example, a politician might find that fundraising for eight hours a week is marginally less effective than seeking donations for ten hours a week, proving that eight hours per week is the ideal amount of time to spend fundraising. Those extra two hours can be re-allocated to a function that needs more attention and that would generate a bigger return.

This approach to time management could be revolutionary for elected officials and any government employee that has too little time to carry out too many responsibilities. A responsible distribution of time commitments may result in a more efficient government that's better equipped to serve the needs of its community.

Challenges of Using Six Sigma in the Government Industry

Checks and Balances
The United States Constitution was written with an emphasis on checks and balances. In other words, none of the three branches of government - judicial, executive and legislative - should be able to obtain too much power. In the event that one of those three branches becomes more prominent than the others, the remaining two branches have the wherewithal to use their power to check the growing branch. On paper, this ensures that no one branch of the government can garner too much influence.
(http://www.usconstitution.net/consttop_cnb.html)

Today, the threat over gaining power isn't so much the traditional model of checks and balances as it is the party system that's used in the United States. Republican officials are inclined to vote for Republican measures while voting down Democratic initiatives, and vice versa. The selling point of staying within party lines is one of solidarity. If a congressman is a Democrat and he or she wants to get a specific action passed, he or she will receive much more support if that congressman typically supports his or her party on a regular basis.

Note that these decisions often have little to do with the actual preferences of the individuals in question. That is to say, politicians routinely pass laws they don't truly believe in and veto measures they actually like just to stay in good standing with their political parties. Once again, the idea is that the entire party will stand behind a politician if he or she works with that party on their ideas. However, the potential always remains for a perfectly good improvement proposal to die on the voting floor, even if it's been backed by a Six Sigma project and the data clearly shows that it's a good idea.

Limited Amount of Time

Elected government officials come into office with the confidence of the people and their respective parties. Unfortunately, the one thing they don't have on their side is time.

Terms of service for elected officials ensure that there are a variety of voices contributing to solving the problems posed by the people of a given area. They also make sure that no politician can rest on his or her laurels. They need to generate results, and they need to do so in enough time that voters can take note of the improvements before the next election.

Six Sigma can be helpful to government officials in so many ways. However, the solutions that are realized as a result of Six Sigma aren't always time-sensitive. Gathering data, evaluating a broken process and devising ways to improve that process all take time, as do creating the ultimate solution and training employees on this revised model. It's entirely possible that the desired changes won't be seen until after the official has left office.

These occurrences are unfortunate, but they can't be avoided without compromising the quality of the solution. It's the job of the government to do whatever's necessary to help people, even if the timeframe for those improvements goes beyond an official's term. It's up to each individual serving to make sure the future incorporates the updated processes and efficient workflow that have been implemented through Six Sigma.

Getting Buy-In

The unfortunate reality of politics and government is that not everyone is willing to respect the wishes of other politicians. Every politician has his or her idea of how things should be, and any elected official is eager to see those ideas implemented as soon as possible.

At the same time, politicians with a great vision for the future might see their ideas throttled by the people above them. This can happen for a variety of reasons. The aforementioned party line issue may change the minds of politicians; additionally, personal philosophies may take center stage, or senior politicians may simply want to take credit for the ideas of people that are lower on the food chain.

No matter what the situation may be, the fact is that not every good idea comes to fruition, and it's often because of a politician's ability to lobby the necessary support. This is unfortunate, yet unavoidable because of the Catch-22 involved. Six Sigma requires total buy-in from all stakeholders who may benefit from a project, but most senior politicians won't consider an improved process unless they can see the projected results of the initiative. This results in improvements that are partially carried out - or not carried out at all - through no fault of the Six Sigma project team. This can happen even if the team asked for permission before embarking on the project.

Six Sigma Case Study - Process Improvement in Houston, Texas

Houston, Texas is the fourth largest city in the United States. While the city's population has grown steadily over the years - Houston currently boasts more than 2 million residents - finances haven't kept up with the population increase. Despite Houston's $2 billion budget, the city found itself facing a $140 million deficit in July 2015.
(http://performance.houstontx.gov/sites/default/files/Industrial%20Engineer%20-%20Case%20Study%20-%202015-02.pdf)

Six Sigma has been a part of Houston's infrastructure in varying forms throughout the 2010s. However, when the deficit grew to such a high number in 2015, it was time for Houston to get its most tenured employees involved. Since many city employee had put in between 20 and 30 years on the job, this change was necessary in order for those employees to keep their jobs and keep contributing to the welfare of the city.

Houston's Six Sigma team began looking for ways where broken processes could become more efficient. A major source of defects was not hard to find. The city's Outside Services department was responsible for confirmation and payment associated with renting city equipment to other groups. Unfortunately, the department suffered from rampant inefficiency. It typically took Outside Services 111 days to resolve invoices received from vendors. This was a far cry from the city's desired goal of 30 days. At the department's lowest point, vendors were shutting off services and directly calling the mayor's office to demand answers.

The Six Sigma team implemented a series of process improvement measures that helped them to develop a revised process for handling the outside vendors. These methods included process mapping, eliminating waste and developing a system for verifying that Outside Services was actually responsible for a given invoice. The improved methods proved highly successful. After beginning with an average cycle time of 111 days, Outside Services brought its average turnaround time down to 2.5 days. Additionally, the group was able to reduce its staff from six employees to one.

However, this did not mean that those extra employees lost their jobs. In fact, Houston has re-invested a variety of resources into its Six Sigma projects, including human capital.

Houston's employee pool now features 1,000 Six Sigma yellow belts and more than 50 Six Sigma green belts. The city is also developing a program for training black belts. What's more, the increased efficiency found across all of the city's processes means that Houston doesn't have to hire new employees, saving $1 million a year on hiring costs.

The long-time employees of Houston not only get to continue serving the community, but they are able to do so in new and exciting ways that have invigorated the entire staff of city employees. The future is bright for Houston, as it is for any city that implements Six Sigma and continues to invest in its solutions.

Tips for Using Six Sigma in the Government Industry

Six Sigma is a great resource for both government employees and elected officials. Since any improvement in government operations has a trickle-down effect that ultimately helps many people, even the smallest Six Sigma initiative can have large-scale benefits.

Inefficiency in the government hurts everyone - elected officials and government staffers all feel the strain of broken processes, and nobody faces the impact of these processes more than the citizens of these affected areas. Bringing up any ideas that can help to improve the flow of government - ideas, money, time, etc. - stands to benefit operations tremendously.

Government officials may be reluctant to undertake Six Sigma projects out of fear that they might highlight the things they're doing wrong. However, reaching out for help is the best way to use Six Sigma to its fullest potential. Talking to everyone involved with a process - from the most important people to the lowest-ranking officials - will help bring about a solution that benefits all parties involved.

Politicians must always remind themselves that the purpose of any Six Sigma project is to streamline internal operations in order to help the people that truly need assistance. The focus should never deviate from that objective. Re-elections and raising money must come a distant second to what really matters.

Source

http://www.villanovau.com/resources/military/six-sigma-for-defense/
http://www.dtic.mil/dtic/tr/fulltext/u2/a493547.pdf
https://www.minitab.com/en-us/Press-Releases/Department-of-Defense-Saves-Billions-with-Lean-Six-Sigma-and-Minitab/

http://performance.houstontx.gov/sites/default/files/Industrial%20Engineer%20-%20Case%20Study%20-%202015-02.pdf

https://www.isixsigma.com/industries/government-non-profit/six-sigma-government-focusing-customer/

INDEX

Lightning Source UK Ltd.
Milton Keynes UK
UKHW03f1047261018
331251UK00006B/644/P